QUANTUM MECHANICS

NUMERICAL VALUES OF SOME PHYSICAL QUANTITIES

$\hbar = 1.054 \times 10^{-27}$ erg-sec (Planck's constant divided by 2π)

$e = 4.80 \times 10^{-10}$ esu (magnitude of electron charge)

$m = 0.911 \times 10^{-27}$ g (electron mass)

$M = 1.672 \times 10^{-24}$ g (proton mass)

$a_0 = \hbar^2/me^2 = 5.29 \times 10^{-9}$ cm (Bohr radius)

$e^2/a_0 = 27.2$ ev (twice binding energy of hydrogen)

$c = 3.00 \times 10^{10}$ cm/sec (speed of light)

$\hbar c/e^2 = 137$ (reciprocal fine structure constant)

$e\hbar/2mc = 0.927 \times 10^{-20}$ erg/oersted (Bohr magneton)

$mc^2 = 5.11 \times 10^5$ ev (electron rest energy)

$Mc^2 = 938$ Mev (proton rest energy)

1 ev $= 1.602 \times 10^{-12}$ erg

Wavelength associated with 1 ev/c = 12,400 Å

Temperature associated with 1 ev = 11,600°K

INTERNATIONAL SERIES IN PURE AND APPLIED PHYSICS
Leonard I. Schiff, Consulting Editor

QUANTUM MECHANICS

THIRD EDITION

LEONARD I. SCHIFF
Professor of Physics
Stanford University

McGraw-Hill, Inc.
New York St. Louis San Francisco Auckland Bogotá
Caracas Lisbon London Madrid Mexico Milan
Montreal New Delhi Paris San Juan Singapore
Sydney Tokyo Toronto

TO FRANCES

PREFACE

This volume has a threefold purpose: to explain the physical concepts of quantum mechanics, to describe the mathematical formalism, and to present illustrative examples of both the ideas and the methods. The book is intended to serve as a text at the graduate level and also as a reference book. It is assumed that the reader is reasonably familiar with classical mechanics, electromagnetic theory, atomic structure, and differential equations; prior acquaintance with matrices or group theory is not necessary. In addition, he should have had some contact with complex variables (for Chap. 9) and the special theory of relativity (for Chap. 13).

The author believes that the analytical methods employed in the book will satisfy most theoretical physicists even though no attempt is made to achieve mathematical rigor. For example, there is little or no discussion of the justification for the interchange of sum, derivative, and integral operations or for the use of the δ function. On the other hand, the physical reasons for the nature of the results obtained are investigated wherever possible.

Problems are given at the end of each chapter. They are often used to illustrate or amplify points discussed in the text. Original theoretical papers are referred to throughout the book; the list is representative rather than exhaustive. Experimental results are, for the most part, quoted without reference, since the large amount of documentation required for an adequate survey seems out of place in a book on theoretical physics. Several other books and review articles on quantum mechanics and related subjects are referred to for more detailed discussions of particular topics.

The scope of this volume is best outlined if the book is divided into three parts. The first three chapters constitute an introduction to quantum mechanics, in which the physical concepts are discussed and the Schrödinger wave formalism is established. The next nine chapters present exact solutions of the wave equation for both bound-state and collision problems, the Heisenberg matrix formalism and transformation theory, symmetry, approximation methods, the scattering matrix, particle identity, radiation theory, and some applications to atomic systems. Since Chaps. 5 to 12 include most of the material given in a first-year graduate course, it seems desirable to include a semiclassical treatment of electromagnetic radiation (Chap. 11) even though some of the results are obtained again in Chap. 14. The last two chapters are an introduction to relativistic particle theory and to quantized fields.

The first edition of this book was completed 20 years ago, and relatively few changes were made in the second edition. Thus the present revision is of necessity extensive; at the same time it is intended to retain the comprehensiveness of the original volume without a substantial increase in length. The principal additions are a section on complex potentials and the reciprocity and optical theorems (Sec. 20); a much fuller account of matrices and transformation theory (Chap. 6); a new chapter that discusses geometrical and dynamical symmetries and includes a fairly detailed account of angular momentum (Chap. 7); a considerably expanded treatment of approximation methods for bound-state and collision problems, including the scattering matrix and its applications, analytic properties, and dispersion relations (Chaps. 8 and 9); and a new section on the density operator and matrix (Sec. 42). The principal topics dropped from the second edition are the variational treatment of scattering, the theory of the Cerenkov effect, and the quantization of the Dirac equation; also, the last two sections of the second edition are somewhat condensed and combined into one (Sec. 57) in the present volume. Some changes in notation have been made to conform to current usage, and a table of the numerical values of some physical quantities has been added inside the back cover.

The author wishes again to record his indebtedness to the late Prof. J. R. Oppenheimer and to Prof. Robert Serber in connection with the preparation of the first edition of this book. He is also grateful to several of those who have studied and taught from the earlier revision for their many helpful suggestions. In particular, Prof. E. H. Wichmann prepared a thorough review of the second edition that contributed substantially to the present volume. The author also thanks the many students who studied from the various drafts of the third edition for their comments, and especially Prof. J. D. Walecka for his constructive criticism of particular sections.

Leonard I. Schiff

CONTENTS

Quantization of a classical system. Motion of a particle in an electromagnetic field. Evaluation of commutator brackets Velocity and acceleration of a charged particle. The Lorentz force. Virial theorem.

QUANTUM MECHANICS

1
The Physical Basis of Quantum Mechanics

At the present stage of human knowledge, quantum mechanics can be regarded as the fundamental theory of atomic phenomena. The experimental data on which it is based are derived from physical events that lie almost entirely beyond the range of direct human perception. It is not surprising, therefore, that the theory embodies physical concepts that are foreign to common daily experience. These concepts did not appear in the historical development of quantum mechanics, however, until a quite complete mathematical formalism had been evolved. The need for quantitative comparison with observation, which is the ultimate test of any physical theory, in this case led first to the formalism and only later to its interpretation in physical terms.

It seems desirable in introducing the subject of quantum mechanics to depart from the historical order and preface the mathematical development with a discussion of the physical concepts.[1] In this chapter we first review briefly the experimental background and the ideas of the old

[1] For a detailed study of the historical development, see M. Jammer, "The Conceptual Development of Quantum Mechanics" (McGraw-Hill, New York, 1966).

quantum theory, then discuss the newer physical concepts of uncertainty and complementarity, and finally lay the groundwork for the formalism that will be developed in its most familiar form in Chap. 2.   No attempt will be made to deduce the structure of the formalism from the fundamental experiments; we shall try to make the theoretical development seem plausible rather than unique.   The justification for the theory, then, will rest on the agreement between deductions made from it and experiments, and on the simplicity (in principle more than in practice) and consistency of the formalism.

1□EXPERIMENTAL BACKGROUND

Experimental physics prior to 1900 had demonstrated the existence of a wide variety of phenomena, which for the most part were believed to be explicable in terms of what we now call *classical* theoretical physics. The motions of mechanical objects were successfully discussed in terms of Newton's equations on both celestial and terrestrial scales.   Application of this theory to molecular motions produced useful results in the kinetic theory of gases, and the discovery of the electron by J. J. Thomson in 1897 consisted in showing that it behaved like a newtonian particle. The wave nature of light had been strongly suggested by the diffraction experiments of Young in 1803 and was put on a firmer foundation by Maxwell's discovery in 1864 of the connection between optical and electrical phenomena.

INADEQUACY OF CLASSICAL PHYSICS

The difficulties in the understanding of experimental results that remained at the beginning of this century were largely concerned with the development of a suitable atomic model and with the late discoveries of x-rays and radioactivity.   However, there were also difficulties associated with phenomena that should have been understood but actually were not: such things as the spectral distribution of thermal radiation from a blackbody, the low-temperature specific heats of solids, and the appearance of only 5 degrees of freedom in the motion of a free diatomic molecule at ordinary temperatures.

The beginning of an understanding of the second class of difficulties was made by Planck in 1900, when he was able to explain the blackbody spectrum in terms of the assumed emission and absorption of electromagnetic radiation in discrete *quanta*, each of which contains an amount of energy E that is equal to the frequency of the radiation ν multiplied by a universal constant h (called *Planck's constant*):

$$E = h\nu \tag{1.1}$$

This quantum idea was later used by Einstein in accounting for some of the experimental observations on the photoelectric effect. In this way the dual character of electromagnetic radiation became established: It sometimes behaves like a wave motion and sometimes like a stream of corpuscular quanta.

At about this time, the existence of discrete values for the measurable parameters of atomic systems (not only of electromagnetic radiation) became apparent through Einstein's and Debye's theories of the specific heats of solids, Ritz's classification of spectral lines, the experiment of Franck and Hertz on the discrete energy losses of electrons on collision with atoms, and (somewhat later) the experiment of Stern and Gerlach, which showed that the component of the magnetic moment of an atom along an external magnetic field has discrete values.

SUMMARY OF PRINCIPAL EXPERIMENTS AND INFERENCES

The theoretical physics of the first quarter of this century thus contained two important inferences, obtained from the experiments and their interpretations, that had not existed in 1900: the dual character of electromagnetic radiation and the existence of discrete values for physical quantities. The relations between the principal experimental conclusions and the theoretical inferences are shown schematically in Table 1; for a more detailed discussion and a bibliography, reference should be made to a book on atomic physics.[1]

A third theoretical inference appeared in 1924 with the suggestion by de Broglie that matter also has a dual (particlelike and wavelike) character; he assumed that the relation between the momentum p of any particle and the length λ of the corresponding wave is[2]

$$\lambda = \frac{h}{p} \tag{1.2}$$

Up to that time all the evidence had indicated that matter was composed of discrete newtonian particles; in particular, sharp tracks of charged particles such as electrons and helium nuclei had been observed in expansion cloud chambers like that invented by C. T. R. Wilson in 1911. Shortly after this, however, Davisson and Germer (1927) and G. P. Thomson (1928) independently observed the diffraction of electrons by crystals and thus confirmed de Broglie's principal supposition.

[1] See, for example, F. K. Richtmyer, E. H. Kennard, and T. Lauritsen, "Introduction to Modern Physics" (McGraw-Hill, New York, 1955); M. Born, "Atomic Physics" (Hafner, New York, 1951); G. P. Harnwell and W. E. Stephens, "Atomic Physics" (McGraw-Hill, New York, 1955).

[2] Equation (1.2) is also valid for light quanta, as may be seen by dividing both sides of Eq. (1.1) by the velocity of light, c; for a directed beam of light $p = E/c$ and $\lambda = c/\nu$.

Table 1 Relations between experimental interpretations and theoretical inferences

Diffraction (Young 1803, Laue 1912)	Electromagnetic waves
Blackbody radiation (Planck 1900)	
Photoelectric effect (Einstein 1904)	
Compton effect (1923)	Electromagnetic quanta
Combination principle (Ritz-Rydberg 1908)	
Specific heats (Einstein 1907, Debye 1912)	Discrete values for physical quantities
Franck-Hertz experiment (1913)	
Stern-Gerlach experiment (1922)	

2☐THE OLD QUANTUM THEORY

What is now called the *old quantum theory*[1] was initiated by the work of Planck on blackbody radiation and was carried farther by Einstein and Debye.   However, only after Rutherford's discovery in 1911 that an atom consists of a small, massive, positively charged nucleus surrounded by electrons could the theory be applied to a quantitative description of atoms.

BOHR–SOMMERFELD QUANTIZATION RULES

The first step in this direction was taken by Bohr in 1913, when he made two postulates concerning the electronic or extranuclear structure of an atom.   The first of these was that an atomic system can exist in particular stationary or quantized states, each of which corresponds to a definite energy of the system.   Transitions from one stationary state to another are accompanied by the gain or loss, as the case may be, of an amount of energy equal to the energy difference between the two states; the energy gained or lost appears as a quantum of electromagnetic radiation, or as internal or kinetic energy of another system.   The second postulate (in agreement with that of Planck and Einstein) was that a radiation quantum has a frequency equal to its energy divided by Planck's constant h.

These two postulates by themselves provided some insight into the Ritz combination principle and the Franck-Hertz experiment.   To obtain specific results for hydrogen, Bohr proposed a simple rule for the selection of the circular orbits that are to constitute stationary states: The angular momentum must be an integral multiple of $h/2\pi$.   A more general quantization rule was discovered independently by W. Wilson (1915) and by

---

[1] For a more detailed discussion than is presented in this section, see the books cited above, and L. Pauling and E. B. Wilson, Jr., "Introduction to Quantum Mechanics," chap. II (McGraw-Hill, New York, 1935).

Sommerfeld (1916), thus making possible the application of Bohr's postulates to a wider variety of atomic systems. This rule is applicable to hamiltonian systems in which the coordinates are cyclic variables; it states that the integral of each canonical momentum with respect to its coordinate over a cycle of its motion must be an integral multiple of h. The rule was applied with considerable success to the computation of the fine structure of hydrogen, the spectra of diatomic molecules, and other problems.

PRACTICAL DIFFICULTIES

The old quantum theory encountered practical difficulties in several different respects. It could not be applied to aperiodic systems, it provided only a qualitative and incomplete treatment of the intensities of spectral lines, and it did not give a satisfactory account of the dispersion of light. Moreover, improvements in experimental techniques soon showed that there were problems, such as the rotational spectra of some diatomic molecules, to which the theory gave unambiguous but incorrect answers.

The correspondence principle was introduced by Bohr in 1923 in an effort to make use of the classical theory as a limiting case to infer some properties of atomic systems, especially the intensities of spectral lines. Although much was achieved in this way, it was clear in the early 1920's that the quantum theory as it then existed was unsatisfactory.

CONCEPTUAL DIFFICULTIES

Quite apart from the practical difficulties outlined above, the old quantum theory failed to give a conceptually satisfactory account of the fundamental phenomena. It was difficult to understand why the electrostatic interaction between a hydrogen nucleus and an electron should be effective when the ability of the accelerated electron to emit electromagnetic radiation disappeared in a stationary state. The mechanism of emission and absorption of radiation in transitions between stationary states was obscure. The quantization rules were arbitrary even when they were most effective. And the assumption of a dual character for light (particle-like on emission and absorption and wavelike in transit) seemed to be self-contradictory.

In order to illustrate the conceptual difficulties and the way in which they are dealt with by the new quantum mechanics, we consider in some detail a simple diffraction experiment, which is illustrated schematically in Fig. 1. A light source S illuminates a diaphragm A in which two slits are cut. A diffraction pattern appears at a photosensitive screen B, and the ejected photoelectrons are most numerous at the diffraction peaks. Here we have the radiation behaving as a wave during its passage

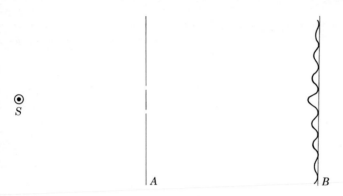

Fig. 1 A diffraction experiment in which light from S passes through the two slits in A to form a diffraction pattern at B.

from source through slits to screen, but behaving as a stream of light quanta or photons when it ejects electrons from B.   We now know that a similar experiment could be set up with matter instead of radiation.   The diffraction pattern of electrons scattered from a crystal (analogous to the slits in A) may be detected as a distribution of electron tracks in a Wilson cloud chamber (analogous to the screen B), so that the wave and particle aspects of matter appear in the same experiment.

In the situation illustrated in Fig. 1, we might at first suppose that the diffraction pattern is due to an interference between different photons passing through the two slits, thus explaining the observations entirely in terms of the particle picture.   That this is not a sufficient explanation may be shown by decreasing the intensity of the light until an average of only one photon at a time is in transit between source and screen.   The diffraction pattern still appears as the distribution of the large number of photons accumulated over a sufficiently long time.   Thus we must conclude that diffraction is a statistical property of a single photon and does not involve an interaction between photons.   From the point of view of the particle picture, we may then ask how it is that a stream of independent photons, each of which presumably can go through only one of the slits, can produce a diffraction pattern that appears only when both slits are open.   Or to put the question in another way, how can the presence of a slit through which a photon does not go prevent that photon from reaching a part of the screen it would be likely to reach if that slit were closed?

QUANTUM-MECHANICAL VIEWPOINT

In this question is implicit the assumption that the photon actually does go through a particular one of the two slits.   This assumption is natural from the point of view of the classical theory or the old quantum theory, since these theories regard a photon or other particle as having a definite and determinable position at each instant of time. The quantum mechanics, however, discards this assumption and asserts instead that the position of a photon has meaning only when the experiment includes a position determination. Moreover, this part of the experiment will affect the remainder of the experiment and cannot be considered separately. Thus from the point of view of quantum mechanics, the question asked in the preceding paragraph is without meaning, since it assumes that the photon goes through a particular one of the two slits (thus making it possible to close the other slit) when there is no provision in the experiment for determining through which slit the photon actually goes.

The quantum mechanics resolves the situation by telling us that the diffraction pattern is destroyed if a sufficiently careful attempt is made to determine through which slit each photon passes (see Sec. 4). We must then be prepared to forgo the customary mental picture of a photon (or an electron) as a classical particle that has at each instant of time a position that can be determined without damage to diffraction patterns of the type discussed here. Thus classical causality, which requires that the motion of a particle at any time be uniquely determinable from its motion at an earlier time, must also be abandoned. The new theory that is forced upon us in this way is so successful in other respects as well that, at the present state of knowledge, we must regard such classically incomplete descriptions as a fundamental property of nature.

3□UNCERTAINTY AND COMPLEMENTARITY

Before presenting a more quantitative discussion of the diffraction experiment outlined in Sec. 2, we consider two principles that express in qualitative terms the physical content of the theory of quantum mechanics. We restrict ourselves here to a discussion of their meaning and give arguments for their validity in Sec. 4.

UNCERTAINTY PRINCIPLE

The first of these is the *uncertainty principle*, developed by Heisenberg[1] in 1927. According to this principle, it is impossible to specify precisely and simultaneously the values of both members of particular pairs of physical variables that describe the behavior of an atomic system. The members of these pairs of variables are canonically conjugate to each other in the hamiltonian sense: a rectangular coordinate x of a particle and the corresponding component of momentum p_x, a component J_z of angular momentum of a particle and its angular position ϕ in the perpendicular

[1] W. Heisenberg, *Z. Physik* **43**, 172 (1927).

(xy) plane, the energy E of a particle and the time t at which it is measured, etc. Put more quantitatively, the uncertainty principle states that the order of magnitude of the product of the uncertainties in the knowledge of the two variables must be at least Planck's constant h divided by $2\pi(\hbar \equiv h/2\pi = 1.0545 \times 10^{-27}$ erg-sec),[1] so that

$$\Delta x \cdot \Delta p_x \gtrsim \hbar \qquad (3.1)$$

$$\Delta \phi \cdot \Delta J_z \gtrsim \hbar \qquad (3.2)$$

$$\Delta t \cdot \Delta E \gtrsim \hbar \qquad (3.3)$$

The relation (3.1) means that a component of the momentum of a particle cannot be precisely specified without loss of all knowledge of the corresponding component of its position at that time, that a particle cannot be precisely localized in a particular direction without loss of all knowledge of its momentum component in that direction, and that in intermediate cases the product of the uncertainties of the simultaneously measurable values of corresponding position and momentum components is at least of the order of magnitude of $\hbar$. Similarly, Eq. (3.2) means, for example, that the precise measurement of the angular position of a particle in an orbit carries with it the loss at that time of all knowledge of the component of angular momentum perpendicular to the plane of the orbit.[2] Equation (3.3) means that an energy determination that has an accuracy ΔE must occupy at least a time interval $\Delta t \sim \hbar/\Delta E$; thus if a system maintains a particular state of motion not longer than a time Δt, the energy of the system in that state is uncertain by at least the amount $\Delta E \sim \hbar/\Delta t$, since Δt is the longest time interval available for the energy determination. The smallness of h makes the uncertainty principle of interest primarily in connection with systems of atomic size.

As we shall see in Sec. 12, the uncertainty principle may be obtained directly from the mathematical formulation of the theory, and this is actually the way in which it was first obtained by Heisenberg.

COMPLEMENTARITY PRINCIPLE

In order to understand the implications of the uncertainty principle in more physical terms, Bohr[3] introduced the *complementarity principle* in 1928. This principle states that atomic phenomena cannot be described with the completeness demanded by classical dynamics; some of the elements that complement each other to make up a complete classical description are actually mutually exclusive, and these complementary

---

[1] E. R. Cohen and J. W. M. DuMond, *Rev. Mod. Phys.* **37**, 537 (1965).

[2] Because of the cyclic nature of ϕ, Eq. (3.2) merits further attention; see M. M. Nieto, *Phys. Rev. Letters* **18**, 182 (1967).

[3] N. Bohr, *Nature* **121**, 580 (1928); "Atomic Theory and the Description of Nature," especially pt. II (Cambridge, London, 1934); *Phys. Rev.* **48**, 696 (1935).

elements are all necessary for the description of various aspects of the phenomena. From the point of view of the experimenter, the complementarity principle asserts that the physical apparatus available to him has such properties that more precise measurements than those indicated by the uncertainty principle cannot be made.

This is not to be regarded as a deficiency of the experimenter or of his techniques. It is rather a law of nature that, whenever an attempt is made to measure precisely one of the pair of canonical variables, the other is changed by an amount that cannot be too closely calculated without interfering with the primary attempt. This is fundamentally different from the classical situation, in which a measurement also disturbs the system that is under observation, but the amount of the disturbance can be calculated and taken into account. Thus the complementarity principle typifies the fundamental limitations on the classical concept that the behavior of atomic systems can be described independently of the means by which they are observed.

LIMITATIONS ON EXPERIMENT

In the atomic field, we must choose between various experimental arrangements, each designed to measure the two members of a pair of canonical variables with different degrees of precision that are compatible with the uncertainty relations. In particular, there are two extreme arrangements, each of which measures one member of the pair with great precision. According to classical theory, these extreme experimental arrangements complement each other; the results of both may be obtained at once and are necessary to supply a complete classical description of the system. In actuality, however, the extreme complementary experiments are mutually exclusive and cannot be performed together.

It is in this sense that the classical concept of causality disappears in the atomic field. There is causality insofar as the quantum laws that describe the behavior of atoms are perfectly definite; there is not, however, a causal relationship between successive configurations of an atomic system when we attempt to describe these configurations in classical terms.

4□DISCUSSION OF MEASUREMENT

In this section we consider three fairly typical measurement experiments from the point of view of the new quantum mechanics. The first two are designed to determine the position and momentum of a particle by optical methods; the third is the diffraction experiment in Sec. 2.

LOCALIZATION EXPERIMENT

We consider a particular example of the validity of the uncertainty principle, making use of a position-momentum determination that is typical

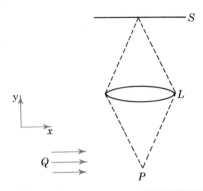

Fig. 2 An experiment for the localization of a particle P by means of one of the
scattered quanta Q, which is focused by
the lens L to form an image on the screen S.

of a number of somewhat similar experiments that have been discussed
in connection with measurements on particles and radiation fields.[1]   We
shall consider here the accuracy with which the x components of the
position and momentum vectors of a material particle can be determined
at the same time by observing the particle through a rather idealized
microscope by means of scattered light.

The best resolving power of the lens L shown in Fig. 2 is known
(either experimentally or from the theory of wave optics) to provide an
accuracy

$$\Delta x \sim \frac{\lambda}{\sin \epsilon} \tag{4.1}$$

in a position determination, where λ is the wavelength of the radiation
that enters the lens, and ϵ is the half angle subtended at the particle P
by the lens.   For simplicity, we consider the case in which only one of
the light quanta Q is scattered onto the screen S.   Because of the finite
aperture of the lens, the precise direction in which the photon is scattered
into the lens is not known.   Then since Eq. (1.2) states that the momentum of the photon after it is scattered is h/λ,[2] the uncertainty in the x
component of its momentum is approximately $(h/\lambda) \sin \epsilon$.

The x components of the momenta of the photon and the particle
can be accurately known before the scattering takes place, since there is
no need then to know the x components of their positions.   Also, if our
position measurement refers to the displacement of the particle with
respect to the microscope, there is no reason why the total momentum of
the system (particle, photon, and microscope) need be altered during the
scattering.   Then the uncertainty Δp_x in the x component of the momen-

---

[1] See, for example, W. Heisenberg, "The Physical Principles of the Quantum Theory,"
chaps. II, III (University of Chicago Press, Chicago, 1930); D. Bohm, "Quantum
Theory," chap. 5 (Prentice-Hall, Englewood Cliffs, N.J., 1951).

[2] See footnote 2, page 3.

tum of the particle after the scattering is equal to the corresponding uncertainty for the photon.

$$\Delta p_x \sim \frac{h}{\lambda} \sin \epsilon \tag{4.2}$$

If we combine Eq. (4.1) with Eq. (4.2), we see that just after the scattering process

$$\Delta x \cdot \Delta p_x \sim h \tag{4.3}$$

is the best that we can do for the particle. Thus a realistic accounting of the properties of the radiation gives a result in agreement with the uncertainty relation (3.1) for the particle.

This experiment may also be considered from the point of view of the complementarity principle. The complementary arrangements differ in the choice of wavelength of the observed radiation: Sufficiently small λ permits an accurate determination of the position of the particle just after the scattering process, and large λ of its momentum.

MOMENTUM DETERMINATION EXPERIMENT

The experiment just discussed assumes that the momentum of the particle is accurately known before the measurement takes place, and then it measures the position. It is found that the measurement not only gives a somewhat inaccurate position determination but also introduces an uncertainty into the momentum.

We now consider a different experiment in which the position is accurately known at the beginning and the momentum is measured. We shall see that the measurement not only gives a somewhat inaccurate momentum determination but also introduces an uncertainty into the position. We assume that the particle is an atom in an excited state, which will give off a photon that has the frequency ν_0 if the atom is at rest. Because of the doppler effect, motion of the atom toward the observer with speed v means that the observed frequency is given approximately by

$$\nu \approx \nu_0 \left(1 + \frac{v}{c} \right) \tag{4.4}$$

so that

$$v \approx c \left(\frac{\nu}{\nu_0} - 1 \right) \tag{4.5}$$

Accurate measurement of the momentum mv by measurement of the frequency ν requires a relatively long time τ; the minimum error in the frequency measurement can be shown to be

$$\Delta \nu \sim \frac{1}{\tau} \qquad (4.6)$$

The instant at which the photon is emitted is uncertain by τ; at this instant, the momentum of the atom decreases by $h\nu/c$, and its velocity decreases by $h\nu/mc$. This makes the subsequent position of the atom uncertain by the amount

$$\Delta x = \frac{h\nu\tau}{mc} \qquad (4.7)$$

since the later the photon is emitted, the longer the atom has the higher velocity and the farther it will have traveled. This position uncertainty arises entirely because of the finiteness of τ. If τ were zero, and we knew the velocity and the velocity change on emission of the photon, we would know where the atom is at each instant; it is because τ is finite that we do not know when the velocity changed and hence where the atom is at later times.

The momentum uncertainty is obtained with the help of Eqs. (4.5) and (4.6):

$$\Delta p_x = m\,\Delta v \approx \frac{mc\,\Delta\nu}{\nu_0} \sim \frac{mc}{\nu_0\tau} \qquad (4.8)$$

In the nonrelativistic case considered here, $v/c \ll 1$, and Eq. (4.4) shows that $\nu \approx \nu_0$. Then combination of Eqs. (4.7) and (4.8) leads to the minimum uncertainty relation (3.1).

ANALYSIS OF DIFFRACTION EXPERIMENT

Finally, we analyze the diffraction experiment of Sec. 2 from the point of view of the complementarity principle, assuming that the uncertainty principle is valid. Two contrasting arrangements, which would complement each other classically, are considered here. One of these is illustrated in Fig. 1. Since it is assumed that the distance from A to B is large compared with the distance between the two slits, and this in turn is large compared with the wavelength of the light, the distribution of intensity in the diffraction pattern determines to good approximation the angular distribution of the photons leaving the slits in A and hence determines the distribution of the y components of momentum of the photons beyond A. The second arrangement, shown in Fig. 3, determines through which of the two slits each photon passes and hence provides information on the y coordinates of the photons.

In the second arrangement each photon registers itself as it passes through a slit by bouncing off one of a number of indicators C placed

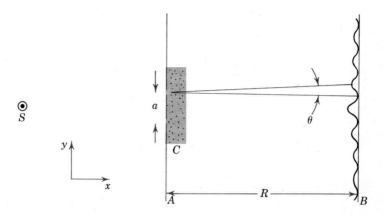

Fig. 3 The experimental arrangement of Fig. 1, modified by the addition of photon indicators C.

close to A, giving up to it a y component of momentum that may be uncertain by the amount Δp_y. If we do not want the resultant diffraction pattern of many such photons to be destroyed by these events, the uncertainty in p_y for a particular photon produced by its encounter with an indicator must be substantially smaller than would be required to throw the photon from a maximum of the diffraction pattern at B into a neighboring minimum. With a photon of momentum p_x, this requires that

$$\Delta p_y \ll \theta p_x \qquad (4.9)$$

For the simple case in which $R \gg a \gg \lambda$, the angle θ is known experimentally (or from the theory of wave optics) to be given by

$$\theta = \frac{\lambda}{2a} \qquad (4.10)$$

in terms of the optical wavelength λ and the distance a between the slits. At the same time, we have not learned through which slit this photon passed unless the uncertainty Δy of the y position of the indicator that recoiled is less than half the distance between slits.

$$\Delta y < \tfrac{1}{2}a \qquad (4.11)$$

It then follows from Eqs. (4.9) to (4.11) and (1.2) that the requirement that we be able to determine through which slit each photon passes without destroying the diffraction pattern at B is equivalent to the requirement that

$$\Delta y \cdot \Delta p_y \ll \tfrac{1}{4}h \qquad (4.12)$$

for each indicator that is used.   Since Eq. (4.12) is in disagreement with the uncertainty relation (3.1), we may conclude that it is impossible to determine through which slits the photons pass without destroying the diffraction pattern.

DISCUSSION OF DIFFRACTION EXPERIMENT

The situation just analyzed shows the intimate connection between the theoretical principles of uncertainty and complementarity and the experimental observations related to localization and diffraction.   It provides an explicit demonstration of the validity of the complementarity principle (represented in this case by the choice between the mutually exclusive but classically complementary experiments for observing the diffraction and for localizing the photon) when taken in conjunction with the experimentally observable properties of matter and radiation.   It shows that no fundamental difficulty need be encountered with the photon picture so long as we do not insist on the degree of detail in describing the situation that is entailed by classical concepts.

It is, of course, still necessary to ascribe unfamiliar properties to the photons in order to explain the experimental observations.   The foregoing discussion does not show how an individual photon can interfere with itself to produce the diffraction pattern, nor, on the other hand, does it show how an electromagnetic wave can eject photoelectrons from the screen.   Such demonstrations lie beyond the scope of the qualitative discussion of this chapter and require the use of the mathematical formalism of quantum mechanics.[1]   However, analysis of the diffraction experiment from the point of view of quantum mechanics removes the difficulty encountered in Sec. 2; the diffraction pattern disappears whenever a successful attempt is made to determine through which slit each photon passes.[2]

5☐WAVE PACKETS IN SPACE AND TIME

The relation (1.2) between momentum and wavelength, which is known experimentally to be valid for both photons and particles, suggests that it might be possible to use concentrated bunches of waves to describe localized particles of matter and quanta of radiation.   To fix our ideas,

---

[1] Chapter 14 shows how the theory of the electromagnetic field can be modified to include quantum effects.

[2] The matters discussed in this section are discussed more fully in the early chapters of the books by R. P. Feynman and A. R. Hibbs, "Quantum Mechanics and Path Integrals," (McGraw-Hill, New York, 1965) and by R. P. Feynman, R. B. Leighton, and M. Sands, "The Feynman Lectures on Physics," vol. III (Addison-Wesley, Reading, Mass., 1965).

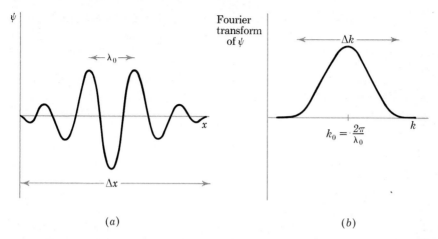

Fig. 4 Plots of a typical wave packet $\psi(x)$ and its Fourier transform.

we shall consider a *wave amplitude or wave function* that depends on the space coordinates x, y, z and the time t.   This quantity ψ is assumed to have three basic properties.   First, it can interfere with itself, so that it can account for the results of diffraction experiments.   Second, it is large in magnitude where the particle or photon is likely to be and small elsewhere.   And third, ψ will be regarded as describing the behavior of a single particle or photon, not the statistical distribution of a number of such quanta.   This last is an essential requirement in view of the conclusion of Sec. 2 that a single quantum of matter or radiation interferes with itself rather than with other quanta.   In this section we shall confine ourselves to a qualitative discussion of the one-dimensional case, in which the wave function ψ depends only on x and t, and leave the quantitative development for Chap. 2.

SPACE PACKETS

A typical form for a concentrated bunch of waves, which we shall call a *wave packet*, is shown in Fig. 4a, where $\psi(x,t)$ is plotted against x for a particular time t.   The average wavelength λ_0 and the approximate extension Δx of the packet are indicated in the diagram.   The Fourier integral analysis[1] of ψ with respect to x is now of interest since it shows how ψ may be built up out of continuous harmonic waves of various lengths.   This is indicated in Fig. 4b, in which the Fourier transform of ψ is plotted schematically against the *propagation number* $k = 2\pi/\lambda$.

[1] See, for example, P. M. Morse and H. Feshbach, "Methods of Theoretical Physics," sec. 4.8 (McGraw-Hill, New York, 1953).

It can be shown by standard mathematical methods that

$$\Delta k \gtrsim \frac{1}{\Delta x} \tag{5.1}$$

where Δk is the approximate spread in propagation number associated with the packet. If now we correlate wavelength and momentum as in Eq. (1.2) we see that the spread Δk corresponds to a momentum spread

$$\Delta p = \Delta \left(\frac{h}{\lambda}\right) = \frac{h}{2\pi} \Delta k = \hbar \cdot \Delta k \tag{5.2}$$

Combination of Eq. (5.1) with Eq. (5.2) gives

$$\Delta x \cdot \Delta p \gtrsim \hbar \tag{5.3}$$

which agrees with the uncertainty relation (3.1). Thus the uncertainty principle for position and momentum of a quantum of matter or radiation follows directly from the wave-packet description and Eq. (1.2).

TIME PACKETS

In analogous fashion, we may examine the dependence of ψ on the time t for a point x that is typical of the packet, and we obtain a time Fourier transform that shows how ψ can be built up out of continuous harmonic waves of various frequencies ν. In this case the relation between the spread in time of ψ and the spread in frequency of the time Fourier transform of ψ is

$$\Delta t \cdot \Delta \nu \gtrsim \frac{1}{2\pi} \tag{5.4}$$

Equation (5.4) may be brought into correspondence with the uncertainty principle by associating the energy E of a quantum with the frequency of the wave that represents it in a manner similar to the association of momentum with wavelength given by Eq. (1.2). We shall make this connection through Eq. (1.1):

$$E = h\nu \tag{5.5}$$

which may be inferred in the case of photons from the experimental discussion of Sec. 1. Combination of Eq. (5.4) with Eq. (5.5) then gives the uncertainty relation (3.3).

The assumption that Eq. (5.5) is valid for matter as well as for radiation may be made plausible by computing the group velocity[1] of a wave packet that represents a nonrelativistic particle of mass m, kinetic energy E, and momentum p for which λ and ν are given by Eqs. (1.2) and (5.5), respectively. The group velocity, which is the velocity of the center of

[1] Born, *op. cit.*, pp. 88, 330.

the packet, is equal to

$$\frac{d\nu}{d(1/\lambda)} = \frac{dE}{dp} = \frac{d(p^2/2m)}{dp} = \frac{p}{m} \tag{5.6}$$

in agreement with the classical expression for the velocity. This shows that, with Eq. (5.5), the wave-packet description of the motion of a particle agrees with the classical description when the circumstances are such that we can ignore the size and internal structure of the packet.

WAVE FORMALISM

We see then that quanta of matter or radiation can be represented in agreement with the uncertainty principle by wave packets that may be superposed to produce interference and whose magnitudes give a measure of likelihood of location, provided that use is made of the experimentally inferred relations (1.2) and (5.5). It is then possible to set up a quantitative formalism based on the mathematical analysis of wave motion. This will be done for matter in Chap. 2, using the physical principles outlined in this chapter as a guide and requiring always that the result of any calculation reduce to the result of the corresponding classical calculation in the appropriate limit. This requirement is a way of stating Bohr's correspondence principle, which was mentioned in Sec. 2. At the present time, when a reasonably complete quantum theory exists, the correspondence principle is mainly of interest in assuring that the formalism has the proper classical limit, although it may also be of heuristic value in performing new calculations or extending the boundaries of the theory.

It might at first be thought that the exclusive use of a wave formalism for the description of matter in the next four chapters would conflict with the observed particle-wave duality discussed in Sec. 1 and hence disagree with the complementarity principle. This is not the case, however, for the formalism actually provides an understanding of all the measurable properties of matter, including, for example, the production of particle tracks in a cloud chamber. Thus it will be shown in Sec. 38 that, if a single material particle is represented by a wave function of definite momentum and hence completely undetermined position, the probability of ionization of two or more molecules of the cloud-chamber gas is negligibly small unless the molecules lie very nearly along a line parallel to the momentum vector.

It must be emphasized that these remarks are true only if a wave function of the type described in this section is always interpreted as representing just one particle of matter and not the statistical distribution of a number of particles. When we wish to describe more than one particle, we must make use of a wave function that depends on the coordinates of all of them. The analogous analytical description of light quanta, which will be taken up quantitatively in Chap. 14, makes use of a somewhat different approach. This is mainly because photons (unlike particles as we consider them here) can be emitted or absorbed through interaction with matter, so that their number is not fixed. Thus a photon wave function would have to depend on a variable number of parameters, and it is desirable to avoid such a situation.

PROBLEMS

1. Give a brief description of each of the experiments referred to in Table 1, together with their interpretations.

2. Describe briefly the Davisson-Germer and Thomson experiments and the use of the Wilson cloud chamber for the observation of particle tracks.

3. A beam of silver atoms for a Stern-Gerlach experiment is produced by collimating atoms that vaporize from silver held in a furnace at 1200°C. If the beam travels 1 meter, use the uncertainty relation to find the order of magnitude of the smallest spot that can be obtained at the detector.

4. A 1-ounce rifle bullet takes 0.5 sec to reach its target. Regarding the bullet as a mass point, and neglecting effects of air resistance and earth motion, find the order of magnitude of the spread of successive shots at the target under optimum conditions of aiming and firing.

5. A perfectly elastic ping-pong ball is dropped in vacuum from a height equal to ten times its radius onto a perfectly elastic fixed sphere of the same radius. Neglecting effects due to earth motion, estimate the largest number of bounces against the fixed sphere that the ball can be expected to make under optimum conditions of release.

6. A beam of monoenergetic electrons is used to excite a particular level of an atom in a Franck-Hertz experiment. If this level is of short duration, owing to radiation back to the ground state, show that the inelastically scattered electrons that have lost energy to produce the excited level will not all be expected to have the same final energy. If the excited level lasts about 10^{-10} sec, what is the order of magnitude of the electron energy spread, measured in electron-volts?

7. Discuss any connections you can think of that exist between the three uncertainty relations (3.1), (3.2), and (3.3).

8. Derive the expression for the group velocity that is given as the left side of Eq. (5.6).

2
The Schrödinger
Wave Equation

This and the next several chapters are concerned with the nonrelativistic motion of a particle in a force field that can be represented by a potential energy.[1] A quantitative description of the motion in terms of a differential equation, the *Schrödinger wave equation*, is developed in this chapter and applied to a simple one-dimensional problem. Various assumptions have to be made as regards the structure of the wave equation, the boundary and continuity conditions on its solutions, and the physical meaning of these solutions. These assumptions are given a high degree of plausibility in this chapter and the next by relating them to experimental results, mainly those that deal with the diffraction of material particles and with the existence of a classical limit to the quantum mechanics. However, no attempt is made to derive the formalism uniquely from a consideration of the experiments. The definitive test

---

[1] This is an idealization of the true situation, in which special relativity must be taken into account, particles can be created and destroyed, and interactions cannot be described by potentials. Nevertheless, it is extraordinarily useful in dealing with atoms, molecules, condensed matter, and atomic nuclei.

of the theory must, of course, be its internal consistency and the success with which deductions from it agree with particular experimental measurements; some examples will be worked out in Chaps. 4 and 5.

6□DEVELOPMENT OF THE WAVE EQUATION

The form of the Schrödinger wave equation is obtained in this section by generalizing the properties of the wave amplitude of Sec. 5. The remainder of this chapter presents a discussion of some of the properties of the equation and its solutions.

TRAVELING HARMONIC WAVES

The first task is to develop in more quantitative fashion the properties of the one-dimensional wave function $\psi(x,t)$ that was discussed qualitatively in Sec. 5. It was shown there that for a continuous traveling harmonic wave, the wavelength and momentum are related by Eq. (1.2) and the energy and frequency by Eq. (5.5). We rewrite these two equations in terms of the universal constant $\hbar = h/2\pi$:

$$p = \hbar k \qquad k = \frac{2\pi}{\lambda} \tag{6.1}$$

$$E = \hbar \omega \qquad \omega = 2\pi \nu \tag{6.2}$$

A wave function $\psi(x,t)$ that represents a particle of completely undetermined position traveling in the positive x direction with precisely known momentum p and kinetic energy E would then be expected to have one of the forms

$$\cos{(kx - \omega t)} \qquad \sin{(kx - \omega t)} \qquad e^{i(kx-\omega t)} \qquad e^{-i(kx-\omega t)} \tag{6.3}$$

or some linear combination of them. This follows from diffraction experiments like those of Davisson and Germer and of Thomson (see Sec. 1) and from the requirement that a wave packet of approximately the propagation number k and angular frequency ω has a group velocity equal to that of a classical free particle of momentum p and energy E [see Eq. (5.6)].

NEED FOR A WAVE EQUATION

In order to go beyond the very simplest problem of a continuous harmonic wave, it is very desirable to have an equation of which both the harmonic waves and more complicated waves are solutions. An example from a more familiar field of physics should help to clarify this point. In the case of three-dimensional sound waves in a gas, it is possible to obtain a solution of the problem of the scattering of sound by a rigid sphere by superposing plane harmonic waves traveling in various directions. But it is far simpler to solve the differential equation for sound waves directly in spherical polar coordinates. If the temperature of the gas changes from point to point, no progress can be made in the general case without such a differential equation. The correct underlying equation for sound waves can be found from direct consideration of the mechanical properties of the gas. Although this is not the case with the equation of which the wave functions of Sec. 5 are solutions, it is no less imperative to find the form of the equation. The need for this becomes more evident when the wave function is to describe the motion of a particle under the influence of external forces; this situation turns out to be analogous to the propagation of sound waves in an inhomogeneous gas. We shall, therefore, find an equation for ψ and, having found it, shall regard it as a more fundamental attribute of the wave functions than the harmonic forms (6.3).

The equation must have two basic properties. First, it must be linear, in order that solutions of it can be superposed to produce interference effects (in the three-dimensional case) and to permit the construction of wave packets. And, second, the coefficients of the equation must involve only constants such as $\hbar$ and the mass and charge of the particle, and not the parameters of a particular kind of motion of the particle (momentum, energy, propagation number, and frequency). The reason for the latter requirement is that we shall want to leave open the possibility of superposing solutions that belong to different values of these parameters; this means that such a more general wave function cannot be a solution of an equation that involves the parameters in its structure. Since differential equations are the easiest to handle, it is worthwhile to try this type first, and it turns out that the requirements can be met by a differential equation.

With all these considerations in mind, we look first at the most familiar one-dimensional wave equation, that which describes the motion of transverse waves on a string or plane sound waves in a gas:

$$\frac{\partial^2 \psi}{\partial t^2} = \gamma \frac{\partial^2 \psi}{\partial x^2} \tag{6.4}$$

where γ is the square of the wave velocity. Substitution of the forms (6.3) into Eq. (6.4) shows that each of the four harmonic solutions, and hence any linear combination of them, satisfies this differential equation if and only if we put

$$\gamma = \frac{\omega^2}{k^2} = \frac{E^2}{p^2} = \frac{p^2}{4m^2} \tag{6.5}$$

where m is the mass of the particle that is to be described by Eq. (6.4). Because of the structure of Eq. (6.5) it is apparent that the coefficient γ that appears in Eq. (6.4) involves the parameters of the motion (E or p); we therefore discard this differential equation.

THE ONE-DIMENSIONAL WAVE EQUATION

In looking further for a suitable equation, it is helpful to note that differentiation with respect to x of wave functions like those of (6.3) has the general effect of multiplication of the function by k (and sometimes also interchanging sine and cosine), whereas differentiation with respect to t has the general effect of multiplication by ω. Then the relation $E = p^2/2m$, which is equivalent to the relation $\omega = \hbar k^2/2m$, suggests that the differential equation for which we are looking contains a first derivative with respect to t and a second derivative with respect to x.

$$\frac{\partial \psi}{\partial t} = \gamma \frac{\partial^2 \psi}{\partial x^2} \tag{6.6}$$

Substitution shows that the first two of the wave functions (6.3) are not solutions of Eq. (6.6) but that either of the last two may be (but not both at once) if the constant γ is suitably chosen. In particular, if we choose

$$\gamma = \frac{i\omega}{k^2} = \frac{i\hbar E}{p^2} = \frac{i\hbar}{2m} \tag{6.7}$$

then the third of the wave functions (6.3) satisfies Eq. (6.6). Moreover, the value of γ given by Eq. (6.7) involves only the constants $\hbar$ and m.

We are thus led to the one-dimensional form of the Schrödinger[1] wave equation for a free particle of mass m, which from Eqs. (6.6) and (6.7) may be written

$$i\hbar \frac{\partial \psi}{\partial t} = -\frac{\hbar^2}{2m} \frac{\partial^2 \psi}{\partial x^2} \tag{6.8}$$

The particular form in which Eq. (6.8) is written is significant insofar as its harmonic solution, the third of the wave functions (6.3), makes the left side $E\psi$ and the right side $(p^2/2m)\psi$. The fact that the solution $e^{i(kx-\omega t)}$ is complex is not in itself a defect of the formalism. We shall have to be certain that all predicted results of possible physical observations are expressible in terms of real numbers, and this will supply a condition on the detailed interpretation of ψ.

EXTENSION TO THREE DIMENSIONS

The foregoing one-dimensional treatment is readily extended to three dimensions. It is natural to rewrite Eq. (6.1) as

$$\mathbf{p} = \hbar \mathbf{k} \qquad k = |\mathbf{k}| = \frac{2\pi}{\lambda} \tag{6.9}$$

---

[1] E. Schrödinger, *Ann. Physik* **79**, 361, 489 (1926); **81**, 109 (1926). The present treatment is somewhat different from that originally given by Schrödinger.

where $\mathbf{k}$ is called the *propagation vector*. Similarly, the third of the wave functions (6.3) becomes

$$\exp i(\mathbf{k} \cdot \mathbf{r} - \omega t) \tag{6.10}$$

where $\mathbf{r}$ is the position vector for the particle. Then, by an obvious extension of the argument that led up to Eq. (6.8), it is seen that the three-dimensional Schrödinger equation for a free particle that is represented by the wave function $\psi(\mathbf{r},t)$ is

$$i\hbar \frac{\partial \psi}{\partial t} = - \frac{\hbar^2}{2m} \nabla^2 \psi \tag{6.11}$$

A comparison of Eqs. (6.9) to (6.11) and the classical energy equation

$$E = \frac{\mathbf{p}^2}{2m} \tag{6.12}$$

suggests that, at least for a free particle, the energy and momentum can be represented by differential operators that act on the wave function ψ.

$$E \rightarrow i\hbar \frac{\partial}{\partial t} \qquad \mathbf{p} \rightarrow -i\hbar \nabla \tag{6.13}$$

The development of Secs. 7, 8, 10, and 11 will show that these are also valid representations when the particle is not free.

INCLUSION OF FORCES

The next problem is to extend the free-particle wave equation (6.11) so that it includes the effects of external forces that may act on the particle. We shall assume for the present that these forces are of such a nature (electrostatic, gravitational, possibly nuclear) that they can be combined into a single force $\mathbf{F}$ that is derivable from a real potential energy V.

$$\mathbf{F}(\mathbf{r},t) = -\nabla V(\mathbf{r},t) \tag{6.14}$$

Just as the classical relation between energy and momentum is used above to infer the structure of Eq. (6.11), so it is desirable now to start from the corresponding classical relation that includes external forces. This is simply expressed in terms of the potential energy

$$E = \frac{\mathbf{p}^2}{2m} + V(\mathbf{r},t) \tag{6.15}$$

where E is now the total energy, and the first and second terms on the right side of Eq. (6.15) are the kinetic and potential energies of the particle, respectively.

Since V does not depend on $\mathbf{p}$ or E, Eqs. (6.15) and (6.13) suggest that Eq. (6.11) be generalized into

$$i\hbar \frac{\partial \psi}{\partial t} = -\frac{\hbar^2}{2m} \nabla^2 \psi + V(\mathbf{r},t)\psi \qquad (6.16)$$

This is the Schrödinger wave equation that describes the motion of a particle of mass m in a force field given by Eq. (6.14).[1] Although the introduction of Eq. (6.16) cannot claim as high a degree of plausibility as the derivation of the free-particle equation (6.11), the further discussion of the next section should make it more convincing. It is, of course, the agreement of solutions of Eq. (6.16) with experiment in particular cases that eventually demonstrates the validity and usefulness of this wave equation.

7☐INTERPRETATION OF THE WAVE FUNCTION

The wave function $\psi(\mathbf{r},t)$, which is a solution of the wave equation (6.16), is now assumed to provide a quantum-mechanically complete description of the behavior of a particle of mass m with the potential energy $V(\mathbf{r},t)$ and hence is analogous to the classical trajectory $\mathbf{r}(t)$. Thus far, the only interpretative guide available to us is that the wave function be large where the particle is likely to be and small elsewhere. This has to be supplemented with more detailed statements that enable us to get out of ψ the maximum amount of information permitted by nature, as was discussed in Sec. 3. As with the structure of the wave equation, the correctness of our interpretation of the wave function must be judged by logical consistency and appeal to experimental results.

STATISTICAL INTERPRETATION

The phrase "likely to be" in the preceding paragraph, together with the discussion of Sec. 3, indicates the need for interpreting ψ in statistical terms. We can imagine a very large number of identical, independent, nonoverlapping regions of space, each large enough to contain all the physically interesting features of the motion, in each of which the behavior of a particle with the potential energy $V(\mathbf{r},t)$ is described by the same wave function $\psi(\mathbf{r},t)$; in each case $\mathbf{r}$ is referred to the origin of the particular region. Or we can imagine a very large number of independent repetitions of the same motion in the same region of space, for each of which t is referred to the particular origin of the time. We then make the

---

[1] The development of the wavefunction in time can also be related to integrals over all possible paths of the particle; see R. P. Feynman, *Rev. Mod. Phys.* **20**, 367 (1948), and the book by R. P. Feynman and A. R. Hibbs, "Quantum Mechanics and Path Integrals" (McGraw-Hill, New York, 1965).

assumption, due to Born,[1] that the numerical result of the measurement at a particular time t (insofar as the time at which the measurement is made can be specified) of any physically meaningful quantity, such as position, momentum, or energy, will in general not be the same for all the regions. Rather, there will be a distribution of these numbers that can be described by a probability function.

For example, we have seen in Sec. 5 that the result of a position determination is to be regarded as uncertain by an amount of the order of the linear dimensions of the wave function. It is natural therefore to regard ψ as a measure of the probability of finding a particle at a particular position with respect to the origin of its region. However, a probability must be real and nonnegative, whereas ψ is complex in general. We therefore assume that the product of ψ and its complex conjugate ψ^* is the *position probability density.*

$$P(\mathbf{r},t) = \psi^*(\mathbf{r},t)\psi(\mathbf{r},t) = |\psi(\mathbf{r},t)|^2 \tag{7.1}$$

This means that $P(\mathbf{r},t)\, dx\, dy\, dz$ is to be the probability of finding a particle in its volume element $dx\, dy\, dz$ about its point $\mathbf{r}$ at the time t, when a large number of precise position measurements are made on independent particles each of which is described by the one-particle wave function $\psi(\mathbf{r},t)$.

NORMALIZATION OF ψ

The probability of finding the particle somewhere in the region must be unity, so that Eq. (7.1) implies that the wave function is *normalized:*

$$\int |\psi(\mathbf{r},t)|^2\, d^3r = 1 \tag{7.2}$$

where the integral extends over the entire region; here d^3r is the three-dimensional volume element $dx\, dy\, dz$. If ψ is a wave packet of the type discussed in Sec. 5, the integral in Eq. (7.2) converges, and the numerical coefficient of ψ may be adjusted so that the integral is unity; such normalization does not change the fact that ψ is a solution of Eq. (6.16), which is homogeneous in ψ. There are, however, wave functions like that given in Eq. (6.10) for which the integral in Eq. (7.2) does not converge if taken over an infinite volume. Such wave functions require special consideration and will be discussed further in Secs. 10 and 11. For the present, we may think of the region of space in which such a wave function is defined as being arbitrarily large but finite; then the integral in Eq. (7.2) is over the finite volume of this region and converges, so that normalization is always possible.

The coefficient of ψ that normalizes it must be independent of the time in order that ψ may satisfy the wave equation (6.16). Thus, if

[1] M. Born, *Z. Physik* **37**, 863 (1926); *Nature* **119**, 354 (1927).

Eq. (7.2) is satisfied at one instant of time, the interpretation of $|\psi|^2$ as a position probability density requires that the normalization integral be independent of the time. That this is actually the case may be shown by computing the time derivative of the integral of P over any fixed volume Ω:

$$\frac{\partial}{\partial t} \int_\Omega P(\mathbf{r},t) \, d^3r = \int_\Omega \left(\psi^* \frac{\partial \psi}{\partial t} + \frac{\partial \psi^*}{\partial t} \psi \right) d^3r$$

$$= \frac{i\hbar}{2m} \int_\Omega [\psi^* \nabla^2 \psi - (\nabla^2 \psi^*)\psi] \, d^3r$$

$$= \frac{i\hbar}{2m} \int_\Omega \nabla \cdot [\psi^* \nabla \psi - (\nabla \psi^*)\psi] \, d^3r$$

$$= \frac{i\hbar}{2m} \int_A [\psi^* \nabla \psi - (\nabla \psi^*)\psi]_n \, dA$$

Here substitution has been made for $\partial \psi / \partial t$ from Eq. (6.16) and for $\partial \psi^* / \partial t$ from the complex conjugate of Eq. (6.16). The last integral is obtained by partial integration (use of Green's theorem), where A is the bounding surface of the region of integration and [ ]$_n$ denotes the component of the vector in brackets in the direction of the outward normal to the surface element dA.[1]

We define a vector $\mathbf{S}(\mathbf{r},t)$,

$$\mathbf{S}(\mathbf{r},t) = \frac{\hbar}{2im} [\psi^* \nabla \psi - (\nabla \psi^*)\psi] \tag{7.3}$$

in terms of which

$$\frac{\partial}{\partial t} \int_\Omega P(\mathbf{r},t) \, d^3r = -\int_\Omega \nabla \cdot \mathbf{S} \, d^3r = -\int_A S_n \, dA \tag{7.4}$$

In the case of a wave packet, for which ψ vanishes at great distances and the normalization integral converges, the surface integral is evidently zero when Ω is the entire space. For a wave function of the type given in Eq. (6.10), ψ can be defined in a finite region Ω so that it vanishes or has a periodic structure along the bounding surfaces (see Sec. 10). In all these cases, it can be shown without difficulty that the surface integral in Eq. (7.4) is zero, so that the normalization integral in Eq. (7.2) is constant in time.

PROBABILITY CURRENT DENSITY

The derivation of Eq. (7.4) also shows that the differential relation

$$\frac{\partial P(\mathbf{r},t)}{\partial t} + \nabla \cdot \mathbf{S}(\mathbf{r},t) = 0$$

[1] It is convenient to adopt an order of factors such that ψ^* precedes ψ [see the discussion of Eq. (7.7) below].

is valid.   This has the familiar form associated with the conservation of
flow of a fluid of density P and current density $\mathbf{S}$, in which there are no
sources or sinks.   It is thus reasonable to interpret $\mathbf{S}(\mathbf{r},t)$ given by Eq.
(7.3) as a *probability current density*.   This interpretation makes more
plausible the identification of $-i\hbar\nabla$ with the momentum in Eq. (6.13),
even when a force is present.   Then $(\hbar/im)\nabla$ is the velocity operator,
and it is apparent that

$$\mathbf{S}(\mathbf{r},t) = \text{real part of } \left(\psi^* \frac{\hbar}{im} \nabla\psi\right)$$

Although this interpretation of $\mathbf{S}$ is suggestive, it must be realized
that $\mathbf{S}$ is not susceptible to direct measurement in the sense in which P is.
It would be misleading, for example, to say that $\mathbf{S}(\mathbf{r},t)$ is the average
measured particle flux at the point $\mathbf{r}$ and the time t, because a measurement of average local flux implies simultaneous high-precision measurements of position and velocity (which is equivalent to momentum) and is
therefore inconsistent with the uncertainty relation (3.1).   Nevertheless,
it is sometimes helpful to think of $\mathbf{S}$ as a flux vector, especially when it
depends only slightly or not at all on $\mathbf{r}$, so that an accurate velocity
determination can be made without impairing the usefulness of the concept of flux.

EXPECTATION VALUE

The existence of the position probability density $P(\mathbf{r},t)$ makes it possible
to calculate what we shall call the *expectation value* of the position vector
of a particle, which is defined as the vector whose components are the
weighted averages of the corresponding components of the position of the
particle.   The expectation value is the mathematical expectation (in the
sense of probability theory) for the result of a single measurement, or
it is the average of the results of a large number of measurements on
independent systems of the type discussed at the beginning of this section.   We write the expectation value of $\mathbf{r}$ as

$$\langle\mathbf{r}\rangle = \int\mathbf{r}P(\mathbf{r},t)\,d^3r = \int\psi^*(\mathbf{r},t)\mathbf{r}\psi(\mathbf{r},t)\,d^3r \tag{7.5}$$

which is equivalent to the three equations

$$\langle x\rangle = \int\psi^*x\psi\,d^3r \qquad \langle y\rangle = \int\psi^*y\psi\,d^3r \qquad \langle z\rangle = \int\psi^*z\psi\,d^3r$$

where ψ is normalized.   The expectation value is a function only of the
time, since ψ and P depend on t and the space coordinates have been
integrated out.
The expectation values of any other physically meaningful quantities can be found in a similar way if they are functions only of the

particle coordinate **r**. Thus the expectation value of the potential energy is

$$\langle V \rangle = \int V(\mathbf{r},t) P(\mathbf{r},t) \, d^3r = \int \psi^*(\mathbf{r},t) V(\mathbf{r},t) \psi(\mathbf{r},t) \, d^3r \qquad (7.6)$$

A quantity such as momentum or energy must, however, be expressed in terms of **r** and t before a calculation of this type can be made. We assume that it is possible to use the differential-operator representations given in Eq. (6.13) for this purpose and will justify this assumption with the help of the corresponding probability functions in Sec. 10 (for the energy) and in Sec. 11 (for the momentum). The question immediately arises, however, as to how such differential operators are to be combined with the position probability density P.

This question may be answered by imposing on the expectation values the reasonable requirement that

$$\langle E \rangle = \left\langle \frac{\mathbf{p}^2}{2m} \right\rangle + \langle V \rangle$$

in analogy with the classical energy equation (6.15). In terms of differential operators, this may be written

$$\left\langle i\hbar \frac{\partial}{\partial t} \right\rangle = \left\langle -\frac{\hbar^2}{2m} \nabla^2 \right\rangle + \langle V \rangle \qquad (7.7)$$

It is apparent that Eq. (7.7) is consistent with the wave equation (6.16) only if the expectation value is defined in the general case with the operator acting on ψ and multiplied on the left by ψ^*. We therefore obtain, for example,

$$\langle E \rangle = \int \psi^* i\hbar \frac{\partial \psi}{\partial t} \, d^3r \qquad \langle \mathbf{p} \rangle = \int \psi^*(-i\hbar) \nabla \psi \, d^3r \qquad (7.8)$$

Like Eq. (7.5), the second of Eqs. (7.8) is equivalent to the three component equations

$$\langle p_x \rangle = -i\hbar \int \psi^* \frac{\partial \psi}{\partial x} \, d^3r \qquad \langle p_y \rangle = -i\hbar \int \psi^* \frac{\partial \psi}{\partial y} \, d^3r$$

$$\langle p_z \rangle = -i\hbar \int \psi^* \frac{\partial \psi}{\partial z} \, d^3r$$

EHRENFEST'S THEOREM[1]

It is reasonable to expect the motion of a wave packet to agree with the motion of the corresponding classical particle whenever the potential energy changes by a negligible amount over the dimensions of the packet.

[1] P. Ehrenfest, *Z. Physik* **45**, 455 (1927).

If we mean by the "position" and "momentum" vectors of the packet the weighted averages or expectation values of these quantities, we can show that the classical and quantum motions always agree. A component of the "velocity" of the packet will be the time rate of change of the expectation value of that component of the position; since $\langle x \rangle$ depends only on the time and the x in the integrand of Eq. (7.5) is a variable of integration, this is

$$\frac{d}{dt} \langle x \rangle = \frac{d}{dt} \int \psi^* x \psi \, d^3r = \int \psi^* x \frac{\partial \psi}{\partial t} \, d^3r + \int \frac{\partial \psi^*}{\partial t} x \psi \, d^3r$$

This may be simplified by substituting for the time derivatives of the wave function and its complex conjugate from Eq. (6.16) and canceling the V terms, where we continue to assume for the present that V is real:

$$\frac{d}{dt} \langle x \rangle = -\frac{i}{\hbar} \left[\int \psi^* x \left(-\frac{\hbar^2}{2m} \nabla^2 \psi + V\psi \right) d^3r \right.$$
$$\left. - \int \left(-\frac{\hbar^2}{2m} \nabla^2 \psi^* + V\psi^* \right) x\psi \, d^3r \right]$$
$$= \frac{i\hbar}{2m} \int [\psi^* x (\nabla^2 \psi) - (\nabla^2 \psi^*) x\psi] \, d^3r$$

The second integral can be integrated by parts:

$$\int (\nabla^2 \psi^*) x\psi \, d^3r = -\int (\nabla\psi^*) \cdot \nabla(x\psi) \, d^3r + \int_A (x\psi\nabla\psi^*)_n \, dA$$

where the integral of the normal component of $x\psi\nabla\psi^*$ over the infinite bounding surface A is zero because a wave packet ψ vanishes at great distances. A second partial integration, in which the surface integral again vanishes, results in

$$\int (\nabla^2 \psi^*) x\psi \, d^3r = \int \psi^* \nabla^2 (x\psi) \, d^3r$$

Thus

$$\frac{d}{dt} \langle x \rangle = \frac{i\hbar}{2m} \int \psi^* [x\nabla^2 \psi - \nabla^2 (x\psi)] \, d^3r$$
$$= -\frac{i\hbar}{m} \int \psi^* \frac{\partial \psi}{\partial x} \, d^3r = \frac{1}{m} \langle p_x \rangle \tag{7.9}$$

Since $\langle x \rangle$ is seen always to be a real number from the structure of Eq. (7.5), Eq. (7.9) shows quite incidentally that $\langle p_x \rangle$ is real; this can also be shown from the second of Eqs. (7.8) when ψ represents a wave packet, by means of a partial integration.

In similar fashion we can calculate the time rate of change of a component of the "momentum" of the particle as

$$\frac{d}{dt}\langle p_x \rangle = -i\hbar \frac{d}{dt} \int \psi^* \frac{\partial \psi}{\partial x} d^3r$$

$$= -i\hbar \left(\int \psi^* \frac{\partial}{\partial x} \frac{\partial \psi}{\partial t} d^3r + \int \frac{\partial \psi^*}{\partial t} \frac{\partial \psi}{\partial x} d^3r \right)$$

$$= -\int \psi^* \frac{\partial}{\partial x} \left(-\frac{\hbar^2}{2m} \nabla^2 \psi + V\psi \right) d^3r$$

$$+ \int \left(-\frac{\hbar^2}{2m} \nabla^2 \psi^* + V\psi^* \right) \frac{\partial \psi}{\partial x} d^3r$$

$$= -\int \psi^* \left[\frac{\partial}{\partial x} (V\psi) - V \frac{\partial \psi}{\partial x} \right] d^3r$$

$$= -\int \psi^* \frac{\partial V}{\partial x} \psi \, d^3r = \left\langle -\frac{\partial V}{\partial x} \right\rangle \qquad (7.10)$$

again substituting from the wave equation and integrating twice by parts.

Equations (7.9) and (7.10), together with their other components, constitute *Ehrenfest's theorem*. They are analogous to the classical equations of motion:

$$\frac{d\mathbf{r}}{dt} = \frac{\mathbf{p}}{m} \qquad \frac{d\mathbf{p}}{dt} = -\nabla V$$

Ehrenfest's theorem provides an example of the correspondence principle, since it shows that a wave packet moves like a classical particle whenever the expectation value gives a good representation of the classical variable; this is usually the macroscopic limit in which the finite size and the internal structure of the packet can be ignored.

8☐ENERGY EIGENFUNCTIONS

The Schrödinger wave equation (6.16) admits of considerable simplification when the potential energy $V(\mathbf{r})$ does not depend on the time. It is then possible to express its general solution as a sum of products of functions of $\mathbf{r}$ and t separately.

SEPARATION OF THE WAVE EQUATION

We consider a particular solution of Eq. (6.16) that can be written as a product: $\psi(\mathbf{r},t) = u(\mathbf{r})f(t)$. A general solution can then be written as a sum of such separated solutions. If we substitute into Eq. (6.16) and divide through by the product, we obtain

$$\frac{i\hbar}{f} \frac{df}{dt} = \frac{1}{u} \left[-\frac{\hbar^2}{2m} \nabla^2 u + V(\mathbf{r})u \right] \qquad (8.1)$$

Since the left side of Eq. (8.1) depends only on t and the right side only on $\mathbf{r}$, both sides must be equal to the same separation constant, which we call E. Then the equation for f is readily integrated to give

$$f(t) = Ce^{-iEt/\hbar}$$

where C is an arbitrary constant, and the equation for u becomes

$$\left[-\frac{\hbar^2}{2m}\nabla^2 + V(\mathbf{r}) \right] u(\mathbf{r}) = Eu(\mathbf{r}) \tag{8.2}$$

Since Eq. (8.2) is homogeneous in u, the constant C may be chosen to normalize u. Then a particular solution of the wave equation is

$$\psi(\mathbf{r},t) = u(\mathbf{r})e^{-iEt/\hbar} \tag{8.3}$$

SIGNIFICANCE OF THE SEPARATION CONSTANT E

The time-derivative operator given in Eq. (6.13) as a representation of the total energy may be applied to the ψ of Eq. (8.3) to give

$$i\hbar \frac{\partial \psi}{\partial t} = E\psi \tag{8.4}$$

An equation of the type of Eq. (8.4) is called an *eigenvalue equation;* ψ is said to be an *eigenfunction* of the operator that appears on the left, and the multiplying constant E that appears on the right is called the corresponding *eigenvalue.*[1] An energy eigenfunction, like the ψ in Eq. (8.3), is said to represent a *stationary state* of the particle, since $|\psi|^2$ is constant in time.

Equation (8.2) is also an eigenvalue equation. It states that u (and hence also ψ) is an eigenfunction of the operator $-(\hbar^2/2m)\nabla^2 + V(\mathbf{r})$ with the same eigenvalue E. It is, of course, to be expected that ψ is an eigenfunction of this operator if it is an eigenfunction of the time-derivative operator since, according to the wave equation (6.16), the two operators are equivalent not only for separated functions of the form of Eq. (8.3) but also for more general solutions.

We now anticipate the discussion of the physical significance of eigenfunctions and eigenvalues that will be presented in Chap. 3 and assume that the energy eigenvalues E are the only possible results of precise measurements of the total energy of the particle. It is then of interest to inquire whether or not physically interesting solutions $u(\mathbf{r})$ of Eq. (8.2) exist for all real values of E. An answer cannot be obtained until a specification of "physical interest" is found in terms of the boundary conditions that are imposed on $u(\mathbf{r})$. This specification and the

---

[1] The terms *characteristic function* and *characteristic value* are often used in place of *eigenfunction* and *eigenvalue.*

general character of the energy eigenvalues that are associated with various types of potential energy function $V(\mathbf{r})$ are considered in the remainder of this section.

BOUNDARY CONDITIONS AT GREAT DISTANCES

We have thus far encountered two classes of wave functions: wave packets that are well localized and for which the normalization integral $\int|\psi|^2 \, d^3r$ converges, and traveling harmonic waves like the function (6.10) that have a constant magnitude at great distances so that the normalization integral taken over an infinite volume diverges. The first class may be interpreted as representing particles that, if free, are initially well localized or that are restrained to a particular region of space by external forces derived from the potential energy $V(\mathbf{r})$. The second class represents particles that are neither localized nor restrained but travel through the region under consideration from one distant part of space to another; such wave functions will be useful in describing the scattering of particles by a field of force.[1] In either case, the wave functions are bounded at great distances in all directions.

CONTINUITY CONDITIONS

The time-independent wave equation (8.2) is a second-order linear differential equation in $\mathbf{r}$. Thus so long as $V(\mathbf{r})$ is finite, whether or not it is continuous, a knowledge of the wave function and its gradient along a surface makes it possible to integrate the equation to obtain the wave function at any point. It is reasonable, therefore, to require that the wave function and its gradient be continuous, finite, and single-valued at every point in space, in order that a definite physical situation can be represented uniquely by a wave function. These requirements also have the consequence that the position probability density $P(\mathbf{r})$ and the probability current density $\mathbf{S}(\mathbf{r})$, defined in Sec. 7, are finite and continuous everywhere.

BOUNDARY CONDITIONS FOR INFINITE POTENTIAL ENERGY

If $V(\mathbf{r})$ is infinite anywhere, the appropriate boundary condition can be established by a limiting process that starts from a finite V and the above continuity conditions.

Suppose, for example, that there is an infinite discontinuity in V across a continuous surface, so that the potential energy is finite on one side of it and $+\infty$ on the other, and we wish to determine the boundary

---

[1] Another possible class consists of wave functions that become infinite at large distances; however, these are not of physical interest, since we have no reason to be concerned with particles for which the position probability density becomes indefinitely large in remote regions of space.

conditions on $u(\mathbf{r})$ and ∇u at this surface. The essential features of the problem are retained if we replace the continuous surface by the plane that is tangent to it at the point of interest and the continuously changing potential energy on one side of the surface by a constant potential, which can, without loss of generality, be chosen to be zero since any constant change in V is equivalent to an equal change in E. We choose the origin of coordinates at the point of interest and the x axis perpendicular to the tangent plane.

The wave equation (8.2) then separates in the three space coordinates, and the dependence of u on y and z is not affected by the discontinuity in V at the plane $x = 0$. We wish therefore to solve the one-dimensional wave equation

$$-\frac{\hbar^2}{2m}\frac{d^2u}{dx^2} + V(x)u = Eu \qquad (8.5)$$

where $V(x) = 0$ for $x < 0$, $V(x) = V_0$ for $x > 0$, and we eventually pass to the limit $V_0 \to +\infty$. If we assume that $0 \leq E < V_0$, the general solutions of Eq. (8.5) are

$$u(x) = A \sin \alpha x + B \cos \alpha x \qquad x < 0 \qquad \alpha = +\left(\frac{2mE}{\hbar^2}\right)^{\frac{1}{2}}$$

$$u(x) = Ce^{-\beta x} + De^{\beta x} \qquad x > 0 \qquad \beta = +\left[\frac{2m(V_0 - E)}{\hbar^2}\right]^{\frac{1}{2}}$$

The boundary condition that u be bounded at great distances requires that we set $D = 0$. Then the continuity of u at $x = 0$ gives the relation $B = C$, and the continuity of du/dx gives the relation $\alpha A = -\beta C$. Since β becomes infinite when V_0 does, and the solution for $x < 0$ must be finite, the second relation shows that C becomes zero as $V_0 \to \infty$, thus also making B zero; A is not determined from these relations but might be fixed by normalization.

Thus the boundary conditions at a surface at which there is an infinite potential step are that the wave function is zero and the component of the gradient of the wave function normal to the surface is not determined. The assumption above that $E < V_0$ is evidently not a restriction since V_0 eventually becomes infinite. For $E < 0$, the sine and cosine in the solution for $x < 0$ are replaced by hyperbolic sine and cosine (which is permissible since the solution need hold only near $x = 0$), with no change in the final result. It should be noted that both P and S_x vanish as $x \to 0$ from the negative side, so that they are continuous at $x = 0$ even though du/dx is not.

A boundary surface of this type represents a perfectly rigid, impenetrable wall, since in the analogous classical situation a particle of any finite energy would have its x component of momentum reversed instantaneously on contact with the surface.

ENERGY EIGENVALUES IN ONE DIMENSION

Energy eigenfunctions that represent particles that are restrained to a particular region of space by the potential energy (first class) are always characterized by discrete eigenvalues, whereas eigenfunctions that do not vanish at great distances (second class) possess a continuous range of eigenvalues. This may be seen qualitatively by considering the nature of the solutions of the one-dimensional wave equation (8.5).

We shall suppose at first that $V(x)$ becomes equal to some constant value, which may be taken to be zero, for sufficiently large positive and negative x and that $E < 0$. A classical particle with this total energy E cannot escape to infinity and, indeed, can exist in the region only if E is greater than or equal to the smallest value V_{min} of $V(x)$. The permitted form of the wave function for $|x|$ large enough that $V = 0$ is evidently $e^{-\beta|x|}$, where $\beta = +(-2mE/\hbar^2)^{\frac{1}{2}}$. These two solutions for large positive and negative x can be extended in toward some intermediate point, say $x = 0$, by making use of the wave equation and the continuity conditions. At this point, u can always be made continuous by choosing the arbitrary multiplying constants for the positive and negative x solutions appropriately. Then a little reflection shows that, for an arbitrary value of E, they will not meet with the same value of du/dx. There may, however, be particular values of E for which both u and du/dx are continuous at $x = 0$. The conditions for this can be seen in the following way.

In the regions in which $E < V(x)$, $(d^2u/dx^2)/u$ is positive, and so u is convex toward the x axis. Thus the two solutions that are continued in from $\pm \infty$ have opposite signs for their ratios of slope to value, $(du/dx)/u$, so long as they are in regions for which E is always less than V. This is illustrated in Fig. 5b for the potential shown in Fig. 5a; both choices of the sign of u are shown for $x < 0$. The points at which $E = V(x)$ are called the *turning points* (TP) of the classical motion, since they are the limits of the motion of a classical particle of energy E, at which the particle turns around or reverses its motion. At these points $d^2u/dx^2 = 0$, and u has zero curvature.

Clearly what is needed to make the two solutions join smoothly is a region in which $E > V(x)$, in order that $(d^2u/dx^2)/u$ may be negative and u be concave toward the x axis; this may permit the ratios of slope to value to become equal. Figure 5c shows the two solutions carried in until they meet, but for a somewhat small value of E, so that when the u's are made the same at $x = 0$ the slopes are not equal (solid curves), or when the slopes are made the same at $x = 0$ the u's are not equal (dotted curve on left and solid curve on right). Figure 5d shows a somewhat larger (less negative) value of E, and Fig. 5e a still larger value. The values of E and V_{min} are indicated on the u axis, and the turning points are indicated on the x axis, in the last three cases.

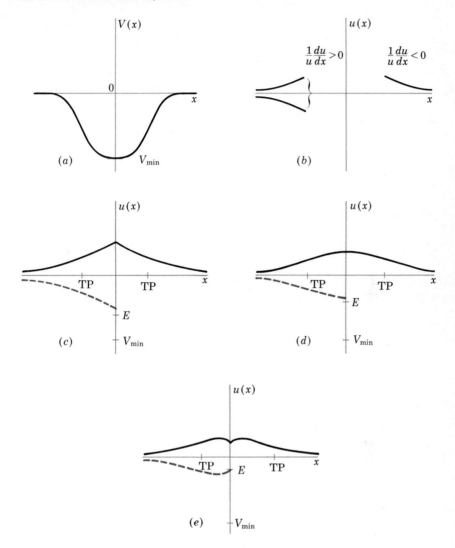

Fig. 5 (a) Potential-energy function and (b) solutions for large $|x|$; (c) and (e) show that either the wave function or its slope is discontinuous at $x = 0$ for values of E that are smaller (more negative) and larger, respectively, than the energy eigenvalue shown in (d).

DISCRETE ENERGY LEVELS

We see then that an eigenfunction that satisfies the boundary and continuity conditions, and that represents a particle bound by the potential energy $V(x)$, can exist for the particular value of E illustrated in Fig. 5d. In analogy with the classical situation, a necessary condition that such an eigenfunction exist is that $V_{min} < 0$, in which case E lies between V_{min} and 0; as in the classical case, this condition is also sufficient in one dimension although it is not in three dimensions (see Prob. 10, Chap. 4, and Secs. 9 and 15).

If the *potential energy well* illustrated in Fig. 5a is sufficiently broad or deep, there will exist another eigenfunction corresponding to a larger energy eigenvalue that is still negative.   Figure 6a, b, and c show a series of wave functions analogous to those shown in Fig. 5c, d, and e for successively increasing (successively less negative) values of E; both signs of u are shown for $x < 0$.   Thus Figs. 5d and 6b show the eigenfunctions for the two lowest energy eigenvalues or *energy levels* of a particle bound by the potential well $V(x)$.   It is easy to see by an extension of the foregoing qualitative arguments that, if there are any higher discrete energy levels, each eigenfunction has one more node than that corresponding to the next lowest eigenvalue.

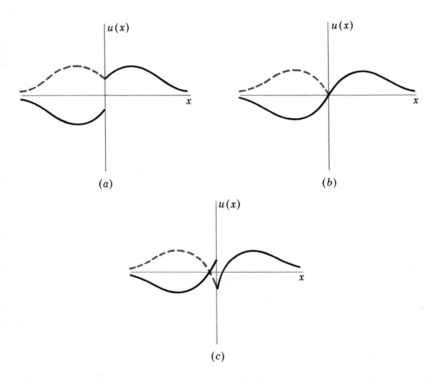

(a)

(b)

(c)

Fig. 6 Solutions for sufficiently broad or deep potential and larger (less negative) values of E than those shown in Fig. 5. E increases from (a) to (b) to (c) and is an eigenvalue in (b), where the wave function and its slope can both be continuous at $x = 0$.

Thus, for a potential energy that approaches a finite constant value as $x \rightarrow \pm \infty$, there may be a finite number of discrete energy levels, or in some cases an infinite number [if $V(x)$ falls off slowly enough for large $|x|$], depending on $V(x)$ and the mass of the particle. However, if $V(x) \rightarrow +\infty$ as $x \rightarrow \pm \infty$, an argument like that given above shows that there will always be an infinite number of discrete energy levels; apart from arbitrary multiplying constants there will be just one eigenfunction $u(x)$ for each of these.

CONTINUOUS ENERGY EIGENVALUES

It is possible to find eigenfunctions that obey the boundary and continuity conditions for all energy eigenvalues that exceed the smaller of the two numbers $V(+\infty)$ and $V(-\infty)$. If, for example, the potential energy has the form illustrated in Fig. 5a, then solutions of the wave equation can be found for all positive values of E. This is because the solutions for large $|x|$ are of the form

$$A \sin \alpha|x| + B \cos \alpha|x| \qquad \alpha = +\left(\frac{2mE}{\hbar^2}\right)^{\frac{1}{2}} \tag{8.6}$$

and there is no reason why both terms should not be kept. Thus it is always possible to adjust the phase of each of the wave functions for large $|x|$ (which is equivalent to adjusting the ratios A/B for the solutions for large positive and negative x) so that they join together smoothly when continued in to $x = 0$.

The classical terms *periodic* (or *multiply periodic*) and *aperiodic* are sometimes used to designate the particle motions associated with discrete and continuous energy eigenvalues, respectively.

DISCRETE AND CONTINUOUS EIGENVALUES IN THREE DIMENSIONS

We shall assume without further discussion that all the foregoing results can be taken over in a natural way for the three-dimensional wave equation (8.2). We can expect that, if $V(\mathbf{r}) \rightarrow +\infty$ as $r \rightarrow \infty$ in all directions, there will be an infinite set of discrete energy levels extending to $+\infty$. If $V(\mathbf{r})$ is bounded as $r \rightarrow \infty$ in some direction, there may be a finite or an infinite number of discrete levels, depending on the form of V. In this case, the discrete energy levels cannot exceed the smallest value that $V(\infty)$ has in any direction. For values of E larger than this smallest $V(\infty)$, the energy eigenvalues cover a continuous range extending to $+\infty$.

9☐ONE-DIMENSIONAL SQUARE WELL POTENTIAL

As a simple explicit example of the calculation of discrete energy levels of a particle in quantum mechanics, we consider the one-dimensional

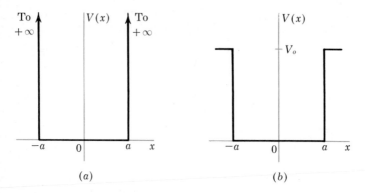

Fig. 7 One-dimensional square well potential with (a) perfectly rigid walls and (b) finite potential step.

motion of a particle that is restrained by reflecting walls that terminate a region of constant potential energy. Two simple types of potential energy are considered. Figure 7a shows a situation in which $V(x) = 0$ for $-a < x < a$, and $V(x) = +\infty$ for $|x| > a$, corresponding to perfectly rigid, impenetrable walls at the points $x = \pm a$. In Fig. 7b the increase in potential energy at the walls is abrupt but finite, so that $V(x) = V_0$ for $|x| > a$; because of its appearance, this is often called a *square well potential*. The motion of a classical particle with total energy E less than V_0 is the same for both these potentials; but, as we shall see, the quantum-mechanical behavior is different. In general, an abrupt finite increase in potential energy at the boundaries of a region forces a particle toward the interior of the region. Such a potential may be thought of as a limiting case of a potential of the type shown in Fig. 5a, for which the force $-dV/dx$ is always directed in toward $x = 0$. The force associated with a square well potential is zero except at the boundaries, so that the particle is acted on by no force except a sudden impulse directed toward the origin as it passes the points $x = \pm a$.

PERFECTLY RIGID WALLS

It was shown in Sec. 8 that the wave function must vanish at the points $x = \pm a$, when the potential energy has the form shown in Fig. 7a. From Eq. (8.5) the wave equation for $|x| < a$ is simply

$$-\frac{\hbar^2}{2m}\frac{d^2u}{dx^2} = Eu \tag{9.1}$$

which has the general solution

$$u(x) = A\sin\alpha x + B\cos\alpha x \qquad \alpha = +\left(\frac{2mE}{\hbar^2}\right)^{\frac{1}{2}} \tag{9.2}$$

Application of the boundary conditions at $x = \pm a$ gives

$$A \sin \alpha a + B \cos \alpha a = 0$$
$$-A \sin \alpha a + B \cos \alpha a = 0$$

from which we obtain

$$A \sin \alpha a = 0 \qquad B \cos \alpha a = 0$$

Now we do not want both A and B to be zero, since this would give the physically uninteresting solution $u = 0$ everywhere. Also, we cannot make both $\sin \alpha a$ and $\cos \alpha a$ zero for a given value of α or E. There are then two possible classes of solutions: For the first class

$$A = 0 \qquad \text{and} \qquad \cos \alpha a = 0$$

and for the second class

$$B = 0 \qquad \text{and} \qquad \sin \alpha a = 0$$

Thus $\alpha a = n\pi/2$, where n is an odd integer for the first class and an even integer for the second class. The two classes of solutions and their energy eigenvalues are then

$$u(x) = B \cos \frac{n\pi x}{2a} \qquad n \text{ odd}$$

$$u(x) = A \sin \frac{n\pi x}{2a} \qquad n \text{ even}$$

$$E = \frac{\pi^2 \hbar^2 n^2}{8ma^2} \qquad \text{in both cases}$$

It is evident that $n = 0$ gives the physically uninteresting result $u = 0$ and that solutions for negative values of n are not linearly independent of those for positive n. The constants A and B can easily be chosen in each case so that the eigenfunctions $u(x)$ are normalized.

There is thus an infinite sequence of discrete energy levels that correspond to all positive integer values of the quantum number n. There is just one eigenfunction for each level, and the number of nodes of the nth eigenfunction that are within the potential well is $n - 1$. These results are in agreement with the discussion of Sec. 8. It is interesting to note that the order of magnitude of the lowest or ground-state energy level is in agreement with the uncertainty relation (3.1). The position uncertainty of order a implies a momentum uncertainty at least of order $\hbar/a$, which in turn implies a minimum kinetic energy of order $\hbar^2/ma^2$.

FINITE POTENTIAL STEP

When the potential energy has the form shown in Fig. 7b, it is necessary to supplement the general solution (9.2), which is still valid for $|x| < a$

since Eq. (9.1) is unaltered there, by a solution for $|x| > a$. The wave equation in this region is

$$-\frac{\hbar^2}{2m}\frac{d^2u}{dx^2} + V_0 u = Eu$$

which has the general solution for $E < V_0$ (bound states)

$$u(x) = Ce^{-\beta x} + De^{\beta x} \qquad \beta = + \left[\frac{2m(V_0 - E)}{\hbar^2}\right]^{\frac{1}{2}} \qquad (9.3)$$

The boundary conditions at $x = \pm\infty$ discussed in Sec. 8 require that we set $D = 0$ if Eq. (9.3) is to represent the solution for $x > a$, and $C = 0$ if the solution is for $x < -a$.

We now impose on the solutions (9.2) and (9.3) the requirements that u and du/dx be continuous at $x = \pm a$.

$$A \sin \alpha a + B \cos \alpha a = Ce^{-\beta a}$$
$$\alpha A \cos \alpha a - \alpha B \sin \alpha a = -\beta Ce^{-\beta a}$$
$$-A \sin \alpha a + B \cos \alpha a = De^{-\beta a}$$
$$\alpha A \cos \alpha a + \alpha B \sin \alpha a = \beta De^{-\beta a}$$

from which we obtain

$$2A \sin \alpha a = (C - D)e^{-\beta a} \qquad 2\alpha A \cos \alpha a = -\beta(C - D)e^{-\beta a} \qquad (9.4)$$

$$2B \cos \alpha a = (C + D)e^{-\beta a} \qquad 2\alpha B \sin \alpha a = \beta(C + D)e^{-\beta a} \qquad (9.5)$$

Unless $A = 0$ and $C = D$, Eqs. (9.4) have as their consequence

$$\alpha \cot \alpha a = -\beta \qquad (9.6)$$

Similarly, unless $B = 0$ and $C = -D$, Eqs. (9.5) give

$$\alpha \tan \alpha a = \beta \qquad (9.7)$$

Now it is impossible for Eqs. (9.6) and (9.7) to be valid at once, since on elimination of β this would require that $\tan^2 \alpha a = -1$, which in turn would make α imaginary and β negative, contrary to Eq. (9.3). Also, we do not want A, B, C, and D all to vanish. Thus the solutions may again be divided into two classes: For the first class

$$A = 0 \qquad C = D \qquad \text{and} \qquad \alpha \tan \alpha a = \beta$$

and for the second class

$$B = 0 \qquad C = -D \qquad \text{and} \qquad \alpha \cot \alpha a = -\beta$$

ENERGY LEVELS

The energy levels are found from a numerical or graphical solution of
Eqs. (9.6) and (9.7) with the definitions for α and β given in Eqs. (9.2)
and (9.3). A simple graphical method for effecting this solution is
described here, since it shows quite clearly the way in which the number
of discrete levels depends on V_0 and a. We put $\xi = \alpha a$, $\eta = \beta a$, whence
Eq. (9.7) becomes $\xi \tan \xi = \eta$, with

$$\xi^2 + \eta^2 = \frac{2mV_0a^2}{\hbar^2}$$

Since ξ and η are restricted to positive values, the energy levels may be
found in this case from the intersections in the first quadrant of the curve
of $\xi \tan \xi$ plotted against ξ, with the circle of known radius $(2mV_0a^2/\hbar^2)^{\frac{1}{2}}$.
The construction is drawn in Fig. 8 for three values of V_0a^2; for each of
the two smaller of these values there is one solution of Eq. (9.7) and for
the largest there are two.

Figure 9 is a similar construction for the solution of Eq. (9.6) in
which the energy levels are obtained from the intersections of the same
circles with the curve of $-\xi \cot \xi$ in the first quadrant. The smallest
value of V_0a^2 gives no solution, and the two larger values each give one.
Thus the three increasing values of V_0a^2 give altogether one, two, and
three energy levels, respectively.

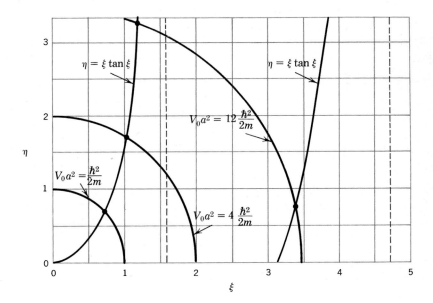

Fig. 8 Graphical solution of Eq. (9.7) for three values of V_0a^2; the vertical dashed
lines are the first two asymptotes of $\eta = \xi \tan \xi$.

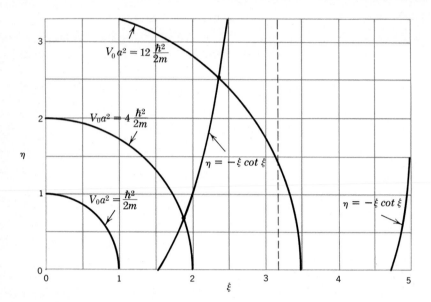

$$V_0 a^2 = 12 \frac{\hbar^2}{2m}$$

$$V_0 a^2 = 4 \frac{\hbar^2}{2m}$$

$$\eta = -\xi \cot \xi$$

$$V_0 a^2 = \frac{\hbar^2}{2m}$$

$$\eta = -\xi \cot \xi$$

Fig. 9 Graphical solution of Eq. (9.6) for three values of $V_c a^2$; the vertical dashed line is the first asymptote of $\eta = -\xi \cot \xi$.

It is clear from Figs. 8 and 9 that, for a given particle mass, the energy levels depend on the parameters of the potential energy through the combination $V_0 a^2$. For $V_0 a^2$ between zero and $\pi^2 \hbar^2 / 8m$, there is just one energy level of the first class; for $V_0 a^2$ between $\pi^2 \hbar^2 / 8m$ and four times this value, there is one energy level of each class, or two altogether. As $V_0 a^2$ increases, energy levels appear successively, first of one class and then of the other. It is not difficult to see from Eq. (9.2) that, when ordered according to increasing eigenvalues, the nth eigenfunction has $n - 1$ nodes.

PARITY

It follows from the foregoing discussion that the eigenfunctions of the first class are even with respect to change in sign of x [$u(-x) = u(x)$], whereas the eigenfunctions of the second class are odd [$u(-x) = -u(x)$]. This division of the eigenfunctions into even and odd types is not accidental and will now be shown to be a direct consequence of the fact that the potential energy function $V(x)$ is symmetric about $x = 0$. If we change the sign of x in the wave equation (8.5)

$$-\frac{\hbar^2}{2m} \frac{d^2 u(x)}{dx^2} + V(x)u(x) = Eu(x) \tag{9.8}$$

and if $V(-x) = V(x)$, we obtain

$$-\frac{\hbar^2}{2m}\frac{d^2u(-x)}{dx^2} + V(x)u(-x) = Eu(-x)$$

Then $u(x)$ and $u(-x)$ are solutions of the same wave equation with the same eigenvalue E. Suppose at first that there is only one linearly independent eigenfunction that corresponds to this energy level; then $u(x)$ and $u(-x)$ can differ only by a multiplicative constant:

$$u(-x) = \epsilon u(x) \tag{9.9}$$

Changing the sign of x in Eq. (9.9) gives $u(x) = \epsilon u(-x)$. From these two equations it follows at once that

$$\epsilon^2 = 1 \qquad \text{or} \qquad \epsilon = \pm 1$$

Thus all such eigenfunctions of a symmetric potential are either even or odd with respect to changes of sign of x. Such wave functions are said to have even or odd *parity*.

If an eigenvalue has more than one linearly independent eigenfunction, the foregoing argument breaks down, and these eigenfunctions need not have a definite parity; they need not be even or odd. However, we can easily see that linear combinations of such eigenfunctions can be found such that each has even or odd parity. Suppose that an eigenfunction $u(x)$ does not have a definite parity. It can always be written

$$u(x) = u_e(x) + u_o(x)$$

where $u_e(x) = \frac{1}{2}[u(x) + u(-x)]$ is even, $u_o(x) = \frac{1}{2}[u(x) - u(-x)]$ is odd, and u_e and u_o are linearly independent. Then if the wave equation (9.8) is symmetric, we can write it as

$$-\frac{\hbar^2}{2m}\frac{d^2u_e}{dx^2} + (V - E)u_e - \frac{\hbar^2}{2m}\frac{d^2u_o}{dx^2} + (V - E)u_o = 0 \tag{9.10}$$

On changing the sign of x in Eq. (9.10), we obtain

$$-\frac{\hbar^2}{2m}\frac{d^2u_e}{dx^2} + (V - E)u_e + \frac{\hbar^2}{2m}\frac{d^2u_o}{dx^2} - (V - E)u_o = 0 \tag{9.11}$$

Addition and subtraction of Eqs. (9.10) and (9.11) show that u_e and u_o are separately solutions of the wave equation with the same eigenvalue E.

A SIMPLIFIED SOLUTION

Knowledge that the solutions possess a definite parity sometimes simplifies the determination of the energy levels, since then we need only find the solution for positive x. Even solutions have zero slope and odd solutions have zero value at $x = 0$. If, for example, we wish to find the even solutions, Eqs. (9.2) and (9.3) can be replaced at once by

$$u(x) = B \cos \alpha x \qquad 0 < x < a$$
$$u(x) = Ce^{-\beta x} \qquad x > a$$

Instead of making both u and du/dx continuous at $x = a$, it is enough to make the ratio $(1/u)(du/dx)$ continuous at $x = a$, since the normalizing constants B and C are eliminated thereby. This gives Eq. (9.7) at once. Similarly, the odd solutions are

$$u(x) = A \sin \alpha x \qquad 0 < x < a$$
$$u(x) = Ce^{-\beta x} \qquad x > a$$

Then continuity of $(1/u)(du/dx)$ at $x = a$ immediately gives Eq. (9.6).

PROBLEMS

1. Use the arguments of Sec. 6 to set up a differential equation for ψ that involves a second time derivative of ψ, in the case of a free particle. Discuss any solutions that this equation has that are not shared by the free-particle Schrödinger equation.

2. Show that the free-particle one-dimensional Schrödinger wave equation (6.8) is invariant with respect to galilean transformations. Do this by showing that, when the transformation $x' = x - vt$, $t' = t$ is applied, the transformed wave function $\psi'(x',t') = f(x,t)\psi(x,t)$ satisfies Eq. (6.8) with respect to the primed variables, where f involves only x, t, $\hbar$, m, and v. Find the form of f, and show that the traveling wave solution $\psi(x,t) = Ae^{i(kx-\omega t)}$ transforms as expected.

3. How must a wave packet ψ fall off for large r in order that the volume integral of P and the surface integral of S_n in Eq. (7.4) converge?

4. Show directly that $\langle p_x \rangle$ is real for a wave packet.

5. Show that for a three-dimensional wave packet

$$\frac{d}{dt} \langle x^2 \rangle = \frac{1}{m} (\langle x p_x \rangle + \langle p_x x \rangle)$$

6. Calculate the energy levels and plot the eigenfunctions for the three bound states in the potential of Fig. 7b when $V_0 a^2 = 6\hbar^2/m$. Compare with the first three states for the potential of Fig. 7a.

7. Discuss the relation between the energy levels for the potential of Fig. 7b and those for the potential $V(x) = +\infty$, $x < 0$; $V(x) = 0$, $0 < x < a$; $V(x) = V_0$, $x > a$.

8. Show that if the potential energy $V(\mathbf{r})$ is changed everywhere by a constant, the time-independent wave functions are unchanged. What is the effect on the energy eigenvalues?

3
Eigenfunctions and Eigenvalues

In Chap. 2, the Schrödinger wave equation was developed and applied to a simple problem. Some discussion of the physical interpretation of the wave function was given in Sec. 7. This relied for the most part on the computation of average or expectation values of operators that represent various physical quantities. In addition, however, a position probability density was introduced. Thus at the present point we are in a position to calculate from the wave function any property that depends on the spatial distribution of a particle (for example, the mean-square deviation of its position from the average), whereas we can calculate only average values of operators other than position. Clearly what is needed to round out our interpretation of the wave function is a means of computing probability functions for operators in general; this would incidentally enable us to obtain the expressions for expectation values used in Sec. 7 without separate assumptions.

In this chapter, we first set up three physical postulates from which a complete interpretation of the wave function can be derived, and we then apply them to a discussion of the total energy and momentum of a particle and to an illustrative problem. The interpretation presented in Sec. 7 can then be seen to be a special case of the more general treatment given here.

10□INTERPRETATIVE POSTULATES AND ENERGY EIGENFUNCTIONS

We start with the wave function $\psi(\mathbf{r},t)$, which is a solution of Eq. (6.16) and describes the motion of a particle that has mass m and potential energy $V(\mathbf{r})$. From this wave function we wish to obtain as complete a description of the properties of the motion of the particle as is consistent with the uncertainty relations discussed in Sec. 3.

DYNAMICAL VARIABLES AS OPERATORS

We first postulate that *each dynamical variable that relates to the motion of the particle can be represented by a linear operator.*[1] The operator may be simply a multiplication operator such as $\mathbf{r}$ for the position, or it may be a differential operator such as $-i\hbar\nabla$ for the momentum.

    With each operator can be associated a linear eigenvalue equation, defined near the beginning of Sec. 8. Thus with the operator Ω may be associated the equation

$$\Omega v_\mu = \omega_\mu v_\mu \tag{10.1}$$

where v_μ is the eigenfunction of Ω corresponding to the eigenvalue ω_μ.

    Our second postulate is that *one or another of the eigenvalues ω_μ is the only possible result of a precise measurement of the dynamical variable represented by Ω.* This implies that the eigenvalues of all operators that represent physically measurable quantities are real numbers.

EXPANSION IN EIGENFUNCTIONS

We assume that all the eigenfunctions of any dynamical variable constitute a complete set of functions in the sense that an arbitrary continuous function can be expanded in terms of them. This is a mathematical, not a physical, assumption and will be discussed further below in connection with energy and momentum eigenfunctions.[2]

    Suppose now that a particular wave function ψ is expanded in terms of the eigenfunctions v_μ of the operator Ω. We adopt the statistical interpretation of ψ given at the beginning of Sec. 7, according to which there are a large number of identical independent regions of space, or

---

[1] An operator Ω is linear if it satisfies the equation $\Omega(a_1\psi_1 + a_2\psi_2) = a_1\Omega\psi_1 + a_2\Omega\psi_2$ for arbitrary complex numbers a_i and functions ψ_i.

[2] For a discussion of completeness, see, for example, R. Courant and D. Hilbert, "Methods of Mathematical Physics," vol. I, p. 369 (Interscience, New York, 1953).

intervals of time, in each of which is a particle described by ψ. We then make measurements of the dynamical variable represented by Ω on each of these particles. Our third physical postulate is that *the number of measurements that result in the eigenvalue ω_μ is proportional to the square of the magnitude of the coefficient of v_μ in the expansion of ψ*. This postulate, due to M. Born (see page 25), enables us to associate a probability function with any dynamical variable.[1] A corollary is that we are certain to measure a particular eigenvalue ω_μ only when the wave function that describes the particle is the corresponding eigenfunction v_μ.

Rather than develop the consequences of these postulates for an arbitrary operator Ω, we consider here the total energy of the particle, and in Sec. 11 the momentum. Most of the results obtained are readily applicable to other physical operators.

THE TOTAL-ENERGY OPERATOR

According to the uncertainty relation (3.3), a precise measurement of the total energy of a particle cannot be made in a finite length of time. Thus if the total energy is to have a definite value, it is essential that the potential energy $V(\mathbf{r})$ be independent of the time. Then the operator $-(\hbar^2/2m)\nabla^2 + V(\mathbf{r})$, which was shown in Sec. 8 to be equivalent to the total-energy operator $i\hbar(\partial/\partial t)$, has eigenfunctions $u(\mathbf{r})$ that need not involve the time. The energy-eigenvalue equation is Eq. (8.2),

$$\left[-\frac{\hbar^2}{2m}\nabla^2 + V(\mathbf{r}) \right] u_E(\mathbf{r}) = E u_E(\mathbf{r}) \tag{10.2}$$

where the eigenfunction $u_E(\mathbf{r})$ corresponds to the eigenvalue E and obeys the boundary and continuity conditions of Sec. 8.

As discussed in Sec. 8, the energy eigenfunctions can be divided into two classes: those which are well localized and are associated with discrete eigenvalues and those which remain finite at great distances and possess a continuous range of eigenvalues.

NORMALIZATION IN A BOX

It is often desirable to be able to treat these two classes on the same basis; this can be accomplished by enclosing the particle under investigation in a box of arbitrarily large but finite volume. The simplest physical situation to which this approach is applicable is one in which the walls of the box are perfectly rigid, so that, as shown in Sec. 8, the wave function vanishes there. Then the discussion of Sec. 8 shows that all the eigen-

---

[1] An alternative deterministic interpretation in terms of "hidden variables" rather than the dynamical variables, which has not been widely accepted, has been proposed by D. Bohm, *Phys. Rev.* **85**, 166, 180 (1952). See also J. S. Bell, *Rev. Mod. Phys.* **38**, 447 (1966); D. Bohm and J. Bub, *Rev. Mod. Phys.* **38**, 453, 470 (1966).

values are discrete.   If the box is large in comparison with the dimensions of physical interest in the problem, the eigenvalues that were discrete in the absence of the box are practically unaffected, since before the walls were introduced the wave functions were extremely small there.   Also, the eigenvalues that were continuously distributed in the absence of the box are very closely spaced; this is shown explicitly for a free particle in Sec. 11.

It is more convenient to assume that the wave functions obey *periodic boundary conditions* at the walls of the box than that they vanish there, since it is then possible to get a simpler description of the momentum eigenfunctions (see Sec. 11).   We choose the finite region to be a cube of edge length L centered at the origin and require each wave function to have the same value at corresponding points of opposite faces of the cube, and the same derivative normal to the wall.   These boundary conditions make the otherwise continuous eigenvalues discrete, since the phase of the eigenfunction at great distances is no longer arbitrary [see the discussion of Eq. (8.6)].   As with the rigid-walled box, the presence of the walls has a negligible effect apart from imparting discreteness to the otherwise continuous eigenvalues and providing a finite volume in which these wave functions can be normalized; we shall continue to use the word "continuous" to describe these functions, even when box normalization is used.

ORTHONORMALITY OF ENERGY EIGENFUNCTIONS

The integral $\int |u_E(\mathbf{r})|^2 \, d^3r$, which converges in any case for the discrete set of eigenfunctions, converges for all eigenfunctions when they are normalized in the box of finite volume L^3.   The coefficient of u_E can then be chosen so that this integral is equal to unity, and the $u_E(\mathbf{r})$ are normalized.

We now show that the eigenfunctions corresponding to two different eigenvalues E and E' are *orthogonal*, that is, that the integral of the product of one of them and the complex conjugate of the other over the common domain of the functions is zero.   From Eq. (10.2) we have that $u_{E'}^*(\mathbf{r})$ satisfies the equation (where V is again assumed to be real)

$$\left[-\frac{\hbar^2}{2m} \nabla^2 + V(\mathbf{r}) \right] u_{E'}^*(\mathbf{r}) = E' u_{E'}^*(\mathbf{r}) \tag{10.3}$$

In accordance with our physical interpretation, we have assumed that E' is real; this is verified below.   We multiply Eq. (10.2) by $u_{E'}^*$ and Eq. (10.3) by u_E, integrate over the volume L^3, and take the difference between the two resulting equations.   The V terms cancel and leave

$$-\frac{\hbar^2}{2m} \int (u_{E'}^* \nabla^2 u_E - u_E \nabla^2 u_{E'}^*) \, d^3r = (E - E') \int u_{E'}^* u_E \, d^3r \tag{10.4}$$

The integral on the left side of Eq. (10.4) can be transformed by Green's theorem into a surface integral over the surface A of the cube:

$$\int (u_{E'}^* \nabla^2 u_E - u_E \nabla^2 u_{E'}^*)\ d^3r = \int \nabla \cdot (u_{E'}^* \nabla u_E - u_E \nabla u_{E'}^*)\ d^3r$$

$$= \int_A (u_{E'}^* \nabla u_E - u_E \nabla u_{E'}^*)_n\ dA \qquad (10.5)$$

where the subscript n designates the component of the vector in the direction of the outward normal to the element of area dA. Since the imposition of periodic boundary conditions gives each wave function and its normal derivative the same values at corresponding points of opposite faces of the cube, the outward normal derivative has opposite signs on opposite faces, and the surface integral in (10.5) vanishes. Then Eq. (10.4) tells us that, if $E \neq E'$, u_E and $u_{E'}$ are orthogonal.[1]

An energy eigenvalue E is said to be *degenerate* when two or more linearly independent eigenfunctions $u_1, u_2, \ldots$ correspond to it. Orthogonal linear combinations of degenerate eigenfunctions can be found in many different ways. For example, $u_a = a_1 u_1 + a_2 u_2$ can be made orthogonal to u_1 by choosing the constant coefficients a_1 and a_2 such that

$$\frac{a_1}{a_2} = -\frac{\int u_1^* u_2\ d^3r}{\int |u_1|^2\ d^3r}$$

This choice does not interfere with the normalization of u_a, and u_a is still an energy eigenfunction with the eigenvalue E. Evidently the choice of orthogonal linear combinations is not unique. By an extension of this procedure, all the energy eigenfunctions can be made orthogonal to each other even though some of the eigenvalues are degenerate.

Such a set of eigenfunctions, each of which is normalized and orthogonal to each of the others, is called an *orthonormal* set of functions. We specify an orthonormal set of nondegenerate energy eigenfunctions by the relation

$$\int u_{E'}^*(\mathbf{r}) u_E(\mathbf{r})\ d^3r = \delta_{EE'} \qquad (10.6)$$

where $\delta_{EE'}$ is the symmetric Kronecker δ symbol that equals unity if $E = E'$ and is zero otherwise. If there is degeneracy, Eq. (10.6) must be replaced by

$$\int u_{E's'}^*(\mathbf{r}) u_{Es}(\mathbf{r})\ d^3r = \delta_{EE'}\ \delta_{ss'} \qquad (10.7)$$

---

[1] It is apparent that this proof of orthogonality can be applied to a discrete set of eigenfunctions even though the box is not introduced, since the u's vanish rapidly at great distances and the surface integral, which is then over a sphere of infinite radius, is zero. The continuous set of energy eigenfunctions can also be treated without using the box normalization (as is the continuous set of momentum eigenfunctions in Sec. 11).

where the index s distinguishes between orthogonal degenerate eigen-functions. It is often convenient to omit explicit mention of s and use Eq. (10.6) for degenerate situations as well, in which case the index s is implied.

REALITY OF THE ENERGY EIGENVALUES

We can now see directly that E is a real number, as has been assumed. We multiply Eq. (10.2) by $u_E^*(\mathbf{r})$ and integrate over the box of volume L^3. If u_E is normalized, the result is

$$E = -\frac{\hbar^2}{2m} \int u_E^* \nabla^2 u_E \, d^3r + \int V(\mathbf{r})|u_E|^2 \, d^3r$$

which may be expressed in terms of expectation values as $(1/2m)\langle \mathbf{p}^2 \rangle + \langle V \rangle$.

The second term $\langle V \rangle$ is real since its integrand is real. The first term can be shown explicitly to be real by means of a partial integration:

$$-\int u_E^* \nabla^2 u_E \, d^3r = \int (\nabla u_E^*) \cdot (\nabla u_E) \, d^3r - \int_A u_E^* (\nabla u_E)_n \, dA$$

The volume integral is evidently real, and the surface integral [like that in Eq. (10.5)] vanishes because of the periodic boundary conditions at the walls of the box. It is interesting to note that $\langle \mathbf{p}^2 \rangle$ cannot be negative.

EXPANSION IN ENERGY EIGENFUNCTIONS

As mentioned near the beginning of this section, we make the mathematical assumption that all the eigenfunctions $u_E(\mathbf{r})$ of the total-energy operator constitute a complete set of functions in the sense that an arbitrary continuous function can be expanded in terms of them. Then, if we have any wave function $\psi(\mathbf{r})$ at a particular instant of time that is normalized in the box L^3 and obeys periodic boundary conditions at the walls, the assumed existence of the expansion

$$\psi(\mathbf{r}) = \sum_E A_E u_E(\mathbf{r}) \tag{10.8}$$

makes it possible to find unique coefficients A_E that do not depend on $\mathbf{r}$.

The coefficients in the expansion (10.8) can be determined by multiplying both sides by $u_{E'}^*$ and integrating over the box. We assume that the order of $\sum_E$ and $\int d^3r$ can be reversed[1] and obtain

---

[1] The propriety of changing the order of summations and integrations must in principle be investigated separately in each case. The mathematical considerations entailed are beyond the scope of this book, and we shall always assume that such interchanges are permissible in situations of physical interest.

$$\int u_{E'}^{*}(\mathbf{r})\psi(\mathbf{r})\, d^3r \;=\; \sum_E A_E \int u_{E'}^{*}(\mathbf{r})u_E(\mathbf{r})\, d^3r \;=\; \sum_E A_E\, \delta_{EE'} \;=\; A_{E'}$$

$$(10.9)$$

with the help of Eq. (10.6) or (10.7).

THE CLOSURE PROPERTY

Substitution of the expression (10.9) for A_E back into Eq. (10.8) gives

$$\psi(\mathbf{r}) \;=\; \sum_E \left[\, \int u_E^{*}(\mathbf{r}')\psi(\mathbf{r}')\, d^3r' \right] u_E(\mathbf{r})$$

which we rearrange to give

$$\psi(\mathbf{r}) \;=\; \int \psi(\mathbf{r}') \left[\sum_E u_E^{*}(\mathbf{r}')u_E(\mathbf{r}) \right] d^3r' \qquad\qquad (10.10)$$

Since $\psi(\mathbf{r})$ is an arbitrary continuous function of $\mathbf{r}$, Eq. (10.10) implies that the bracketed part of the integrand vanishes unless $\mathbf{r}' = \mathbf{r}$, since otherwise the value of ψ at the point $\mathbf{r}$ given by Eq. (10.10) would change when the values of ψ at other points $\mathbf{r}' \neq \mathbf{r}$ are changed, and this is contrary to the assumption that ψ can have an arbitrary form. Moreover, the integral of the term in brackets must be unity when the volume of integration includes the point $\mathbf{r}' = \mathbf{r}$. We conclude therefore that

$$\sum_E u_E^{*}(\mathbf{r}')u_E(\mathbf{r}) = 0 \qquad \mathbf{r}' \neq \mathbf{r}$$

$$\cdot(10.11)$$

$$\int \sum_E u_E^{*}(\mathbf{r}')u_E(\mathbf{r})\, d^3r' = 1$$

if the volume of integration includes the point $\mathbf{r}' = \mathbf{r}$.

Equations (10.11) describe the *closure* property of the orthonormal set of functions $u_E(\mathbf{r})$ and are seen to follow directly from their completeness as expressed by Eq. (10.8), whether or not they happen to be energy eigenfunctions.

PROBABILITY FUNCTION AND EXPECTATION VALUE

The second and third physical postulates presented at the beginning of this section state that the energy eigenvalues are the only possible results of precise measurement of the total energy and that the probability of finding a particular value E when the particle is described by the wave function $\psi(\mathbf{r})$ is proportional to $|A_E|^2$. It is easily seen that the proportionality factor is unity, because if we put for the energy probability function

$$P(E) = |A_E|^2 \tag{10.12}$$

we see that $P(E)$ sums to unity:

$$
\begin{aligned}
\sum_E P(E) &= \sum_E \int u_E^*(\mathbf{r}) \psi(\mathbf{r}) \, d^3r \int u_E(\mathbf{r}') \psi^*(\mathbf{r}') \, d^3r' \\
&= \iint \psi^*(\mathbf{r}') \psi(\mathbf{r}) \left[\sum_E u_E^*(\mathbf{r}) u_E(\mathbf{r}') \right] d^3r \, d^3r' \\
&= \int |\psi(\mathbf{r})|^2 \, d^3r = 1
\end{aligned}
$$

since ψ is normalized; use has been made here of Eqs. (10.11).

We can also compute the average or expectation value of the energy from the probability function:

$$\langle E_\rangle = \sum_E E P(E) = \sum_E \int E u_E^*(\mathbf{r}) \psi(\mathbf{r}) \, d^3r \int u_E(\mathbf{r}') \psi^*(\mathbf{r}') \, d^3r' \tag{10.13}$$

If we substitute for $E u_E^*(\mathbf{r})$ from Eq. (10.3), the first integral in Eq. (10.13) can be integrated twice by parts as follows:

$$
\begin{aligned}
\int E u_E^*(\mathbf{r}) \psi(\mathbf{r}) \, d^3r &= \int \psi(\mathbf{r}) \left[-\frac{\hbar^2}{2m} \nabla^2 + V(\mathbf{r}) \right] u_E^*(\mathbf{r}) \, d^3r \\
&= \int u_E^*(\mathbf{r}) \left[-\frac{\hbar^2}{2m} \nabla^2 + V(\mathbf{r}) \right] \psi(\mathbf{r}) \, d^3r
\end{aligned}
$$

The two surface integrals that result from the partial integrations vanish because of the periodic boundary conditions on u_E and ψ. Thus, with the help of Eqs. (10.11), Eq. (10.13) becomes

$$
\begin{aligned}
\langle E \rangle &= \sum_E \int u_E^*(\mathbf{r}) \left[-\frac{\hbar^2}{2m} \nabla^2 + V(\mathbf{r}) \right] \psi(\mathbf{r}) \, d^3r \int u_E(\mathbf{r}') \psi^*(\mathbf{r}') \, d^3r' \\
&= \iint \psi^*(\mathbf{r}') \left\{ \left[-\frac{\hbar^2}{2m} \nabla^2 + V(\mathbf{r}) \right] \psi(\mathbf{r}) \right\} \left[\sum_E u_E^*(\mathbf{r}) u_E(\mathbf{r}') \right] d^3r \, d^3r' \\
&= \int \psi^*(\mathbf{r}) \left[-\frac{\hbar^2}{2m} \nabla^2 + V(\mathbf{r}) \right] \psi(\mathbf{r}) \, d^3r \tag{10.14}
\end{aligned}
$$

The result embodied in Eq. (10.14) confirms the supposition made in Sec. 7 that the expectation value of an operator is to be calculated by inserting the operator between $\psi^*(\mathbf{r})$ and $\psi(\mathbf{r})$, so that it operates just on the latter, and then integrating over $\mathbf{r}$.

GENERAL SOLUTION OF THE SCHRÖDINGER EQUATION

If the potential energy $V(\mathbf{r})$ is independent of t and we know the solution of the Schrödinger equation (6.16) at a particular time, we can write a formal expression for the solution at any time. We expand $\psi(\mathbf{r},t)$ in energy eigenfunctions at the time t, in which case the expansion coefficients depend on the time.

$$\psi(\mathbf{r},t) = \sum_E A_E(t)u_E(\mathbf{r}) \qquad A_E(t) = \int u_E^*(\mathbf{r})\psi(\mathbf{r},t)\, d^3r \qquad (10.15)$$

Substitution of Eq. (10.15) into the wave equation (6.16) gives

$$i\hbar \sum_E u_E(\mathbf{r})\frac{d}{dt}A_E(t) = \sum_E A_E(t)Eu_E(\mathbf{r}) \qquad (10.16)$$

Because of the orthonormality of the u_E, Eq. (10.16) is equivalent to

$$i\hbar \frac{d}{dt}A_E(t) = EA_E(t)$$

which may be integrated at once to give

$$A_E(t) = A_E(t_0)e^{-iE(t-t_0)/\hbar} \qquad (10.17)$$

Note that $P(E) = |A_E(t)|^2 = |A_E(t_0)|^2$ is constant in time.

Thus, if $\psi(\mathbf{r},t)$ is known at the time $t = t_0$, the solution at any time t is given in terms of Eqs. (10.15) and (10.17):

$$\psi(\mathbf{r},t) = \sum_E A_E(t_0)e^{-iE(t-t_0)/\hbar}u_E(\mathbf{r})$$
$$A_E(t_0) = \int u_E^*(\mathbf{r}')\psi(\mathbf{r}',t_0)\, d^3r' \qquad (10.18)$$

or

$$\psi(\mathbf{r},t) = \int \left[\sum_E u_E^*(\mathbf{r}')u_E(\mathbf{r})e^{-iE(t-t_0)/\hbar}\right]\psi(\mathbf{r}',t_0)\, d^3r' \qquad (10.19)$$

The solution (10.18) is a linear combination of the separated solutions (8.3) obtained earlier.

11□MOMENTUM EIGENFUNCTIONS

The eigenfunctions of the linear momentum operator $-i\hbar\nabla$ provide a second instructive example of the application of the general ideas developed at the beginning of the preceding section. They also are of considerable usefulness in solving problems of physical interest.

FORM OF THE EIGENFUNCTIONS

The momentum eigenfunctions are solutions of the three eigenvalue equations

$$-i\hbar\nabla u_{\mathbf{p}}(\mathbf{r}) = \mathbf{p}u_{\mathbf{p}}(\mathbf{r}) \qquad (11.1)$$

or

$$-i\hbar \frac{\partial}{\partial x} u_p(\mathbf{r}) = p_x u_p(\mathbf{r}) \qquad -i\hbar \frac{\partial}{\partial y} u_p(\mathbf{r}) = p_y u_p(\mathbf{r})$$

$$-i\hbar \frac{\partial}{\partial z} u_p(\mathbf{r}) = p_z u_p(\mathbf{r})$$

They have the form

$$u_p(\mathbf{r}) = C \exp \frac{i(\mathbf{p} \cdot \mathbf{r})}{\hbar}$$

where C is a normalization constant.

It is convenient, as in Sec. 6, to change from the momentum vector $\mathbf{p}$ to the propagation vector $\mathbf{k} = \mathbf{p}/\hbar$ and to rewrite the momentum eigenfunctions

$$u_k(\mathbf{r}) = C \exp (i\mathbf{k} \cdot \mathbf{r}) \tag{11.2}$$

These are eigenfunctions of the momentum operator with the eigenvalues $\hbar\mathbf{k}$.

BOX NORMALIZATION

As with the energy eigenfunctions discussed in Sec. 10, we can restrict the domain of the $u_k(\mathbf{r})$ to an arbitrarily large but finite cubical box of volume L^3 centered at the origin, at the walls of which the functions obey periodic boundary conditions. Then u_k is normalized if $C = L^{-\frac{3}{2}}$. Also, $\mathbf{k}$ is no longer an arbitrary real vector; its components are restricted to the values

$$k_x = \frac{2\pi n_x}{L} \qquad k_y = \frac{2\pi n_y}{L} \qquad k_z = \frac{2\pi n_z}{L} \tag{11.3}$$

where n_x, n_y, and n_z are positive or negative integers or zero. The spacing of neighboring $\mathbf{k}$ vectors and of their energy eigenvalues $\hbar^2 k^2/2m$ can be made as small as desired by making L sufficiently large. It is always assumed that the limit $L \to \infty$ is taken at the end of the calculation.

It is interesting to note that the momentum eigenfunctions (11.2) cannot exist within a box that has perfectly rigid walls, since these eigenfunctions do not vanish anywhere. This is analogous to the classical situation in which the momentum of a particle that is reflected from a rigid wall is not conserved. On the other hand, the cubical box with periodic boundary conditions is equivalent to a situation in which the entire infinite space is divided into adjacent cubes and all wave functions are periodic throughout space with the period L along each of the three cartesian axes. If the periodicity of the space is carried over to the analogous classical situation, a particle passing through a wall would be equivalent to one that strikes that wall and appears at the corresponding point of the opposite wall with its momentum vector unchanged.

The orthonormality of the momentum eigenfunctions

$$u_{\mathbf{k}}(\mathbf{r}) = L^{-\frac{3}{2}} \exp{(i\mathbf{k} \cdot \mathbf{r})} \tag{11.4}$$

is readily established.   For integration over the volume L^3

$$\int u_{\mathbf{l}}^*(\mathbf{r}) u_{\mathbf{k}}(\mathbf{r}) \, d^3r$$

$$= \frac{1}{L^3} \int_{-\frac{1}{2}L}^{\frac{1}{2}L} e^{i(k_x - l_x)x} \, dx \int_{-\frac{1}{2}L}^{\frac{1}{2}L} e^{i(k_y - l_y)y} \, dy \int_{-\frac{1}{2}L}^{\frac{1}{2}L} e^{i(k_z - l_z)z} \, dz$$

$$= \delta_{k_x l_x} \delta_{k_y l_y} \delta_{k_z l_z} \equiv \delta_{\mathbf{kl}} \tag{11.5}$$

where the δ's are Kronecker δ symbols and use is made of Eqs. (11.3). Orthogonality could also have been shown by the more general method used in Sec. 10 for the energy eigenfunctions [see Eq. (10.4)].

THE DIRAC δ FUNCTION

It was stated in Sec. 10 that continuous sets of eigenfunctions can be handled without introducing the box with periodic boundary conditions (which has the effect of making the set discrete with an arbitrarily small spacing of eigenvalues).   This can be shown explicitly for the momentum eigenfunctions with the help of the Dirac δ function,[1] which can be defined by the relations

$$\delta(x) = 0 \qquad \text{if} \qquad x \neq 0 \qquad \int \delta(x) \, dx = 1 \tag{11.6}$$

where the region of integration includes the point $x = 0$.   An equivalent definition is that, for an arbitrary function $f(x)$ that is continuous at $x = 0$, the equation

$$\int f(x) \, \delta(x) \, dx = f(0) \tag{11.7}$$

is valid, where again the integration includes the point $x = 0$.

It is apparent from a comparison of Eqs. (11.6) and (10.11), or of Eqs. (11.7) and (10.10), that the bracketed quantity in Eq. (10.10) can be expressed in terms of δ functions:

$$\sum_E u_E^*(\mathbf{r}') u_E(\mathbf{r}) = \delta(x - x') \, \delta(y - y') \, \delta(z - z') \equiv \delta^3(\mathbf{r} - \mathbf{r}') \tag{11.8}$$

Comparison of Eqs. (11.8) and (10.6) shows that the closure property is a kind of orthonormality of the eigenfunctions with respect to summation over the eigenvalues.

[1] P. A. M. Dirac, "The Principles of Quantum Mechanics," 4th ed., sec. 15 (Oxford, New York, 1958).

A REPRESENTATION OF THE δ FUNCTION

The definition (11.6) or (11.7) shows that $\delta(x)$ is an exceedingly singular function.[1] It may be thought of qualitatively as being zero everywhere except at $x = 0$ and being so large there that the area between it and the x axis is finite and equal to unity. More formally, it can be represented in a number of different ways as the limit of a sequence of analytic functions.

A particular representation that is quite useful involves $(\sin gx)/\pi x$ as a function of x, where g is a positive real number. This has the value g/π at $x = 0$, oscillates with decreasing amplitude and with period $2\pi/g$ as $|x|$ increases, and has unit integral from $x = -\infty$ to $x = +\infty$ independently of the value of g. Thus the limit of this function as $g \to \infty$ has all the properties of the δ function: It becomes infinitely large at $x = 0$, it has unit integral, and the infinitely rapid oscillations as $|x|$ increases mean that the entire contribution to an integral containing this function comes from the infinitesimal neighborhood of $x = 0$. We can therefore put

$$\delta(x) = \lim_{g \to \infty} \frac{\sin gx}{\pi x} \tag{11.9}$$

NORMALIZATION IN TERMS OF THE δ FUNCTION

The representation (11.9) of the δ function can be used to set up an orthonormality integral like that given in Eq. (11.5), where now we do not impose the box normalization but allow the momentum eigenfunctions to have the form (11.2) over all space with all real vectors $\mathbf{k}$. The integral $\int u_1^*(\mathbf{r}) u_{\mathbf{k}}(\mathbf{r}) \, d^3 r$ is the product of three integrals, each of which can be expressed in terms of a δ function:

$$\int_{-\infty}^{\infty} e^{i(k_x - l_x)x} \, dx = \lim_{g \to \infty} \int_{-g}^{g} e^{i(k_x - l_x)x} \, dx$$

$$= \lim_{g \to \infty} \frac{2 \sin g(k_x - l_x)}{k_x - l_x}$$

$$= 2\pi \delta(k_x - l_x) \tag{11.10}$$

Thus the momentum eigenfunctions in infinite space can be written

$$u_k(\mathbf{r}) = (8\pi^3)^{-\frac{1}{2}} \exp(i\mathbf{k} \cdot \mathbf{r}) \tag{11.11}$$

---

[1] A rigorous mathematical basis has been provided for the δ function by L. Schwartz. It may be thought of as a linear functional that operates on a set of sufficiently well-behaved test functions; thus the left side of Eq. (11.7) could be written $\delta[f]$. For detailed discussions, see M. J. Lighthill, "Introduction to Fourier Analysis and Generalized Functions" (Cambridge, New York, 1958); A. Messiah, "Quantum Mechanics," vol. I, App. A (Interscience, New York, 1961).

in which case the orthonormality relation becomes

$$\int u_1^*(\mathbf{r}) u_{\mathbf{k}}(\mathbf{r}) \, d^3r = \delta(k_x - l_x) \, \delta(k_y - l_y) \, \delta(k_z - l_z) \equiv \delta^3(\mathbf{k} - \mathbf{l})$$
$$\text{(11.12)}$$

It will be shown in Sec. 12 that the box and δ-function normalizations of the momentum eigenfunctions give the same final result in a typical problem.

SOME PROPERTIES OF THE δ FUNCTION

It is important to note that, because of its singular character, the δ function cannot be the end result of a calculation and has meaning only so long as a subsequent integration over its argument is carried out. With this understanding we can write some relations between δ functions.[1]

$$\delta(x) = \delta(-x)$$
$$\delta'(x) = -\delta'(-x)$$
$$x \, \delta(x) = 0$$
$$x \, \delta'(x) = -\delta(x) \qquad\qquad\qquad\qquad\qquad \text{(11.13)}$$
$$\delta(ax) = a^{-1} \, \delta(x) \qquad\qquad\qquad\qquad a > 0$$
$$\delta(x^2 - a^2) = (2a)^{-1}[\delta(x - a) + \delta(x + a)] \qquad a > 0$$
$$\int \delta(a - x) \, \delta(x - b) \, dx = \delta(a - b)$$
$$f(x) \, \delta(x - a) = f(a) \, \delta(x - a)$$

Here, a prime denotes differentiation with respect to the argument.

Each of the first six of these equations can be established by multiplying both sides by a continuous, differentiable function $f(x)$ and integrating over x. For example, the fourth of Eqs. (11.13) gives

$$\int f(x) x \, \delta'(x) \, dx = -\int \delta(x) \frac{d}{dx} [xf(x)] \, dx$$
$$= -\int \delta(x)[f(x) + xf'(x)] \, dx = -\int f(x) \, \delta(x) \, dx$$

where the boundary terms that result from the partial integration vanish. Thus $x\delta'(x)$ has the same effect when it is a factor in an integrand as has $-\delta(x)$. Similarly the seventh of Eqs. (11.13) means that the two sides give the same result when multiplied by $f(a)$ or $f(b)$ and integrated over a or b. The last equation is verified by integrating both sides over either x or a.

CLOSURE

The closure property of the momentum eigenfunctions, with both box and δ-function normalization, can be established without the help of the

[1] Dirac, *op. cit.*, p. 60.

completeness assumption that was made in Sec. 10 for the energy eigen-functions.   With box normalization, the expression analogous to the left side of Eq. (11.8) is

$$\sum_{\mathbf{k}} u_{\mathbf{k}}^*(\mathbf{r}')u_{\mathbf{k}}(\mathbf{r}) = L^{-3} \sum_{n_x=-\infty}^{\infty} \sum_{n_y=-\infty}^{\infty} \sum_{n_z=-\infty}^{\infty} e^{2\pi i[n_x(x-x')+n_y(y-y')+n_z(z-z')]/L}$$

This is readily evaluated in the limit of large L, in which case the sum-mand changes by a negligible amount as each n changes by one unit. We can then regard n_x as a continuous variable and replace $\sum_{n_x=-\infty}^{\infty}$ by $\int_{-\infty}^{\infty} dn_x = (L/2\pi) \int_{-\infty}^{\infty} dk_x$.   We thus obtain

$$\sum_{\mathbf{k}} u_{\mathbf{k}}^*(\mathbf{r}')u_{\mathbf{k}}(\mathbf{r}) \xrightarrow[L\to\infty]{}$$
$$(8\pi^3)^{-1} \int_{-\infty}^{\infty} \int_{-\infty}^{\infty} \int_{-\infty}^{\infty} e^{i[k_x(x-x')+k_y(y-y')+k_z(z-z')]} \, dk_x \, dk_y \, dk_z$$
$$= \delta(x - x') \, \delta(y - y') \, \delta(z - z') = \delta^3(\mathbf{r} - \mathbf{r}') \quad (11.14)$$

on making use of Eq. (11.10).

A similar calculation can be carried through, using the δ-function normalization, in which case we obtain from Eqs. (11.11) and (11.10)

$$\int u_{\mathbf{k}}^*(\mathbf{r}')u_{\mathbf{k}}(\mathbf{r}) \, d^3k = \iiint u_{\mathbf{k}}^*(\mathbf{r}')u_{\mathbf{k}}(\mathbf{r}) \, dk_x \, dk_y \, dk_z = \delta^3(\mathbf{r} - \mathbf{r}') \quad (11.15)$$

The closure relation (11.14) or (11.15) shows that the momentum eigenfunctions are orthonormal with respect to summation or integration over the eigenvalue $\mathbf{k}$ as well as with respect to integration over the position vector $\mathbf{r}$.

EXPANSION IN MOMENTUM EIGENFUNCTIONS

An arbitrary continuous function $\psi(\mathbf{r})$ can be written in terms of the δ function as

$$\psi(\mathbf{r}) = \int \psi(\mathbf{r}') \, \delta^3(\mathbf{r} - \mathbf{r}') \, d^3r' \qquad (11.16)$$

If we substitute the left side of Eq. (11.14) in place of $\delta^3(\mathbf{r} - \mathbf{r}')$ in Eq. (11.16), we obtain

$$\psi(\mathbf{r}) = \int \psi(\mathbf{r}') \sum_{\mathbf{k}} u_{\mathbf{k}}^*(\mathbf{r}')u_{\mathbf{k}}(\mathbf{r}) \, d^3r' = \sum_{\mathbf{k}} A_{\mathbf{k}} u_{\mathbf{k}}(\mathbf{r})$$
$$A_{\mathbf{k}} = \int u_{\mathbf{k}}^*(\mathbf{r}')\psi(\mathbf{r}') \, d^3r' \qquad (11.17)$$

Similarly, if we substitute for $\delta^3(\mathbf{r} - \mathbf{r}')$ from Eq. (11.15), we obtain

$$\psi(\mathbf{r}) = \int \psi(\mathbf{r}') \int u_{\mathbf{k}}^*(\mathbf{r}')u_{\mathbf{k}}(\mathbf{r}) \, d^3k \, d^3r' = \int A_{\mathbf{k}} u_{\mathbf{k}}(\mathbf{r}) \, d^3k \qquad (11.18)$$

with the same expression for A_k. Equations (11.17) and (11.18) show that it is possible to expand an arbitrary function in momentum eigenfunctions that are normalized either in a box or by means of δ functions.[1]

PROBABILITY FUNCTION AND EXPECTATION VALUE

The momentum probability function associated with a normalized wave function $\psi(\mathbf{r})$ is proportional to $|A_k|^2$. The proportionality factor is unity, since if we put

$$P(\mathbf{k}) = |A_k|^2 \tag{11.19}$$

it is easily shown in analogy with the summation of Eq. (10.12) that

$$\sum_k P(\mathbf{k}) = 1 \qquad \text{and} \qquad \int P(\mathbf{k}) \, d^3k = 1 \tag{11.20}$$

for the box and δ-function normalization, respectively.

The expectation value of the momentum when box normalization is used is

$$\langle \mathbf{p} \rangle = \hbar \sum_k \mathbf{k} P(\mathbf{k}) = \hbar \sum_k \int \mathbf{k} u_k^*(\mathbf{r})\psi(\mathbf{r}) \, d^3r \int u_k(\mathbf{r}')\psi^*(\mathbf{r}') \, d^3r' \tag{11.21}$$

From the complex conjugate of Eq. (11.2), we can replace $\mathbf{k} u_k^*(\mathbf{r})$ by $i\boldsymbol{\nabla} u_k^*(\mathbf{r})$. Then the first integral in Eq. (11.21) can be integrated by parts, and the surface integral vanishes because of the periodic boundary conditions on ψ and u_k^*. Thus, with the help of Eq. (11.14), Eq. (11.21) becomes

$$\langle \mathbf{p} \rangle = -i\hbar \sum_k \int u_k^*(\mathbf{r})\boldsymbol{\nabla}\psi(\mathbf{r}) \, d^3r \int u_k(\mathbf{r}')\psi^*(\mathbf{r}') \, d^3r'$$

$$= -i\hbar \iint \psi^*(\mathbf{r}')[\boldsymbol{\nabla}\psi(\mathbf{r})] \, \delta^3(\mathbf{r} - \mathbf{r}') \, d^3r \, d^3r'$$

$$= -i\hbar \int \psi^*(\mathbf{r})\boldsymbol{\nabla}\psi(\mathbf{r}) \, d^3r \tag{11.22}$$

This is in agreement with the second of Eqs. (7.8).

When δ-function normalization is used, the details of the calculation are very similar to those given above, except that the surface integral that results from the partial integration is over a sphere of infinite radius; it is zero because ψ becomes vanishingly small at great distances. This is consistent with the supposition that ψ is normalized; otherwise neither $\int P(\mathbf{k}) \, d^3k$ nor $\langle \mathbf{p} \rangle$ have any physical meaning. The result of the calculation in this case is the same as Eqs. (11.22) and (7.8).

---

[1] These results, although not rigorously established here, are equivalent to the mathematical theorems on the expansibility of functions in Fourier series and Fourier integrals.

12□MOTION OF A FREE WAVE PACKET IN ONE DIMENSION

The motion of a free particle (no external forces) in one dimension is described by the Schrödinger wave equation (6.8). The study of this motion provides an interesting application of the expansion techniques developed in Secs. 10 and 11. As a first step, we find the minimum value of the uncertainty product given in Eq. (3.1) and the possible forms of the one-dimensional wave packet that correspond to it, all at a definite instant of time. The structure of this minimum packet is the same whether or not the particle is free, since this form can be regarded simply as an initial condition on the solution of the Schrödinger equation for any V. However, the analytical work involved in finding ψ at other times is especially simple in the force-free case.

THE MINIMUM UNCERTAINTY PRODUCT[1]

In order to find the minimum value for the uncertainty product $\Delta x \cdot \Delta p$, we must first define what we mean by Δx and Δp. Although many expressions are possible, the simplest to handle analytically is the root-mean-square deviation from the mean, where the word "mean" implies the expectation value of Sec. 7.[2]

$$(\Delta x)^2 = \langle (x - \langle x \rangle)^2 \rangle = \langle x^2 \rangle - \langle 2x\langle x \rangle \rangle + \langle \langle x \rangle^2 \rangle = \langle x^2 \rangle - \langle x \rangle^2$$
$$(\Delta p)^2 = \langle (p - \langle p \rangle)^2 \rangle = \langle p^2 \rangle - \langle p \rangle^2 \tag{12.1}$$

Here the equalities follow directly from the general definition of expectation value given in Sec. 7. If now we put

$$\alpha \equiv x - \langle x \rangle \qquad \beta \equiv p - \langle p \rangle = -i\hbar \left(\frac{d}{dx} - \left\langle \frac{d}{dx} \right\rangle \right) \tag{12.2}$$

then

$$(\Delta x)^2 (\Delta p)^2 = \int_{-\infty}^{\infty} \psi^* \alpha^2 \psi \, dx \int_{-\infty}^{\infty} \psi^* \beta^2 \psi \, dx$$
$$= \int_{-\infty}^{\infty} (\alpha^* \psi^*)(\alpha \psi) \, dx \int_{-\infty}^{\infty} (\beta^* \psi^*)(\beta \psi) \, dx \tag{12.3}$$

The transformation of the α integral in Eq. (12.3) is obvious; the similar transformation of the β integral follows from a partial integration when we remember that ψ is a normalized wave packet, which vanishes at $x = \pm \infty$.

---

[1] W. Heisenberg, "The Physical Principles of the Quantum Theory," pp. 17–19 (University of Chicago Press, Chicago, 1930).

[2] Note that Δx and Δp are each calculated separately from ψ. We do not consider the possible existence of a "joint probability distribution" for x and p; see P. Suppes, *Phil. Sci.* **28**, 378 (1961).

The inequality

$$\int \left| f - g \frac{\int fg^* \, dx}{\int |g|^2 \, dx} \right|^2 dx \geq 0$$

where all integrals are from $x = -\infty$ to $+\infty$, is obviously true, and the equality is applicable only if $f = \gamma g$, where γ is a constant. From this inequality we obtain at once

$$\int |f|^2 \, dx \int |g|^2 \, dx \geq |\int f^* g \, dx|^2$$

If now we replace f by $\alpha\psi$ and g by $\beta\psi$, Eq. (12.3) becomes

$$(\Delta x)^2 \, (\Delta p)^2 \geq |\int (\alpha^*\psi^*)(\beta\psi) \, dx|^2 = |\int \psi^* \alpha\beta\psi \, dx|^2 \tag{12.4}$$

The last term in Eq. (12.4) can be written

$$|\int \psi^* [\tfrac{1}{2}(\alpha\beta - \beta\alpha) + \tfrac{1}{2}(\alpha\beta + \beta\alpha)]\psi \, dx|^2$$
$$= \tfrac{1}{4} |\int \psi^*(\alpha\beta - \beta\alpha)\psi \, dx|^2 + \tfrac{1}{4} |\int \psi^*(\alpha\beta + \beta\alpha)\psi \, dx|^2 \tag{12.5}$$

The cross term in the product that is omitted on the right side of Eq. (12.5) can be seen to vanish when use is made of the relation

$$(\int \psi^* \alpha\beta\psi \, dx)^* = \int \psi\alpha^* \beta^* \psi^* \, dx = \int (\beta^*\psi^*)(\alpha\psi) \, dx = \int \psi^* \beta\alpha\psi \, dx$$

which is obtained by using partial integration and remembering that α is real. Now from Eq. (12.2)

$$(\alpha\beta - \beta\alpha)\psi = -i\hbar \left[x \frac{d\psi}{dx} - \frac{d}{dx}(x\psi) \right] = i\hbar\psi \tag{12.6}$$

We thus obtain from Eqs. (12.4) to (12.6)

$$(\Delta x)^2 \, (\Delta p)^2 \geq \tfrac{1}{4}\hbar^2 \qquad \text{or} \qquad \Delta x \cdot \Delta p \geq \tfrac{1}{2}\hbar \tag{12.7}$$

where the equality can hold only if the second term on the right side of Eq. (12.5) is zero. This is the precise expression of the Heisenberg uncertainty relation (3.1), when the uncertainties Δx and Δp are defined as in Eq. (12.1).

FORM OF THE MINIMUM PACKET

It follows from the foregoing derivation that the minimum uncertainty product is attained only when two conditions are fulfilled:

$$\alpha\psi = \gamma\beta\psi \tag{12.8}$$
$$\int \psi^*(\alpha\beta + \beta\alpha)\psi \, dx = 0 \tag{12.9}$$

Equations (12.8) and (12.2) give us a differential equation for ψ

$$\frac{d\psi}{dx} = \left[\frac{i}{\gamma\hbar}(x - \langle x \rangle) + \frac{i\langle p \rangle}{\hbar} \right] \psi$$

which is readily integrated to give

$$\psi(x) = N \exp\left[\frac{i}{2\gamma\hbar}(x - \langle x \rangle)^2 + \frac{i\langle p \rangle x}{\hbar}\right] \tag{12.10}$$

where N is an arbitrary constant.

Equation (12.9), with the help of Eq. (12.8), becomes

$$\left(\frac{1}{\gamma} + \frac{1}{\gamma^*}\right)\int \psi^* \alpha^2 \psi\, dx = 0$$

which evidently requires that γ be pure imaginary. Then, since we want Eq. (12.10) to represent a wave packet for which the integral of $|\psi|^2$ converges, γ must be negative imaginary. The magnitude of the constant N can now be fixed by normalizing ψ.

$$\int |\psi|^2\, dx = 1$$

Similarly, γ can be determined by requiring that

$$\int (x - \langle x \rangle)^2 |\psi|^2\, dx = (\Delta x)^2$$

The integrals are readily evaluated and lead to the normalized minimum wave packet

$$\psi(x) = [2\pi(\Delta x)^2]^{-\frac{1}{4}} \exp\left[-\frac{(x - \langle x \rangle)^2}{4(\Delta x)^2} + \frac{i\langle p \rangle x}{\hbar}\right] \tag{12.11}$$

MOMENTUM EXPANSION COEFFICIENTS

The one-dimensional momentum eigenfunctions analogous to Eqs. (11.4) and (11.11) are

$$u_k(x) = L^{-\frac{1}{2}} e^{ikz} \tag{12.12}$$

for normalization in a one-dimensional "box" of length L, and

$$u_k(x) = (2\pi)^{-\frac{1}{2}} e^{ikz} \tag{12.13}$$

for δ-function normalization. Since for a free particle the wave equation has the simple form of Eq. (6.8)

$$i\hbar \frac{\partial \psi}{\partial t} = -\frac{\hbar^2}{2m}\frac{\partial^2 \psi}{\partial x^2} \tag{12.14}$$

the momentum eigenfunctions are also eigenfunctions of the energy.[1] Thus any solution of the wave equation can be written in a form analogous to Eq. (10.18),

$$\psi(x,t) = \left(\sum_k \text{ or } \int dk\right) A_k e^{-iE_k t/\hbar} u_k(x) \tag{12.15}$$

---

[1] The converse is not necessarily true, since there are two solutions of Eq. (12.16) for k (positive and negative) for each value of E_k.

where the A_k are independent of x and t; the entire time dependence is contained in the exponential factor. Equation (12.15) is readily verified to be a solution of Eq. (12.14) by direct substitution, provided that

$$E_k = \frac{\hbar^2 k^2}{2m} \tag{12.16}$$

The problem of finding the motion of a wave packet is thus resolved into finding the expansion coefficient A_k at some particular time, say $t = 0$, and then using Eqs. (12.15) and (12.16) to find $\psi(x,t)$ at other times. At $t = 0$, the exponential factors in Eq. (12.15) are unity, and we may use the one-dimensional analog of the second of Eqs. (11.17) to find A_k.

$$A_k = \int u_k^*(x)\psi(x,0)\,dx \tag{12.17}$$

The limits on the integral are $x = \pm\frac{1}{2}L$ or $x = \pm\infty$, according as box or δ-function normalization is used. The momentum probability function $P(k) = |A_k e^{-iE_k t/\hbar}|^2 = |A_k|^2$ is independent of the time, so that $\langle p \rangle$ and Δp, for example, are constants.

CHANGE WITH TIME OF A MINIMUM PACKET

As a simple specific example, we take $\psi(x,0)$ to have the form of Eq. (12.11) with $\langle x \rangle = \langle p \rangle = 0$, so that the wave packet initially is centered at $x = 0$ and has zero average momentum. Then, using box normalization, Eq. (12.17) gives

$$A_k = [2\pi L^2(\Delta x)^2]^{-\frac{1}{4}} \int_{-\frac{1}{2}L}^{\frac{1}{2}L} \exp\left[-\frac{x^2}{4(\Delta x)^2} - ikx\right] dx$$

$$= \left[\frac{8\pi(\Delta x)^2}{L^2}\right]^{\frac{1}{4}} e^{-k^2(\Delta x)^2} \tag{12.18}$$

where L is assumed to be so large that the contribution to the integral from $|x| > \frac{1}{2}L$ can be neglected. Substitution into Eq. (12.15) gives the wave function for general values of t:

$$\psi(x,t) = \sum_k A_k e^{-i\hbar k^2 t/2m} u_k(x) \tag{12.19}$$

where $k = 2\pi n/L$ and n takes on all positive and negative integer values and zero. As in Sec. 11, L may be taken arbitrarily large, n can be regarded as a continuous variable, and the summation replaced by $\int dn$, which in turn is the same as $(L/2\pi)\int dk$. Thus

$$\psi(x,t) = \left[\frac{(\Delta x)^2}{2\pi^3}\right]^{\frac{1}{4}} \int_{-\infty}^{\infty} \exp\left[-k^2(\Delta x)^2 - \frac{i\hbar k^2 t}{2m} + ikx\right] dk$$

$$= (2\pi)^{-\frac{1}{4}} \left(\Delta x + \frac{i\hbar t}{2m\,\Delta x}\right)^{-\frac{1}{2}} \exp - \frac{x^2}{4(\Delta x)^2 + 2i\hbar t/m} \tag{12.20}$$

The position probability density is then

$$|\psi(x,t)|^2 = \left\{ 2\pi \left[(\Delta x)^2 + \frac{\hbar^2 t^2}{4m^2(\Delta x)^2} \right] \right\}^{-\frac{1}{2}}$$

$$\exp - \frac{x^2}{2[(\Delta x)^2 + \hbar^2 t^2/4m^2(\Delta x)^2]} \quad (12.21)$$

Equation (12.21) is of the same form as $|\psi(x,0)|^2$, except that $(\Delta x)^2$ is replaced by $(\Delta x)^2 + \hbar^2 t^2/4m^2(\Delta x)^2$, which is equal to $(\Delta x)^2 + (\Delta p)^2 t^2/m^2$. Thus the center of the packet remains at $x = 0$ while the breadth of the packet increases as t departs from zero in both past and future directions. The smaller the initial uncertainty in position, the larger the uncertainty in momentum and the more rapidly the packet spreads; the time-dependent part of the above expression, $t(\Delta p)/m$, is simply the distance traveled by a classical particle of momentum Δp in the time t.

Use of the δ-function normalization does not alter the results of the foregoing calculation. The expression for A_k given in Eq. (12.18) is to be multiplied by $(L/2\pi)^{\frac{1}{2}}$; in Eq. (12.19) the summation is to be replaced directly by $\int dk$, thus eliminating a factor $L/2\pi$; finally, u_k in Eq. (12.19) is to be multiplied by $(L/2\pi)^{\frac{1}{2}}$. These three factors cancel, and so Eqs. (12.20) and (12.21) are unaffected by the choice of normalization of the momentum eigenfunctions.

CLASSICAL LIMIT

We have seen in Sec. 7 that a wave packet always moves like a classical particle insofar as the expectation values of its position and momentum are concerned. However, classical dynamics is useful as a description of the motion only if the spreading of the wave packet can be neglected over times of interest in the particular problem.

As a simple example of the kind of parameter that indicates when the classical limit is realized, we consider a wave packet that corresponds to a classical particle moving in a circular orbit of radius a and period T. We shall assume that this packet is sufficiently well localized so that the potential energy does not vary appreciably over its dimensions. Then the classical theory can provide a useful description of the motion only if a wave packet like that discussed above spreads by an amount that is small in comparison with a during a time that is large in comparison with T. The smallest spread of a packet during a time interval of magnitude t is attained when Δx is chosen to be of order $(\hbar t/m)^{\frac{1}{2}}$. We thus require that $(\hbar t/m)^{\frac{1}{2}} \ll a$ when $t \gg T$. This condition may be simply expressed by saying that the angular momentum $2\pi ma^2/T$ of the particle must be very large in comparison with $\hbar$. Thus for most atomic systems, where the angular momentum of each electron is of order $\hbar$, a wave packet corresponding to a well-localized particle spreads so much in one period that this type of description of the motion is not of physical interest.

PROBLEMS

1. Given three degenerate eigenfunctions that are linearly independent although not necessarily orthogonal, find three linear combinations of them that are orthogonal to each other and are normalized. Are the three new combinations eigenfunctions? If so, are they degenerate?

2. Show that so far as the one-dimensional motion of a particle is concerned, the functions $u_{x'}(x) = \delta(x - x')$ for all real x' constitute a complete orthonormal set and that each of them is an eigenfunction of the position variable x with the eigenvalue x'. Set up the position probability function and compare with that obtained in Sec. 7.

3. If the potential energy $V(x)$ in a one-dimensional problem is a monotonic increasing function of x and independent of the time, show that the functions $u_{V'}(x) = (dV/dx)^{-\frac{1}{2}}_{x=x'}\, \delta(x - x')$ for all real x', where $V' = V(x')$, constitute a complete orthonormal set of eigenfunctions of the potential energy with eigenvalues V'. Find the probability function for the potential energy, and show that it has the properties that would be expected of it.

4. What changes are needed in the discussion of the momentum eigenfunctions given in Sec. 11 if the normalization is carried through in a box of rectangular parallelepiped shape rather than in a box of cubical shape?

5. Find two other representations for the Dirac δ function like that given in Eq. (11.9).

6. Verify each of Eqs. (11.13) involving δ functions.

7. Show that the two Eqs. (11.20) are correct: that the momentum probability function defined in Eqs. (11.19) and (11.17) for a normalized ψ sums or integrates to unity.

8. The expression in brackets in the integrand of Eq. (10.19) enables one to calculate ψ at time t' in terms of ψ at time t. If this expression is called $iG(x',t';x,t)$ in the one-dimensional case, then $\psi(x',t') = i\int G(x',t';x,t)\psi(x,t)\, dx$. Show that for a free particle in one dimension

$$G_0(x',t';x,t) = -i\left[\frac{m}{2\pi i\hbar(t' - t)}\right]^{\frac{1}{2}} e^{im(x'-x)^2/2\hbar(t'-t)}$$

Assume that ψ has the form of the normalized minimum wave packet (12.11) at $t = 0$; use the above result to find ψ and $|\psi|^2$ at another time t'. This G_0 is called the free-particle Green's function in one dimension (see Sec. 36).

9. Let $u_1(\mathbf{r})$ and $u_2(\mathbf{r})$ be two eigenfunctions of the same hamiltonian that correspond to the same energy eigenvalue; they may be the same function, or they may be degenerate. Show that

$$\int u_1^*(\mathbf{r})(xp_x + p_x x)u_2(\mathbf{r})\, d^3r = 0$$

where the momentum operator $p_x = -i\hbar(\partial/\partial x)$ operates on everything to its right. What is the relation of this problem to Prob. 5, Chap. 2?

4

Discrete Eigenvalues: Bound States

The formalism that was developed in Chap. 2 and elaborated in Chap. 3 will now be applied to the explicit computation of discrete energy levels and the corresponding eigenfunctions. The next chapter will take up situations in which the energy eigenvalues are continuously distributed. Thus we are concerned here with bound states in which the particle is restrained by the external forces (potential energy) to a particular region of space, and in the next chapter with collision problems in which the particle can approach from and recede to infinite distance.

The relatively few potential-energy functions $V(\mathbf{r})$ for which analytic solutions of the wave equation (8.2) are possible are important beyond these immediate problems, since they often serve as bases for approximate calculations on more complicated systems.

13☐LINEAR HARMONIC OSCILLATOR

The one-dimensional motion of a point mass attracted to a fixed center by a force that is proportional to the displacement from that center provides one of the fundamental problems of classical dynamics. Its study is important not only for itself but also because more complicated systems can always be analyzed in terms of normal modes of motion whenever the interparticle forces are linear functions of the relative displacements, and these normal modes are formally equivalent to harmonic oscillators. This linearity of the newtonian equations of motion means that the potential energy of the system is a bilinear function of the coordinates; since this aspect carries over into quantum mechanics, harmonic normal modes can again be found. Thus the one-dimensional harmonic oscillator is very important for the quantum-mechanical treatment of such problems as the vibrations of individual atoms in molecules and in crystals. It also provides the key to quantum theory of the electromagnetic field. The vibrations of the electromagnetic field in a cavity can be analyzed into harmonic normal modes, each of which has energy levels of the oscillator type [see Eq. (13.8)]. Excitation of a particular mode of angular frequency ω to the nth excited state means that the energy of the system is increased by $n\hbar\omega$ and corresponds physically to the addition of n photons of this frequency to the system (see Chap. 14).

We shall solve the oscillator problem in this section by starting with the Schrödinger equation. However it can also be solved by algebraic methods, starting with the matrix theory of Chap. 6. The importance of the harmonic oscillator is so great that we shall also carry through the matrix solution in Sec. 25.

ASYMPTOTIC BEHAVIOR

The force $F = -Kx$ can be represented by the potential energy $V(x) = \frac{1}{2}Kx^2$ so that Eq. (8.5) becomes

$$-\frac{\hbar^2}{2m}\frac{d^2u}{dx^2} + \frac{1}{2}Kx^2u = Eu \tag{13.1}$$

It is convenient in dealing with an equation of this type to rewrite it in dimensionless form. To this end we introduce a dimensionless independent variable $\xi = \alpha x$, and a dimensionless eigenvalue λ, and attempt to put Eq. (13.1) in the form

$$\frac{d^2u}{d\xi^2} + (\lambda - \xi^2)u = 0 \tag{13.2}$$

Comparison of Eqs. (13.1) and (13.2) shows that this is possible if

$$\alpha^4 = \frac{mK}{\hbar^2} \qquad \lambda = \frac{2E}{\hbar}\left(\frac{m}{K}\right)^{\frac{1}{2}} = \frac{2E}{\hbar\omega_c} \tag{13.3}$$

where $\omega_c = (K/m)^{\frac{1}{2}}$ is the angular frequency of the corresponding classical harmonic oscillator.

The solution of Eq. (13.2) is facilitated by first examining the dominant behavior of u in the asymptotic region $\xi \to \pm \infty$.[1] For sufficiently large ξ it is apparent that $u(\xi) = \xi^n e^{\pm \frac{1}{2}\xi^2}$ satisfies Eq. (13.2), so far as the leading terms (which are of order $\xi^2 u$) are concerned, when n has any finite value. The boundary conditions of Sec. 8 permit us to keep only the minus sign in the exponent. This suggests that it might be possible to find an exact solution of Eq. (13.2) of the form

$$u(\xi) = H(\xi)e^{-\frac{1}{2}\xi^2} \tag{13.4}$$

where $H(\xi)$ is a polynomial of finite order in ξ. Substitution of Eq. (13.4) into Eq. (13.2) gives as the equation for $H(\xi)$

$$H'' - 2\xi H' + (\lambda - 1)H = 0 \tag{13.5}$$

where primes denote differentiation with respect to ξ.

ENERGY LEVELS

We now find a solution for H in the form

$$H(\xi) = \xi^s(a_0 + a_1\xi + a_2\xi^2 + \cdots) \qquad a_0 \neq 0 \qquad s \geq 0 \tag{13.6}$$

This is necessarily finite for $\xi = 0$. Equation (13.5) is to be valid for all values of ξ, so that, when Eq. (13.6) is substituted into it, the coefficient of each power of ξ can be equated to zero.

$$s(s - 1)a_0 = 0$$
$$(s + 1)sa_1 = 0$$
$$(s + 2)(s + 1)a_2 - (2s + 1 - \lambda)a_0 = 0$$
$$(s + 3)(s + 2)a_3 - (2s + 3 - \lambda)a_1 = 0 \tag{13.7}$$
$$\cdots \cdots \cdots \cdots \cdots \cdots \cdots \cdots \cdots \cdots \cdots$$
$$(s + \nu + 2)(s + \nu + 1)a_{\nu+2} - (2s + 2\nu + 1 - \lambda)a_\nu = 0$$

where ν is an integer. Since a_0 cannot be zero, the first of Eqs. (13.7) tells us that $s = 0$ or $s = 1$. The second equation tells us that $s = 0$, or $a_1 = 0$, or both. Then the third equation gives us a_2 in terms of a_0, the fourth gives us a_3 in terms of a_1, and the general equation gives us $a_{\nu+2}$ in terms of a_ν.

The discussion of parity in Sec. 9 shows that $u(\xi)$, and hence also $H(\xi)$, can be chosen to be either even or odd in ξ. It then follows from Eq. (13.6) that a_1 and all the other odd-subscript coefficients are zero. The wave function is then even or odd according as $s = 0$ or $s = 1$.

It follows from Eqs. (13.7) that the presence in the series (13.6) of a finite or an infinite number of terms depends on the choice of s and the

---

[1] We follow the polynomial method of A. Sommerfeld, "Wave Mechanics," p. 11 (Dutton, New York, 1929).

eigenvalue λ. If the series does not terminate, its dominant asymptotic behavior can be inferred from the coefficients of its high terms:

$$\frac{a_{\nu+2}}{a_\nu} \xrightarrow[\nu \to \infty]{} \frac{2}{\nu}$$

This ratio is the same as that of the series for $\xi^n e^{\xi^2}$ with any finite value of n. Equation (13.4) shows that this behavior for H violates the boundary conditions on u for large $|\xi|$.

Thus the series (13.6) must terminate. This means that

$$\lambda = 2s + 2\nu + 1$$

ν must be an even integer, since $a_0 \neq 0$ and otherwise the even-subscript terms would form an infinite series. The index s can still be either 0 or 1, and corresponding to these two values λ is equal to $2\nu + 1$ or $2\nu + 3$, where ν is an even integer. We may express both cases in terms of a quantum number n:

$$\lambda = 2n + 1 \qquad E_n = (n + \tfrac{1}{2})\hbar\omega_c \qquad n = 0, 1, 2, \ldots \quad (13.8)$$

It follows from Eqs. (13.8) and (13.7) that n is the highest value of $s + \nu$ in the series (13.6) for H. If we denote the corresponding polynomial by $H_n(\xi)$, we see that H_n is of degree n in ξ and is wholly even or odd according as n is even or odd. Since $e^{-\frac{1}{2}\xi^2}$ is even and has no nodes, the corresponding eigenfunction $u_n(\xi)$ has the parity of n and has n nodes.

ZERO-POINT ENERGY

The infinite sequence of energy levels (13.8) has the equal spacing postulated in 1900 by Planck, which is in agreement with the quantization rules of the old quantum theory. However, the finite value of the ground-state energy level $\frac{1}{2}\hbar\omega_c$, which is called the *zero-point energy*, is characteristic of the quantum mechanics and is related to the uncertainty principle in the same manner as is the finite lowest energy level for the square well with perfectly rigid walls (Sec. 9). The total energy is of order $(\Delta p)^2/m + K(\Delta x)^2$, where Δp and Δx are measures of the spreads in momentum and position, as defined in Sec. 12; if this is minimized, taking account of the uncertainty relation (3.1), it is easily seen that the minimum Δp is of order $(Km\hbar^2)^{\frac{1}{4}}$, so that the minimum total energy is of order $\hbar(K/m)^{\frac{1}{2}}$ or $\hbar\omega_c$.

HERMITE POLYNOMIALS

The polynomial of order n that has the parity of n and is a solution of Eq. (13.5) with $\lambda = 2n + 1$

$$H_n'' - 2\xi H_n' + 2nH_n = 0 \qquad\qquad (13.9)$$

is called the nth *Hermite polynomial* $H_n(\xi)$.   It is clear from the foregoing solution of Eq. (13.5) that these conditions define H_n uniquely
except for an arbitrary multiplying constant.   It is not necessary, then,
to use the recursion relations (13.7) to study the detailed properties of
the H_n if some other formulation of them can be found that is consistent
with these conditions.   A far more convenient formulation is actually
available, which expresses the H_n in terms of a *generating function* $S(\xi,s)$.

$$S(\xi,s) = e^{\xi^2-(s-\xi)^2} = e^{-s^2+2s\xi}$$

$$= \sum_{n=0}^{\infty} \frac{H_n(\xi)}{n!} s^n \tag{13.10}$$

If the exponential in Eq. (13.10) is expanded out in powers of s and ξ, it is
seen that a given power of s is associated only with powers of ξ that are
equal to that power or less than it by an even integer.   Thus $H_n(\xi)$
defined in this way is a polynomial of order n that has the parity of n.

To show that this H_n satisfies the differential equation (13.9), we
differentiate both sides of Eq. (13.10) first with respect to ξ and then with
respect to s.

$$\frac{\partial S}{\partial \xi} = 2se^{-s^2+2s\xi} = \sum_n \frac{2s^{n+1}}{n!} H_n(\xi) = \sum_n \frac{s^n}{n!} H_n'(\xi)$$

$$\frac{\partial S}{\partial s} = (-2s + 2\xi)e^{-s^2+2s\xi} = \sum_n \frac{(-2s + 2\xi)s^n}{n!} H_n(\xi)$$

$$= \sum_n \frac{s^{n-1}}{(n-1)!} H_n(\xi)$$

Equating equal powers of s in the sums of these two equations gives,
respectively,

$$H_n' = 2nH_{n-1}$$
$$H_{n+1} = 2\xi H_n - 2nH_{n-1} \tag{13.11}$$

The lowest-order differential equation involving only H_n that can be
constructed from Eqs. (13.11) is easily seen to be Eq. (13.9).   Thus the
$H_n(\xi)$ given by Eq. (13.10) are the Hermite polynomials.

The relations (13.11) may be used for the calculation of the H_n and
their derivatives, or an explicit expression obtainable directly from the
generating function may be used.   If $S(\xi,s)$ is differentiated n times with
respect to s and s is then set equal to 0, Eq. (13.10) shows that the result
is simply $H_n(\xi)$.   Now for any function of the form $f(s - \xi)$ it is apparent
that

$$\frac{\partial f}{\partial s} = -\frac{\partial f}{\partial \xi}$$

Thus

$$\frac{\partial^n S}{\partial s^n} = e^{\xi^2} \frac{\partial^n}{\partial s^n} e^{-(s-\xi)^2} = (-1)^n e^{\xi^2} \frac{\partial^n}{\partial \xi^n} e^{-(s-\xi)^2}$$

This gives an expression for the nth Hermite polynomial:

$$H_n(\xi) = (-1)^n e^{\xi^2} \frac{\partial^n}{\partial \xi^n} e^{-\xi^2} \qquad (13.12)$$

The first three polynomials calculated from Eq. (13.12) are

$$H_0(\xi) = 1 \qquad H_1(\xi) = 2\xi \qquad H_2(\xi) = 4\xi^2 - 2$$

HARMONIC–OSCILLATOR WAVE FUNCTIONS

The generating function is also useful for the calculation of integrals involving the harmonic-oscillator wave functions (13.4):

$$u_n(x) = N_n H_n(\alpha x) e^{-\frac{1}{2}\alpha^2 x^2} \qquad (13.13)$$

Suppose, for example, that we wish to normalize $u_n(x)$; this is equivalent to choosing the constant N_n such that

$$\int_{-\infty}^{\infty} |u_n(x)|^2 \, dx = \frac{|N_n|^2}{\alpha} \int_{-\infty}^{\infty} H_n{}^2(\xi) e^{-\xi^2} \, d\xi = 1$$

The integral on the right can be expressed as a series coefficient in the expansion of an integral containing the product of two generating functions.

$$\int_{-\infty}^{\infty} e^{-s^2+2s\xi} e^{-t^2+2t\xi} e^{-\xi^2} \, d\xi = \sum_{n=0}^{\infty} \sum_{m=0}^{\infty} \frac{s^n t^m}{n!m!} \int_{-\infty}^{\infty} H_n(\xi) H_m(\xi) e^{-\xi^2} \, d\xi \qquad (13.14)$$

The integral on the left of Eq. (13.14) is readily evaluated directly to give

$$\pi^{\frac{1}{2}} e^{2st} = \pi^{\frac{1}{2}} \sum_{n=0}^{\infty} \frac{(2st)^n}{n!} \qquad (13.15)$$

If equal powers of s and t are equated in the series on the right sides of Eqs. (13.14) and (13.15), we obtain the results

$$\int_{-\infty}^{\infty} H_n{}^2(\xi) e^{-\xi^2} \, d\xi = \pi^{\frac{1}{2}} 2^n n!$$

$$\int_{-\infty}^{\infty} H_n(\xi) H_m(\xi) e^{-\xi^2} \, d\xi = 0 \qquad n \neq m \qquad (13.16)$$

The first of Eqs. (13.16) tells us that the normalizing constant can be chosen to be

$$N_n = \left(\frac{\alpha}{\pi^{\frac{1}{2}} 2^n n!} \right)^{\frac{1}{2}} \qquad (13.17)$$

where a constant multiplicative complex phase factor of unit magnitude is still arbitrary. The second of these equations tells us that $u_n(x)$ and $u_m(x)$ are orthogonal to each other if $n \neq m$; this is in agreement with the general result obtained in Sec. 10 for nondegenerate energy eigenfunctions, since, in accordance with Eq. (13.8), $E_n \neq E_m$ if $n \neq m$, and so there is no degeneracy.

The integral

$$\int_{-\infty}^{\infty} u_n^*(x) x u_m(x) \, dx = \frac{N_n^* N_m}{\alpha^2} \int_{-\infty}^{\infty} \xi H_n(\xi) H_m(\xi) e^{-\xi^2} \, d\xi$$

is typical of others that can be evaluated with the help of the generating function. The two series expressions for the integral,

$$\int_{-\infty}^{\infty} e^{-s^2+2s\xi} e^{-t^2+2t\xi} \xi e^{-\xi^2} \, d\xi = \sum_{n=0}^{\infty} \sum_{m=0}^{\infty} \frac{s^n t^m}{n! \, m!} \int_{-\infty}^{\infty} \xi H_n(\xi) H_m(\xi) e^{-\xi^2} \, d\xi$$

and

$$\pi^{\frac{1}{2}}(s + t) e^{2st} = \pi^{\frac{1}{2}} \sum_{n=0}^{\infty} \frac{2^n (s^{n+1} t^n + s^n t^{n+1})}{n!}$$

may be equated term by term. With the help of Eq. (13.17), we get

$$\int_{-\infty}^{\infty} u_n^*(x) x u_m(x) \, dx = \begin{cases} \dfrac{1}{\alpha} \left(\dfrac{n+1}{2} \right)^{\frac{1}{2}} & m = n + 1 \\[2ex] \dfrac{1}{\alpha} \left(\dfrac{n}{2} \right)^{\frac{1}{2}} & m = n - 1 \\[2ex] 0 & \text{otherwise} \end{cases} \qquad (13.18)$$

CORRESPONDENCE WITH CLASSICAL THEORY

Plots of the first six harmonic-oscillator wave functions are shown in Fig. 10. It is apparent that the position probability densities $|u_n|^2$ associated with these stationary wave functions have little resemblance to the corresponding densities for the classical harmonic oscillator; the latter are proportional to $(\xi_0^2 - \xi^2)^{-\frac{1}{2}}$, where ξ_0 is the amplitude of the classical oscillator whose energy is equal to the quantum-mechanical eigenvalue. The agreement between classical and quantum probability densities improves rapidly with increasing n. Figure 11 contains a plot of $|u_n|^2$ for $n = 10$ (solid curve) and of the density of a classical oscillator of total energy $\frac{21}{2} \hbar \omega_c$ (dashed curve). The agreement is fairly good, on the average, the principal discrepancy being the rapid oscillations in $|u_n|^2$.

The expectation value for the potential energy can be obtained from Eq. (7.6):

$$\langle V \rangle_n = \int_{-\infty}^{\infty} u_n^*(x) \tfrac{1}{2} K x^2 u_n(x) \, dx$$

$$= \tfrac{1}{2} K \frac{2n + 1}{2\alpha^2} = \tfrac{1}{2} (n + \tfrac{1}{2}) \hbar \omega_c = \tfrac{1}{2} E_n$$

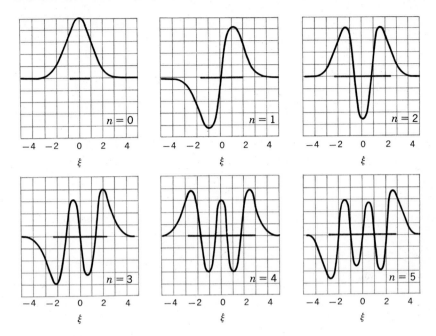

Fig. 10 Energy eigenfunctions for the first six states of the harmonic oscillator. [*After L. Pauling and E. B. Wilson, Jr., "Introduction to Quantum Mechanics," pp. 74–75 (McGraw-Hill, New York, 1935).*]

where $\int x^2 |u_n|^2\, dx$ can be calculated with the help of the generating function in analogy with the evaluation of Eq. (13.18).   Thus, for any value of n, the average potential and kinetic energies are each half of the total energy, just as is the case with the classical oscillator.

In similar fashion it can be shown that $\langle x \rangle = \langle p \rangle = 0$ for any harmonic-oscillator wave function, so that Eq. (12.1) tells us that $(\Delta x)^2 = \langle x^2 \rangle$ and $(\Delta p)^2 = \langle p^2 \rangle$. It is then easy to see that the uncertainty product is

$$\Delta x \cdot \Delta p = (n + \tfrac{1}{2})\hbar$$

This has the minimum possible value $\tfrac{1}{2}\hbar$ of Eq. (12.7) for the ground-state eigenfunction

$$u_0(x) = \frac{\alpha^{\frac{1}{2}}}{\pi^{\frac{1}{4}}}\, e^{-\frac{1}{2}\alpha^2 x^2} \tag{13.19}$$

which, as would be expected, is of the form of the minimum packet (12.11). Thus the minimum packet happens to be an eigenfunction of the harmonic-oscillator wave equation if its Δx is properly related to K and m.

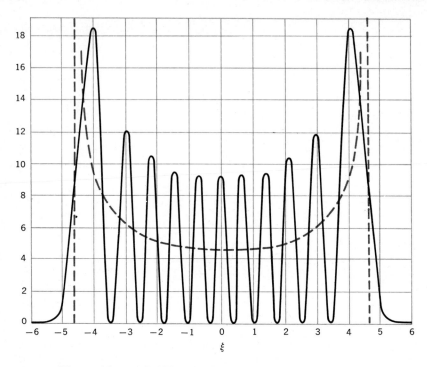

Fig. 11 The position probability density for the state $n = 10$ of a harmonic oscillator (solid curve) and for a classical oscillator of the same total energy (dashed curve). [*After L. Pauling and E. B. Wilson, Jr., "Introduction to Quantum Mechanics," p. 76 (McGraw-Hill, New York, 1935).*]

OSCILLATING WAVE PACKET

In accordance with Eq. (10.18), the general solution of the time-dependent Schrödinger equation for the harmonic oscillator

$$i\hbar \frac{\partial}{\partial t} \psi(x,t) = \left(-\frac{\hbar^2}{2m} \frac{\partial^2}{\partial x^2} + \tfrac{1}{2} K x^2 \right) \psi(x,t)$$

can be expanded in terms of stationary wave functions

$$\psi(x,t) = \sum_{n=0}^{\infty} A_n u_n(x) e^{-iE_n t/\hbar} = e^{-\frac{1}{2} i \omega_c t} \sum_{n=0}^{\infty} A_n u_n(x) e^{-in\omega_c t} \qquad (13.20)$$

where the A_n are arbitrary constants. Thus, apart from the phase factor $e^{-\frac{1}{2} i \omega_c t}$, $\psi(x,t)$ is a periodic function of t with the period of the classical oscillator $2\pi/\omega_c$. This suggests that it might be possible to find a solution in the form of a wave packet whose center of gravity oscillates with the period of the classical motion.[1]

[1] E. Schrödinger, *Naturwiss.* **14**, 664 (1926).

To investigate this possibility, we assume that at $t = 0$ the ψ of Eq. (13.20) has the form of the normalized minimum packet (13.19), except that the center of gravity is displaced in the positive x direction by an amount a.

$$\psi(x,0) = \sum_{n=0}^{\infty} A_n u_n(x) = \frac{\alpha^{\frac{1}{2}}}{\pi^{\frac{1}{4}}} e^{-\frac{1}{2}\alpha^2(x-a)^2} \tag{13.21}$$

We can make use of the orthonormality of the u_n to calculate a particular coefficient A_m by multiplying Eq. (13.21) through by $u_m^*(x)$ and integrating over x.

$$A_m = \int_{-\infty}^{\infty} u_m^*(x)\psi(x,0)\ dx = \frac{N_m^*}{\pi^{\frac{1}{4}}\alpha^{\frac{1}{2}}} \int_{-\infty}^{\infty} H_m(\xi)e^{-\frac{1}{2}\xi^2}e^{-\frac{1}{2}(\xi-\xi_0)^2}\ d\xi$$

$$\xi_0 \equiv \alpha a$$

The integral on the right can be evaluated with the help of the generating function by equating term by term the two series expressions for the integral:

$$\int_{-\infty}^{\infty} e^{-s^2+2s\xi}e^{-(\xi^2-\xi\xi_0+\frac{1}{2}\xi_0^2)}\ d\xi = \sum_{n=0}^{\infty} \frac{s^n}{n!} \int_{-\infty}^{\infty} H_n(\xi)e^{-(\xi^2-\xi\xi_0+\frac{1}{2}\xi_0^2)}\ d\xi$$

and

$$\pi^{\frac{1}{2}}e^{-\frac{1}{4}\xi_0^2+s\xi_0} = \pi^{\frac{1}{2}}e^{-\frac{1}{4}\xi_0^2} \sum_{n=0}^{\infty} \frac{(s\xi_0)^n}{n!}$$

On making use of Eq. (13.17), we obtain

$$A_n = \frac{\xi_0^n e^{-\frac{1}{4}\xi_0^2}}{(2^n n!)^{\frac{1}{2}}} \tag{13.22}$$

Substitution of these A_n into Eq. (13.20) gives

$$\psi(x,t) = \frac{\alpha^{\frac{1}{2}}}{\pi^{\frac{1}{4}}} e^{-\frac{1}{2}\xi^2-\frac{1}{4}\xi_0^2-\frac{1}{2}i\omega_c t} \sum_{n=0}^{\infty} \frac{H_n(\xi)}{n!} \left(\tfrac{1}{2}\xi_0 e^{-i\omega_c t}\right)^n$$

$$= \frac{\alpha^{\frac{1}{2}}}{\pi^{\frac{1}{4}}} \exp\left(-\tfrac{1}{2}\xi^2 - \tfrac{1}{4}\xi_0^2 - \tfrac{1}{2}i\omega_c t - \tfrac{1}{4}\xi_0^2 e^{-2i\omega_c t} + \xi\xi_0 e^{-i\omega_c t}\right)$$

$$= \frac{\alpha^{\frac{1}{2}}}{\pi^{\frac{1}{4}}} \exp\left[-\tfrac{1}{2}(\xi - \xi_0 \cos\omega_c t)^2\right.$$

$$\left. - i(\tfrac{1}{2}\omega_c t + \xi\xi_0 \sin\omega_c t - \tfrac{1}{4}\xi_0^2 \sin 2\omega_c t)\right]$$

where the sum is evaluated with the help of the generating function (13.10). The absolute square of this wave function gives a position probability density

$$|\psi(x,t)|^2 = \frac{\alpha}{\pi^{\frac{1}{2}}} e^{-\alpha^2(x-a\cos\omega_c t)^2}$$

This shows that ψ represents a wave packet that oscillates without change of shape about $x = 0$, with amplitude a and the classical frequency.

As $a \to 0$, ψ approaches the lowest energy eigenfunction $u_0(x)e^{-\frac{1}{2}i\omega_c t}$. The larger a becomes, the larger the number of stationary states that contribute significantly to the packet, and the larger the quantum number n_0 for which A_n of Eq. (13.22) has a maximum. For $n \gg 1$, we can use Stirling's formula to maximize $\ln A_n$; neglecting terms of order $\ln n$ and lower

$$\ln A_n \approx n(\ln \xi_0 - \tfrac{1}{2} \ln 2) - \tfrac{1}{2}n(\ln n - 1)$$

$$n_0 \approx \tfrac{1}{2}\xi_0^2 = \frac{Ka^2}{2\hbar\omega_c} \qquad (13.23)$$

Thus the energy level $E_{n_0} = (n_0 + \tfrac{1}{2})\hbar\omega_c$, from whose neighborhood most of the contribution to ψ comes, is approximately equal to the energy $\tfrac{1}{2}Ka^2$ of the classical oscillator that has the same amplitude.

14□SPHERICALLY SYMMETRIC POTENTIALS IN THREE DIMENSIONS

It is generally impossible to obtain analytic solutions of the three-dimensional wave equation (8.2) unless it can be separated into total differential equations in each of the three space coordinates. It has been shown[1] that there are 11 coordinates systems in which the free-particle wave equation [Eq. (8.2) with $V = 0$] can be separated. One of the most important of these is the spherical polar coordinate system, in terms of which the rectangular coordinates are given by (see Fig. 12)

$$x = r \sin \theta \cos \phi$$

$$y = r \sin \theta \sin \phi$$

$$z = r \cos \theta$$

If the potential energy is spherically symmetric, so that $V(\mathbf{r}) = V(r)$ is a function only of the magnitude r of $\mathbf{r}$ measured from some origin, the wave equation can always be separated in spherical coordinates. Many problems of physical interest can be represented exactly or approximately in terms of spherically symmetric potentials of various shapes. In this section we effect the separation and solve the resulting total differential equations in θ and ϕ. The next two sections deal with the solution of the radial equation for particular forms of $V(r)$.

[1] L. P. Eisenhart, *Phys. Rev.* **45**, 428 (1934). See also L. Pauling and E. B. Wilson, Jr., "Introduction to Quantum Mechanics," App. IV (McGraw-Hill, New York, 1935).

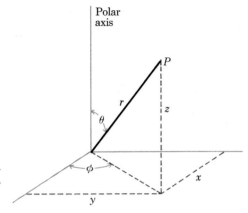

Fig. 12 The relation between rectangular and spherical polar coordinates of a point P.

SEPARATION OF THE WAVE EQUATION

The wave equation (8.2) with a spherically symmetric potential energy may be written in spherical coordinates:

$$-\frac{\hbar^2}{2m}\left[\frac{1}{r^2}\frac{\partial}{\partial r}\left(r^2\frac{\partial}{\partial r}\right) + \frac{1}{r^2\sin\theta}\frac{\partial}{\partial\theta}\left(\sin\theta\frac{\partial}{\partial\theta}\right) + \frac{1}{r^2\sin^2\theta}\frac{\partial^2}{\partial\phi^2}\right]u$$

$$+ V(r)u = Eu \quad (14.1)$$

We first separate the radial and the angular parts by substituting

$$u(r,\theta,\phi) = R(r)Y(\theta,\phi)$$

into Eq. (14.1) and dividing through by u.

$$\frac{1}{R}\frac{d}{dr}\left(r^2\frac{dR}{dr}\right) + \frac{2mr^2}{\hbar^2}[E - V(r)]$$

$$= -\frac{1}{Y}\left[\frac{1}{\sin\theta}\frac{\partial}{\partial\theta}\left(\sin\theta\frac{\partial Y}{\partial\theta}\right) + \frac{1}{\sin^2\theta}\frac{\partial^2 Y}{\partial\phi^2}\right] \quad (14.2)$$

Since the left side of Eq. (14.2) depends only on r, and the right side depends only on θ and ϕ, both sides must be equal to a constant that we call λ. Thus Eq. (14.2) gives us a radial equation

$$\frac{1}{r^2}\frac{d}{dr}\left(r^2\frac{dR}{dr}\right) + \left\{\frac{2m}{\hbar^2}[E - V(r)] - \frac{\lambda}{r^2}\right\}R = 0 \quad (14.3)$$

and an angular equation

$$\frac{1}{\sin\theta}\frac{\partial}{\partial\theta}\left(\sin\theta\frac{\partial Y}{\partial\theta}\right) + \frac{1}{\sin^2\theta}\frac{\partial^2 Y}{\partial\phi^2} + \lambda Y = 0 \quad (14.4)$$

The angular equation (14.4) can be further separated by substituting $Y(\theta,\phi) = \Theta(\theta)\Phi(\phi)$ into it and following the same procedure to obtain

$$\frac{d^2\Phi}{d\phi^2} + \nu\Phi = 0 \tag{14.5}$$

$$\frac{1}{\sin\theta}\frac{d}{d\theta}\left(\sin\theta\frac{d\Theta}{d\theta}\right) + \left(\lambda - \frac{\nu}{\sin^2\theta}\right)\Theta = 0 \tag{14.6}$$

The ϕ equation (14.5) can be solved at once; its general solution may be written

$$\Phi(\phi) = Ae^{i\nu^{\frac{1}{2}}\phi} + Be^{-i\nu^{\frac{1}{2}}\phi} \qquad \nu \neq 0$$

$$\Phi(\phi) = A + B\phi \qquad \nu = 0 \tag{14.7}$$

The requirement of Sec. 8 that $\Phi(\phi)$ and $d\Phi/d\phi$ be continuous throughout the domain 0 to 2π of ϕ demands that ν be chosen equal to the square of an integer. We thus replace Eqs. (14.7) by

$$\Phi_m(\phi) = (2\pi)^{-\frac{1}{2}}e^{im\phi} \tag{14.8}$$

where now all physical meaningful solutions are included if m is allowed to be a positive or negative integer or zero;[1] the multiplying constant is chosen equal to $(2\pi)^{-\frac{1}{2}}$ in order that Φ be normalized to unity over the range of ϕ.

LEGENDRE POLYNOMIALS

Unless $V(r)$ is specified, the farthest we can carry our treatment is the solution of the θ equation (14.6), where now $\nu = m^2$. It is convenient to substitute $w = \cos\theta$ for θ and put

$$\Theta(\theta) = P(w)$$

when Eq. (14.6) becomes

$$\frac{d}{dw}\left[(1-w^2)\frac{dP}{dw}\right] + \left(\lambda - \frac{m^2}{1-w^2}\right)P = 0 \tag{14.9}$$

Since the domain of θ is 0 to π, the domain of w is 1 to -1. The procedure for solving Eq. (14.9) is in many respects similar to the solution of the harmonic-oscillator wave equation presented in Sec. 13 and will not be given in detail here.[2] Since Eq. (14.9) is a second-order differential equation, it has two linearly independent solutions. Except for particular values of λ, both of these are infinite at $w = \pm 1$ and, in accordance

---

[1] At the very slight risk of confusion with the mass of the particle, we make use of the customary symbol m for the quantum number associated with the coordinate ϕ.

[2] For a complete discussion of this equation, see E. T. Whittaker and G. N. Watson, "A Course of Modern Analysis," 4th ed., chap. XV (Cambridge, London, 1935).

with Sec. 8, are not physically acceptable. If, however, $\lambda = l(l + 1)$, where l is a positive integer or zero, one of the solutions is finite at $w = \pm 1$ (the other is not); this finite solution has the form $(1 - w^2)^{\frac{1}{2}|m|}$ times a polynomial of order $l - |m|$ in w and has the parity of $l - |m|$.

The physically acceptable solutions of Eq. (14.9) when $m = 0$ are called the *Legendre polynomials* $P_l(w)$. Just as is the case with the Hermite polynomials, their properties may be discussed in terms of a generating function

$$T(w,s) = (1 - 2sw + s^2)^{-\frac{1}{2}}$$

$$= \sum_{l=0}^{\infty} P_l(w)s^l \qquad s < 1 \tag{14.10}$$

Differentiation of the generating function with respect to w and s leads to relations that are analogous to Eqs. (13.11) for the Hermite polynomials.

$$(1 - w^2)P_l' = -lwP_l + lP_{l-1}$$
$$(l + 1)P_{l+1} = (2l + 1)wP_l - lP_{l-1} \tag{14.11}$$

where primes denote differentiation with respect to w. The lowest-order differential equation involving only P_l that can be constructed from Eqs. (14.11) is easily seen to be Eq. (14.9) with $\lambda = l(l + 1)$ and $m = 0$.

For m not necessarily equal to zero, Eq. (14.9) has physically acceptable solutions if $\lambda = l(l + 1)$ and $|m| \leq l$. These solutions, which are called *associated Legendre functions*, are expressible in terms of the Legendre polynomials:

$$P_l^m(w) = (1 - w^2)^{\frac{1}{2}|m|} \frac{d^{|m|}}{dw^{|m|}} P_l(w) \tag{14.12}$$

This can be shown by substitution of Eq. (14.12) into the equation that is obtained by differentiating $|m|$ times the equation for $P_l(w)$. The generating function for the associated Legendre functions is obtained by differentiating Eq. (14.10) $|m|$ times with respect to w and multiplying by $(1 - w^2)^{\frac{1}{2}|m|}$.

$$T_m(w,s) = \frac{(2|m|)!(1 - w^2)^{\frac{1}{2}|m|}s^{|m|}}{2^{|m|}(|m|)!(1 - 2sw + s^2)^{|m|+\frac{1}{2}}}$$

$$= \sum_{l=|m|}^{\infty} P_l^m(w)s^l \tag{14.13}$$

SPHERICAL HARMONICS

The angular part $Y_{lm}(\theta,\phi)$ of the complete wave function, which is a solution of Eq. (14.4) when $\lambda = l(l + 1)$, is called a *spherical harmonic*.

It is apparent that

$$Y_{lm}(\theta,\phi) = N_{lm}P_l{}^m(\cos\theta)\Phi_m(\phi) \tag{14.14}$$

where $\Phi_m(\phi)$ is given by Eq. (14.8), and N_{lm} is the normalization constant for the associated Legendre function.

The same proof that was given in Sec. 10 for the orthogonality of the energy eigenfunctions may be used to show that solutions of Eq. (14.4) corresponding to different eigenvalues λ or l are orthogonal. The eigenvalue l is, however, $(2l + 1)$-fold degenerate, since there exist linearly independent solutions $Y_{lm}(\theta,\phi)$ for this value of l and all integer values of m between $+l$ and $-l$. The choice of Eq. (14.8) for $\Phi_m(\phi)$ makes these degenerate eigenfunctions orthogonal. We have then that the integral

$$\int_0^\pi \int_0^{2\pi} Y_{lm}^*(\theta,\phi)Y_{l'm'}(\theta,\phi)\sin\theta\,d\theta\,d\phi = \int_{-1}^1 \int_0^{2\pi} Y_{lm}^* Y_{l'm'}\,dw\,d\phi$$

vanishes unless $l = l'$ and $m = m'$. It is interesting to note that there is no more orthogonality present than is necessary to make this integral vanish when it should. Thus the ϕ part of the integral vanishes when $m \neq m'$ without regard for the l values; the θ or w part of the integral vanishes only when $l \neq l'$ and $|m| = |m'|$, since for $m \neq m'$ the orthogonality is taken care of by the integration over ϕ.

The integral

$$\int_{-1}^1 P_l{}^m(w)P_{l'}{}^m(w)\,dw \tag{14.15}$$

can be evaluated in various ways, for example, by using the generating function (14.13) in a manner similar to that described in Sec. 13. As expected, the integral (14.15) vanishes unless $l = l'$, when it has the value $[2/(2l + 1)][(l + |m|)!/(l - |m|)!]$; thus N_{lm} is the reciprocal of the square root of this quantity, except for an arbitrary complex phase factor of unit magnitude. For later convenience we choose the spherical harmonics to be

$$Y_{lm}(\theta,\phi) = \epsilon\left[\frac{2l + 1}{4\pi}\frac{(l - |m|)!}{(l + |m|)!}\right]^{\frac{1}{2}} P_l{}^m(\cos\theta)e^{im\phi} \tag{14.16}$$

where $\epsilon = (-1)^m$ for $m > 0$ and $\epsilon = 1$ for $m \leq 0$. The first few spherical harmonics are

$$Y_{0,0} = \frac{1}{(4\pi)^{\frac{1}{2}}} \qquad\qquad Y_{1,0} = \left(\frac{3}{4\pi}\right)^{\frac{1}{2}}\cos\theta$$

$$Y_{1,\pm1} = \mp\left(\frac{3}{8\pi}\right)^{\frac{1}{2}}\sin\theta\,e^{\pm i\phi} \qquad\qquad Y_{2,0} = \left(\frac{5}{16\pi}\right)^{\frac{1}{2}}(3\cos^2\theta - 1)$$

$$Y_{2,\pm1} = \mp\left(\frac{15}{8\pi}\right)^{\frac{1}{2}}\sin\theta\cos\theta\,e^{\pm i\phi} \qquad\qquad Y_{2,\pm2} = \left(\frac{15}{32\pi}\right)^{\frac{1}{2}}\sin^2\theta\,e^{\pm 2i\phi}$$

PARITY

The concept of parity introduced in Sec. 9 can now be extended to three-dimensional problems of the type discussed in this section.   Suppose that the position coordinate **r** is reflected through the origin so that **r** is replaced by $-\mathbf{r}$; this corresponds to replacing x by $-x$, y by $-y$, and z by $-z$, or to replacing θ by $\pi - \theta$, ϕ by $\phi + \pi$, and leaving r unchanged.   It is clear that the only change in the wave equation (14.1) is that $u(r,\theta,\phi)$ is replaced by $u(r, \pi - \theta, \phi + \pi)$, the rest of the equation being unaffected. Then the discussion of Sec. 9 shows that orthogonal linear combinations of degenerate eigenfunctions can be found that have definite parities and that a nondegenerate eigenfunction must have a definite parity.

The energy levels for a spherically symmetric potential are degenerate at least with respect to the quantum number m, for $l > 0$.   In this case, the degenerate eigenfunctions all have the same parity, which we now show to be the parity of l.   When **r** is reflected through the origin, the radial part $R(r)$ of the solution is unchanged, the ϕ part $\Phi(\phi)$ given by Eq. (14.8) has the parity of $|m|$, and the θ part $P_l^m(\cos\theta)$ has the parity of $l - |m|$, since $P_l^m(w)$ is equal to an even part $(1 - w^2)^{\frac{1}{2}|m|}$ times a polynomial in w that has the parity of $l - |m|$ with respect to change in sign of w or $\cos\theta$.   Thus $Y_{lm}(\theta,\phi)$, and hence $u(\mathbf{r})$, has the parity of l.

ANGULAR MOMENTUM

The radial wave equation (14.3) may be rewritten in a form that resembles the one-dimensional wave equation (8.5).   If we put $R(r) = \chi(r)/r$, the equation for the modified radial wave function χ may be written

$$-\frac{\hbar^2}{2m}\frac{d^2\chi}{dr^2} + \left[V(r) + \frac{l(l+1)\hbar^2}{2mr^2}\right]\chi = E\chi \qquad (14.17)$$

Thus the radial motion is similar to the one-dimensional motion of a particle in a potential

$$V(r) + \frac{l(l+1)\hbar^2}{2mr^2} \qquad (14.18)$$

The additional "potential energy" can be seen physically to be connected with the angular momentum in the following way.   A classical particle that has angular momentum L about the axis through the origin perpendicular to the plane of its orbit has the angular velocity $\omega = L/mr^2$ when its radial distance from the origin is r.   An inward force

$$m\omega^2 r = \frac{L^2}{mr^3}$$

is required to keep the particle in this path; this "centripetal force" is supplied by the potential energy and hence adds to the $V(r)$ that appears in the radial motion an additional "centrifugal potential energy" $L^2/2mr^2$. This has exactly the form of the extra term in (14.18) if we put

$$L = [l(l+1)]^{\frac{1}{2}}\hbar$$

The foregoing physical argument for identifying the quantum number l with the angular momentum of the particle can be put in quantitative form by finding the operators that correspond to the three components of the angular-momentum vector. Classically, we have that $\mathbf{L} = \mathbf{r} \times \mathbf{p}$, so that in quantum mechanics we take

$$L_x = yp_z - zp_y = -i\hbar\left(y\frac{\partial}{\partial z} - z\frac{\partial}{\partial y}\right)$$

$$L_y = zp_x - xp_z = -i\hbar\left(z\frac{\partial}{\partial x} - x\frac{\partial}{\partial z}\right) \tag{14.19}$$

$$L_z = xp_y - yp_x = -i\hbar\left(x\frac{\partial}{\partial y} - y\frac{\partial}{\partial x}\right)$$

Equations (14.19) can be transformed into spherical polar coordinates to give

$$L_x = i\hbar\left(\sin\phi\frac{\partial}{\partial\theta} + \cot\theta\cos\phi\frac{\partial}{\partial\phi}\right)$$

$$L_y = i\hbar\left(-\cos\phi\frac{\partial}{\partial\theta} + \cot\theta\sin\phi\frac{\partial}{\partial\phi}\right) \tag{14.20}$$

$$L_z = -i\hbar\frac{\partial}{\partial\phi}$$

The operator that represents the square of the total angular momentum is then found from Eqs. (14.20) to be

$$\mathbf{L}^2 = L_x{}^2 + L_y{}^2 + L_z{}^2$$

$$= -\hbar^2\left[\frac{1}{\sin\theta}\frac{\partial}{\partial\theta}\left(\sin\theta\frac{\partial}{\partial\theta}\right) + \frac{1}{\sin^2\theta}\frac{\partial^2}{\partial\phi^2}\right] \tag{14.21}$$

Comparison of Eqs. (14.21) and (14.4) shows that $Y_{lm}(\theta,\phi)$ is an eigenfunction of $\mathbf{L}^2$ with the eigenvalue $l(l+1)\hbar^2$:

$$\mathbf{L}^2 Y_{lm}(\theta,\phi) = l(l+1)\hbar^2 Y_{lm}(\theta,\phi) \tag{14.22}$$

In similar fashion, it follows from the structure of Eq. (14.8) and the last of Eqs. (14.20) that $\Phi_m(\phi)$, and hence also $Y_{lm}(\theta,\phi)$, is an eigenfunction of L_z with the eigenvalue $m\hbar$:

$$L_z Y_{lm}(\theta,\phi) = m\hbar Y_{lm}(\theta,\phi) \tag{14.23}$$

Thus the separation of the wave equation in spherical polar coordinates results in wave functions that are eigenfunctions of both the total angular momentum and the component of angular momentum along the polar axis. The quantum number l that appears in Eq. (14.22) is called the *azimuthal* or *orbital-angular-momentum quantum number*. The quantum number m that appears in Eq. (14.23) is called the *magnetic quantum number*, since it is of importance in the theory of the Zeeman effect (see Sec. 31), which involves the component of angular momentum along the magnetic field (z axis). It should be noted that in general the wave equation cannot be separated in this way and angular-momentum eigenfunctions obtained if the potential energy $V(\mathbf{r})$ is not spherically symmetric. This corresponds to the classical result that the angular momentum is a constant of the motion only for a central field of force (which is describable by a spherically symmetric potential). There is, however, the characteristic difference between classical and quantum theory that all three components of $\mathbf{L}$ can be precisely specified at once in the classical theory, whereas only L_z and $\mathbf{L}^2$ can, in general, be precisely specified at once in the quantum theory, since $Y_{lm}(\theta,\phi)$ is not an eigenfunction of L_x and L_y (except for the case $l = 0$). The choice of the direction of the polar axis that distinguishes L_z from L_x and L_y is, of course, completely arbitrary; it corresponds to the arbitrariness of the direction of space quantization in the absence of external fields in the old quantum theory.

15□THREE-DIMENSIONAL SQUARE WELL POTENTIAL

We are now in a position to find the bound-state·energy levels that correspond to particular choices of the potential energy $V(r)$ and of the angular-momentum quantum number l, by solving the radial wave equation (14.3). As a first example, we consider the square well potential of finite depth, for which $V(r) = -V_0$, $r < a$, $V(r) = 0$, $r > a$, where V_0 is positive (see Fig. 13). A spherical region of this type in which the potential is less than that of the surroundings serves to attract a particle just as in the one-dimensional case considered in Sec. 9.

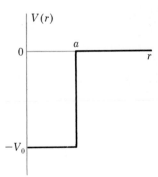

Fig. 13 A spherically symmetric square well potential of depth V_0 and radius a.

ZERO ANGULAR MOMENTUM

When $l = 0$, it is easier to solve the wave equation in the form (14.17) than in the form (14.3). In this case, $R(r) = \chi(r)/r$, and the wave equation is

$$-\frac{\hbar^2}{2m}\frac{d^2\chi}{dr^2} - V_0\chi = E\chi \qquad r < a$$

$$-\frac{\hbar^2}{2m}\frac{d^2\chi}{dr^2} = E\chi \qquad r > a \tag{15.1}$$

The solution of Eqs. (15.1) is the same as that obtained for the finite potential step in Sec. 9, except for three points: First, the energy scale is lowered everywhere in the present problem by an amount V_0; second, the domain of r is 0 to $+\infty$, in place of the domain $-\infty$ to $+\infty$ for x; and third, the boundary condition that the wave function not become infinite at $x = -\infty$ is now replaced by the same condition at $r = 0$.

From the discussion of Sec. 9, it is apparent that the solutions of Eqs. (15.1) are

$$\chi(r) = A \sin \alpha r + B \cos \alpha r$$

$$\alpha = \left[\frac{2m(V_0 - |E|)}{\hbar^2}\right]^{\frac{1}{2}} \qquad r < a \tag{15.2}$$

$$\chi(r) = Ce^{-\beta r} \qquad \beta = \left(\frac{2m|E|}{\hbar^2}\right)^{\frac{1}{2}} \qquad r > a$$

where we are interested in bound-state energy levels for which $E < 0$. The requirement that $R(r)$ be finite at $r = 0$ demands that we set $B = 0$ in the first of Eqs. (15.2). Thus the solution has the form of the odd parity solution of the one-dimensional problem. The energy levels are obtained by equating the two values of $(1/\chi)(d\chi/dr)$ at $r = a$ [this is equivalent to making $(1/R)(dR/dr)$ continuous there] and are given by solving

$$\alpha \cot \alpha a = -\beta \tag{15.3}$$

which is the same as Eq. (9.6). Then it follows from the discussion of Fig. 9 that there is no energy level unless $V_0 a^2 > \pi^2\hbar^2/8m$; there is one bound state if $\pi^2\hbar^2/8m < V_0 a^2 \leq 9\pi^2\hbar^2/8m$, etc.

INTERIOR SOLUTIONS FOR ARBITRARY l

For nonzero values of l, it is more convenient to work with the original radial equation (14.3) than with the equation for χ. If we put $\rho = \alpha r$, where α is defined in Eq. (15.2), the wave equation for $r < a$ becomes

$$\frac{d^2R}{d\rho^2} + \frac{2}{\rho}\frac{dR}{d\rho} + \left[1 - \frac{l(l+1)}{\rho^2}\right]R = 0 \tag{15.4}$$

The strong resemblance between Eq. (15.4) and Bessel's equation suggests that $R(r)$ can be expressed in terms of Bessel functions. This is, in fact, the case; if we define the "spherical Bessel function" $j_l(\rho)$ that is regular at $\rho = 0$ by[1]

$$j_l(\rho) = \left(\frac{\pi}{2\rho}\right)^{\frac{1}{2}} J_{l+\frac{1}{2}}(\rho) \tag{15.5}$$

where J is an ordinary Bessel function of half-odd-integer order, it is easily verified that $j_l(\rho)$ satisfies Eq. (15.4). In similar fashion, the "spherical Neumann function" is

$$n_l(\rho) = (-1)^{l+1}\left(\frac{\pi}{2\rho}\right)^{\frac{1}{2}} J_{-l-\frac{1}{2}}(\rho)$$

It can be shown[2] that $J_{l+\frac{1}{2}}(\rho)$, where l is a positive or negative integer or zero, is expressible as a sum of products of $\sin \rho$ and $\cos \rho$ with polynomials of odd order in $\rho^{-\frac{1}{2}}$. In particular, explicit expressions for the first three j's and n's are

$$j_0(\rho) = \frac{\sin \rho}{\rho} \qquad\qquad n_0(\rho) = -\frac{\cos \rho}{\rho}$$

$$j_1(\rho) = \frac{\sin \rho}{\rho^2} - \frac{\cos \rho}{\rho} \qquad n_1(\rho) = -\frac{\cos \rho}{\rho^2} - \frac{\sin \rho}{\rho}$$

$$j_2(\rho) = \left(\frac{3}{\rho^3} - \frac{1}{\rho}\right)\sin \rho - \frac{3}{\rho^2}\cos \rho \tag{15.6}$$

$$n_2(\rho) = -\left(\frac{3}{\rho^3} - \frac{1}{\rho}\right)\cos \rho - \frac{3}{\rho^2}\sin \rho$$

The leading terms for small ρ are[3]

$$j_l(\rho) \xrightarrow[\rho \to 0]{} \frac{\rho^l}{(2l+1)!!} \qquad n_l(\rho) \xrightarrow[\rho \to 0]{} -\frac{(2l-1)!!}{\rho^{l+1}} \tag{15.7}$$

$$(2l+1)!! \equiv 1 \cdot 3 \cdot 5 \cdots (2l+1)$$

---

[1] This definition and the properties of the j_l and n_l are taken from P. M. Morse and K. U. Ingard, "Theoretical Acoustics," pp. 337–338 (McGraw-Hill, New York, 1968).

[2] G. N. Watson, "Theory of Bessel Functions," 2d ed., p. 52 (Macmillan, New York, 1945).

[3] Equations (15.7) are useful approximations for ρ^2 somewhat less than $4l + 6$ and 2, respectively (Watson, op. cit., p. 44).

and the leading terms in the asymptotic expansions are[1]

$$j_l(\rho) \xrightarrow[\rho \to \infty]{} \frac{1}{\rho} \cos [\rho - \tfrac{1}{2}(l + 1)\pi]$$

$$n_l(\rho) \xrightarrow[\rho \to \infty]{} \frac{1}{\rho} \sin [\rho - \tfrac{1}{2}(l + 1)\pi]$$

(15.8)

Some properties of the j's and n's are

$$\int j_0{}^2(\rho)\rho^2\, d\rho = \tfrac{1}{2}\rho^3[j_0{}^2(\rho) + n_0(\rho)j_1(\rho)]$$

$$\int n_0{}^2(\rho)\rho^2\, d\rho = \tfrac{1}{2}\rho^3[n_0{}^2(\rho) - j_0(\rho)n_1(\rho)]$$

$$n_{l-1}(\rho)j_l(\rho) - n_l(\rho)j_{l-1}(\rho) = \frac{1}{\rho^2} \qquad l > 0 \qquad\qquad (15.9)$$

$$j_l(\rho) \frac{d}{d\rho} n_l(\rho) - n_l(\rho) \frac{d}{d\rho} j_l(\rho) = \frac{1}{\rho^2}$$

The following are properties of both the j's and the n's:

$$j_{l-1}(\rho) + j_{l+1}(\rho) = \frac{2l + 1}{\rho} j_l(\rho) \qquad\qquad\qquad l > 0$$

$$\frac{d}{d\rho} j_l(\rho) = \frac{1}{2l + 1} [l j_{l-1}(\rho) - (l + 1)j_{l+1}(\rho)]$$

$$= j_{l-1}(\rho) - \frac{l + 1}{\rho} j_l(\rho)$$

$$\frac{d}{d\rho} [\rho^{l+1}j_l(\rho)] = \rho^{l+1}j_{l-1}(\rho) \qquad\qquad l > 0 \quad (15.10)$$

$$\frac{d}{d\rho} [\rho^{-l}j_l(\rho)] = -\rho^{-l}j_{l+1}(\rho)$$

$$\int j_1(\rho)\, d\rho = -j_0(\rho)$$

$$\int j_0(\rho)\rho^2\, d\rho = \rho^2 j_1(\rho)$$

$$\int j_l{}^2(\rho)\rho^2\, d\rho = \tfrac{1}{2}\rho^3[j_l{}^2(\rho) - j_{l-1}(\rho)j_{l+1}(\rho)] \qquad l > 0$$

Since $R(r)$ must be finite for $r = 0$, the desired solution for $r < a$ is

$$R(r) = A j_l(\alpha r) \qquad\qquad\qquad\qquad (15.11)$$

EXTERIOR SOLUTIONS FOR ARBITRARY l

The wave equation for $r > a$ can be put in the form (15.4) if we redefine ρ to be $i\beta r$, where β is given in Eq. (15.2). Since the domain of ρ does not

---

[1] Equations (15.8) are useful approximations for ρ somewhat larger than $\tfrac{1}{2}l(l + 1)$ (Watson, *op. cit.*, p. 199); however, the magnitudes (although not the phases) of j_l and n_l are given to good approximation by (15.8) if ρ is somewhat larger than l, which is approximately the value of ρ for which the magnitude of j_l is greatest.

now extend in to zero, there is no reason why n_l cannot appear in the solution. The linear combination of j_l and n_l to be selected will be determined by the asymptotic form, which must fall off exponentially for large r. This suggests that we define *spherical Hankel functions*

$$h_l^{(1)}(\rho) = j_l(\rho) + in_l(\rho)$$
$$h_l^{(2)}(\rho) = j_l(\rho) - in_l(\rho)$$

(15.12)

which from Eqs. (15.8) have the asymptotic forms

$$h_l^{(1)}(\rho) \xrightarrow[\rho \to \infty]{} \frac{1}{\rho} e^{i[\rho - \frac{1}{2}(l+1)\pi]}$$

$$h_l^{(2)}(\rho) \xrightarrow[\rho \to \infty]{} \frac{1}{\rho} e^{-i[\rho - \frac{1}{2}(l+1)\pi]}$$

(15.13)

It can be shown that the asymptotic expansions, of which Eqs. (15.13) give the leading terms, contain no terms for which the exponent has the opposite sign to that given.

The desired solution for $r > a$ is then

$$R(r) = Bh_l^{(1)}(i\beta r) = B[j_l(i\beta r) + in_l(i\beta r)]$$

(15.14)

The first three of these functions are

$$h_0^{(1)}(i\beta r) = -\frac{1}{\beta r} e^{-\beta r}$$

$$h_1^{(1)}(i\beta r) = i\left(\frac{1}{\beta r} + \frac{1}{\beta^2 r^2}\right) e^{-\beta r}$$

$$h_2^{(1)}(i\beta r) = \left(\frac{1}{\beta r} + \frac{3}{\beta^2 r^2} + \frac{3}{\beta^3 r^3}\right) e^{-\beta r}$$

(15.15)

ENERGY LEVELS

The energy levels are obtained by requiring that $(1/R)(dR/dr)$ be continuous at $r = a$. When this condition is applied to the interior solution (15.11) and the exterior solution (15.15) with $l = 0$, we obtain Eq. (15.3). This may be written as

$$\xi \cot \xi = -\eta \qquad \xi^2 + \eta^2 = \frac{2mV_0a^2}{\hbar^2}$$

(15.16)

where, as in Sec. 9, we have put $\xi = \alpha a$ and $\eta = \beta a$. The same condition applied to the solutions for $l = 1$ reduces, with the help of Eqs. (15.6) and (15.15), to

$$\frac{\cot \xi}{\xi} - \frac{1}{\xi^2} = \frac{1}{\eta} + \frac{1}{\eta^2} \qquad \xi^2 + \eta^2 = \frac{2mV_0a^2}{\hbar^2}$$

(15.17)

Equations (15.17) may be solved numerically or graphically, by the methods indicated for the solution of Eqs. (15.16) in Sec. 9. In general, there is no degeneracy between the eigenvalues obtained from the solution of equations like (15.16) and (15.17) for various values of l.

It is easy to see how many energy levels Eqs. (15.17) give for various values of $V_0 a^2$ without going through the numerical work. A new level appears whenever η is zero or cot ξ is infinite. This occurs at $\xi = \pi$, $2\pi, \ldots$. Thus there is no energy level with $l = 1$ when

$$V_0 a^2 \leq \frac{\pi^2 \hbar^2}{2m}$$

there is one bound state with $l = 1$ if $\pi^2 \hbar^2 / 2m < V_0 a^2 \leq 2\pi^2 \hbar^2 / m$, etc.

The smallest value of $V_0 a^2$ for which there exists a bound state with $l = 1$ is greater than the corresponding value of $V_0 a^2$ for $l = 0$; this is reasonable from a physical point of view. The interpretation in Sec. 14 of the l term in the radial wave equation as an additional potential energy, which corresponds to the repulsive "centrifugal force," suggests that a particle possessing angular momentum requires a stronger attractive potential to bind it than a particle with no angular momentum. Indeed, it turns out that the minimum square well potential "strength" $V_0 a^2$ required to bind a particle of orbital-angular-momentum quantum number l increases monotonically with increasing l.[1]

16□THE HYDROGEN ATOM

The potential energy $V(r) = -Ze^2/r$, which represents the attractive coulomb interaction between an atomic nucleus of charge $+Ze$ and an electron of charge $-e$, provides another wave equation that can be solved analytically. This problem is of direct physical interest, since apart from relativistic effects (see Chap. 13), the calculated energy eigenvalues are in agreement with the observed energy levels of the hydrogen atom $(Z = 1)$, the singly charged helium ion $(Z = 2)$, etc.

REDUCED MASS

The Schrödinger wave equation developed in Sec. 6 describes the motion of a single particle in an external field of force. Now, however, we are interested in the motion of two particles (nucleus and electron) that are attracted to each other by a force that depends only on the distance between them. The form of the wave equation to be used for two particles is suggested by the extension of the wave equation from one to three

---

[1] It can be shown that bound states appear with zero energy for a particular l value when $[(1/R)(dR/dr)]_{r=a} = -(l + 1)/a$; for $l > 0$ this is equivalent to the condition $j_{l-1}(\xi) = 0$ where now $\xi = (2mV_0 a^2/\hbar^2)^{\frac{1}{2}}$.

dimensions that was given in Sec. 6. This extension involved making the wave function depend on the three rectangular coordinates x, y, and z, instead of just on x, and introducing the momenta corresponding to the new coordinates as they appear in the classical expression for the energy.

A similar extension from three to six rectangular coordinates leads directly to the Schrödinger wave equation for two particles of masses m_1 and m_2:

$$i\hbar \frac{\partial}{\partial t} \psi(x_1,y_1,z_1,x_2,y_2,z_2,t) = \left[-\frac{\hbar^2}{2m_1} \left(\frac{\partial^2}{\partial x_1{}^2} + \frac{\partial^2}{\partial y_1{}^2} + \frac{\partial^2}{\partial z_1{}^2} \right) \right.$$

$$-\frac{\hbar^2}{2m_2} \left(\frac{\partial^2}{\partial x_2{}^2} + \frac{\partial^2}{\partial y_2{}^2} + \frac{\partial^2}{\partial z_2{}^2} \right)$$

$$\left. + V(x_1,y_1,z_1,x_2,y_2,z_2,t) \right] \psi(x_1,y_1,z_1,x_2,y_2,z_2,t) \quad (16.1)$$

where the potential energy is assumed to depend in an arbitrary manner on all six coordinates and the time. If now the potential energy depends only on the relative coordinates, so that $V = V(x_1 - x_2, y_1 - y_2, z_1 - z_2)$, an important simplification can be made. We define relative coordinates x, y, z and coordinates of the center of mass X, Y, Z by

$$x = x_1 - x_2 \qquad y = y_1 - y_2 \qquad z = z_1 - z_2$$

$$MX = m_1x_1 + m_2x_2 \qquad MY = m_1y_1 + m_2y_2 \qquad MZ = m_1z_1 + m_2z_2$$
$$(16.2)$$

Here, $M = m_1 + m_2$ is the total mass of the system. Equation (16.1) can be rewritten in terms of the new coordinates

$$i\hbar \frac{\partial \psi}{\partial t} = \left[-\frac{\hbar^2}{2M} \left(\frac{\partial^2}{\partial X^2} + \frac{\partial^2}{\partial Y^2} + \frac{\partial^2}{\partial Z^2} \right) \right.$$

$$\left. -\frac{\hbar^2}{2\mu} \left(\frac{\partial^2}{\partial x^2} + \frac{\partial^2}{\partial y^2} + \frac{\partial^2}{\partial z^2} \right) + V(x,y,z) \right] \psi \quad (16.3)$$

where

$$\mu = \frac{m_1m_2}{m_1 + m_2} \quad (16.4)$$

is called the *reduced mass*.

Two separations of the wave equation (16.3) can now be made. First, the time dependence can be separated out, as in Sec. 8, and, second, a separation can be made into a product of functions of the relative coordinates and center-of-mass coordinates. The process is straightforward and simple and results in

$$\psi(x,y,z,X,Y,Z,t) = u(x,y,z)U(X,Y,Z)e^{-i(E+E')t/\hbar}$$

$$-\frac{\hbar^2}{2\mu}\nabla^2 u + Vu = Eu \tag{16.5}$$

$$-\frac{\hbar^2}{2M}\nabla^2 U = E'U$$

where the ∇^2 operators in the second and third equations imply differentiation with respect to the relative and center-of-mass coordinates, respectively. The second of Eqs. (16.5) describes the relative motion of the two particles and is the same as the equation for the motion of a particle that has the reduced mass μ in an external potential energy V. The third of Eqs. (16.5) tells us that the center of mass of the system of two particles moves like a free particle of mass M.

In the hydrogen-atom problem, we shall be interested in the energy levels E associated with the relative motion. In this case, the reduced mass μ is only slightly smaller than the electronic mass, since atomic nuclei are far more massive than electrons.

ASYMPTOTIC BEHAVIOR

The separation of the relative motion in spherical coordinates is made as in Sec. 14. The radial equation that corresponds to the angular-momentum quantum number l is then

$$-\frac{\hbar^2}{2\mu}\frac{1}{r^2}\frac{d}{dr}\left(r^2\frac{dR}{dr}\right) - \frac{Ze^2}{r}R + \frac{l(l+1)\hbar^2}{2\mu r^2}R = ER \tag{16.6}$$

where $E < 0$ for a bound state.[1] We follow the polynomial method used in the treatment of the harmonic-oscillator equation that was given in Sec. 13, and we first attempt to rewrite Eq. (16.6) in dimensionless form by introducing a dimensionless independent variable $\rho = \alpha r$. Unlike Eq. (13.1), however, where the leading term for large x was the potential-energy term $\frac{1}{2}Kx^2$, the leading term in Eq. (16.6) for large r is the eigenvalue term E. We therefore choose α so that the E term becomes a fixed number; this makes the dominant asymptotic behavior of the solution independent of the eigenvalue. We rewrite Eq. (16.6) as

$$\frac{1}{\rho^2}\frac{d}{d\rho}\left(\rho^2\frac{dR}{d\rho}\right) + \left[\frac{\lambda}{\rho} - \frac{1}{4} - \frac{l(l+1)}{\rho^2}\right]R = 0 \tag{16.7}$$

where the particular choice of the number $\frac{1}{4}$ for the eigenvalue term is arbitrary but convenient for the following development. Comparison

---

[1] E. Schrödinger, *Ann. Physik* **79**, 361 (1926).

of Eqs. (16.6) and (16.7) shows that

$$\alpha^2 = \frac{8\mu|E|}{\hbar^2} \qquad \lambda = \frac{2\mu Ze^2}{\alpha\hbar^2} = \frac{Ze^2}{\hbar}\left(\frac{\mu}{2|E|}\right)^{\frac{1}{2}} \qquad (16.8)$$

As with the harmonic-oscillator equation, we first find the dominant behavior of $R(\rho)$ in the asymptotic region $\rho \to \infty$. For sufficiently large ρ, it is apparent that $R(\rho) = \rho^n e^{\pm\frac{1}{2}\rho}$ satisfies Eq. (16.7) so far as the leading terms (which are of order R) are concerned, when n has any finite value. This suggests that we look for an exact solution of Eq. (16.7) of the form

$$R(\rho) = F(\rho)e^{-\frac{1}{2}\rho} \qquad (16.9)$$

where $F(\rho)$ is a polynomial of finite order in ρ. Substitution of Eq. (16.9) into Eq. (16.7) gives as the equation for $F(\rho)$

$$F'' + \left(\frac{2}{\rho} - 1\right)F' + \left[\frac{\lambda - 1}{\rho} - \frac{l(l+1)}{\rho^2}\right]F = 0 \qquad (16.10)$$

where primes denote differentiation with respect to ρ.

ENERGY LEVELS

We now find a solution for F in the form

$$F(\rho) = \rho^s(a_0 + a_1\rho + a_2\rho^2 + \cdots)$$
$$\equiv \rho^s L(\rho) \qquad a_0 \neq 0 \qquad s \geq 0 \quad (16.11)$$

This is necessarily finite for $\rho = 0$. Substitution of Eq. (16.11) into Eq. (16.10) gives as the equation for L

$$\rho^2 L'' + \rho[2(s+1) - \rho]L' + [\rho(\lambda - s - 1)$$
$$+ s(s+1) - l(l+1)]L = 0$$

If ρ is set equal to zero in this equation, it follows from the form of L implied by Eq. (16.11) that $s(s+1) - l(l+1) = 0$. This quadratic equation in s has two roots: $s = l$ and $s = -(l+1)$. The boundary condition that $R(\rho)$ be finite at $\rho = 0$ requires that we choose $s = l$. The equation for L then becomes

$$\rho L'' + [2(l+1) - \rho]L' + (\lambda - l - 1)L = 0 \qquad (16.12)$$

Equation (16.12) can be solved by substituting in a power series of the form indicated by Eq. (16.11). The recursion relation between the coefficients of successive terms of the series is readily seen to be

$$a_{\nu+1} = \frac{\nu + l + 1 - \lambda}{(\nu + 1)(\nu + 2l + 2)} a_\nu \qquad (16.13)$$

If the series does not terminate, its dominant asymptotic behavior can be inferred from the coefficients of its high terms:

$$\frac{a_{\nu+1}}{a_\nu} \xrightarrow[\nu \to \infty]{} \frac{1}{\nu}$$

This ratio is the same as that of the series for $\rho^n e^\rho$ with any finite value of n. Equations (16.9) and (16.11) show that this behavior for L violates the boundary condition on R for large ρ.

Thus the series for L must terminate. If the highest power of ρ in L is $\rho^{n'}(n' \geq 0)$, we must choose λ equal to a positive integer n,[1] such that

$$\lambda = n = n' + l + 1 \tag{16.14}$$

n' is called the *radial quantum number* and n the *total quantum number*. Since n' and l can take on positive integer or zero values, n can have the values 1, 2, ... The energy eigenvalues are given by Eq. (16.8)

$$E_n = - |E_n| = - \frac{\mu Z^2 e^4}{2\hbar^2 n^2} \tag{16.15}$$

in agreement with the old quantum theory and with experiment. Unlike the square well potential problem considered in Sec. 15, the coulomb field problem gives rise to an infinite number of discrete energy levels extending from $-\mu Z^2 e^4/2\hbar^2$ up to zero, for any finite value of Z. This is due to the slow decrease in magnitude of the coulomb potential at large r.

LAGUERRE POLYNOMIALS

The physically acceptable solutions of Eq. (16.12) with $\lambda = n$ may be expressed in terms of the *Laguerre polynomials* $L_q(\rho)$, which can be defined in terms of a generating function

$$U(\rho,s) = \frac{e^{-\rho s/(1-s)}}{1 - s}$$

$$= \sum_{q=0}^{\infty} \frac{L_q(\rho)}{q!} s^q \qquad s < 1 \tag{16.16}$$

Differentiation of the generating function with respect to ρ and s leads to relations that are analogous to Eqs. (13.11) for the Hermite polynomials and (14.11) for the Legendre polynomials:

$$L_q' - qL_{q-1}' = -qL_{q-1}$$
$$L_{q+1} = (2q + 1 - \rho)L_q - q^2 L_{q-1} \tag{16.17}$$

---

[1] The result that the allowed values of λ are integers, rather than multiples of integers, derives from the choice of $\frac{1}{4}$ for the eigenvalue term in the dimensionless radial wave equation (16.7).

The lowest-order differential equation involving only L_q that can be constructed from Eqs. (16.17) is easily seen to be

$$\rho L_q'' + (1 - \rho)L_q' + q L_q = 0 \tag{16.18}$$

Equation (16.18) resembles Eq. (16.12) but is not quite the same. We define the *associated Laguerre polynomial*

$$L_q^p(\rho) = \frac{d^p}{d\rho^p} L_q(\rho) \tag{16.19}$$

On differentiating Eq. (16.18) p times, it is seen that $L_q^p(\rho)$ satisfies

$$\rho L_q^{p\prime\prime} + (p + 1 - \rho)L_q^{p\prime} + (q - p)L_q^p = 0 \tag{16.20}$$

Comparison of Eq. (16.12) with $\lambda = n$ and Eq. (16.20) shows that the desired polynomial solutions are the associated Laguerre polynomials $L_{n+l}^{2l+1}(\rho)$, which are of order $(n + l) - (2l + 1) = n - l - 1$ in agreement with Eq. (16.14).

Differentiation of Eq. (16.16) p times with respect to ρ gives the generating function for the associated Laguerre polynomials:

$$U_p(\rho,s) = \frac{(-s)^p e^{-\rho s/(1-s)}}{(1 - s)^{p+1}} = \sum_{q=p}^{\infty} \frac{L_q^p(\rho)}{q!} s^q \tag{16.21}$$

The following explicit expression may be verified by substituting it into Eq. (16.21), with $n + l = q$ and $2l + 1 = p$, and interchanging the order of the two summations:

$$L_{n+l}^{2l+1}(\rho) = \sum_{k=0}^{n-l-1} (-1)^{k+2l+1} \frac{[(n + l)!]^2 \rho^k}{(n - l - 1 - k)!(2l + 1 + k)!k!} \tag{16.22}$$

HYDROGEN–ATOM WAVE FUNCTIONS

The radial wave function is of the form $e^{-\frac{1}{2}\rho}\rho^l L_{n+l}^{2l+1}(\rho)$. The normalization constant may be found by using the generating function to evaluate the integral

$$\int_0^{\infty} e^{-\rho}\rho^{2l}[L_{n+l}^{2l+1}(\rho)]^2 \rho^2 \, d\rho = \frac{2n[(n + l)!]^3}{(n - l - 1)!} \tag{16.23}$$

Thus the normalized energy eigenfunctions for the hydrogen atom are

$$u_{nlm}(r,\theta,\phi) = R_{nl}(r) Y_{lm}(\theta,\phi)$$

$$R_{nl}(r) = - \left\{ \left(\frac{2Z}{na_0} \right)^3 \frac{(n - l - 1)!}{2n[(n + l)!]^3} \right\}^{\frac{1}{2}} e^{-\frac{1}{2}\rho}\rho^l L_{n+l}^{2l+1}(\rho) \tag{16.24}$$

$$a_0 = \frac{\hbar^2}{\mu e^2} \qquad \rho = \frac{2Z}{na_0} r$$

where $Y_{lm}(\theta,\phi)$ is the normalized spherical harmonic given in Eq. (14.16); a_0 is the radius of the first (circular) Bohr orbit for hydrogen ($Z = 1$) in the old quantum theory. The energy levels (16.15) may be written

$$E_n = -\frac{Z^2 e^2}{2a_0 n^2}$$

The first three radial functions, which are found from Eqs. (16.22) and (16.24), are

$$R_{10}(r) = \left(\frac{Z}{a_0}\right)^{\frac{3}{2}} 2e^{-Zr/a_0}$$

$$R_{20}(r) = \left(\frac{Z}{2a_0}\right)^{\frac{3}{2}} \left(2 - \frac{Zr}{a_0}\right) e^{-Zr/2a_0}$$

$$R_{21}(r) = \left(\frac{Z}{2a_0}\right)^{\frac{3}{2}} \frac{Zr}{a_0\sqrt{3}} e^{-Zr/2a_0}$$

A much more complete set of these functions, with graphs of some of them, is given by Pauling and Wilson.[1]

It is interesting to note that each of the eigenfunctions for which $l = 0$ has a discontinuous gradient at $r = 0$, since $dR_{n0}/dr \neq 0$ there and Y_{00} is independent of θ and ϕ. This is a consequence of the infinite potential energy at that point, as can be shown by means of a limiting process similar to that used in Sec. 8 to derive the boundary conditions at a perfectly rigid wall.

DEGENERACY

The energy eigenvalues (16.15) depend only on n and so are degenerate with respect to both l and m. Thus, for each value of n, l can vary from 0 to $n - 1$, and for each of these l values, m can vary from $-l$ to $+l$. The total degeneracy of the energy level E_n is then

$$\sum_{l=0}^{n-1} (2l + 1) = 2\frac{n(n - 1)}{2} + n = n^2$$

It follows from the discussion of Sec. 14 that the degeneracy with respect to m is characteristic of any central force field, for which V depends only on the radial distance r from some point. The l degeneracy, however, is characteristic of the coulomb field, as distinguished from most other central force fields.[2] In some problems, such as the motion of the valence electron of an alkali atom, the potential energy of the electron

---

[1] Pauling and Wilson, *op. cit.*, sec. 21.

[2] The special symmetry of the coulomb field that leads to this degeneracy is discussed in Sec. 30.

is central but only approximately of the coulomb form. This prevents the n energy levels that have the same total quantum number n and different l from being coincident, so that the nth hydrogen-like level splits up into n distinct levels. If also some external field (such as a magnetic field) that destroys the spherical symmetry is imposed, the $(2l + 1)$-fold m degeneracy disappears, and the nth hydrogen-like level is split up into n^2 distinct levels.

The existence of degenerate energy eigenvalues means that linear combinations of the corresponding eigenfunctions are solutions of the wave equation with the same energy. In the case of the m degeneracy, such linear combinations of the spherical harmonics $Y_{lm}(\theta, \phi)$ can be found that correspond to a new choice of the polar axis. It is reasonable to expect that linear combinations of the degenerate hydrogen-atom eigenfunctions that have the same n and different l exist that also correspond to some new choice of the coordinates. This is, in fact, the case, since it turns out that the hydrogen-atom wave equation can be separated in parabolic coordinates. In general, degeneracy will occur whenever the wave equation can be solved in more than one way (in different coordinate systems, or in a single coordinate system oriented in different ways), since if there were no degeneracy the wave functions obtained in the different coordinate systems would have to be identical except for a multiplying constant, and that is usually not possible. For a general central field, an exception occurs when $l = 0$, since then the wave function is spherically symmetric and has the same form for all orientations of the polar axis, so that there is no degeneracy. A similar exception occurs in the hydrogen-atom problem when $n = 1$, in which case it turns out that the solutions obtained by spherical and parabolic separation of the wave equation are identical.

SEPARATION IN PARABOLIC COORDINATES

The parabolic coordinates ξ, η, ϕ are given in terms of the spherical polar coordinates by the relations

$$\xi = r - z = r(1 - \cos\theta)$$
$$\eta = r + z = r(1 + \cos\theta) \qquad\qquad (16.25)$$
$$\phi = \phi$$

The surfaces of constant ξ are a set of confocal paraboloids of revolution about the z or polar axis, with focus at the origin, that open in the direction of positive z or $\theta = 0$. The surfaces of constant η are a similar set of confocal paraboloids that open in the direction of negative z or $\theta = \pi$. The surfaces of constant ϕ are the same as in the spherical coordinate system: planes through the polar axis.

The wave equation for the hydrogen atom in parabolic coordinates is

$$
-\frac{\hbar^2}{2\mu} \left\{ \frac{4}{\xi+\eta} \left[\frac{\partial}{\partial\xi}\left(\xi\frac{\partial u}{\partial\xi} \right) + \frac{\partial}{\partial\eta}\left(\eta\frac{\partial u}{\partial\eta} \right) \right] \right.
$$
$$
\left. + \frac{1}{\xi\eta}\frac{\partial^2 u}{\partial\phi^2} \right\} - \frac{2Ze^2}{\xi+\eta}u = Eu \qquad E < 0 \quad (16.26)
$$

The separation is accomplished by substituting

$$
u(\xi,\eta,\phi) = f(\xi)g(\eta)\Phi(\phi)
$$

into Eq. (16.26) and dividing through by u; the ϕ part of the equation separates at once[1]:

$$
\frac{4\xi\eta}{\xi+\eta}\left[\frac{1}{f}\frac{d}{d\xi}\left(\xi\frac{df}{d\xi} \right) + \frac{1}{g}\frac{d}{d\eta}\left(\eta\frac{dg}{d\eta} \right) \right]
$$
$$
+ \frac{4\mu Ze^2\xi\eta}{\hbar^2(\xi+\eta)} - \frac{2\mu|E|\xi\eta}{\hbar^2} = -\frac{1}{\Phi}\frac{d^2\Phi}{d\phi^2} \quad (16.27)
$$

Since the left side of Eq. (16.27) depends only on ξ and η, and the right side only on ϕ, both sides must be equal to a constant that we call m^2; in accordance with the discussion of Sec. 14, this gives normalized ϕ solutions that are the same as (14.8):

$$
\Phi_m(\phi) = (2\pi)^{-\frac{1}{2}}e^{im\phi} \qquad m = 0, \pm 1, \pm 2, \ldots \quad (16.28)
$$

The rest of Eq. (16.27) can be separated into ξ and η parts:

$$
\frac{1}{f}\frac{d}{d\xi}\left(\xi\frac{df}{d\xi} \right) - \frac{m^2}{4\xi} - \frac{\mu|E|}{2\hbar^2}\xi + \frac{\mu Ze^2}{\hbar^2}
$$
$$
= -\left[\frac{1}{g}\frac{d}{d\eta}\left(\eta\frac{dg}{d\eta} \right) - \frac{m^2}{4\eta} - \frac{\mu|E|}{2\hbar^2}\eta \right] = \nu \quad (16.29)
$$

where the separation constant ν is to be determined by the boundary conditions. Thus the equations for f and g are

$$
\frac{d}{d\xi}\left(\xi\frac{df}{d\xi} \right) - \left(\frac{m^2}{4\xi} + \frac{\mu|E|\xi}{2\hbar^2} - \frac{\mu Ze^2}{\hbar^2} + \nu \right)f = 0
$$
$$
\frac{d}{d\eta}\left(\eta\frac{dg}{d\eta} \right) - \left(\frac{m^2}{4\eta} + \frac{\mu|E|\eta}{2\hbar^2} - \nu \right)g = 0
$$
(16.30)

Since these two equations are of the same form and differ only in their constant terms, it is sufficient to solve one of them.

---

[1] E. Schrödinger, *Ann. Physik* **80**, 437 (1926); P. S. Epstein, *Phys. Rev.* **28**, 695 (1926); I. Waller, *Z. Physik* **38**, 635 (1926).

ENERGY LEVELS

The first of Eqs. (16.30) may be solved by the method used to solve (16.6). The substitution $\zeta = \alpha \xi$ puts it into the dimensionless form

$$\frac{1}{\zeta} \frac{d}{d\zeta} \left(\zeta \frac{df}{d\zeta} \right) + \left(\frac{\lambda_1}{\zeta} - \frac{1}{4} - \frac{m^2}{4\zeta^2} \right) f = 0 \qquad (16.31)$$

if we choose the parameters α and λ_1 to be given by

$$\alpha^2 = \frac{2\mu|E|}{\hbar^2} \qquad \lambda_1 = \frac{1}{\alpha} \left(\frac{\mu Z e^2}{\hbar^2} - \nu \right) \qquad (16.32)$$

The second of Eqs. (16.30) is also of the form (16.31) if we put $\zeta = \alpha \eta$ with α given by (16.32); λ_1 is replaced by

$$\lambda_2 = \frac{\nu}{\alpha} \qquad (16.33)$$

We now treat Eq. (16.31) as we did (16.7). The asymptotic behavior is dominated by the factor $e^{\pm \frac{1}{2}\zeta}$, where we must take the minus sign in the exponent. The series that multiplies this starts with a term ζ^s, where it is readily shown that $s = \pm \frac{1}{2}m$. We therefore substitute

$$f(\zeta) = e^{-\frac{1}{2}\zeta} \zeta^{\frac{1}{2}|m|} L(\zeta) \qquad (16.34)$$

into (16.31) and obtain as the equation for L

$$\zeta L'' + (|m| + 1 - \zeta)L' + [\lambda_1 - \tfrac{1}{2}(|m| + 1)]L = 0 \qquad (16.35)$$

As with Eq. (16.12), the nonterminating solutions for L cause the wave function (16.34) to become infinite for large ζ. The terminating solutions are the associated Laguerre polynomials; comparison of Eqs. (16.20) and (16.35) shows that they are $L_{n_1+|m|}^{|m|}(\zeta)$, where

$$n_1 = \lambda_1 - \tfrac{1}{2}(|m| + 1) \qquad (16.36)$$

is a positive integer or zero.

In similar fashion, the solution of the η equation shows that the number

$$n_2 = \lambda_2 - \tfrac{1}{2}(|m| + 1) \qquad (16.37)$$

is a positive integer or zero. From Eqs. (16.36) and (16.37) we obtain

$$\lambda_1 + \lambda_2 = n_1 + n_2 + |m| + 1 \equiv n \qquad (16.38)$$

where n is a nonzero positive integer. The energy levels are given by combining Eqs. (16.32), (16.33), and (16.38):

$$E_n = -|E_n| = -\frac{\hbar^2 \alpha^2}{2\mu} = -\frac{\mu Z^2 e^4}{2\hbar^2 n^2}$$

in agreement with Eq. (16.15). The energy level E_n is degenerate, since according to (16.38) there are various ways in which the three quantum numbers n_1, n_2, and m can be combined to make up n. For $m = 0$, there are n ways of choosing n_1 and n_2; for $|m| > 0$, there are two ways of choosing m $(= \pm|m|)$, and $n - |m|$ ways of choosing n_1 and n_2. Thus the total degeneracy of the energy level E_n is

$$n + 2 \sum_{|m|=1}^{n-1} (n - |m|) = n + 2 \left[n(n-1) - \frac{n(n-1)}{2} \right] = n^2$$

in agreement with the earlier result.

WAVE FUNCTIONS

It is clear from the foregoing discussion that the unnormalized hydrogen-atom wave functions in parabolic coordinates are

$$u_{n_1 n_2 m}(\xi, \eta, \phi) = e^{-\frac{1}{2}\alpha(\xi+\eta)} (\xi\eta)^{\frac{1}{2}|m|} L_{n_1+|m|}^{|m|}(\alpha\xi) L_{n_2+|m|}^{|m|}(\alpha\eta) e^{im\phi}$$

$$\alpha = \frac{\mu Z e^2}{\hbar^2 (n_1 + n_2 + |m| + 1)}$$

For a particular energy level E_n and magnetic quantum number m $(n > |m|)$, the parabolic quantum numbers n_1 and n_2 can be chosen such that $n_1 + n_2 = n - |m| - 1$, that is, in $n - |m|$ different ways. Similarly, for given n and m, the azimuthal quantum number l in the spherical solution can be chosen such that $|m| \leq l \leq n - 1$, and so also in $n - |m|$ different ways. Thus the $n - |m|$ products of the ξ and η functions are linear combinations of the $n - |m|$ products of the r and θ functions.

The ground-state energy level provides a particularly simple illustration of the connection between the parabolic and spherical solutions. In this case, $n_1 = n_2 = m = 0$, and the parabolic solution is simply $e^{-\mu Z e^2(\xi+\eta)/2\hbar^2}$. Also, $n = 1$, $l = m = 0$, and the spherical solution is $e^{-\mu Z e^2 r/\hbar^2}$. It is apparent from Eq. (16.25) that these two solutions are identical.

PROBLEMS

1. Apply the Bohr-Sommerfeld quantization rules (see Sec. 2) to the determination of the energy levels of a harmonic oscillator and of the circular orbits in a hydrogen atom. Compare with the results obtained in this chapter.

2. What is the order of magnitude of the spread of quantum numbers and energies of the states that contribute significantly to the oscillating-wave-packet solution for the harmonic oscillator?

3. Use the generating function for the Hermite polynomials to evaluate

$$\int_{-\infty}^{\infty} u_n^*(x) x^2 u_m(x) \, dx$$

where the u's are normalized harmonic-oscillator wave functions.

4. Use the generating function for the Legendre polynomials to evaluate

$$\int_{-1}^{1} P_l(w)P_{l'}(w)\ dw$$

5. Obtain an approximate analytic expression for the energy level in a square well potential ($l = 0$) when V_0a^2 is slightly greater than $\pi^2\hbar^2/8m$.

6. Show that for a square well potential the limiting values of V_0a^2 that just bind new energy levels with an l value greater than zero are given by $\hbar^2z^2/2m$, where the numbers z are the nonvanishing solutions of the equation $j_{l-1}(z) = 0$ (see footnote 1, page 88).

7. Assume that the interaction between the neutron and the proton that make up a deuteron can be represented by a square well potential with $a = 2.00 \times 10^{-13}$ cm. If the lowest ($l = 0$) energy level of the system is -2.23 Mev (million electron volts), calculate V_0 in Mev to three significant figures. How does the answer compare with that which would be obtained from the approximate formula derived in Prob. 5?

8. Consider Eq. (14.17) with $l = 0$ and $V(r) = -V_0e^{-r/a}$. Change variables from r to $z = e^{-r/2a}$, and show that Bessel's equation results. What boundary conditions are to be imposed on χ as a function of z, and how can these be used to determine the energy levels? What is the lower limit to V_0 for which a bound state exists?

9. Find expressions for the eigenfunctions and energy levels of a particle in a two-dimensional circular box that has perfectly rigid walls.

10. It is shown in Sec. 9 that a one-dimensional square well potential has a bound state for any positive V_0a^2, and in Sec. 15 that a three-dimensional spherically symmetric square well potential has a bound state only for $V_0a^2 > \pi^2\hbar^2/8m$. What is the analogous situation for a two-dimensional circularly symmetric square well potential? What, if any, is the physical significance of these results?

11. The Schrödinger equation for a rigid body that is constrained to rotate about a fixed axis and that has a moment of inertia I about this axis is

$$i\hbar \frac{\partial\psi}{\partial t} = -\frac{\hbar^2}{2I}\frac{\partial^2\psi}{\partial\phi^2}$$

where $\psi(\phi,t)$ is a function of the time t and of the angle of rotation, ϕ, about the axis. What boundary conditions must be applied to the solutions of this equation? Find the normalized energy eigenfunctions and eigenvalues. Is there any degeneracy?

12. Find the energy levels of a three-dimensional isotropic harmonic oscillator $[V(r) = \frac{1}{2}Kr^2]$ by solving the wave equation in cartesian coordinates. What is the degeneracy of each level? Show that this equation can also be separated in spherical and in cylindrical coordinates.

13. Show that the expectation value of the potential energy of an electron in the nth quantum state of a hydrogen atom is $-Z^2e^2/a_0n^2$. From this result, find the expectation value of the kinetic energy.

14. Find the normalized hydrogen-atom wave functions in parabolic coordinates for $n = 2$, $m = 0$. Express them as linear combinations of the corresponding wave functions in spherical coordinates.

15. Discuss the parities, if any, of the hydrogen-atom wave functions in parabolic coordinates.

5
Continuous Eigenvalues: Collision Theory

Problems for which the energy eigenvalues are continuously distributed usually arise in connection with the collision of a particle with a force field. The method of approach is different from that employed in the preceding chapter. There the boundary conditions at great distances were used to determine the discrete energy levels of the particle. In a collision problem, the energy is specified in advance, and the behavior of the wave function at great distances is found in terms of it. This asymptotic behavior can then be related to the amount of scattering of the particle by the force field.

As in Chap. 4, the relatively few exact solutions that are obtained here are of wider application than might at first seem to be the case, since they can serve as foundations for approximate calculations on more complicated systems. It is interesting to note that the study of collisions is particularly important in connection with atomic nuclei and elementary particles, where relatively little information can be obtained in other ways.

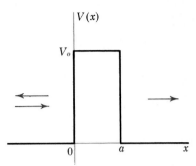

Fig. 14 A one-dimensional square potential barrier of height V_0 and thickness a.

17□ONE–DIMENSIONAL SQUARE POTENTIAL BARRIER

We consider first the one-dimensional collision of a particle with the square potential barrier $V(x)$ shown in Fig. 14. In this problem we are interested in a particle that approaches from the region of negative x and is reflected or transmitted by the barrier. In the corresponding classical problem, the particle is always reflected if its energy is less than that of the top of the barrier, and it is always transmitted if its energy is greater. We shall see that, in the quantum problem, both reflection and transmission occur with finite probability for most energies of the particle. Because of the lack of symmetry between positive and negative x that is introduced from the beginning, it is disadvantageous to deal with solutions that have definite parities, and so there is no reason for making $V(x)$ symmetrical about $x = 0$, as was done in Sec. 9. We assume, therefore, that $V(x) = 0$ for $x < 0$ and $x > a$, and $V(x) = V_0$ for $0 < x < a$, where V_0 is positive.

ASYMPTOTIC BEHAVIOR

We are interested in representing a particle that approaches from the left with energy $E > 0$ and may be turned back by the potential barrier or penetrate through it. Thus the asymptotic behavior [in the regions where $V(x) = 0$] is as follows: For $x < 0$, we want the wave function to represent a particle moving to the left (reflected particle) as well as to the right (incident particle); for $x > a$, we want the wave function to represent only a particle moving to the right (transmitted particle).

A particle in a force-free region that is moving in a definite direction with a definite energy necessarily has a definite momentum and hence can be represented by a one-dimensional momentum eigenfunction $u(x) \propto e^{ipx/\hbar}$ if the particle is moving in the positive x direction with the momentum p, and $u(x) \propto e^{-ipx/\hbar}$ if the particle is moving in the negative x direction with the same energy. Thus, since the wave equation in the regions where $V(x) = 0$ is

$$-\frac{\hbar^2}{2m}\frac{d^2u}{dx^2} = Eu$$

our asymptotic solutions are

$$
\begin{aligned}
u(x) &= Ae^{ikx} + Be^{-ikx} & x &\le 0 \\
u(x) &= Ce^{ikx} & x &\ge a
\end{aligned}
\tag{17.1}
$$

where $k = p/\hbar = +(2mE/\hbar^2)^{\frac{1}{2}}$ is the magnitude of the propagation number. The solutions (17.1) are appropriate for the force-free regions that are external to any scattering potential, whether or not it has the simple form shown in Fig. 14.

NORMALIZATION

The physical meaning of the coefficients A, B, and C can be inferred by substituting (17.1) into the one-dimensional form of the probability current density given by Eq. (7.3).

$$
\begin{aligned}
S(x) &= v(|A|^2 - |B|^2) & x &< 0 \\
S(x) &= v|C|^2 & x &> a
\end{aligned}
\tag{17.2}
$$

where $v = \hbar k/m$ is the speed of a particle with propagation number k. Since these expressions are independent of x, the discussion of Sec. 7 shows that they may be interpreted as the net flux (positive to the right) in the two regions. This interpretation is consistent with the statement above that A, B, and C are the amplitudes of the incident, reflected, and transmitted wave functions, respectively.

The absolute normalization of the wave functions (17.1) is unimportant for this problem; this is because we are interested only in the ratios of $|B|^2$ and $|C|^2$ to $|A|^2$, which are, respectively, the reflection and transmission coefficients for the barrier. It is sometimes convenient, however, to normalize the incident wave function to unit flux; this corresponds to taking $A = 1/v^{\frac{1}{2}}$. Such a normalization must not be interpreted as indicating that $u(x)$ represents more than one particle; rather it means that we choose a large enough number of systems [each described by $u(x)$] that are identical and independent in the sense of Sec. 7, so that the total incident flux in all of them is unity. A more precise but sometimes less convenient normalization would assume a one-dimensional "box" of length L with periodic boundary conditions and require that $\int_{(L)} |u(x)|^2 \, dx = 1$.

SCATTERING COEFFICIENTS

The character of the solution inside the potential barrier depends on whether E is greater or less than V_0. Suppose first that $E > V_0$, so that we can define a propagation number inside the barrier: $\alpha = [2m(E - V_0)/\hbar^2]^{\frac{1}{2}}$. Then the solution inside is

$$u(x) = Fe^{i\alpha x} + Ge^{-i\alpha x} \qquad 0 \leq x \leq a \qquad (17.3)$$

The continuity of u and du/dx at $x = 0$ and $x = a$ required by the boundary conditions provides four relations between the five coefficients. We can eliminate F and G and solve for the ratios B/A and C/A.

$$\frac{B}{A} = \frac{(k^2 - \alpha^2)(1 - e^{2i\alpha a})}{(k + \alpha)^2 - (k - \alpha)^2 e^{2i\alpha a}}$$

$$\frac{C}{A} = \frac{4k\alpha e^{i(\alpha-k)a}}{(k + \alpha)^2 - (k - \alpha)^2 e^{2i\alpha a}} \qquad (17.4)$$

The absolute squares of the ratios (17.4) are the scattering (reflection and transmission) coefficients

$$\left|\frac{B}{A}\right|^2 = \left[1 + \frac{4k^2\alpha^2}{(k^2 - \alpha^2)^2 \sin^2 \alpha a}\right]^{-1} = \left[1 + \frac{4E(E - V_0)}{V_0^2 \sin^2 \alpha a}\right]^{-1}$$

$$\left|\frac{C}{A}\right|^2 = \left[1 + \frac{(k^2 - \alpha^2)^2 \sin^2 \alpha a}{4k^2\alpha^2}\right]^{-1} = \left[1 + \frac{V_0^2 \sin^2 \alpha a}{4E(E - V_0)}\right]^{-1} \qquad (17.5)$$

It is readily verified from (17.5) that $|B/A|^2 + |C/A|^2 = 1$, as would be expected.

Equations (17.5) show that the transmission coefficient approaches

$$\left(1 + \frac{mV_0 a^2}{2\hbar^2}\right)^{-1} \qquad (17.6)$$

when the particle energy approaches the energy of the top of the barrier $(E \to V_0)$. For increasing E $(E > V_0)$, the transmission coefficient oscillates between a steadily increasing lower envelope and unity (see Fig. 15). There is perfect transmission when $\alpha a = \pi, 2\pi, \ldots$, that is, whenever the barrier contains an integral number of half wavelengths.[1] Interference phenomena of this type are well known in the transmission of light through thin refracting layers.

The reflection and transmission coefficients for $0 < E < V_0$ are most easily obtained by replacing α by $i\beta$ in Eqs. (17.4), where

$$\beta = \left[\frac{2m(V_0 - E)}{\hbar^2}\right]^{\frac{1}{2}}$$

The result for the transmission coefficient is

$$\left|\frac{C}{A}\right|^2 = \left[1 + \frac{V_0^2 \sinh^2 \beta a}{4E(V_0 - E)}\right]^{-1} \qquad (17.7)$$

[1] This effect also occurs when $V_0 < 0$, in which case the square barrier becomes a square well. The scattering coefficients are given by (17.5) if the sign of V_0 is changed there and in the expression for α.

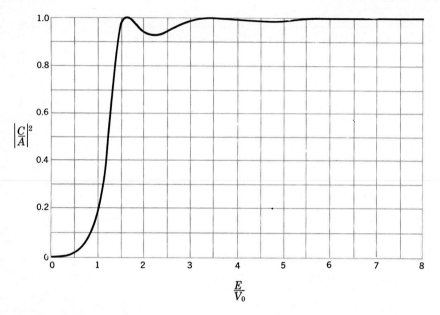

Fig. 15 The transmission coefficient of a square barrier as a function of particle energy for $mV_0a^2/\hbar^2 = 8$.

which decreases monotonically from the value (17.6) as E decreases below V_0. This behavior is often referred to as *tunneling* through the barrier. When $\beta a \gg 1$, the transmission coefficient (17.7) becomes very small and is given approximately by

$$\frac{16E(V_0 - E)}{V_0{}^2}\, e^{-2\beta a} \tag{17.8}$$

Figure 15 is a plot of the transmission coefficient computed from Eqs. (17.5) and (17.7) for a rather "opaque" barrier: $mV_0a^2/\hbar^2 = 8$.

SCATTERING OF A WAVE PACKET

The foregoing treatment of scattering makes use of stationary solutions of the time-independent wave equation (8.2) that correspond to particular values of the incident momentum. It is also possible to work with the time-dependent equation (6.16), although this is more difficult since even in the one-dimensional case we must deal with a partial differential equation in two independent variables, x and t. There is, however, the advantage that we can then study the motion of a wave packet of the general form discussed in Sec. 12 and see in what way it is reflected from and transmitted by the potential.

There are two ways of approaching this problem. The solution can be expanded in energy eigenfunctions, as in Eq. (12.15), and the summation carried out explicitly as in the transition from Eqs. (12.18) and (12.19) to (12.20). Although this could be done analytically in Sec. 12 for a free particle, it is generally impossible when a potential is present. The other approach consists in performing a numerical integration of Eq. (6.16), choosing small but finite time intervals, and approximating the differential equation in the time by a difference equation. Even in the one-dimensional case this is feasible only with a high-speed computer, and special computational techniques must be invented to make the problem manageable. Some typical graphs are reproduced here from a very large number that form the basis of computer-generated motion pictures.[1]

In these computations, units are chosen such that $\hbar = 1$ and $m = \frac{1}{2}$. The unit of length can still be chosen arbitrarily and is slightly longer than the total length of the abscissa shown in each graph. Then the time and the reciprocal of the energy are each expressed in terms of a unit that is the square of the length unit. The incident wave packet is of the gaussian form (12.11), with $\Delta x = 0.035$ and $\langle p \rangle = 50\pi$, 70.7π, and 100π. The potential has breadth $a = 0.064$ and strength $V_0 = \pm(70.7\pi)^2$, so that the mean energy of the incident wave packet is $\frac{1}{2}|V_0|$, $|V_0|$, and $2|V_0|$. Succeeding frames of the motion picture are shown in Fig. 16 when the mean energy of the wave packet is half the barrier height, and in Fig. 17 when the mean energy is equal to V_0. Figures 18 and 19 show the attractive case in which the mean energy is half of the well depth and equal to the well depth, respectively. In all these cases, $|\psi|^2$ is plotted as ordinate and x as abscissa, and the potential width and position are indicated; the number in each frame denotes the time in arbitrary units. Figure 17 is especially interesting, since it shows how the probability decays slowly and bounces back and forth within the barrier when the mean kinetic energy of the particle in the barrier is zero.

18☐COLLISIONS IN THREE DIMENSIONS

We are primarily concerned in this chapter with collisions in three dimensions, in which a particle collides with a fixed force field or two particles collide with each other. It was shown in Sec. 16 that the problem of the nonrelativistic motion of two particles, when the only forces present depend on their relative positions, can be broken up into two one-particle problems, of which one describes the motion of the particles relative to each other or to their center of mass, and the other describes the free motion of the center of mass. Although the center of mass can be

[1] A. Goldberg, H. M. Schey, and J. L. Schwartz, *Am. J. Phys.* **35**, 177 (1967).

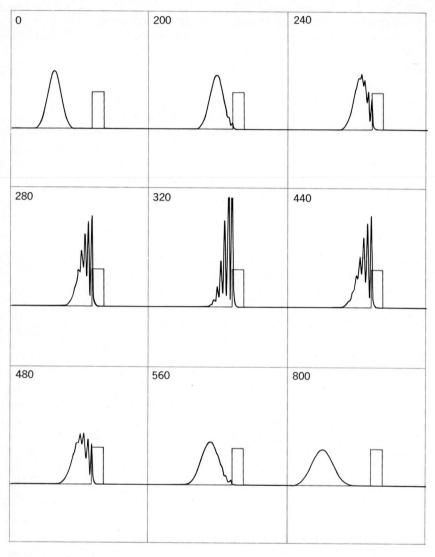

Fig. 16 Gaussian wave-packet scattering from a square barrier when the mean energy of the packet is half the barrier height.

taken to be at rest in calculating the energy levels of the internal motion, as in Sec. 16, it has a definite motion in a collision that cannot be ignored in calculating the outcome of such an experiment. This is because the customary laboratory procedure consists in bombarding a particle that is initially at rest with another particle that carries the total energy $E_0 = E + E'$ of Eq. (16.5). Thus the energy E of the relative motion of

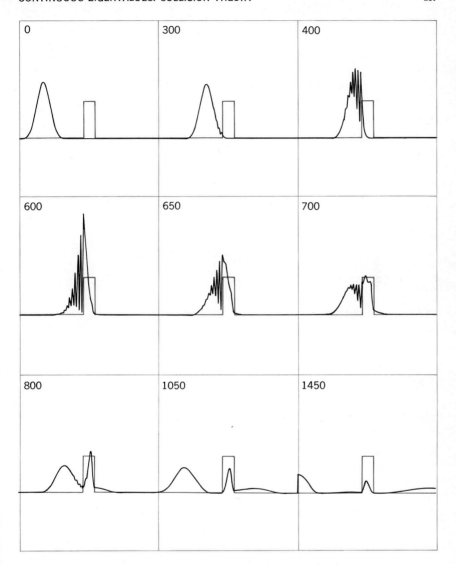

Fig. 17 Same as Fig. 16, with the mean energy equal to the barrier height.

the two particles is different from the bombarding energy E_0, and the observed scattering depends on whether the struck particle or the center of mass is initially at rest.

We call the coordinate system in which the bombarded particle is initially at rest the *laboratory coordinate system* and the coordinate system in which the center of mass of the two colliding particles is (initially

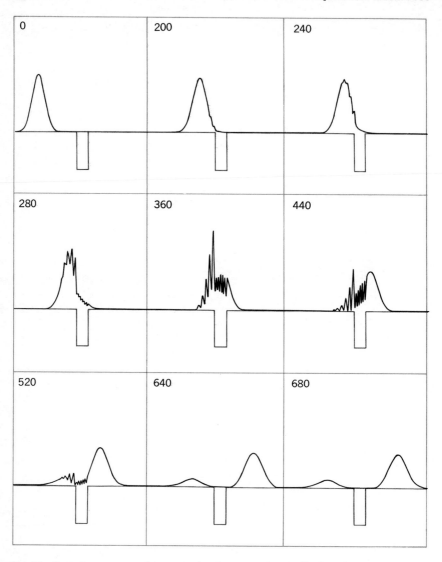

Fig. 18 Gaussian wave-packet scattering from a square well when the mean energy of the packet is half the well depth.

and always) at rest the *center-of-mass coordinate system*. It is evidently easier to calculate the result of a collision experiment in the center-of-mass system than in the laboratory system, since only 3 degrees of freedom appear in the former as compared with 6 in the latter system. The collision process in the center-of-mass system may then be thought of as one in which a particle that has the reduced mass $\mu = m_1 m_2 / (m_1 + m_2)$

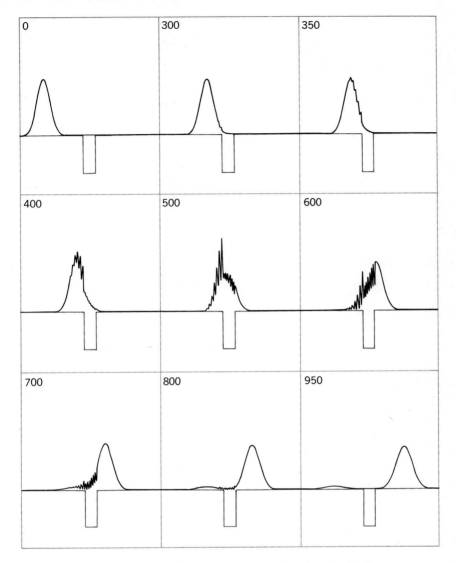

Fig. 19 Same as Fig. 18, with the mean energy equal to the well depth.

of Eq. (16.4) and an initial velocity v collides with a fixed scattering center [see the discussion of Eq. (18.9) below]. The distribution in angle of the scattered particles will be affected by the transformation between the center-of-mass coordinate system, in which the calculations are made, and the laboratory coordinate system, in which the observations are made.

SCATTERING CROSS SECTION

The angular distribution of particles scattered by a fixed center of force or by other particles is conveniently described in terms of a scattering cross section. Suppose that we bombard a group of n particles or scattering centers with a parallel flux of N particles per unit area per unit time and count the number of incident particles that emerge per unit time in a small solid angle $\Delta\omega_0$ centered about a direction that has polar angles θ_0 and ϕ_0 with respect to the bombarding direction as polar axis. This number will be proportional to N, n, and $\Delta\omega_0$, provided that the flux is small enough so that there is no interference between bombarding particles and no appreciable diminution of the bombarded particles by their recoil out of the target region, and provided also that the bombarded particles are far enough apart so that each collision process involves only one of them.

Then the number of incident particles that emerge per unit time in $\Delta\omega_0$ can be written

$$nN\sigma_0(\theta_0,\phi_0)\,\Delta\omega_0 \tag{18.1}$$

where the proportionality factor $\sigma_0(\theta_0,\phi_0)$ is called the *differential scattering cross section*. Since (18.1) has the dimensions of reciprocal time, $\sigma_0(\theta_0,\phi_0)$ has the dimensions of an area. $\sigma_0(\theta_0,\phi_0)\,\Delta\omega_0$ is equal to the cross-sectional area of the parallel incident beam that contains the number of particles scattered into $\Delta\omega_0$ by a single target particle or scattering center. The integral of $\sigma_0(\theta_0,\phi_0)$ over the sphere is called the *total scattering cross section*

$$\sigma_0 = \int \sigma_0(\theta_0,\phi_0)\,d\omega_0 \tag{18.2}$$

For the collision of a particle with a fixed scattering center, the definition (18.1) of differential scattering cross section is equally valid in the laboratory and center-of-mass coordinate systems, since a scattering center that is fixed has an infinite effective mass and so the center of mass of the system does not move. For a collision between two particles of finite mass, however, the differential cross section (18.1) applies in general only to the laboratory coordinate system and to the observation of the scattered incident particle. It does not describe the observation of the recoil bombarded particle in the laboratory system, although it is of course possible to obtain a differential cross section for the recoil particle from $\sigma_0(\theta_0,\phi_0)$. In the center-of-mass system the differential cross section $\sigma(\theta,\phi)$ may be defined in analogy with (18.1), where again the scattered incident particle is the one that is observed and the flux N of the incident particle is computed with respect to the bombarded particle, not the center of mass. Since in this coordinate system the two particles move in opposite directions away from each other after the collision, it is clear that the differential cross section for observation of the recoil bombarded particle in the direction θ, ϕ is just $\sigma(\pi - \theta, \phi + \pi)$.

RELATIONS BETWEEN ANGLES IN THE LABORATORY AND CENTER–OF–MASS SYSTEMS

The relation between the differential cross sections and angles in the laboratory system and in the center-of-mass system can be found by translating the laboratory system in the direction of the incident particle with sufficient speed to bring the center of mass to rest. Figure 20a shows a particle of mass m_1 and initial speed v striking a particle of mass m_2 that is initially at rest; the center of mass moves to the right with the speed $v' = m_1 v / (m_1 + m_2)$, as may be seen from the conservation of momentum. Thus in the center-of-mass system the particles of masses m_1 and m_2 approach the center of mass with speeds

$$v'' = v - v' = \frac{m_2 v}{m_1 + m_2}$$

and v', respectively. If the collision is elastic, they evidently recede from the center of mass after the collision with the same speeds (see Fig. 20b). It follows from the geometry of the situation that θ and ϕ are related to θ_0 and ϕ_0 by

$$v'' \cos \theta + v' = v_1 \cos \theta_0$$
$$v'' \sin \theta = v_1 \sin \theta_0 \tag{18.3}$$
$$\phi = \phi_0$$

From the first two of Eqs. (18.3) we obtain, on elimination of v_1,

$$\tan \theta_0 = \frac{\sin \theta}{\gamma + \cos \theta} \qquad \gamma = \frac{v'}{v''} = \frac{m_1}{m_2} \tag{18.4}$$

Equations (18.3) and (18.4) can be valid for inelastic collisions as well. Consider a general binary collision (for example, a nuclear reaction) in which a particle of mass m_1 strikes a particle of mass m_2 initially at rest and, after the collision, particles of masses m_3 and m_4 emerge, where $m_1 + m_2 = m_3 + m_4$. If also an amount of energy, Q, is converted from internal energy to kinetic energy of the emergent particles (Q is positive for exothermic and negative for endothermic collisions) and the particle of mass m_3 is observed, the first of Eqs. (18.4) is still valid. In this case γ is still equal to the ratio of the speed of the center of mass in the laboratory system to the speed of the observed particle in the center-of-mass system. However, γ is no longer m_1/m_2 but can be shown to be given by

$$\gamma = + \left(\frac{m_1 m_3}{m_2 m_4} \frac{E}{E + Q} \right)^{\frac{1}{2}} \tag{18.5}$$

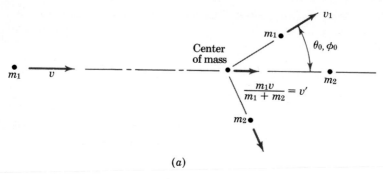

(a)

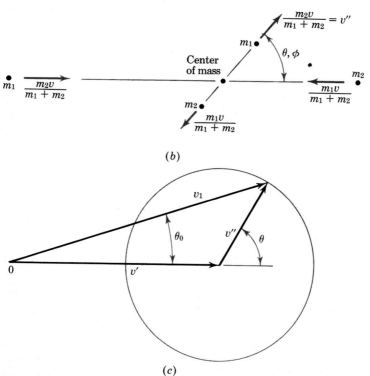

(b)

(c)

Fig. 20 (a) Laboratory coordinate system, in which the target particle of mass m_2 is initially at rest. (b) Center-of-mass coordinate system, in which the center of mass is initially and always at rest. (c) Vector addition of velocity of center of mass in laboratory system $(\mathbf{v}')$ to velocity of observed particle in center-of-mass system $(\mathbf{v}'')$ to give velocity observed in laboratory system $(\mathbf{v}_1)$; if $v'' < v'$, θ_0 cannot exceed the angle $\sin^{-1}(v''/v')$.

where $E = m_1 m_2 v^2 / 2(m_1 + m_2)$ is the energy initially associated with the relative motion in the center-of-mass system [see the discussion of Eq. (18.9) below].

RELATION BETWEEN CROSS SECTIONS

The relation between the cross sections in the laboratory and center-of-mass coordinate systems can be obtained from their definitions, which imply that the same number of particles are scattered into the differential solid angle $d\omega_0$ about θ_0, ϕ_0 as are scattered into $d\omega$ about θ, ϕ.

$$\sigma_0(\theta_0, \phi_0) \sin \theta_0 \, d\theta_0 \, d\phi_0 = \sigma(\theta, \phi) \sin \theta \, d\theta \, d\phi \tag{18.6}$$

With the help of the last of Eqs. (18.3) and the first of Eqs. (18.4), Eq. (18.6) gives

$$\sigma_0(\theta_0, \phi_0) = \frac{(1 + \gamma^2 + 2\gamma \cos \theta)^{\frac{3}{2}}}{|1 + \gamma \cos \theta|} \sigma(\theta, \phi) \tag{18.7}$$

where in general γ is given by Eq. (18.5). It should be noted that the total cross section is the same for both laboratory and center-of-mass systems and also for both the outgoing particles, since the total number of collisions that take place is independent of the mode of description of the process.

DEPENDENCE ON γ

For $\gamma < 1$, Eq. (18.4) shows that θ_0 increases monotonically from 0 to π as θ increases from 0 to π. For $\gamma = 1$, $\theta_0 = \frac{1}{2}\theta$ and varies from 0 to $\frac{1}{2}\pi$ as θ varies from 0 to π; in this case

$$\sigma_0(\theta_0, \phi_0) = 4 \cos \theta_0 \sigma(2\theta_0, \phi_0)$$

and no particles appear in the backward hemisphere in the laboratory system. For $\gamma > 1$, θ_0 first increases from 0 to a maximum value $\sin^{-1}(1/\gamma)$, which is less than $\frac{1}{2}\pi$, as θ increases from 0 to $\cos^{-1}(-1/\gamma)$; θ_0 then decreases to 0 as θ increases further to π. In this case $\sigma_0(\theta_0, \phi_0)$ is usually infinite at the maximum value of θ_0, although this singularity gives a finite contribution to the total cross section; no particles appear beyond the maximum θ_0 in the laboratory system. The two values of θ that give rise to a particular value of θ_0 between 0 and $\sin^{-1}(1/\gamma)$ can be distinguished by the energy of the observed particle, which is greater for the smaller θ.

This last case ($\gamma > 1$) is illustrated schematically in Fig. 20c. The resultant of the velocity $\mathbf{v}''$ of the observed particle in the center-of-mass system and the velocity $\mathbf{v}'$ of the center of mass in the laboratory system gives the velocity $\mathbf{v}_1$ of the observed particle in the laboratory system. The locus of the terminal points of $\mathbf{v}_1$ when its origin is at the point O

is the circle of radius v''.   Thus, when $v'' < v'$, the angle θ_0 of the resultant $\mathbf{v}_1$ with the bombarding direction cannot exceed the angle

$$\sin^{-1}\frac{v''}{v'} = \sin^{-1}\frac{1}{\gamma}$$

As the ratio $\gamma = v'/v''$ decreases, the circle gets relatively larger and the angular range of $\mathbf{v}_1$ increases.

The use of geometrical relationships in the foregoing discussion is valid in a quantum-mechanical system as well as in a classical system. This is because they are essentially relations between momentum vectors that are applied in the asymptotic region where the particles need not be precisely localized in space and hence can have definite momenta.

It is interesting to note that the difference between laboratory and center-of-mass systems is negligible in the collisions of electrons with atoms, because of the large mass ratio of the colliding particles.   In nuclear collisions, however, the difference between the two coordinate systems is usually significant.

ASYMPTOTIC BEHAVIOR

The differential scattering cross section $\sigma(\theta,\phi)$ in the center-of-mass coordinate system can be found from the asymptotic form of the solution of the second of Eqs. (16.5),

$$-\frac{\hbar^2}{2\mu}\nabla^2 u + Vu = Eu \tag{18.8}$$

which is the wave equation for the relative motion.   The wave function u may be written as a function of the angles θ, ϕ of Fig. 20b and the radial distance r between the two particles.   From Eq. (16.4) the reduced mass is $\mu = m_1 m_2/(m_1 + m_2)$.   The energy E associated with the relative motion is easily seen from Fig. 20 to be

$$E = \frac{m_2}{m_1 + m_2} E_0 \tag{18.9}$$

where E_0 is the initial energy of the bombarding particle.   It is interesting to note that E is equal to the kinetic energy of a particle whose mass is the reduced mass μ and whose speed is the relative speed v.   Thus we can think of Eq. (18.8) as representing the elastic collision of a particle of mass μ, initial speed v, and kinetic energy $E = \frac{1}{2}\mu v^2$, with a fixed scattering center that is described by the potential energy $V(\mathbf{r})$; then $\mathbf{r}$ is the vector distance from the fictitious particle μ to the origin of the scattering potential.

As in Sec. 17, the scattering is determined by the asymptotic form of $u(r,\theta,\phi)$ in the region where $V = 0$.   When the colliding particles are far apart, we want u to contain a part that represents an incident particle of mass μ moving in a particular direction with speed v, and a part that represents a radially outgoing particle:

$$u(r,\theta,\phi) \xrightarrow[r \to \infty]{} A[e^{ikz} + r^{-1}f(\theta,\phi)e^{ikr}] \qquad k = \frac{\mu v}{\hbar} \qquad (18.10)$$

The first term in Eq. (18.10) represents a particle moving in the positive z direction, or along the polar axis $\theta = 0$, since $z = r \cos \theta$; it is an infinite plane wave of the form of the momentum eigenfunction (11.2), where the propagation vector $\mathbf{k}$ has the magnitude k and is directed along the polar axis. The second term in Eq. (18.10) represents a particle that is moving radially outward; its amplitude depends on θ and ϕ and is inversely proportional to r, since the radial flux must fall off as the inverse square of the distance. It is readily verified that Eq. (18.10) satisfies the wave equation (18.8) asymptotically through terms of order $1/r$ in the region in which $V = 0$, for any form of the function $f(\theta,\phi)$.

NORMALIZATION

The physical meaning of the coefficient A and the angular function f can be inferred from a calculation of the particle flux, as in Sec. 17. A straightforward substitution of Eq. (18.10) into Eq. (7.3), however, yields interference terms between the incident and scattered waves that do not appear in most experimental arrangements; that they do not appear can be seen in the following way.

In practice, the incident and scattered particles are separated from each other by collimating one or the other. Suppose, for example, that the experimental arrangement is as shown schematically in Fig. 21, so that the bombarding particles from the source S are collimated by dia-

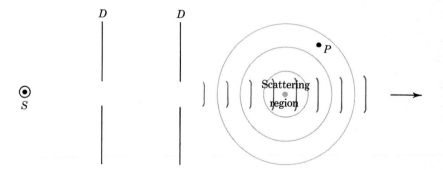

Fig. 21 Schematic diagram of a laboratory arrangement for the measurement of scattering, in which there is no interference between the incident and scattered waves at the point of observation, P.

phragms DD into a fairly well-defined beam. Such a collimated beam is not an infinite plane wave of the form e^{ikz} but can be made up by superposing infinite plane waves that have propagation vectors of slightly different magnitudes and directions. The total angular spread in radians will be of the order of the ratio of the wavelength of the particle to the diameter of the collimating aperture and so can be made extremely small in a practical case. Now f usually does not vary rapidly with angle, so that the small directional spread of the incident propagation vectors does not affect f significantly. Thus at the point of observation, P, only the f term is present, and it is essentially the same as that which appears in Eq. (18.10). The incident flux can be calculated from the plane-wave term alone, since if we go far enough from the scattering region, the f term can be made negligible. Thus in the region of observation, the interference terms are a consequence of the idealization implicit in assuming an infinite plane wave in Eq. (18.10), and they usually have no physical significance.[1]

Substitution of the two terms of Eq. (18.10) separately into Eq. (7.3) shows that the incident flux is of magnitude $v|A|^2$ along the polar axis and that the leading term in the scattered flux is of magnitude

$$\frac{v|A|^2|f(\theta,\phi)|^2}{r^2}$$

along the outward radius. From the definition of cross section, it follows that

$$\sigma(\theta,\phi) = |f(\theta,\phi)|^2 \tag{18.11}$$

As discussed in Sec. 17, the choice of the coefficient A is unimportant so far as the calculation of the scattering is concerned. The wave function may be normalized to unit incident flux by choosing $A = 1/v^{\frac{1}{2}}$, or it may be normalized by making $\int|u|^2\,d^3r = 1$ over a large box that has periodic boundary conditions. We shall often simply set A equal to unity.

19□SCATTERING BY SPHERICALLY SYMMETRIC POTENTIALS

The asymptotic behavior of the wave function determines the differential scattering cross section but cannot itself be found without solving the wave equation (18.8) throughout all space. As was the case with the calculation of energy levels considered in Chap. 4, this can be done only when the wave equation is separable, and a particular case of great physical interest is that in which the potential energy is spherically symmetric. We assume here that V is a function only of r, and we find

[1] For a somewhat exceptional case, see the discussion at the end of Sec. 20.

the connection between the solutions separated in spherical polar coordinates and the asymptotic form (18.10); this procedure is called the *method of partial waves.*

In the remainder of this chapter we shall not, for the most part, distinguish between collisions of a particle with a fixed scattering center and collisions between two particles treated in the center-of-mass coordinate system.

Elastic scattering, for which V is real, is considered in this section. The situation in which V is complex is discussed in Sec. 20 and is of interest since certain inelastic processes can be described approximately in this way.

ASYMPTOTIC BEHAVIOR

It is apparent that the problem now possesses symmetry about the polar axis, so that u, f, and σ are independent of the angle ϕ. The general solution of Eq. (18.8) can then be written as a sum of products of radial functions and Legendre polynomials (see Sec. 14); for later convenience we write this in the form

$$u(r,\theta) = \sum_{l=0}^{\infty} (2l + 1)i^l R_l(r) P_l(\cos \theta)$$

$$= \sum_{l=0}^{\infty} (2l + 1)i^l r^{-1} \chi_l(r) P_l(\cos \theta) \qquad (19.1)$$

where P_l is the Legendre polynomial of order l, and χ_l satisfies the equation

$$\frac{d^2\chi_l}{dr^2} + \left[k^2 - U(r) - \frac{l(l + 1)}{r^2} \right] \chi_l = 0$$

$$k = \left(\frac{2\mu E}{\hbar^2}\right)^{\frac{1}{2}} \qquad U(r) = \frac{2\mu V(r)}{\hbar^2} \xrightarrow[r \to \infty]{} 0 \qquad (19.2)$$

The boundary condition at $r = 0$ that R_l be finite or χ_l vanish determines the asymptotic form of the solution (19.2) except for an arbitrary multiplicative constant.

In order to find the general nature of this asymptotic behavior, we consider r to be so large that the U and l terms in Eq. (19.2) can be neglected. Then the solution of Eq. (19.2) is one of the forms $e^{\pm ikr}$. To get a better approximation, we put

$$\chi_l(r) = A \exp\left[\int_a^r f(r') \, dr' \right] e^{\pm ikr} \qquad (19.3)$$

where A and a are constants. The first exponential is assumed to be a slowly varying function of r for large r, which implies that $f(r)$ falls off more rapidly than r^{-1} as $r \to \infty$. Substitution of (19.3) into (19.2) gives the following equation for f:

$$f' + f^2 \pm 2ikf = U(r) + \frac{l(l+1)}{r^2} \equiv W(r) \tag{19.4}$$

where the prime denotes differentiation with respect to r. If now $W(r)$ falls off like r^{-s} for large r ($s > 0$), the last term on the left side is the leading term, and f also falls off like r^{-s}. In this case, χ_l varies like $e^{\pm ikr}$ for large r if $s > 1$, since then the integral in the exponent of Eq. (19.3) converges for large r. If, on the other hand, W falls off like an exponential or error function of r (which implies that $l = 0$), the first and third terms on the left side of Eq. (19.4) may both have to be considered. It can then be shown without difficulty that χ_l again varies like $e^{\pm ikr}$ for large r. The coulomb field, for which U and W vary like r^{-1} for large r regardless of the value of l, is the only case of physical interest that requires special attention and will be discussed in Sec. 21.

The asymptotic form of $\chi_l(r)$ can then be written quite generally

$$\chi_l(r) \xrightarrow[r \to \infty]{} A'_l \sin(kr + \delta'_l) \tag{19.5}$$

where thus far A'_l and δ'_l can be complex. The solution of (19.2) that vanishes at $r = 0$ is unique except for a multiplying constant. It can be shown that this solution is real everywhere if it starts out to be real at $r = 0$, since k, U, and l are all real. Thus δ'_l must be real, although A'_l need not be. This being the case, it is readily verified that the total radial flux of particles through a large sphere vanishes:

$$\lim_{r \to \infty} 2\pi r^2 \int_0^\pi S_r \sin \theta \, d\theta = 0 \tag{19.6}$$

where S_r is the radial component of the vector (7.3) calculated by substituting $u(r,\theta)$ from Eq. (19.1) into it. This means that no sources or sinks of particles are present, and the particles that are scattered radially outward are supplied by the incident plane wave.

DIFFERENTIAL CROSS SECTION

It is convenient to redefine the amplitude A'_l and phase angle δ'_l that appear in Eq. (19.5) in terms of a somewhat more specialized problem. It will be assumed that $U(r)$ can be neglected for r greater than some distance a; in cases of practical interest, a may be small enough so that the l term in (19.2) is not negligible. We can then divide the domain of r into three regions. In the first, $U(r)$ cannot be neglected, and the form of $R_l(r)$ depends on U. In the second, $U(r)$ can be neglected, but the l term in (19.2) is not negligible. Then the most general form for $R_l(r)$ that is real (except possibly for a complex multiplying constant) is shown in Sec. 15 to be

$$R_l(r) = A_l[\cos \delta_l j_l(kr) - \sin \delta_l n_l(kr)] \tag{19.7}$$

where δ_l is real. In the third region, the l term as well as U is negligible, and $R_l(r)$ is obtained from the asymptotic formulas (15.8):

$$R_l(r) \xrightarrow[r \to \infty]{} (kr)^{-1} A_l \sin (kr - \tfrac{1}{2}l\pi + \delta_l) \tag{19.8}$$

Equations (19.5) and (19.8) agree if $A_l = kA_l'$ and $\delta_l = \delta_l' + \tfrac{1}{2}l\pi$.

We now wish to identify the asymptotic form of (19.1) with (18.10). To do this, we require an expansion of $e^{ikz} = e^{ikr\cos\theta}$ in Legendre polynomials:[1]

$$e^{ikr\cos\theta} = \sum_{l=0}^{\infty} (2l + 1)i^l j_l(kr) P_l(\cos \theta) \tag{19.9}$$

Substituting the asymptotic form of (19.9) into (18.10) with $A = 1$, and equating this to the asymptotic form of (19.1), we obtain

$$\sum_{l=0}^{\infty} (2l + 1)i^l(kr)^{-1} \sin (kr - \tfrac{1}{2}l\pi) P_l(\cos \theta) + r^{-1}f(\theta)e^{ikr}$$

$$= \sum_{l=0}^{\infty} (2l + 1)i^l A_l(kr)^{-1} \sin (kr - \tfrac{1}{2}l\pi + \delta_l) P_l(\cos \theta)$$

When the sine functions are written in complex exponential form, the coefficients of e^{ikr} and of e^{-ikr} on the two sides of this equation must be equal to each other:

$$2ikf(\theta) + \sum_{l=0}^{\infty} (2l + 1)i^l e^{-\frac{1}{2}il\pi} P_l(\cos \theta)$$

$$= \sum_{l=0}^{\infty} (2l + 1)i^l A_l e^{i(\delta_l - \frac{1}{2}l\pi)} P_l(\cos \theta) \tag{19.10}$$

$$\sum_{l=0}^{\infty} (2l + 1)i^l e^{\frac{1}{2}il\pi} P_l(\cos \theta) = \sum_{l=0}^{\infty} (2l + 1)i^l A_l e^{-i(\delta_l - \frac{1}{2}l\pi)} P_l(\cos \theta)$$

Since these are true for all values of θ and the Legendre polynomials are orthogonal to each other, the second of Eqs. (19.10) becomes

$$A_l = e^{i\delta_l}$$

Substitution of this into the first of Eqs. (19.10) gives for the scattering amplitude

$$f(\theta) = (2ik)^{-1} \sum_{l=0}^{\infty} (2l + 1)(e^{2i\delta_l} - 1) P_l(\cos \theta) \tag{19.11}$$

[1] G. N. Watson, "Theory of Bessel Functions," rev. ed., p. 128 (Macmillan, New York, 1944).

Thus the differential cross section is

$$\sigma(\theta) = |f(\theta)|^2 = \frac{1}{k^2}\left|\sum_{l=0}^{\infty}(2l+1)e^{i\delta_l}\sin\delta_l\,P_l(\cos\theta)\right|^2 \qquad (19.12)$$

It is useful to note that Eqs. (18.10), (19.11), and (19.12), which refer to the asymptotic behavior of the wave function, are also valid when special relativity is taken into account. So long as we are dealing with motion in the center-of-mass coordinate system, which can be described by a function u of the relative coordinates, we can specify the scattering in this way in terms of the δ_l, where $\hbar k$ is the relative momentum. This is true even when the interaction cannot be described by a potential.

TOTAL ELASTIC CROSS SECTION

The total elastic cross section is the integral of Eq. (19.12) over the sphere. Because of the orthogonality of the Legendre polynomials, it contains no products of factors involving different values of l.

$$\sigma = 2\pi\int_0^\pi \sigma(\theta)\sin\theta\,d\theta = \frac{4\pi}{k^2}\sum_{l=0}^{\infty}(2l+1)\sin^2\delta_l \qquad (19.13)$$

The total cross section can also be related to $f(0)$. It follows from the generating function (14.10) for the Legendre polynomials that $P_l(1) = 1$ for all l, so that Eq. (19.11) gives for $\theta = 0$

$$f(0) = (2ik)^{-1}\sum_{l=0}^{\infty}(2l+1)(e^{2i\delta_l} - 1)$$

Comparison with Eq. (19.13) then shows that

$$\sigma = \frac{2\pi}{ik}[f(0) - f^*(0)] = \frac{4\pi}{k}\operatorname{Im}f(0) \qquad (19.14)$$

where Im denotes the imaginary part of the expression that follows.

The physical interpretation of Eq. (19.14) is as follows: In order for scattering to take place, particles must be removed in an amount proportional to σ from the incident beam, so that its intensity is smaller behind the scattering region ($\theta \approx 0$) than in front of it. This can occur only by interference between the two terms in the asymptotic expression (18.10). Since such an interference term must be a linear function of the forward-scattered amplitude, we expect a relation of the general form of Eq. (19.14). An actual calculation of this interference term shows that Eq. (19.14) holds much more generally: when f depends on ϕ as well as on θ, and when σ includes inelastic scattering and absorption as well as elastic scattering. (See the end of Sec. 20.)

PHASE SHIFTS

The angle δ_l is called the *phase shift* of the lth partial wave, since according to (19.8) it is the difference in phase between the asymptotic forms of the actual radial function $R_l(r)$ and the radial function $j_l(kr)$ in the absence of scattering potential $(U = 0)$. The phase shifts completely determine the scattering, and the scattering cross section vanishes when each of the δ_l is 0° or 180°.

It should be noted that the derivation of (19.11) is valid whether or not there exists the assumed radius a beyond which $U(r)$ is negligible, provided that $U(r)$ falls off more rapidly than $1/r$. However, the method of partial waves is most useful for computing scattering cross sections if such a radius a does exist, especially if ka is of the order of or less than unity. The reason for this is that the first and largest maximum of $j_l(kr)$ lies roughly at $r = l/k$; for r much smaller than this, j_l is small and increases about as r^l [see Eq. (15.7)]. Thus if $a \ll l/k$, j_l will be very small where U is appreciable; then the lth partial wave will hardly be affected by the potential, the phase shift δ_l will be very small, and the contribution to the scattering from that l will be negligible. It follows then that the scattering cross section consists of a series of terms extending from $l = 0$ to a maximum l that is of the order of ka. Since the computation of the phase shifts is usually a tedious affair, the smaller the magnitude of ka, the easier the method is to apply. Thus this method of partial waves is most useful at low bombarding energies.

It is interesting to note that the classical distance of closest approach of a free particle of mass μ, velocity v, and angular momentum $l\hbar$ to the origin is $l\hbar/\mu v = l/k$. Thus the foregoing remarks are analogous to the statement that a classical particle is not scattered if it has sufficient angular momentum so that it does not enter the potential region $r < a$.

CALCULATION OF δ_l

The phase shift δ_l is computed by fitting the radial wave function $R_l(r)$ for $r < a$, which may have an analytic form and can always be found numerically if necessary, to the solution (19.7). The boundary condition at $r = a$ is that $(1/R_l)(dR_l/dr)$ be continuous. Thus if γ_l is the ratio of slope to value of the interior wave function, we have that

$$\frac{k[j_l'(ka) \cos \delta_l - n_l'(ka) \sin \delta_l]}{j_l(ka) \cos \delta_l - n_l(ka) \sin \delta_l} = \gamma_l$$

where the derivatives j_l' and n_l' may be rewritten with the help of (15.10). Then δ_l is given by

$$\tan \delta_l = \frac{kj_l'(ka) - \gamma_l j_l(ka)}{kn_l'(ka) - \gamma_l n_l(ka)} \tag{19.15}$$

Equation (19.15) can be used at once to obtain an approximate expression for δ_l when l is large and δ_l is expected to be small. In this case, γ_l will differ little from the ratio of slope to value of the solution in the absence of a scattering potential, so that we put

$$\gamma_l = k \left[\frac{j_l'(ka)}{j_l(ka)} + \epsilon_l \right] \qquad |\epsilon_l| \ll \left| \frac{j_l'(ka)}{j_l(ka)} \right| \tag{19.16}$$

Equation (19.15) can be rewritten with the help of (15.9) as

$$\tan \delta_l = \frac{\epsilon_l(ka)^2 j_l^2(ka)}{\epsilon_l(ka)^2 j_l(ka) n_l(ka) - 1} \tag{19.17}$$

which is still exact. If now we make use of the power series expansion for j_l from (15.7) when $l \gg (ka)^2$, and use (15.7) and (15.8) to estimate the order of magnitude of n_l, the inequality in (19.16) becomes

$$|\epsilon_l| \ll \frac{l}{ka} \tag{19.18}$$

and (19.17) may be approximated as

$$\delta_l \approx - \frac{\epsilon_l(ka)^{2l+2}}{[(2l+1)!!]^2} = - \frac{\epsilon_l 2^{2l}(l!)^2(ka)^{2l+2}}{[(2l+1)!]^2} \tag{19.19}$$

Equation (19.19) can be used to verify the convergence of the sums over partial waves such as appear in (19.11). We use Stirling's formula to find the leading terms in $\ln |\delta_l|$ when l is large, and we neglect terms of order $\ln l$ and lower.

$$\ln |\delta_l| \approx \ln |\epsilon_l| + 2l[\ln (ka) + 1 - \ln 2] - 2l \ln l$$

Thus even if $|\epsilon_l|$ has the maximum value indicated by (19.18), δ_l falls off like the inverse factorial of l (faster than exponentially), and the series that appear in the expressions for the scattering converge quite rapidly for large l.

RELATION BETWEEN SIGNS OF δ_l AND $V(r)$

It is apparent from (19.19) that, when $l \gg (ka)^2$, δ_l has the opposite sign from ϵ_l. If now the potential-energy term V or U is positive, corresponding to forces that are mainly repulsive, Eq. (19.2) shows that the ratio of curvature to value for the radial wave function is more positive than in the force-free case. This means that the ratio of slope to value is more positive at $r = a$ than is the case if $U = 0$. Thus a repulsive potential makes ϵ_l positive and δ_l negative. A negative phase shift means that the radial wave function is "pushed out" in comparison with the force-free wave function.

In similar fashion, we see that a negative potential makes ϵ_l negative

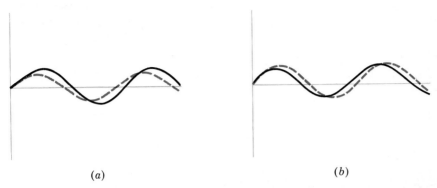

$$(a) \qquad\qquad\qquad\qquad (b)$$

Fig. 22 Graphs of the effects of (a) positive (repulsive) potential and (b) negative (attractive) potential on the force-free radial wave function $rj_0(kr)$ (dotted curves). The solid curves are $\chi_0(r)$. (*Graphs supplied by J. L. Schwartz and H. M. Schey.*)

and δ_l positive. This means that the radial wave function is "pulled in" by the attractive potential.

This may be seen graphically by comparing $rj_0(kr)$ and $\chi_0(r)$ when they are arbitrarily made to start out with the same slope at $r = 0$. Figure 22a and b show the results of numerical computations performed for repulsive and attractive square potentials, respectively. The units chosen are such that $\hbar = 1$, $m = \frac{1}{2}$, and the length unit is one-fifth of the total length of the abscissa shown in the graphs. The potential has radius $a = 1$ and strength $V_0 = \pm 2$; the energy is $E = 4$, so that $ka = 2$. In each case the dotted curve is $rj_0(kr)$ and the solid curve is $\chi_0(r)$.

RAMSAUER–TOWNSEND EFFECT

Figure 22b suggests that an attractive potential might be strong enough so that the $l = 0$ partial wave is pulled in by just half a cycle and its phase shift is 180°. If this were the case, the corresponding term in the expression (19.11) for $f(\theta)$ would vanish, and there would be no contribution to the scattering. This situation is shown in Fig. 23 which, like Fig. 22, was computed numerically. Here $a = 2$, $V_0 = -5$, and $E = 1$, so that $ka = 2$. The dotted curve is $rj_0(kr)$, and the solid curve is $\chi_0(r)$; the potential width is also indicated.

In such a situation, the possibility arises that ka can be small enough and the attractive potential strong enough so that all other phase shifts are negligibly small when $\delta_0 = 180°$. The scattering amplitude $f(\theta)$ then vanishes for all θ, and there is no scattering. This is the explanation[1] of the *Ramsauer-Townsend effect*, the extremely low mini-

[1] This explanation, suggested by N. Bohr, was shown to be quantitatively reasonable by H. Faxén and J. Holtsmark, *Z. Physik* **45**, 307 (1927).

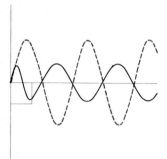

Fig. 23 Graphs of $r j_0(kr)$ (dotted curve) and $\chi_0(r)$
(solid curve) when the attractive square well potential
is strong enough to make $\delta_0 = 180°$. The two wave
functions start out with the same slope at $r = 0$, and
$\chi_0(r)$ is pulled in by half a cycle. (*Graphs supplied by
J. L. Schwartz and H. M. Schey.*)

mum observed in the scattering cross section of electrons by rare-gas
atoms at about 0.7-ev bombarding energy. A rare-gas atom, which
consists entirely of closed shells, is relatively small, and the combined
force of nucleus and atomic electrons exerted on an incident electron is
strong and sharply defined as to range. It is clear that this minimum
cross section will occur at a definite energy, since the shape of the wave
function inside the potential is insensitive to the relatively small bombarding energy whereas the phase of the force-free wave function depends
rapidly on it.

Physically, the Ramsauer-Townsend effect may be thought of as a
diffraction of the electron around the rare-gas atom, in which the wave
function inside the atom is distorted in just such a way that it fits on
smoothly to an undistorted wave function outside. This effect is analogous to the perfect transmission found at particular energies in the one-
dimensional problem considered earlier [see discussion of Eq. (17.5)].
Unlike the situation in one dimension, however, the Ramsauer-Townsend
effect cannot occur with a repulsive potential, since ka would have to be
at least of order unity to make $\delta_0 = -180°$, and a potential of this large
range would produce higher l phase shifts.

SCATTERING BY A PERFECTLY RIGID SPHERE

As a first example of the method of partial waves, we compute the scattering by a perfectly rigid sphere, which is represented by the potential
$V(r) = +\infty$ for $r < a$, and $V(r) = 0$ for $r > a$. The solution for $r > a$
is just Eq. (19.7). The boundary condition, obtained in Sec. 8, that

$u(a,\theta) = 0$, is equivalent to the requirement that all the radial functions vanish at $r = a$. The phase shifts may then be obtained by setting either $R_l(a)$ given by (19.7) equal to zero, or γ_l in (19.15) equal to infinity:

$$\tan \delta_l = \frac{j_l(ka)}{n_l(ka)} \tag{19.20}$$

The calculation of the scattering is particularly simple in the low-energy limit: $ka = 2\pi a/\lambda \ll 1$. Then substitution of (15.7) into (19.20) gives as an approximation for the phase shifts

$$\tan \delta_l \approx - \frac{(ka)^{2l+1}}{(2l+1)[(2l-1)!!]^2} \tag{19.21}$$

Thus δ_l falls off very rapidly as l increases, in agreement with (19.19). All the phase shifts vanish as $k \to 0$; however, the $l = 0$ partial wave gives a finite contribution to the scattering because of the factor $1/k^2$ that appears in (19.12) and (19.13). We thus obtain

$$\sigma(\theta) \approx a^2 \qquad \sigma \approx 4\pi a^2 \tag{19.22}$$

The scattering is spherically symmetrical, and the total cross section is four times the classical value.

In the high-energy limit ($ka \gg 1$), we might expect to get the classical result, since it is then possible to make wave packets that are small in comparison with the size of the scattering region, and these can follow the classical trajectories without spreading appreciably. This corresponds to the ray limit in the wave theory of light or sound. The differential scattering cross section is rather difficult to find, and we only indicate the computation of the leading term in the total cross section. Substitution of (19.20) into (19.13) gives

$$\sigma = \frac{4\pi}{k^2} \sum_{l=0}^{\infty} \frac{(2l+1)j_l^2(ka)}{j_l^2(ka) + n_l^2(ka)} \tag{19.23}$$

We can make use of asymptotic expansions of Bessel functions that are valid when the argument is large and the order is smaller than, of the order of, and larger than the argument.[1] The calculation shows that most of the contribution to the sum in (19.23) comes from

$$l < (ka) - C(ka)^{\frac{1}{3}}$$

where C is a number of order unity; the leading term here is $\frac{1}{2}(ka)^2$. The other two parts of the sum, for $(ka) - C(ka)^{\frac{1}{3}} < l < (ka) + C(ka)^{\frac{1}{3}}$ and for $l > (ka) + C(ka)^{\frac{1}{3}}$, each contribute terms of order $(ka)^{\frac{4}{3}}$ and

[1] Watson, *op. cit.*, chap. VIII.

hence may be neglected in the high-energy limit.   Thus

$$\sigma \approx 2\pi a^2 \tag{19.24}$$

which is twice the classical value.[1]

The reason for the apparently anomalous result (19.24) is that the asymptotic form of the wave function is so set up in Eq. (18.10) that in the classical limit the scattering is counted twice: once in the true scattering (which turns out to be spherically symmetric as it is in the classical problem) and again in the shadow of the scattering sphere that appears in the forward direction, since this shadow is produced by interference between the incident plane wave e^{ikz} and the scattered wave $f(\theta)e^{ikr}/r$ [see also the discussion of Eq. (19.14)].   However, so long as ka is finite, diffraction around the sphere in the forward direction actually takes place, and the total measured cross section (if the measurement can be made so that it includes the strong forward diffraction peak) is approximately $2\pi a^2$.

SCATTERING BY A SQUARE WELL POTENTIAL

As a second example of the method of partial waves, we consider the somewhat more complicated problem of the scattering from the spherically symmetric square well potential illustrated in Fig. 13, Sec. 15. The interior $(r < a)$ wave function that is finite at $r = 0$ is seen by analogy with Eq. (15.11) to be

$$R_l(r) = B_l j_l(\alpha r) \qquad \alpha = \left[\frac{2\mu(E + V_0)}{\hbar^2} \right]^{\frac{1}{2}} \tag{19.25}$$

Thus the phase shifts are given by Eq. (19.15), where the ratio of slope to value of the lth partial wave at $r = a$ is

$$\gamma_l = \frac{\alpha j_l'(\alpha a)}{j_l(\alpha a)} \tag{19.26}$$

In the low-energy limit $(ka \ll 1)$, substitution of (15.7) into (19.15) gives for the first two phase shifts

$$\tan \delta_0 \approx -\frac{\gamma_0 k a^2}{1 + \gamma_0 a}$$

$$\tan \delta_1 \approx \frac{(ka)^3}{3} \frac{1 - \gamma_1 a}{2 + \gamma_1 a} \tag{19.27}$$

---

[1] The next term has been calculated by S. I. Rubinow and T. T. Wu, *J. Appl. Phys.* **27**, 1032 (1956); the result is

$$\sigma = 2\pi a^2 \left[1 + \frac{0.99615}{(ka)^{\frac{2}{3}}} + \cdots \right]$$

Unless $\gamma_0 a = -1$ or $\gamma_1 a = -2$, both of these vanish as $k \to 0$. As with the rigid sphere, however, the $l = 0$ partial wave gives a finite contribution to the scattering because of the factor $1/k^2$ that appears in (19.12) and (19.13). From Eq. (19.26), we see that $\gamma_0 a = \alpha a \cot \alpha a - 1$, so that

$$\sigma \approx 4\pi a^2 \left(1 - \frac{\tan \alpha a}{\alpha a} \right)^2 \tag{19.28}$$

The scattering is spherically symmetrical.

The conclusion reached here and in connection with the rigid sphere that the low-energy scattering is substantially independent of bombarding energy and angle of observation is almost always valid for any potential that has a finite range. Exceptions can arise, as pointed out after Eq. (19.27), if any one of the γ_l is such that the denominator of the expression for $\tan \delta_l$ is very small. In such a situation, the lth partial wave is said to be in *resonance* with the scattering potential; then it usually dominates the scattering.

RESONANCE SCATTERING

An approximate expression for the resonance cross section can be obtained by making use of the fact that γ_l decreases linearly with increasing α when α is sufficiently close to $\alpha_0 \equiv (2\mu V_0/\hbar^2)^{\frac{1}{2}}$. Increasing α causes the interior wave function to bend over more rapidly and so decreases the ratio of slope to value at $r = a$. Now

$$\alpha = (\alpha_0{}^2 + k^2)^{\frac{1}{2}} \approx \alpha_0 + \frac{k^2}{2\alpha_0}$$

when k is small, so that we can write to lowest order in k

$$\gamma_l a \approx \gamma_l{}^0 a - b_l (ka)^2$$

where $\gamma_l{}^0$ is the value of γ_l when $\alpha = \alpha_0$, and b_l is a positive number of order unity.[1] Substitution into (19.27) and then into (19.12) gives for the leading term in the differential cross section, in the two cases for which the value of l for the partial wave that is in resonance is 0 and is 1,

$$\sigma(\theta) \approx \frac{a^2}{(\zeta_0 - b_0 k^2 a^2)^2 + (ka)^2} \qquad l = 0 \tag{19.29}$$

$$\sigma(\theta) \approx \frac{9a^2 \cos^2 \theta \, (ka)^4}{(\zeta_1 - b_1 k^2 a^2)^2 + (ka)^6} \qquad l = 1 \tag{19.30}$$

We have put $\zeta_0 = \gamma_0{}^0 a + 1$ and $\zeta_1 = \gamma_1{}^0 a + 2$; for resonance, $|\zeta_0|$ and $|\zeta_1|$ are small compared with unity. It is easy to show then that (19.29)

[1] It can be shown that the lth partial wave is exactly in resonance at zero bombarding energy when $\gamma_l{}^0 a = -(l+1)$; in this case $b_l = \frac{1}{2}$ for all l. Compare with footnote 1, page 88. See also B. W. Downs, *Am. J. Phys.* **30**, 248 (1962).

is a monotonically decreasing function of ka; however (19.30) has a sharp maximum at $ka \approx (\zeta_1/b_1)^{\frac{1}{2}}$ if ζ_1 is positive, and a much lower maximum at $ka \approx (2|\zeta_1|b_1)^{\frac{1}{4}}$ if ζ_1 is negative.

If we make use of the relation $\zeta_0 = \alpha_0 a \cot \alpha_0 a$, we see from (19.29) that a suitable approximation for the total cross section when the $l = 0$ partial wave is in resonance is

$$\sigma \approx \frac{4\pi}{k^2 + \alpha_0{}^2 \cot^2 \alpha_0 a} \tag{19.31}$$

It is apparent that the $l = 0$ partial wave is in resonance at low bombarding energies whenever $\alpha_0 a$ is approximately an odd multiple of $\pi/2$, so that $V_0 a^2 \approx \pi^2 \hbar^2/8\mu, 9\pi^2 \hbar^2/8\mu$, etc. The discussion of Eq. (15.3) shows that these are just the values of $V_0 a^2$ for which new energy levels with $l = 0$ appear. It is true quite generally that a potential well (not necessarily square) that has an energy level nearly at zero exhibits a resonance in the low-energy scattering of particles with the same l value (not necessarily zero) as the energy level. From a physical point of view, we can say that an incident particle that has nearly the right energy to be bound by the potential tends to concentrate there and produce a large distortion in the wave function and hence a large amount of scattering.

Sharp resonance maxima in the low-energy scattering like that found above for $l = 1$ with positive ζ_1 can appear for any l value except $l = 0$, provided that the potential well is not quite deep or broad enough to contain a new energy level of that angular momentum (this corresponds in the case of the square well to having ζ_1 small and positive). We can think of such a potential physically as containing a *virtual energy level* slightly above zero. Although a discrete energy level cannot exist with positive energy, the positive "centrifugal potential" $l(l + 1)\hbar^2/2\mu r^2$ [see the discussion of Eq. (14.18)] for $l > 0$ acts as a potential barrier that impedes the escape of a particle that is in the virtual energy level. Figure 24 illustrates this barrier, which is characterized by a small transmission at low energies in the same way as is the barrier of Fig. 14 [see the discus-

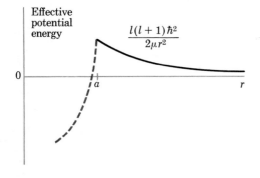

Fig. 24 The effective potential energy $[V(r)$ plus "centrifugal potential"] for $l > 0$, when $V = 0$ for $r > a$. The dashed portion for $r < a$ depends on the shape of V. The effective potential barrier $(r \gtrsim a)$ resembles the barrier of Fig. 14 in that it has a small transmission for E slightly greater than zero.

sion of Eq. (17.7)]. Thus the virtual level has a kind of transient existence and produces a greater distortion of the incident wave function at its energy than at neighboring energies. In the limit of zero energy, it can be shown that the transmission of the centrifugal barrier is zero (see Sec. 34), so that the particle cannot leak out if $l > 0$. Resonance at zero energy thus leads to a true bound state if l is not zero.

ANGULAR DISTRIBUTION AT LOW ENERGIES

When the bombarding energy is small but not zero, the partial wave $l = 1$ may have an observable effect on the scattering. If only δ_0 and δ_1 are appreciably different from zero, Eqs. (19.12) and (19.13) become

$$\sigma(\theta) = \frac{1}{k^2} [\sin^2 \delta_0 + 6 \sin \delta_0 \sin \delta_1 \cos (\delta_1 - \delta_0) \cos \theta$$
$$+ 9 \sin^2 \delta_1 \cos^2 \theta] \quad (19.32)$$

$$\sigma = \frac{4\pi}{k^2} (\sin^2 \delta_0 + 3 \sin^2 \delta_1)$$

In the absence of resonance, we see from Eqs. (19.27) and (19.32) that the ratio of the contributions to the total cross section of the partial waves $l = 1$ and $l = 0$ is of order $(ka)^4$. However, the ratio of the largest angle-dependent term in the differential cross section (which is proportional to $\cos \theta$) to the constant term is of order $(ka)^2$.

Thus the partial wave $l = 1$ manifests itself in the angular distribution at a lower energy than that at which it becomes significant in the total cross section; this is because of its interference with the stronger partial wave $l = 0$. For example, if $\delta_0 = 20°$ and $\delta_1 = 2°$ at a particular bombarding energy, the partial wave $l = 1$ contributes only 3 percent to the total cross section but it makes the forward scattering ($\theta = 0°$) 3.5 times as great as the backward scattering ($\theta = 180°$).

20☐SCATTERING BY COMPLEX POTENTIALS

It has been assumed thus far that the potential energy $V(\mathbf{r})$ is real. This is a natural assumption since V has been taken over from classical mechanics in accordance with Eq. (6.14). However, there are situations in which it is convenient to make use of a complex potential as a highly abbreviated description of a much more complicated physical system. For example, neutrons may be scattered elastically or inelastically from atomic nuclei. In the first case the nucleus is left in its original state, and the sum of the kinetic energies of neutron and nucleus is the same before and after the collision. In an inelastic collision the nucleus is left in an excited state, and the quantity Q, defined in connection with

Eq. (18.5), is negative. Inelastic scattering and the absorption of the neutron to form a different nucleus are both processes in which neutrons are taken out of the incident beam and do not reappear as part of the scattering amplitude $f(\theta,\phi)$.

So far as the effect of these other processes on the elastic scattering is concerned, a useful approximation consists in regarding the interaction between neutron and nucleus as being represented by a complex potential.[1] It is usually called the *optical-model potential*, in analogy with the long-standing use of a complex refractive index for discussing the optical properties of partially absorbing media. This section describes the modifications in the theory thus far developed that are necessitated by the assumption that V may be complex.

CONSERVATION OF PROBABILITY

It was shown in Sec. 7 that the position probability density $P(\mathbf{r},t)$ and the probability current density $\mathbf{S}(\mathbf{r},t)$, defined by Eqs. (7.1) and (7.3), obey a differential conservation relation. The derivation of this relation made essential use of the assumption that V is real. If we now assume that V is complex and write it for future convenience in the form

$$V = V_R - iV_I$$

where V_R and V_I are real, a repetition of the derivation shows that the conservation relation is replaced by

$$\frac{\partial P(\mathbf{r},t)}{\partial t} + \mathbf{\nabla} \cdot \mathbf{S}(\mathbf{r},t) = -\frac{2V_I}{\hbar} P(\mathbf{r},t) \qquad (20.1)$$

Since P is nonnegative, the right side of this equation acts as a source of probability if V_I is negative and as a sink if V_I is positive. For the physical reasons discussed above, we shall always assume that $V_I \geq 0$. If there is a region in which $\mathbf{\nabla} \cdot \mathbf{S} = 0$, Eq. (20.1) shows that P decays exponentially in time, $P \propto e^{-2V_I t/\hbar}$, so that the wave function is expected to have the time dependence $\psi \propto e^{(-iE-V_I)t/\hbar}$.

Integration of Eq. (20.1) over a fixed volume Ω bounded by the surface A leads to

$$\frac{\partial}{\partial t} \int_\Omega P(\mathbf{r},t)\, d^3r = -\int_A S_n dA - \frac{2}{\hbar} \int_\Omega V_I P\, d^3r \qquad (20.2)$$

in place of Eq. (7.4). If ψ is sufficiently well bounded at large distances so that the surface integral vanishes when Ω is the entire space, we see

[1] It was first used for this purpose by H. Feshbach, C. E. Porter, and V. F. Weisskopf, *Phys. Rev.* **96**, 448 (1954). For reviews of the subject, see P. E. Hodgson, "The Optical Model of Elastic Scattering" (Oxford, New York, 1963); A. L. Fetter and K. M. Watson in "Advances in Theoretical Physics" (Academic, New York, 1965).

that the normalization integral decreases in time.   This is to be expected since particles are being absorbed.

It is more interesting to apply Eq. (20.2) to a scattering situation. In this case we require ψ to be stationary, so that it has the time dependence $\psi \propto e^{-iEt/\hbar}$. The discussion of Eq. (20.1) then shows that there is no region in which $V_I \neq 0$ and $\nabla \cdot \mathbf{S} = 0$.   The left side of (20.2) is now zero, and as Ω becomes large the first term on the right side, $- \int_A S_n \, dA$, becomes the total inward flux of particles entering Ω from very large distances.   In the discussion of Eq. (19.6) it was pointed out that the vanishing of this integral implied that the particles scattered outward are supplied by the incident plane wave.   In the present situation we see that this integral is the flux of particles removed from the incident plus elastically scattered wave by the complex potential, provided that ψ is normalized to a plane wave of unit amplitude at infinity.   It may therefore be set equal to $v\sigma_{abs}$, where v is the relative velocity and σ_{abs} is the sum of the total absorption and inelastic cross sections.   We thus obtain the relation

$$\sigma_{abs} = \frac{2}{\hbar v} \int V_I |\psi|^2 \, d^3r \tag{20.3}$$

Although this equation is valid whenever ψ is properly normalized, it is useful only if ψ is known in the region where $V_I \neq 0$.

COMPLEX PHASE SHIFTS

If the potential is spherically symmetric, the method of partial waves can be employed whether or not V is complex.   The discussion of Eq. (19.5) showed that the phase shifts are real if the potential is.   The same argument shows that δ_l is generally complex if V is complex, and so we put

$$\delta_l = \alpha_l + i\beta_l$$

where α_l and β_l are real, and also define

$$S_l \equiv e^{2i\delta_l} = e^{2i\alpha_l - 2\beta_l}$$

The derivation of the expression for the scattering amplitude is unchanged, so that Eq. (19.11) becomes

$$f(\theta) = (2ik)^{-1} \sum_{l=0}^{\infty} (2l + 1)(S_l - 1)P_l(\cos \theta) \tag{20.4}$$

The differential elastic scattering cross section is $|f(\theta)|^2$, and the total elastic cross section is

$$\sigma_{el} = 2\pi \int_0^\pi |f(\theta)|^2 \sin\theta \, d\theta$$

$$= \frac{\pi}{k^2} \sum_{l=0}^\infty (2l+1)(1 - 2e^{-2\beta_l}\cos 2\alpha_l + e^{-4\beta_l})$$

$$= \frac{\pi}{k^2} \sum_{l=0}^\infty (2l+1)|1 - S_l|^2 \tag{20.5}$$

This reduces to Eq. (19.13) when $\beta_l = 0$, as expected.

The absorption cross section can also be expressed in terms of the phase shifts. As pointed out above, it is equal to $-v^{-1}\int_A S_n \, dA$, where it is now convenient to choose the surface A to be a large sphere of radius r:

$$\sigma_{abs} = -\frac{1}{v}\lim_{r\to\infty} r^2 \int_0^{2\pi}\int_0^\pi S_r \sin\theta \, d\theta \, d\phi$$

$$= -\frac{1}{v}\lim_{r\to\infty} 2\pi r^2 \int_0^\pi S_r \sin\theta \, d\theta \tag{20.6}$$

The radial flux is

$$S_r = \frac{\hbar}{2i\mu}\left(u^*\frac{\partial u}{\partial r} - \frac{\partial u^*}{dr}u\right)$$

Differentiation of Eq. (19.1) gives

$$\frac{\partial u}{\partial r} = \sum_{l=0}^\infty \frac{1}{r}\frac{\partial \chi_l}{\partial r}P_l(\cos\theta) + O\left(\frac{1}{r^2}\right)$$

so that Eq. (20.6) becomes

$$\sigma_{abs} = \frac{2\pi i}{k}\sum_{l=0}^\infty \frac{1}{2l+1}\left(\chi_l^*\frac{\partial \chi_l}{\partial r} - \frac{\partial \chi_l^*}{\partial r}\chi_l\right) \tag{20.7}$$

evaluated at $r = \infty$. The asymptotic form (19.8) shows that

$$\left(\chi_l^*\frac{\partial \chi_l}{\partial r} - \frac{\partial \chi_l^*}{\partial r}\chi_l\right) \xrightarrow[r\to\infty]{}$$

$$\frac{|A_l|^2}{k}[\sin(kr - \tfrac{1}{2}l\pi + \alpha_l - i\beta_l)\cos(kr - \tfrac{1}{2}l\pi + \alpha_l + i\beta_l)$$

$$- \cos(kr - \tfrac{1}{2}l\pi + \alpha_l - i\beta_l)\sin(kr - \tfrac{1}{2}l\pi + \alpha_l + i\beta_l)]$$

$$= \frac{|A_l|^2}{k}\sin(-2i\beta_l) = -\frac{i|A_l|^2}{k}\sinh 2\beta_l$$

Substitution of this and the expression $|A_l|^2 = (2l + 1)^2 e^{-2\beta_l}$ into Eq. (20.7) yields

$$\sigma_{\text{abs}} = \frac{\pi}{k^2} \sum_{l=0}^{\infty} (2l + 1)(1 - e^{-4\beta_l})$$

$$= \frac{\pi}{k^2} \sum_{l=0}^{\infty} (2l + 1)(1 - |S_l|^2) \tag{20.8}$$

We thus expect that $\beta_l \geq 0$.

The total cross section is defined to be the sum of the elastic and absorption cross sections. From Eqs. (20.5) and (20.8) it is

$$\sigma_{\text{tot}} = \frac{2\pi}{k^2} \sum_{l=0}^{\infty} (2l + 1)(1 - e^{-2\beta_l} \cos 2\alpha_l)$$

$$= \frac{2\pi}{k^2} \sum_{l=0}^{\infty} (2l + 1)[1 - \text{Re}\,(S_l)] \tag{20.9}$$

where Re denotes the real part of what follows.

ASYMPTOTIC RELATIONS

Three interesting and useful relations, the reciprocity theorem, the generalized optical theorem, and the optical theorem, can be derived from a consideration of the asymptotic behavior of the scattering wave function. We now obtain them in the order just given, although this is not the historical sequence.[1]

It is convenient to rewrite Eq. (18.10), with $A = 1$, in a form that does not emphasize the special role played by the z axis:

$$u_{\mathbf{k}}(\mathbf{r}) \xrightarrow[r \to \infty]{} \exp\,(i\mathbf{k} \cdot \mathbf{r}) + r^{-1}f(\mathbf{k}_r, \mathbf{k})e^{ikr} \tag{20.10}$$

Here the plane wave is incident along the direction of $\mathbf{k}$, and the amplitude $f(\mathbf{k}_r, \mathbf{k})$ corresponds to scattering from $\mathbf{k}$ to $\mathbf{k}_r$, which is a vector that has the magnitude k and the direction of $\mathbf{r}$. For another solution that corresponds to the initial direction $-\mathbf{k}'$,

$$u_{-\mathbf{k}'}(\mathbf{r}) \xrightarrow[r \to \infty]{} \exp\,(-i\mathbf{k}' \cdot \mathbf{r}) + r^{-1}f(\mathbf{k}_r, -\mathbf{k}')e^{ikr} \tag{20.11}$$

Since $u_{\mathbf{k}}(\mathbf{r})$ and $u_{-\mathbf{k}'}(\mathbf{r})$ both satisfy Eq. (18.8) with the same value of E, it follows that

$$u_{-\mathbf{k}'}\nabla^2 u_{\mathbf{k}} - u_{\mathbf{k}}\nabla^2 u_{-\mathbf{k}'} = 0 \tag{20.12}$$

whether V is real or complex.

[1] The optical theorem [Eq. (20.23) below] was first derived in this way by E. Feenberg, *Phys. Rev.* **40**, 40 (1932). This approach was subsequently generalized to yield the other two theorems by R. Glauber and V. Schomaker, *Phys. Rev.* **89**, 667 (1953).

Equation (20.12) may be integrated over a large spherical volume Ω of radius r, and this integral can be transformed into an integral over the surface of the sphere:

$$\int_\Omega (u_{-\mathbf{k}'}\nabla^2 u_{\mathbf{k}} - u_{\mathbf{k}}\nabla^2 u_{-\mathbf{k}'})\, d^3r$$

$$= r^2 \int_0^{2\pi}\int_0^\pi \left(u_{-\mathbf{k}'}\frac{\partial u_{\mathbf{k}}}{\partial r} - u_{\mathbf{k}}\frac{\partial u_{-\mathbf{k}'}}{\partial r}\right)\sin\theta_r\, d\theta_r\, d\phi_r = 0$$

where θ_r, ϕ_r are the polar angles of $\mathbf{r}$ with respect to some arbitrarily chosen polar axis. Substitution of the asymptotic forms (20.10) and (20.11) gives in the limit of large r

$$r^2 \int_0^{2\pi}\int_0^\pi \left\{ ik(\cos\theta + \cos\theta')e^{ikr(\cos\theta-\cos\theta')} \right.$$

$$+ \left[\frac{ik}{r}(1+\cos\theta') - \frac{1}{r^2}\right]f(\mathbf{k}_r,\mathbf{k})e^{ikr(1-\cos\theta')}$$

$$\left. - \left[\frac{ik}{r}(1-\cos\theta) - \frac{1}{r^2}\right]f(\mathbf{k}_r,-\mathbf{k}')e^{ikr(1+\cos\theta)} \right\} \sin\theta_r\, d\theta_r\, d\phi_r = 0$$

where θ is the angle between $\mathbf{k}$ and $\mathbf{r}$, and θ' is that between $\mathbf{k}'$ and $\mathbf{r}$. The first term in the integrand can be seen to vanish on integration over the directions of $\mathbf{r}$, since for every pair of angles θ, θ' there is a canceling pair $\pi - \theta'$, $\pi - \theta$. The $1/r^2$ terms in the integrand, as well as other terms of order $1/r^2$ that were ignored in the expansion (20.10), can be neglected for a reason that will become clear from the discussion of (20.14) below.

We are thus left with the equation

$$ikr \int_0^{2\pi}\int_0^\pi [(1+\cos\theta')f(\mathbf{k}_r,\mathbf{k})e^{ikr(1-\cos\theta')}$$

$$- (1-\cos\theta)f(\mathbf{k}_r,-\mathbf{k}')e^{ikr(1+\cos\theta)}]\sin\theta_r\, d\theta_r\, d\phi_r = 0 \quad (20.13)$$

which is to be evaluated in the limit $r \to \infty$. In the first term we can shift the polar axis from its original arbitrary choice to the direction $\mathbf{k}'$ and thus replace the variables of integration θ_r, ϕ_r by θ', ϕ'. Then, with $w \equiv \cos\theta'$, we consider the integral

$$r\int_{-1}^1 F(w,\phi')e^{ikr(1-w)}\, dw \qquad (20.14)$$

in the limit of large r, where $F(w,\phi') \equiv ik(1+w)f(\mathbf{k}_r,\mathbf{k})$. Integration by parts gives

$$\frac{i}{k}F(w,\phi')e^{ikr(1-w)}\bigg|_{-1}^{1} - \frac{i}{k}\int_{-1}^1 \frac{\partial F}{\partial w}e^{ikr(1-w)}\, dw$$

It is apparent that further partial integrations lead to successively higher powers of r in the denominator, so that only the first term need be kept in the limit $r \to \infty$. This is the reason why the above-mentioned terms of order $1/r^2$ could be neglected. We thus find that the limit of (20.14) is

$$\frac{i}{k} [F(1,\phi') - F(-1,\phi')e^{2ikr}] \tag{20.15}$$

With the above form for $F(w,\phi')$, we see that $F(-1,\phi') = 0$. However the second term of (20.15) could have been dropped in any event, since the factor e^{2ikr} oscillates about zero as $r \to \infty$. This is an application of the method of stationary phase, which is sometimes useful in obtaining asymptotic expressions for integrals.[1] In this case the point $w = 1$ is called the *stationary phase point*, since the phase of the integrand of (20.14) is stationary as w approaches unity.

RECIPROCITY THEOREM

The stationary phase point of the first term in (20.13) is $\cos \theta' = 1$ or $\theta' = 0$. This corresponds to $\mathbf{r}$ being along $\mathbf{k}'$ or to the substitution of $\mathbf{k}'$ for $\mathbf{k}_r$ in the scattering amplitude $f(\mathbf{k}_r,\mathbf{k})$. Further, the integrand does not depend on ϕ', so that the ϕ' integration only introduces a multiplicative factor 2π. In similar fashion, the second term in (20.13) has its stationary phase point at $\cos \theta = -1$ or $\theta = \pi$, so that $\mathbf{k}_r$ is replaced by $-\mathbf{k}$ in $f(\mathbf{k}_r,-\mathbf{k}')$.

We thus obtain the *reciprocity theorem*

$$f(\mathbf{k}',\mathbf{k}) = f(-\mathbf{k},-\mathbf{k}') \tag{20.16}$$

which states that the amplitude for scattering from $\mathbf{k}$ to $\mathbf{k}'$ is equal to that for scattering from the reversed final direction $-\mathbf{k}'$ to the reversed initial direction $-\mathbf{k}$. It is important to note that this theorem is valid whether V is real or complex.

It often happens that $V(\mathbf{r}) = V(-\mathbf{r})$, so that V possesses space-inversion symmetry (see Sec. 29). Then all vectors in the scattering problem may be inverted without altering the physical situation, and we have that

$$f(-\mathbf{k},-\mathbf{k}') = f(\mathbf{k},\mathbf{k}') \tag{20.17}$$

Combination of Eqs. (20.16) and (20.17) yields a slightly specialized reciprocity theorem:

$$f(\mathbf{k}',\mathbf{k}) = f(\mathbf{k},\mathbf{k}') \tag{20.18}$$

GENERALIZED OPTICAL THEOREM

The procedure followed in the two preceding subsections can now be repeated, starting with $u_{\mathbf{k}'}^*$ in place of $u_{-\mathbf{k}'}$. Then Eq. (20.12) is replaced

---

[1] See, for example, C. Eckart, *Rev. Mod. Phys.* **20**, 399 (1948).

by

$$u_{\mathbf{k}'}^* \nabla^2 u_{\mathbf{k}} - u_{\mathbf{k}} \nabla^2 u_{\mathbf{k}'}^* + \frac{4i\mu}{\hbar^2} V_I u_{\mathbf{k}'}^* u_{\mathbf{k}} = 0$$

Integration over a large spherical volume Ω of radius r leads to

$$r^2 \int_0^{2\pi} \int_0^{\pi} \left(u_{\mathbf{k}'}^* \frac{\partial u_{\mathbf{k}}}{\partial r} - u_{\mathbf{k}} \frac{\partial u_{\mathbf{k}'}^*}{\partial r} \right) \sin \theta_r \, d\theta_r \, d\phi_r + \frac{4i\mu}{\hbar^2} \int_\Omega V_I u_{\mathbf{k}'}^* u_{\mathbf{k}} \, d^3r = 0$$

Substitution of asymptotic forms like (20.10) in the first term then gives in the limit of large r

$$r^2 \int_0^{2\pi} \int_0^{\pi} \left\{ ik(\cos\theta + \cos\theta') e^{ikr(\cos\theta - \cos\theta')} \right.$$

$$+ \left[\frac{ik}{r} (1 + \cos\theta') - \frac{1}{r^2} \right] f(\mathbf{k}_r, \mathbf{k}) e^{ikr(1-\cos\theta')}$$

$$+ \left[\frac{ik}{r} (1 + \cos\theta) + \frac{1}{r^2} \right] f^*(\mathbf{k}_r, \mathbf{k}') e^{-ikr(1-\cos\theta)}$$

$$\left. + \frac{2ik}{r^2} f^*(\mathbf{k}_r, \mathbf{k}') f(\mathbf{k}_r, \mathbf{k}) \right\} \sin\theta_r \, d\theta_r \, d\phi_r$$

$$+ \frac{4i\mu}{\hbar^2} \int V_I u_{\mathbf{k}'}^* u_{\mathbf{k}} \, d^3r = 0 \quad (20.19)$$

where the volume integral is now over all space.

As before, the first term integrates to zero, and the terms that are products of $1/r^2$ and exponentials can again be neglected. The two remaining exponential terms can be evaluated by the method of stationary phase. The first term has its stationary phase point at the same place: $\cos\theta' = 1$ or $\mathbf{k}_r = \mathbf{k}'$. However, the second term now has its stationary phase point at $\cos\theta = 1$ or $\mathbf{k}_r = \mathbf{k}$, rather than at $\mathbf{k}_r = -\mathbf{k}$ as before; there is also a sign change that arises from the altered sign in the exponent. Equation (20.19) thus becomes

$$-4\pi f(\mathbf{k}', \mathbf{k}) + 4\pi f^*(\mathbf{k}, \mathbf{k}') + 2ik \int_0^{2\pi} \int_0^{\pi} f^*(\mathbf{k}_r, \mathbf{k}') f(\mathbf{k}_r, \mathbf{k}) \sin\theta_r \, d\theta_r \, d\phi_r$$

$$+ \frac{4i\mu}{\hbar^2} \int V_I u_{\mathbf{k}'}^* u_{\mathbf{k}} \, d^3r = 0 \quad (20.20)$$

As it stands, this relation is not useful, since the last term is difficult to evaluate and in general has no simple physical interpretation. We thus consider first the case in which V is real, so that $V_I = 0$. Equation (20.20) is then called the *generalized optical theorem*:

$$\int_0^{2\pi} \int_0^{\pi} f^*(\mathbf{k}_r, \mathbf{k}') f(\mathbf{k}_r, \mathbf{k}) \sin\theta_r \, d\theta_r \, d\phi_r = \frac{2\pi i}{k} \left[f^*(\mathbf{k}, \mathbf{k}') - f(\mathbf{k}', \mathbf{k}) \right]$$

$$(20.21)$$

If V possesses inversion symmetry, Eq. (20.18) may be used to simplify this relation:

$$\int_0^{2\pi} \int_0^{\pi} f^*(\mathbf{k'},\mathbf{k}_r) f(\mathbf{k}_r,\mathbf{k}) \sin \theta_r \, d\theta_r \, d\phi_r = \frac{4\pi}{k} \, \mathrm{Im} \, [f(\mathbf{k'},\mathbf{k})] \qquad (20.22)$$

It is important to note that Eqs. (20.21) and (20.22) are valid only if V is real.

Equation (20.22) may be used in conjunction with the Born approximation (see Sec. 38) in the following way. The Born approximation gives an extremely simple approximate expression for the scattering amplitude f which is of first order in V, and this f is real when V is real. Thus Eq. (20.22) enables us to calculate the imaginary part of f that is of lowest order in V and shows that it is actually of second order.

OPTICAL THEOREM

There is one situation in which the volume integral in Eq. (20.20) has a simple physical interpretation, that is, when $\mathbf{k'} = \mathbf{k}$. Then, in accordance with (20.3),

$$\int V_I u_{\mathbf{k}}^* u_{\mathbf{k}} \, d^3r = \tfrac{1}{2} \hbar v \sigma_{\mathrm{abs}}$$

since the normalization of $u_{\mathbf{k}}$ agrees with that used earlier for ψ. Then Eq. (20.20) becomes

$$\int_0^{2\pi} \int_0^{\pi} |f(\mathbf{k}_r,\mathbf{k})|^2 \sin \theta_r \, d\theta_r \, d\phi_r + \sigma_{\mathrm{abs}} = \frac{4\pi}{k} \, \mathrm{Im} \, [f(\mathbf{k},\mathbf{k})]$$

The first term on the left side is the total elastic cross section σ_{el}, so that the left side is equal to σ_{tot}.

We thus obtain the *optical theorem:*

$$\sigma_{\mathrm{tot}} = \sigma_{\mathrm{el}} + \sigma_{\mathrm{abs}} = \frac{4\pi}{k} \, \mathrm{Im} \, [f(\mathbf{k},\mathbf{k})] \qquad (20.23)$$

This is a generalization of Eq. (19.14) in that it applies as well when V is neither spherically symmetric nor real. In actuality, the optical theorem is even more generally valid than the preceding sentence indicates, since it can be derived without reference to a potential. All that is needed is the asymptotic form of the probability current density $\mathbf{S}(\mathbf{r},t)$, obtained by substituting (20.10) into (7.3). Then the integral of its radial component over an infinite sphere is proportional to the rate of disappearance of particles from the plane plus scattered wave and hence is proportional to σ_{abs}. Equation (20.23) then follows at once from application of the method of stationary phase. The optical theorem is also valid when special relativity is taken into account.

It is apparent that $f(\mathbf{k},\mathbf{k})$ enters into the optical theorem through an interference between the plane and scattered waves in (20.10). This interference is characterized by the phase factor $e^{ikr(1-\cos\theta)}$, which, as a function of θ, oscillates rapidly about zero for large r except in the neighborhood of $\theta = 0$. Thus the asymptotic probability current density consists of a part from the plane wave alone that is everywhere in the direction of $\mathbf{k}$, a part from the scattered wave alone that is always radially outward and integrates to σ_{el}, and a part that arises from interference. The last is appreciable only when $kr(1 - \cos\theta) \lesssim 1$; for large kr and small θ, this is equivalent to $\theta \lesssim (kr)^{-\frac{1}{2}}$. Within this angular region the scattered wave interferes destructively with the plane wave, thus removing from the plane wave just enough of the incident flux to account for absorption and inelastic scattering and for elastic scattering at all but infinitesimal angles.

In the asymptotic region, this angular range of interference may be thought of as the remnant of the shadow cast by the scatterer. This shadow remnant has a diameter $d \sim r(kr)^{-\frac{1}{2}} \sim (r/k)^{\frac{1}{2}}$. The true shadow cannot extend beyond a distance r_s such that the interfering or imaginary part of the forward-scattered amplitude, $\mathrm{Im}[f(\mathbf{k},\mathbf{k})]/r_s$, is of the order of the plane wave amplitude, which is unity, so that $r_s \sim \mathrm{Im}[f(\mathbf{k},\mathbf{k})] \sim k\sigma_{tot}$. At this limiting distance, the shadow diameter is $d \sim (r_s/k)^{\frac{1}{2}} \sim (\sigma_{tot})^{\frac{1}{2}}$. Now σ_{tot} is of the order of the square of the diameter of the scatterer in the short wavelength or classical limit. Thus scatterer and shadow are roughly of the same size at the limiting distance at which the shadow exists, as would be expected.[1]

21□SCATTERING BY A COULOMB FIELD

It was noted in Sec. 19 that the coulomb field is an exceptional scatterer so far as the application of the method of partial waves is concerned. If $V(r) = ZZ'e^2/r$ for a collision between particles of charges Ze and $Z'e$, it is easily seen that Eq. (19.3) becomes asymptotically

$$\chi_l(r) \propto e^{\pm i(kr - n \ln r)} \tag{21.1}$$

Here $n = \mu ZZ'e^2/\hbar^2 k = ZZ'e^2/\hbar v$, where v is the relative velocity and μ is the reduced mass. Thus the radial solutions never approach the sinusoidal free-particle solutions, since there is always a logarithmic contribution to the phase at great distances that cannot be neglected. Although it is still possible to obtain a solution of this scattering problem in spherical coordinates (this is given below), the phase shifts δ_l introduced in Sec. 19 are altered in meaning. This section presents the analytical

---

[1] For an extension of the discussion in this paragraph and its relation to the uncertainty principle, see L. I. Schiff, *Prog. Theoret. Phys.* (Kyoto) **11**, 288 (1954).

work in outline and quotes the principal results from more extended treatments.[1]

PARABOLIC COORDINATES

So long as $\sigma(\theta)$ for a pure coulomb field is all that is desired, it is simpler to work with the separation of the wave equation in parabolic coordinates (see Sec. 16) than in spherical coordinates. The reason for this is that the desired solution depends almost entirely on the variable ξ defined in Eq. (16.25) and not on the other two variables η and ϕ. It is apparent that the solution will not involve ϕ, because of the axial symmetry of the problem; if now the incident plane wave term e^{ikz} is taken out as a factor, it can be made plausible that the rest of the solution does not involve η. We put

$$u_c = e^{ikz}f \tag{21.2}$$

where u_c represents the complete coulomb wave function (incident plus scattered wave). Now u_c must contain a part whose dominant asymptotic behavior is of the form $r^{-1}e^{ikr}$, but no part that goes like $r^{-1}e^{-ikr}$ [see Eq. (18.10)]. Since an expression $e^{ikz}f(r - z)$ can be of this form, whereas an expression $e^{ikz}f(r + z)$ cannot, we anticipate that the function f appearing in (21.2) will depend only on $\xi = r - z$.

We substitute Eq. (21.2) into Eq. (16.26), after replacing Z by $-ZZ'$, and remember that $E > 0$. The differential equation for f is then

$$\xi \frac{d^2f}{d\xi^2} + (1 - ik\xi)\frac{df}{d\xi} - nkf = 0 \tag{21.3}$$

The confluent hypergeometric equation

$$z \frac{d^2F}{dz^2} + (b - z)\frac{dF}{dz} - aF = 0 \tag{21.4}$$

which has the solution $F(a,b,z)$, is equivalent to Eq. (21.3) if we put

$$f(\xi) = CF(-in,1,ik\xi) \tag{21.5}$$

where C is a constant.

[1] W. Gordon, Z. Physik **48**, 180 (1928); N. F. Mott and H. S. W. Massey, "The Theory of Atomic Collisions," 2d ed., chap. III (Oxford, New York, 1949). For the mathematical background, see E. T. Whittaker and G. N. Watson, "A Course of Modern Analysis," 4th ed., chap. XVI (Cambridge, London, 1935).

CONFLUENT HYPERGEOMETRIC FUNCTION

The solution of Eq. (21.4) that is regular at $z = 0$ can be written as a power series:

$$F(a,b,z) = \sum_{s=0}^{\infty} \frac{\Gamma(a + s)\Gamma(b)z^s}{\Gamma(a)\Gamma(b + s)\Gamma(1 + s)}$$

$$= 1 + \frac{az}{b1!} + \frac{a(a + 1)z^2}{b(b + 1)2!} + \cdots \tag{21.6}$$

It is convenient to put $F(a,b,z) = W_1(a,b,z) + W_2(a,b,z)$, where W_1 and W_2 are separately solutions of Eq. (21.4). An asymptotic expansion for F can then be obtained from the following relations:

$$W_1(a,b,z) = \frac{\Gamma(b)}{\Gamma(b - a)} (-z)^{-a} g(a, a - b + 1, -z)$$

$$W_2(a,b,z) = \frac{\Gamma(b)}{\Gamma(a)} e^z z^{a-b} g(1 - a, b - a, z) \tag{21.7}$$

$$g(\alpha,\beta,z) \xrightarrow[z \to \infty]{} 1 + \frac{\alpha\beta}{z1!} + \frac{\alpha(\alpha + 1)\beta(\beta + 1)}{z^2 2!} + \cdots$$

The solution of Eq. (21.4) that is irregular at the origin can be taken to be

$$G(a,b,z) = iW_1(a,b,z) - iW_2(a,b,z) \tag{21.8}$$

We shall require the irregular solution for problems in which the coulomb field does not extend in to $r = 0$.

The asymptotic form of the coulomb wave function can be obtained from Eqs. (21.1), (21.5), and (21.7). The result through terms of order r^{-1} is

$$u_c \xrightarrow[r \to \infty]{} \frac{Ce^{\frac{1}{2}n\pi}}{\Gamma(1 + in)} \left\{ e^{i[kz + n \ln k(r-z)]} \left[1 + \frac{n^2}{ik(r - z)} \right] \right.$$

$$\left. + r^{-1} f_c(\theta) e^{i(kr - n \ln 2kr)} \right\} \tag{21.9}$$

where[1]

$$f_c(\theta) = \frac{\Gamma(1 + in)}{i\Gamma(- in)} \frac{e^{-in \ln (\sin^2 \frac{1}{2}\theta)}}{2k \sin^2 \frac{1}{2}\theta}$$

$$= \frac{n}{2k \sin^2 \frac{1}{2}\theta} e^{-in \ln (\sin^2 \frac{1}{2}\theta) + i\pi + 2i\eta_0} \tag{21.10}$$

$$\eta_0 = \arg \Gamma(1 + in)$$

[1] The real quantity $\phi = \arg z$ is defined by the relation $z = |z| e^{i\phi}$.

SCATTERING CROSS SECTION AND NORMALIZATION

The f_c term on the right side of Eq. (21.9) represents the outgoing scattered wave, since it is the only term in which the factor $r^{-1}e^{ikr}$ appears. The first term in Eq. (21.9) similarly corresponds to the incident "plane" wave; the multiplicative factor $-n^2/ik(r-z)$ can be ignored in the asymptotic region.   Both the incident and scattered waves are distorted at infinite distances by logarithmic phase factors.   In accordance with Eq. (18.11), the differential scattering cross section is

$$\sigma_c(\theta) = |f_c(\theta)|^2 = \left(\frac{n}{2k\sin^2\frac{1}{2}\theta}\right)^2$$

$$= \left(\frac{ZZ'e^2}{2\mu v^2}\right)^2 \operatorname{cosec}^4 \tfrac{1}{2}\theta \tag{21.11}$$

This is just the formula obtained by Rutherford from classical dynamics, which was verified experimentally for the collisions of alpha particles (helium nuclei) with heavier nuclei.   It should be noted, however, that the angle-dependent part of the phase factor in the scattered amplitude $f_c(\theta)$ given in Eq. (21.10) can manifest itself in a nonclassical way when the colliding particles are identical (see Sec. 40).

If the incident beam is normalized to unit flux, the constant C must be chosen to be

$$C = v^{-\frac{1}{2}}\Gamma(1+in)e^{-\frac{1}{2}n\pi}$$

so that the coulomb wave function is

$$u_c = v^{-\frac{1}{2}}\Gamma(1+in)e^{-\frac{1}{2}n\pi}e^{ikr}F(-in,1,ik\xi)$$

$$= v^{-\frac{1}{2}}\Gamma(1+in)e^{-\frac{1}{2}n\pi}e^{ikr\cos\theta}F(-in, 1, 2ikr\sin^2\tfrac{1}{2}\theta) \tag{21.12}$$

Then the particle density at $r = 0$ is found from the power series expansion (21.6) to be

$$|u_c(0)|^2 = |C|^2 = v^{-1}|\Gamma(1+in)|^2 e^{-n\pi}$$

$$= \frac{2n\pi}{v(e^{2n\pi}-1)} \tag{21.13}$$

For small collision speeds ($|n| \gg 1$), Eq. (21.13) tells us that

$$|u_c(0)|^2 \approx \frac{2\pi|n|}{v} \qquad \text{attractive case, } n < 0$$

$$|u_c(0)|^2 \approx \frac{2\pi n}{v} e^{-2n\pi} \qquad \text{repulsive case, } n > 0 \tag{21.14}$$

The second of Eqs. (21.14) is of some practical interest.   The exponential is the dominant factor in the rate of reactions between positively charged nuclei at low bombarding energies, when the nuclear radii may be assumed small enough so that the colliding nuclei have to tunnel through the coulomb potential barrier to zero distance in order to initiate a reaction. In this case $e^{-2\pi ZZ'e^2/hv}$ is called the *Gamow factor*[1] and is the dominant term in the rate of many nuclear reactions at low bombarding energies.

SOLUTION IN SPHERICAL COORDINATES

In nuclear collision problems, such as that of the scattering of protons of several million electron-volts energy in hydrogen, the departures from the coulomb law of interaction at small distances between the colliding particles can affect the scattering cross section. Such problems can be treated by a modification of the method of partial waves, developed in Sec. 19, in which an expansion in spherical harmonics is made for the pure coulomb field, and modifications introduced for the first few l values. In order to apply such a technique, we require first a solution for the pure coulomb scattering in spherical partial waves.

We put

$$u_c = \sum_{l=0}^{\infty} R_l(r) P_l(\cos \theta) \tag{21.15}$$

where the radial wave equation is

$$\frac{1}{r^2} \frac{d}{dr} \left(r^2 \frac{dR_l}{dr} \right) + \left[k^2 - \frac{2nk}{r} - \frac{l(l+1)}{r^2} \right] R_l = 0 \tag{21.16}$$

If we substitute $R_l(r) = r^l e^{ikr} f_l(r)$, the equation for f_l becomes

$$r \frac{d^2 f_l}{dr^2} + [2ikr + 2(l+1)] \frac{df_l}{dr} + [2ik(l+1) - 2nk]f_l = 0 \tag{21.17}$$

This is equivalent to the confluent hypergeometric equation (21.4) and has as its solution that is regular at $r = 0$

$$f_l(r) = C_l F(l + 1 + in, 2l + 2, -2ikr) \tag{21.18}$$

The asymptotic form of (21.18) can be found from (21.7) and gives for the radial wave function at great distances

$$R_l(r) \xrightarrow[r \to \infty]{} \frac{C_l e^{\frac{1}{2}n\pi + in_l}\Gamma(2l+2)}{(2k)^l \Gamma(l+1+in)kr} \sin\left(kr - \tfrac{1}{2}l\pi - n \ln 2kr + \eta_l\right) \tag{21.19}$$

where $\eta_l = \arg \Gamma(l + 1 + in)$.

The coefficients C_l must be determined so that the partial wave expansion (21.15) is identical with the solution (21.12) in parabolic

---

[1] G. Gamow, *Z. Physik* **51**, 204 (1928); R. W. Gurney and E. U. Condon, *Phys. Rev.* **33**, 127 (1929).

coordinates. Because of the orthogonality of the Legendre polynomials, we have the relation

$$R_l(r) = \frac{2l+1}{2} \int_0^\pi P_l(\cos\theta) u_c(r,\theta) \sin\theta \, d\theta \tag{21.20}$$

where $u_c(r,\theta)$ is given by the second of Eqs. (21.12). The complete evaluation of this integral can be avoided by making use of the fact that we know all about the function $R_l(r)$ except the constant multiplying factor C_l. C_l can then be found by matching the known form of $R_l(r)$ to Eq. (21.20) near $r = 0$; it is

$$C_l = \frac{(2ik)^l e^{-\frac{1}{2}n\pi} \Gamma(l+1+in)}{v^{\frac{1}{2}}(2l)!}$$

We thus obtain as an alternative expression to (21.12)

$$u_c = v^{-\frac{1}{2}} e^{-\frac{1}{2}n\pi} \sum_{l=0}^\infty \frac{\Gamma(l+1+in)}{(2l)!} (2ikr)^l e^{ikr}$$
$$F(l+1+in, \, 2l+2, \, -2ikr)P_l(\cos\theta) \tag{21.21}$$

It is also possible to expand $f_c(\theta)$, given by Eq. (21.10), in a series of Legendre polynomials; the result is

$$f_c(\theta) = \frac{1}{2ik} \sum_{l=0}^\infty (2l+1)e^{2i\eta_l} P_l(\cos\theta) \tag{21.22}$$

This seems surprising at first, since $f_c(\theta)$ does not appear to vanish in the limit $n \to 0$, which corresponds to no interaction; we obtain instead

$$\lim_{n\to 0} f_c(\theta) = \frac{1}{2ik} \sum_{l=0}^\infty (2l+1)P_l(\cos\theta)$$

The series on the right can be summed to give

$$\sum_{l=0}^\infty (2l+1)P_l(\cos\theta) = 4\delta(1-\cos\theta) \tag{21.23}$$

Equation (21.23) can be verified by multiplying both sides by $P_{l'}(\cos\theta)$, integrating $\sin\theta \, d\theta$ from 0 to π, and remembering that the integral on the right is carried to but not through the point $\theta = 0$. We thus find that $f_c(\theta)$ does indeed vanish in the limit $n \to 0$ for $\theta \neq 0$ but that it has a δ-function singularity at $\theta = 0$ such that

$$\lim_{n\to 0} \int_0^{\theta_0} f_c(\theta) \sin\theta \, d\theta = -\frac{i}{k} \tag{21.24}$$

for any finite θ_0. Equation (21.24) is easily verified by direct integration of (21.10), provided that the value of the integral at the lower limit is interpreted to be the average of its value at ϵ as $\epsilon \to 0$. This peculiar behavior arises from the long-range character of the coulomb field. No matter how weak the interaction is made, it always causes particles that pass at very great distances to be deflected through very small angles.

MODIFIED COULOMB FIELD

If the actual potential deviates from the coulomb form only at small values of r, we expect in analogy with the partial wave treatment of Sec. 19 that only the first few terms in the sum (21.21) will be altered. Since each partial radial wave function must be a solution of (21.16) outside of the potential anomaly, the only change we can make in the function f_l and still have it a solution of (21.17) is to add in some of the irregular solution $G(l + 1 + in, 2l + 2, -2ikr)$ defined by (21.8). The manner in which G is to be added in is determined by the requirement that the complete wave function shall represent asymptotically a coulomb incident plus scattered wave, plus an extra *outgoing* scattered wave.

We must, therefore, substitute for each F term in (21.21) a linear combination of F and G in which the amount of the ingoing term W_2 is not changed. Such a combination is

$$e^{i\delta_l}(F \cos \delta_l + G \sin \delta_l) = W_1 e^{2i\delta_l} + W_2$$

The modified wave function, which is a solution of the wave equation outside of the potential anomaly, can then be written

$$u_m = u_c + v^{-\frac{1}{2}}e^{-\frac{1}{2}n\pi} \sum_{l=0}^{\infty} \frac{\Gamma(l + 1 + in)}{(2l)!} (2ikr)^l e^{ikr}$$
$$(e^{2i\delta_l} - 1)W_1(l + 1 + in, 2l + 2, -2ikr)P_l(\cos \theta) \quad (21.25)$$

The asymptotic form of u_m is

$$u_m \xrightarrow[r \to \infty]{} v^{-\frac{1}{2}} \sum_{l=0}^{\infty} (2l + 1)i^l e^{i(\eta_l + \delta_l)}(kr)^{-1}$$
$$\sin (kr - \tfrac{1}{2}l\pi - n \ln 2kr + \eta_l + \delta_l)P_l(\cos \theta) \quad (21.26)$$

As shown in connection with Eq. (19.5), if V is real each term on the right side of (21.26) must be a real function of r, except for complex multiplying factors, so that the δ_l must be real.

The additional phase shifts δ_l can be found by matching each partial radial wave in Eq. (21.25) to the interior solution at the edge of the potential anomaly, in just the same way as the phase shifts were found in Sec. 19. Although in Sec. 19 the phase shifts δ_l represented the departure of the wave function from that of a free particle, they here represent the departure from the wave function of a particle scattered by a pure coulomb field.[1] It can be shown from Eq. (21.25) that the asymptotic form of u_m may be written in the form of (21.9), where $f_c(\theta)$ is replaced by

$$f_m(\theta) = f_c(\theta) + \sum_{l=0}^{\infty} k^{-1}(2l + 1)e^{i(2\eta_l+\delta_l)} \sin \delta_l P_l(\cos \theta) \qquad (21.27)$$

The differential scattering cross section is just $|f_m(\theta)|^2$ and in general contains interference terms between the coulomb scattered amplitude $f_c(\theta)$ and the extra terms that are determined by the δ_l.

It is important to note that these δ_l are not equal to those that would be obtained from the potential anomaly in the absence of the coulomb field.

CLASSICAL LIMIT FOR A PURE COULOMB FIELD

As was discussed in Sec. 12, we expect the results of quantum and classical theory to coincide whenever it is possible to construct wave packets that follow the classical trajectory without spreading appreciably and are small enough so that the forces are sensibly constant over their dimensions. The smallest spread of a wave packet during a time interval t was found there to be of order $(\hbar t/\mu)^{\frac{1}{2}}$ or $(\hbar d/\mu v)^{\frac{1}{2}} = (\lambdabar d)^{\frac{1}{2}}$, where $d = vt$ is the distance traveled by the packet in the time t, and $\lambdabar \equiv \lambda/2\pi = \hbar/\mu v$ is the reduced wavelength for the relative motion. Thus the classical theory can be used when $(\lambdabar d)^{\frac{1}{2}} \ll d$, or $(d/\lambdabar)^{\frac{1}{2}} \gg 1$, where d is the distance over which the force varies by an appreciable fraction of itself. For a repulsive coulomb field, d is of the order of the classical distance of closest approach $|ZZ'e^2/\frac{1}{2}\mu v^2|$. This also provides a useful estimate for an attractive coulomb field, since in all the collisions, except the relatively few for which the particles are scattered through large angles, they never get closer than this distance from each other.

The condition for the validity of the classical theory is then

$$|n|^{\frac{1}{2}} = \left| \frac{ZZ'e^2}{\hbar v} \right|^{\frac{1}{2}} \gg 1$$

Large n implies that the angle-dependent part of the phase of $f_c(\theta)$ given by Eq. (21.10) varies rapidly with θ, so that these rapid oscillations in the scattering amplitude should have little effect on the scattering when the colliding particles are identical (see Prob. 6, Chap. 10).

It is interesting to note that for the coulomb field the classical limit is approached for small v, whereas for potentials that have a finite range

[1] The computation of the δ_l in Eq. (21.25) requires knowledge of G at small r; useful formulas have been given by F. L. Yost, J. A. Wheeler, and G. Breit, *Phys. Rev.* **49,** 174 (1936).

a, such as are discussed in Sec. 19, the classical limit is approached when $(a/\lambda)^{\frac{1}{3}} \gg 1$, that is, for large v. This is because the "size" $|ZZ'e^2/\mu v^2|$ of the coulomb field increases more rapidly than $\lambda = \hbar/\mu v$ as v decreases.

PROBLEMS

1. Show that the coefficients of scattering by a one-dimensional square well potential (like Fig. 14 except that $V_0 < 0$) are given by Eqs. (17.5) if the sign of V_0 is changed there and in the expression for α. Discuss the dependence of transmission coefficient on E in this case.

2. Show that Eqs. (18.4) and (18.7) are valid for a general binary collision if γ is given by (18.5); make use of conservation of energy and mass.

3. Show that, when a particle of mass m_1 collides elastically with a particle of mass m_2 that is initially at rest, all the recoil (mass m_2) particles are scattered in the forward hemisphere in the laboratory coordinate system. If the angular distribution is spherically symmetrical in the center-of-mass system, what is it for m_2 in the laboratory system?

4. Express the scattering wave function (19.1) outside the scattering potential (but not necessarily in the asymptotic region) as the sum of a plane wave and an infinite series of spherical Hankel functions of the first kind [see Eqs. (15.12)]. From this expression and the discussion of Eqs. (15.13), show that the scattered wave is purely outgoing, even inside of the asymptotic region.

5. Two objects, A and B, have irregular forms and are identical in size and shape. Object A is filled with a positively infinite (impenetrable) potential and scatters particles of mass m. Object B is made of metal and has a certain electrostatic capacity C when isolated from other objects. Derive expressions for the differential and total cross sections for elastic scattering of particles of mass m by object A in the limit $k \to 0$, in terms of the capacity C of object B.

6. Find a general expression for the phase shift produced by a scattering potential $V(r) = A/r^2$, where $A > 0$. Is the total cross section finite? If not, does the divergence come from small or large scattering angles, and why? What modifications are necessary in the calculation if $A < 0$? Are any difficulties encountered in the latter case?

7. What must $V_0 a^2$ be for a three-dimensional square well potential in order that the scattering cross section be zero at zero bombarding energy (Ramsauer-Townsend effect)? Find the leading term in the expressions for the differential and total cross sections for small bombarding energy. Show that partial waves with $l > 2$ can be neglected.

8. State clearly the assumptions that go into the derivation of Eq. (19.31), and verify that it is a suitable approximation for the total cross section at low bombarding energies when the $l = 0$ wave is in resonance.

9. Make use of Eq. (19.31) and the result of Prob. 5, Chap. 4, to obtain an approximate expression for the total scattering cross section by a particular potential in terms of the bombarding energy E and the binding energy ϵ of a particle in that potential, when E and ϵ are small in comparison with V_0.

10. Compute and make a polar plot of the differential scattering cross section for a perfectly rigid sphere when $ka = \frac{1}{2}$, using the first three partial waves ($l = 0,1,2$). What is the total cross section in this case, and what is the approximate accuracy of this result when the three terms are used?

11. Calculate the elastic scattering and absorption cross sections for a potential of the form $V(r) = -V_0(1 + i\xi)$, $r < a$; $V(r) = 0$, $r > a$. V_0 and ξ are positive; assume that k and ξ are very small and that there is neither a resonance nor a Ramsauer-Townsend effect. Keep only the leading term in k and ξ in each cross section.

12. Show that the following inequality holds for any potential:

$$\sigma_{el}(0) \geq \left(\frac{k\sigma_{tot}}{4\pi}\right)^2$$

The quantity on the left side is the differential elastic scattering cross section in the forward direction.

13. Protons of 200,000-ev energy are scattered from aluminum. The directly back-scattered intensity ($\theta = 180°$) is found to be 96 percent of that computed from the Rutherford formula. Assume this to be due to a modification of the coulomb potential that is of sufficiently short range so that only the phase shift for $l = 0$ is affected. Is this modification attractive or repulsive? Find the sign and magnitude of the change in phase shift for $l = 0$ produced by the modification.

6

Matrix Formulation of Quantum Mechanics

In the four preceding chapters the Schrödinger wave equation was developed and its solutions obtained in some cases of physical interest. We now turn to a different formulation of quantum mechanics, in which dynamical variables such as the coordinates, momentum components, and energy of a particle appear explicitly in the equations of motion of the system without their having to multiply or differentiate a wave function. The classical equations are just of this structure, and so it might be expected that there would be a closer resemblance between the classical and quantum formalism here than in the Schrödinger theory.

This is actually the case; the principal formal difference is that the quantum-dynamical variables do not obey the commutative law of multiplication. It is convenient to represent such noncommutative dynamical variables, which are often simply called *operators*, as matrices. Matrix theory provides an especially flexible representation scheme, since there are an arbitrarily large number of ways of choosing the rows and columns of a matrix, all of which are of equal validity. It is because of the close formal resemblance between quantum matrix mechanics and classical dynamics that this was historically the first formulation of quantum theory to be discovered, by Heisenberg in 1925.[1]

In this chapter we first review briefly the more important properties of matrices and then show their connection with quantum theory and their usefulness in particular problems.

22☐MATRIX ALGEBRA

We restrict our discussion at first to matrices that have a finite number of rows and columns, and then indicate how the results obtained can be taken over to matrices that have an infinite number of rows and columns.[2]

MATRIX ADDITION AND MULTIPLICATION

A *matrix* is a square or rectangular array of numbers that can be added to or multiplied into another matrix according to certain rules. We denote a matrix by a capital letter, such as A, and the numbers or *elements* that make it up by the same letter with subscripts, such as A_{kl}; here, k designates the row and l the column in which the matrix element A_{kl} appears. Two matrices can be added when they have the same *rank*, i.e., the same number of rows and the same number of columns. Addition is commutative:

$$A + B = B + A \tag{22.1}$$

If the sum matrix is called C, then

$$C_{kl} = A_{kl} + B_{kl} \tag{22.2}$$

A matrix A can be multiplied from the left into a matrix B if the number of columns of A is equal to the number of rows of B; then the product matrix C has the number of rows of A and the number of columns of B.

$$C = AB \qquad C_{kl} = \sum_m A_{km} B_{ml} \tag{22.3}$$

where the summation is over the subscript m, which denotes the columns of A and the rows of B. It follows at once from Eqs. (22.2) and (22.3)

---

[1] W. Heisenberg, *Z. Physik* **33**, 879 (1925); M. Born, W. Heisenberg, and P. Jordan, *Z. Phys.* **35**, 557 (1925). The connection between quantum matrix mechanics and the wave equation was established by E. Schrödinger, *Ann. Physik* **79**, 734 (1926), and C. Eckart, *Phys. Rev.* **28**, 711 (1926). The historical development has been reviewed by S.-I. Tomonaga, "Quantum Mechanics," chap. 5 (Interscience, New York, 1962).

[2] For a fuller discussion, see J. von Neumann, "Mathematische Grundlagen der Quantenmechanik," chap. II (Springer, Berlin, 1932; reprinted by Dover, New York).

that the distributive law of multiplication is valid.

$$A(B + C) = AB + AC \tag{22.4}$$

Also, the associative law of multiplication is seen to be valid:

$$A(BC) = (AB)C \tag{22.5}$$

where the left side means that A is multiplied from the left into the product of B and C, and the right side means that the product of A and B is multiplied from the left into C. The product (22.5) is written simply as ABC and, from (22.3), has the explicit expression

$$D = ABC \qquad D_{kl} = \sum_{m,n} A_{km}B_{mn}C_{nl} \tag{22.6}$$

It is clear from Eq. (22.3) that AB is not, in general, equal to BA; thus the commutative law of multiplication is not generally valid.

NULL, UNIT, AND CONSTANT MATRICES

For an arbitrary square matrix A, the *null matrix* O is defined by the equations

$$OA = O \qquad AO = O \tag{22.7}$$

from which it follows that all the elements of O are zero. If A is not square, the elements of O are still all zero, but the O's that appear at different places in (22.7) do not all have the same numbers of rows and columns.

The *unit matrix* 1 is defined by

$$1A = A \qquad B1 = B \tag{22.8}$$

for arbitrary matrices A and B. From Eqs. (22.8) it follows that 1 is a square matrix whose rank (number of rows or columns) equals the number of rows of A or the number of columns of B. Moreover, 1 must have unit elements along its principal diagonal ($k = l$) and zeros elsewhere, so that the elements of 1 equal the Kronecker symbol δ_{kl} introduced in Sec. 10.

The product of a number c and a matrix A is the matrix cA that results from multiplying each element of A by c. Thus if we define a *constant matrix* C to be a multiple of a unit matrix so that each nonvanishing element is c instead of unity, then

$$cA = CA \qquad \text{where } C_{kl} = c\delta_{kl} \tag{22.9}$$

are the matrix elements of the constant matrix C.

TRACE, DETERMINANT, AND INVERSE OF A MATRIX

The *trace* of a matrix, often called the *spur* or the *diagonal sum*, is the sum of the diagonal elements of the matrix:

$$\text{tr } (A) = \sum_k A_{kk} \tag{22.10}$$

It is easily shown, with the help of (22.3), that the trace possesses the cyclic property

$$\text{tr } (ABC \cdots EF) = \text{tr } (BC \cdots EFA) \tag{22.11}$$

The *determinant* of a square matrix, denoted by det (A), is found from the usual rule for the computation of the determinant of a square array of numbers. If A and B are square and of the same rank, then

$$\det (AB) = \det (A) \cdot \det (B) \tag{22.12}$$

A matrix may or may not possess an *inverse* A^{-1}, which is defined by the relations

$$AA^{-1} = 1 \qquad A^{-1}A = 1 \tag{22.13}$$

A is said to be *nonsingular* if it possesses an inverse, and *singular* if it does not. If A is nonsingular and of finite rank, it can be shown to be square, and either of Eqs. (22.13) implies the other (see Prob. 2). The kl element of A^{-1} is just the cofactor of A_{kl} divided by det (A); thus A is singular if its determinant vanishes. It is readily verified that for nonsingular matrices A, B, C

$$(ABC)^{-1} = C^{-1}B^{-1}A^{-1} \tag{22.14}$$

HERMITIAN AND UNITARY MATRICES

The *hermitian adjoint* $A^\dagger$ of a matrix A is the matrix obtained by interchanging rows and columns and taking the complex conjugate of each element; thus if

$$B = A^\dagger \qquad \text{then} \qquad B_{kl} = A_{lk}^* \tag{22.15}$$

It is readily verified that the hermitian adjoint of the product of a series of matrices is the product of their adjoints in the reverse order:

$$(ABC)^\dagger = C^\dagger B^\dagger A^\dagger \tag{22.16}$$

A matrix is *hermitian* or *self-adjoint* if it is equal to its hermitian adjoint; thus H is a hermitian matrix if

$$H = H^\dagger \tag{22.17}$$

Evidently only square matrices can be hermitian.

A matrix is *unitary* if its hermitian adjoint is equal to its inverse; thus U is a unitary matrix if

$$U^\dagger = U^{-1} \quad \text{or if} \quad UU^\dagger = 1 \quad \text{and} \quad U^\dagger U = 1 \quad (22.18)$$

Unitary matrices of finite rank must be square, and then either of the latter two of Eqs. (22.18) implies the other.

TRANSFORMATION AND DIAGONALIZATION OF MATRICES

We define the *transformation* of a square matrix A into a square matrix A' by a nonsingular matrix S, by the following equation:

$$SAS^{-1} = A' \quad (22.19)$$

It is evident then that S^{-1} transforms A' back into A.

The form of a matrix equation is unaffected by transformation. Thus the equation

$$AB + CDE = F$$

may be transformed into

$$SABS^{-1} + SCDES^{-1} = SFS^{-1}$$

which is equivalent to

$$SAS^{-1} \cdot SBS^{-1} + SCS^{-1} \cdot SDS^{-1} \cdot SES^{-1} = SFS^{-1}$$

or to

$$A'B' + C'D'E' = F'$$

where the primes denote transformed matrices. This invariance of matrix equations with respect to transformations makes it possible to work with any convenient transformation of a set of matrices without affecting the validity of any results obtained. It should also be noted that tr (A) and det (A) are unchanged by transformation.

A square matrix is *diagonal* if it has nonvanishing elements only along the principal diagonal $(k = l)$. The diagonal elements are then called the *eigenvalues* of the matrix. It is easily seen that the nth power of a diagonal matrix is also diagonal and has as its eigenvalues the nth powers of the eigenvalues of the original matrix. The matrix A in Eq. (22.19) is said to be *diagonalized* by the matrix S if the matrix A' that results from the transformation is diagonal, so that $A'_{kl} = A'_k \delta_{kl}$. To find A' explicitly, we multiply (22.19) through on the right by S, where we assume that such an S exists.

$$SA = A'S \quad (22.20)$$

The set of linear algebraic equations that are obtained by writing the elements of Eq. (22.20) for a particular row k and all columns l is

$$\sum_m S_{km} A_{ml} = A'_k S_{kl} \qquad \text{or} \qquad \sum_m S_{km} (A_{ml} - A'_k \, \delta_{ml}) = 0 \quad (22.21)$$

where A'_k is a particular eigenvalue of A' and the subscript m is summed over from unity to the rank N of the matrix A.

Now (22.21) may be regarded as a set of N homogeneous algebraic equations for the transformation matrix elements S_{km}, where k is fixed. The necessary and sufficient condition that these equations have a solution is that the determinant of their coefficients vanish, or that the determinant of the square matrix $(A_{ml} - A'_k \, \delta_{ml})$ be zero. This provides a single algebraic equation, called the *secular equation*, which is of order N and has N roots A'_k. Thus the eigenvalues of the diagonal matrix A' resulting from A by transformation are the same no matter how A is diagonalized, except perhaps for the order in which they are arranged; for this reason they are also called the eigenvalues of the original non-diagonal matrix A. A' and A are said to be *degenerate* when two or more eigenvalues are equal.

It is not difficult to see that, in general, equations that involve both A and $A^\dagger$ are not invariant with respect to transformation unless the transformation matrix S is unitary.

FUNCTIONS OF MATRICES

A function of a matrix can often be defined in terms of a power series. Thus, if $f(z)$ is a polynomial in the number z, then $f(A)$ is the same polynomial in the matrix A. With an infinite series, some attention must be paid to convergence. It is apparent that, if A can be diagonalized and is put in its diagonal form $A' = SAS^{-1}$, then S will also transform $f(A)$ into the diagonal form $f(A')$ and the kth eigenvalue of $f(A')$ is simply $f(A'_k)$. Thus, if the power series $f(z)$ converges when z is equal to each eigenvalue of A, the power series $S^{-1} f(A') S = f(A)$ is well defined. This last may provide a useful definition of $f(A)$ even when $f(z)$ cannot be represented by a power series.

Exponential and trigonometric functions of matrices can be represented by power series that converge for all finite values of their arguments and hence are well defined. It is easily seen, for example, that $(e^A)^\dagger = e^{A^\dagger}$, so that e^{iH} is unitary if H is hermitian.

Another useful result is the relation (see Prob. 3)

$$\det (e^A) = e^{\text{tr} \, (A)} \qquad (22.22)$$

MATRICES OF INFINITE RANK

The rules (22.2) and (22.3) for addition and multiplication of matrices may be taken over in an obvious way for matrices that have an infinite number of rows and columns, provided that the infinite sum in (22.3) converges. We sometimes deal with matrices that have a nondenumerably infinite number of rows or columns or both; in this case, one or both of the matrix subscripts becomes a continuous variable, and the usual summation over a subscript is replaced by integration over this variable. We do not consider these possibilities in detail here but simply assume that all reasonable results can be taken over from finite- to infinite-rank matrices without difficulty.[1] The statement that a hermitian matrix of infinite rank is square means that its rows and columns are labeled in the same way. A unitary matrix of infinite rank need not be square. Its rows and columns can be labeled differently; for example, the number of rows may be denumerably infinite and the number of columns nondenumerably infinite.

We are concerned primarily in quantum mechanics with hermitian and unitary matrices, mainly of infinite rank. A fundamental theorem that we shall assume without proof is that any hermitian matrix can be diagonalized by a unitary transformation; a corollary of this theorem is that the resulting eigenvalues of the hermitian matrix are unique, except perhaps for the order in which they are arranged. Starting from this theorem, it is not difficult to show (see Prob. 1) that the necessary and sufficient condition that two hermitian matrices can be diagonalized by the same unitary transformation is that they *commute* (matrices A and B commute if $AB = BA$).

It also follows from this theorem that the eigenvalues of a hermitian matrix are real. If the S and A in (22.19) are unitary and hermitian, respectively, that equation can be rewritten

$$SAS^\dagger = A' \tag{22.23}$$

The hermitian adjoint of Eq. (22.23) is, from (22.16),

$$SAS^\dagger = A'^\dagger$$

Since then $A'^\dagger = A'$, this shows that the hermitian property is maintained during transformation by a unitary matrix. If A' is diagonal as well as hermitian, it follows from (22.15) that its eigenvalues are real. It is easily seen that the converse is also true: a matrix that can be diagonalized by a unitary transformation and has real eigenvalues is hermitian.

It is important to note with matrices of infinite rank that both of Eqs. (22.13) must be valid in order for A^{-1} to be the inverse of A. Similarly, both of the latter pair of Eqs. (22.18) must be valid if U is to be unitary.

---

[1] A more thorough discussion of this point and a proof of the following theorem are given by von Neumann, *loc. cit.*

23☐TRANSFORMATION THEORY

The appearance of matrices in quantum mechanics can be connected in a simple way with the solution of the Schrödinger equation (8.2). In this section we adopt the hamiltonian notation and justify it in detail in Sec. 24. We rewrite Eq. (8.2) as

$$Hu_k(\mathbf{r}) = E_k u_k(\mathbf{r}) \tag{23.1}$$

where the subscript k denotes the different members of the complete orthonormal set of energy eigenfunctions $u_k(\mathbf{r})$ and their corresponding eigenvalues E_k. k specifies the energy and also distinguishes between degenerate eigenfunctions; it thus includes both E and s of Eq. (10.7). For example, k represents k_x, k_y, and k_z in the case of plane waves and n_x, n_y, and n_z in the case of three-dimensional harmonic-oscillator eigenfunctions.

The hamiltonian or energy operator H is given by

$$H = \frac{\mathbf{p}^2}{2m} + V(\mathbf{r}) = -\frac{\hbar^2}{2m}\nabla^2 + V(\mathbf{r}) \tag{23.2}$$

where we shall assume throughout this chapter that V is real, so that the E_k are also real. In accordance with the discussion of Sec. 8, k may be a discrete or a continuous variable or (as in the case of a hydrogen atom) discrete over part of its range and continuous over the rest. We shall use the generalized summation symbol S or S_k to denote both a summation $\sum_k$ over discrete values of the subscript k and an integration $\int dk$ over the continuous part of its range. We shall also use the subscript "op" whenever it seems desirable to distinguish between an operator like (23.2) and its equivalent matrix.

UNITARY MATRIX W

Suppose that we have a second complete orthonormal set of functions $v_\mu(\mathbf{r})$, which are eigenfunctions of some operator Ω with real eigenvalues ω_μ:

$$\Omega v_\mu(\mathbf{r}) = \omega_\mu v_\mu(\mathbf{r}) \tag{23.3}$$

Ω might, for example, be the momentum operator (6.13) with eigenfunctions (11.4) or (11.11), or the hamiltonian for some potential other than that of Eq. (23.2). The v_μ can be expanded in terms of the u_k with expansion coefficients $w_{k\mu}$:

$$v_\mu(\mathbf{r}) = S_k w_{k\mu} u_k(\mathbf{r}) \tag{23.4}$$

Both sides of this equation may be multiplied by $u_k^*(\mathbf{r})$ and integrated to obtain

$$w_{k\mu} = \int u_k^*(\mathbf{r}) v_\mu(\mathbf{r})\ d^3r \qquad (23.5)$$

The completeness of the set u_k was used to obtain Eq. (23.4), and its orthonormality to obtain Eq. (23.5). In similar fashion, u_k may be expanded in terms of the v_μ:

$$u_k(\mathbf{r}) = S_\mu w_{k\mu}^* v_\mu(\mathbf{r}) \qquad (23.6)$$

We can now show that the matrix W, of which $w_{k\mu}$ are the elements, is unitary by calculating a typical matrix element of $WW^\dagger$:

$$
\begin{aligned}
(WW^\dagger)_{kl} = S_\mu w_{k\mu} w_{l\mu}^* &= S_\mu \int u_k^*(\mathbf{r}) v_\mu(\mathbf{r})\ d^3r \int v_\mu^*(\mathbf{r}') u_l(\mathbf{r}')\ d^3r' \\
&= \iint u_k^*(\mathbf{r})\ \delta^3(\mathbf{r} - \mathbf{r}') u_l(\mathbf{r}')\ d^3r\ d^3r' = \int u_k^*(\mathbf{r}) u_l(\mathbf{r})\ d^3r \quad (23.7)
\end{aligned}
$$

Use has been made here of the closure property of any complete orthonormal set of functions, discussed in connection with Eq. (10.11), which now takes the form

$$S_\mu v_\mu(\mathbf{r}) v_\mu^*(\mathbf{r}') = \delta^3(\mathbf{r} - \mathbf{r}') \qquad (23.8)$$

The last integral on the right side of Eq. (23.7) is either a Kronecker δ symbol or a Dirac δ function according as k is one of a discrete or continuous set of subscripts. In either case, this integral is equivalent to an element of the unit matrix, so that $WW^\dagger = \mathbf{1}$. In similar fashion, it can be established that

$$(W^\dagger W)_{\mu\nu} = S_k w_{k\mu}^* w_{k\nu} = (\mathbf{1})_{\mu\nu} \qquad (23.9)$$

TRANSFORMATION OF THE HAMILTONIAN WITH W

We have shown that W is a unitary matrix that relates two sets of functions u_k and v_μ. It can also be used to transform the hamiltonian matrix H', which we define through its matrix elements

$$H_{kl}' = \int u_k^*(\mathbf{r}) H_{\text{op}} u_l(\mathbf{r})\ d^3r = E_k \delta_{kl} \qquad \text{or} \qquad E_k \delta(k - l) \qquad (23.10)$$

where H_{op} is the differential operator (23.2). Use has been made here of Eq. (23.1) to show that H' is in diagonal form with diagonal elements that are just the energy eigenvalues E_k. Another hamiltonian matrix H'' can be constructed by using the functions v_μ:

$$H_{\mu\nu}'' = \int v_\mu^*(\mathbf{r}) H_{\text{op}} v_\nu(\mathbf{r})\ d^3r \qquad (23.11)$$

This is not in diagonal form.

We now follow the definition (22.19) and transform H'' with W:

$$
\begin{aligned}
(WH''W^\dagger)_{kl} &= S_\mu S_\nu w_{k\mu} H_{\mu\nu}'' w_{l\nu}^* \\
&= S_\mu S_\nu \int u_k^*(\mathbf{r}') v_\mu(\mathbf{r}')\ d^3r' \\
&\qquad\qquad \int v_\mu^*(\mathbf{r}) H_{\text{op}} v_\nu(\mathbf{r})\ d^3r \int v_\nu^*(\mathbf{r}'') u_l(\mathbf{r}'')\ d^3r'' \\
&= \iiint u_k^*(\mathbf{r}') \delta^3(\mathbf{r}' - \mathbf{r}) H_{\text{op}} \delta^3(\mathbf{r} - \mathbf{r}'') u_l(\mathbf{r}'')\ d^3r'\ d^3r\ d^3r''
\end{aligned}
$$

where H_{op} operates only on the variable $\mathbf{r}$ to its right. The integration over $\mathbf{r}''$ may be performed by taking H_{op} outside of the $\mathbf{r}''$ integral:

$$\int H_{op}\, \delta^3(\mathbf{r} - \mathbf{r}'')\, u_l(\mathbf{r}'')\, d^3r'' = H_{op}\int \delta^3(\mathbf{r} - \mathbf{r}'')\, u_l(\mathbf{r}'')\, d^3r'' = H_{op}u_l(\mathbf{r})$$

We thus obtain

$$(WH''W^\dagger)_{kl} = \int u_k^*(\mathbf{r})H_{op}u_l(\mathbf{r})\, d^3r = H'_{kl}$$

This may be written without explicit use of subscripts as the matrix equation

$$WH''W^\dagger = H' \tag{23.12}$$

Thus we see that W is the unitary matrix that transforms the non-diagonal matrix H'' into the diagonal form H'; also, $W^\dagger$ transforms H' into H''.

Another way of putting what has been done thus far is to state that the process of solving the Schrödinger equation (23.1) is completely equivalent to the process of diagonalizing a particular matrix. The matrix H'' may be calculated from the operator H_{op} of Eq. (23.2) by using any complete orthonormal set of functions $v_\mu(\mathbf{r})$ that is convenient. If this diagonalization can be carried through, both the diagonal form H', which consists of the energy eigenvalues E_k, and the diagonalizing matrix W are obtained in the process. Once W is known, the eigenfunctions $u_k(\mathbf{r})$ may be obtained by using Eq. (23.6).

It is interesting to note that W is not necessarily a square matrix; that is, its rows and columns may be labeled differently. For example, the functions u_k may be the eigenfunctions of a three-dimensional harmonic oscillator, which form a completely discrete set, and the functions v_μ may be momentum eigenfunctions, which form a completely continuous set. However the hamiltonian matrices H' and H'' are both square.

It is apparent that H' and H'' are hermitian, since their eigenvalues are real. The discussion of Sec. 10 developed the interpretation that the eigenvalues of any operator that represents a physically measureable quantity are real, since they are the only possible results of precise measurement of that quantity. Thus a dynamical variable that is physically measurable is represented by a hermitian matrix when it is in diagonal form; it then follows from the discussion of Eq. (22.23) that any unitary transformation of this matrix is also hermitian.

TRANSFORMATION OF THE HAMILTONIAN WITH U

There is no need to think of the operator H given in Eq. (23.2) as having a fundamentally different status from the matrices H' and H'' defined by Eqs. (23.10) and (23.11). The natural matrix form for H_{op} is one in which the rows and columns are labeled by coordinates $\mathbf{r}$ and $\mathbf{r}'$. The corresponding unit matrix is taken to be

$$(1)_{rr'} = \delta^3(r - r')$$

in analogy with the right side of Eq. (23.7) when k is one of a continuous set of subscripts. A diagonal matrix can then be written as $f(r)\, \delta^3(r - r')$, where f is any multiplicative function of r but not a differential operator; it might, for example, be the potential energy. We then expect the matrix form of the hamiltonian operator to be

$$H_{rr'} = H_{op}\, \delta^3(r - r') \tag{23.13}$$

where on the right side H_{op} operates only on the variable r. We shall refer to this matrix as H whenever the subscripts are not written explicitly. It is important to note that $H_{rr'}$ is not diagonal, since H_{op} is not a multiplicative function but contains differential operators in its kinetic-energy part. Equation (23.13) has nonvanishing matrix elements that are infinitesimally removed from the diagonal $r = r'$.

Equation (23.12) shows that W transforms H'' into H'. It is of interest to inquire what the unitary matrix U is that transforms H, as defined by (23.13), into H':

$$UHU^\dagger = H' \tag{23.14}$$

This equation may be written $HU^\dagger = U^\dagger H'$, which becomes, when expressed in matrix elements, $(HU^\dagger)_{rk} = (U^\dagger H')_{rk}$, or

$$S_{r'}H_{rr'}(U^\dagger)_{r'k} = S_l(U^\dagger)_{rl}H'_{lk} \tag{23.15}$$

Here $S_{r'}$ is the same as $\int d^3r'$. On substitution from Eq. (23.13), the left side of (23.15) becomes

$$\int H_{op}\, \delta^3(r - r')(U^\dagger)_{r'k}\, d^3r' = H_{op}\int \delta^3(r - r')(U^\dagger)_{r'k}\, d^3r'$$
$$= H_{op}(U^\dagger)_{rk}$$

where H_{op} operates on the r dependence of $(U^\dagger)_{rk}$. The right side of Eq. (23.15) may be rewritten by making use of (23.10), so that it becomes $(U^\dagger)_{rk}E_k$. Thus Eq. (23.15) is equivalent to

$$H_{op}(U^\dagger)_{rk} = E_k(U^\dagger)_{rk}$$

Comparison with the Schrödinger equation (23.1) shows that $(U^\dagger)_{rk}$ must be identified with the energy eigenfunction $u_k(r)$.

We are thus led naturally to an extension of the formalism according to which a complete orthonormal set of functions $u_k(r)$ may be regarded as a unitary matrix U:

$$U_{kr} = u_k^*(r) \tag{23.16}$$

In this particular case, U transforms H into H' in accordance with Eq. (23.14). It is easily verified that U is, in fact, unitary; for example,

$$(UU^\dagger)_{kl} = S_r U_{kr}(U^\dagger)_{rl} = \int u_k^*(\mathbf{r})u_l(\mathbf{r}) \, d^3r = (\mathbf{1})_{kl}$$

by orthonormality, and

$$(U^\dagger U)_{rr'} = S_k(U^\dagger)_{rk}U_{kr'} = S_k u_k(\mathbf{r})u_k^*(\mathbf{r}') = (\mathbf{1})_{rr'}$$

by closure.

TRANSFORMATION OF THE HAMILTONIAN WITH V

The set of functions $v_\mu(\mathbf{r})$ can, in accordance with Eq. (23.16), also be regarded as a unitary matrix V:

$$V_{\mu r} = v_\mu^*(\mathbf{r})$$

where again the unitarity of V follows from the orthonormality and closure of the set $v_\mu(\mathbf{r})$. As would be expected, transformation of H with V gives H'':

$$VHV^\dagger = H'' \tag{23.17}$$

The $\mu\nu$ matrix elements of the two sides of this equation are precisely the two sides of Eq. (23.11).

The matrix H can be eliminated between Eqs. (23.14) and (23.17) as follows:

$$H = V^\dagger H'' V$$

$$H' = UHU^\dagger = UV^\dagger H'' V U^\dagger$$

This agrees with Eq. (23.12) if we set

$$W = UV^\dagger \tag{23.18}$$

In matrix-element form this is

$$(W)_{k\mu} = S_r U_{kr}(V^\dagger)_{r\mu}$$

or

$$w_{k\mu} = \int u_k^*(\mathbf{r})v_\mu(\mathbf{r}) \, d^3r$$

which is the same as Eq. (23.5). Equation (23.18) can also be written in the forms $V^\dagger = U^\dagger W$ and $U^\dagger = V^\dagger W^\dagger$, which are the same as Eqs. (23.4) and (23.6), respectively.

REPRESENTATIONS OF OPERATORS

The three hamiltonian matrices H, H', H'' are referred to as different *representations* of the same operator H_{op}. Each representation is characterized by the quantity whose eigenvalues are used to label the rows and columns of the matrix $(\mathbf{r}, E_k, \omega_\mu$, or, more concisely, $\mathbf{r}, k, \mu)$. Thus H, H', and H'' are the hamiltonian in the coordinate, energy, and Ω representations, respectively. A unitary matrix whose rows and columns are labeled by the eigenvalues of A and B, respectively, transforms an operator from the B to the A representation. For example, U transforms any operator from the coordinate to the energy representation, and $U^\dagger$ from the energy to the coordinate representation. In similar fashion, V transforms from the coordinate to the Ω representation, and W from the Ω to the energy representation. Thus application of V followed by W transforms from the coordinate to the Ω representation and then to the energy representation; the overall effect is represented by the product WV, since the transformation farthest to the right acts first. Equation (23.18) shows that $WV = U$, as it should since U transforms from the coordinate to the energy representation. An operator is diagonal in the representation in which the rows and columns are labeled by the eigenvalues of that operator; thus H' is diagonal since it is the hamiltonian expressed in the energy representation.

The remarks in the preceding paragraph can be illustrated by applying them to the operator Ω. In the coordinate representation it is expected to have the form

$$\Omega_{\mathbf{rr}'} = \Omega_{\mathrm{op}}\, \delta^3(\mathbf{r} - \mathbf{r}') \tag{23.19}$$

where on the right side Ω_{op} operates only on the variable $\mathbf{r}$. We call this matrix Ω and find its transformation into the energy representation, which should be $U\Omega U^\dagger$:

$$\begin{aligned}(U\Omega U^\dagger)_{kl} &= \mathrm{S_r S_{r'}}\, U_{kr}\Omega_{\mathbf{rr}'}(U^\dagger)_{r'l} \\ &= \int u_k^*(\mathbf{r})\Omega_{\mathrm{op}}u_l(\mathbf{r})\, d^3r\end{aligned}$$

as expected. Similarly, transformation to the Ω representation gives

$$(V\Omega V^\dagger)_{\mu\nu} = \omega_\mu(\mathbf{1})_{\mu\nu}$$

which is in diagonal form.

A USEFUL IDENTITY

Equation (23.19) can be used to write

$$\Omega_{\mathrm{op}}\psi_\beta(\mathbf{r}) = \int \Omega_{\mathbf{rr}'}\psi_\beta(\mathbf{r}')\, d^3r'$$

where $\psi_\beta(\mathbf{r})$ is an arbitrary function. Then

$$\int \psi_\alpha^*(\mathbf{r})[\Omega_{\mathrm{op}}\psi_\beta(\mathbf{r})]\, d^3r = \int\int \psi_\alpha^*(\mathbf{r})\Omega_{\mathbf{rr}'}\psi_\beta(\mathbf{r}')\, d^3r\, d^3r' \tag{23.20}$$

where $\psi_\alpha(\mathbf{r})$ is another arbitrary function. We are not necessarily assuming that the $\psi_\alpha(\mathbf{r})$ are members of a complete orthonormal set of functions.

Since $\Omega_{rr'}$ is a matrix with rows and columns labeled by r and r' and hence is not the same as the operator Ω_{op}, we can rearrange terms on the right side of Eq. (23.20) to give

$$\int[\int(\Omega^\dagger)_{r'r}\psi_\alpha(r)\,d^3r]^*\psi_\beta(r')\,d^3r'$$

where $(\Omega^\dagger)_{r'r} = \Omega^*_{rr'}$ is the r',r element of the matrix $\Omega^\dagger$ that is the hermitian adjoint of Ω. Equation (23.19) can also be used to define the hermitian adjoint operator $\Omega_{op}{}^\dagger$ in accordance with

$$\Omega_{op}{}^\dagger\psi_\alpha(r) = \int(\Omega^\dagger)_{rr'}\psi_\alpha(r')\,d^3r'$$

Thus Eq. (23.20) may be rewritten

$$\int\psi^*_\alpha(r)[\Omega_{op}\psi_\beta(r)]\,d^3r = \int[\Omega_{op}{}^\dagger\psi_\alpha(r)]^*\psi_\beta(r)\,d^3r \tag{23.21}$$

Equation (23.21) is sometimes useful, since an integral of this type may be more conveniently evaluated when Ω_{op} operates on one of the functions ψ_α, ψ_β rather than on the other. The partial integrations in Eqs. (7.9), (7.10), and (12.3) are examples of the application of Eq. (23.21). In those cases, Ω_{op} is a differential operator, and its coordinate representation involves derivatives of $\delta^3(r - r')$. However, Ω_{op} need not be of this specialized type but might have nonvanishing matrix elements for finite $r - r'$. In any event, if Ω_{op} is to represent a physically measurable dynamical variable, it must be hermitian, in which case $\Omega_{op}{}^\dagger$ can be replaced by Ω_{op} on the right side of Eq. (23.21).

ROW AND COLUMN MATRICES

We have been dealing thus far with square matrices like H and Ω, which represent dynamical variables and are often hermitian, and rectangular matrices like U, V, and W, which transform from one representation to another and are unitary. A particular state α of a system can be represented by a function $\psi_\alpha(r)$, which may be thought of as a matrix with one column, in which the rows are labeled by the coordinate r; as remarked above, α need not label a complete set of functions but can be considered by itself. Since the $u_k(r)$ are a complete set, ψ_α can be expanded in terms of them:

$$\psi_\alpha(r) = S_k a_{\alpha k} u_k(r) \tag{23.22}$$

where the coefficients $a_{\alpha k}$ are given by

$$a_{\alpha k} = \int u^*_k(r)\psi_\alpha(r)\,d^3r \tag{23.23}$$

These equations may be written in matrix form as

$$\psi_\alpha = U^\dagger a_\alpha \qquad \text{and} \qquad a_\alpha = U\psi_\alpha \tag{23.24}$$

respectively, where a_α is a one-column matrix whose rows are labeled by k. Thus, just as U transforms an operator like H from the coordinate to the energy representation through Eq. (23.14), it also transforms a state function from the coordinate to the energy representation through the second of Eqs. (23.24).

In similar fashion we can write

$$\psi_\alpha(\mathbf{r}) = S_\mu b_{\alpha\mu} v_\mu(\mathbf{r}) \qquad \text{and} \qquad b_{\alpha\mu} = \int v_\mu^*(\mathbf{r}) \psi_\alpha(\mathbf{r}) \, d^3r$$

in matrix form as

$$\psi_\alpha = V^\dagger b_\alpha \qquad \text{and} \qquad b_\alpha = V\psi_\alpha \qquad (23.25)$$

Combination of Eqs. (23.22), (23.23), and (23.18) gives

$$a_\alpha = U\psi_\alpha = UV^\dagger b_\alpha = Wb_\alpha$$

so that W transforms the state function from the Ω representation b_α to the energy representation a_α, as expected.

An important property of unitary transformations is that they leave the *norm* of a state function unchanged. In the coordinate representation, the norm is just the normalization integral, which may be written as

$$\int \psi_\alpha^*(\mathbf{r})\psi_\alpha(\mathbf{r}) \, d^3r = S_\mathbf{r} \psi_\alpha^*(\mathbf{r})\psi_\alpha(\mathbf{r}) = \psi_\alpha^\dagger \psi_\alpha$$

The right side is the matrix product of the one-row matrix $\psi_\alpha^\dagger$, which is the hermitian adjoint of ψ_α and has its columns labeled by the coordinate $\mathbf{r}$, and the one-column matrix ψ_α. The result is a one-row, one-column matrix, which is simply a number. It is evident that the norm is real and nonnegative. With the help of Eq. (23.24), the norm may be written

$$\psi_\alpha^\dagger \psi_\alpha = a_\alpha^\dagger UU^\dagger a_\alpha = a_\alpha^\dagger a_\alpha$$

which is equal to $S_k |a_{\alpha k}|^2$. In similar fashion, $\psi_\alpha^\dagger \psi_\alpha = b_\alpha^\dagger b_\alpha$, so that all three representations of the state function have the same norm. A state function for which the norm exists (i.e., is not infinite) may be *normalized* by dividing it by $(\psi_\alpha^\dagger \psi_\alpha)^{\frac{1}{2}}$, in which case its norm becomes equal to unity.

It is interesting to note that the identity (23.21) becomes trivially valid when rewritten in terms of coordinate matrix representations of the state functions ψ_α and ψ_β:

$$\psi_\alpha^\dagger \Omega \psi_\beta = (\Omega^\dagger \psi_\alpha)^\dagger \psi_\beta$$

Equation (22.16) shows that the two sides are the same. The structure of the matrix products is such that each side is a one-row, one-column matrix and hence a number.

HILBERT SPACE

A geometrical picture that is often used regards a state function such as ψ_α, a_α, or b_α as a *state vector* in an infinite-dimensional *Hilbert space*.[1] Each dimension corresponds to one of the rows of the one-column matrix that describes the state, and the component of the state vector along that axis of the Hilbert space is numerically equal to the corresponding element of the matrix.   Different choices for the orientation of the axes in the Hilbert space correspond to different choices for the representation. For example, the energy representation corresponds to choosing axes in such a way that a state vector oriented along one of these axes is an eigenstate of the hamiltonian.   More generally, the vector a_α has the component $a_{\alpha k}$ along the axis that goes with the energy eigenvalue E_k.

The norm of a state function is just the square of the length of the corresponding state vector in Hilbert space, where "length" is suitably generalized to take account of components that may be complex numbers. The norm is a special case of the *inner product* of two state vectors ψ_α and ψ_β, which is defined as

$$(\psi_\alpha,\psi_\beta) = \psi_\alpha{}^\dagger\psi_\beta = \int\psi_\alpha^*(\mathbf{r})\psi_\beta(\mathbf{r})\ d^3r \tag{23.26}$$

and is also a number.   When α and β are the same state, this is equal to the norm.   When the inner product vanishes, the state vectors are said to be *orthogonal*.   The inner products of these state vectors, expressed in the energy and the Ω representations, are

$$(a_\alpha,a_\beta) = a_\alpha{}^\dagger a_\beta \qquad \text{and} \qquad (b_\alpha,b_\beta) = b_\alpha{}^\dagger b_\beta$$

respectively.   It is apparent from Eqs. (23.24) and (23.25) that the inner product is independent of the representation, just as is the norm.   It follows that a unitary transformation from one representation to another corresponds to a *rotation of axes* in the Hilbert space, without change in the state vectors.   A particular state vector has different components when referred to different axes, and these constitute the different representations of the state.

It also follows that operation on ψ_β with Ω_{op} performs a transformation on the state vector ψ_β so that it becomes another state vector $\Omega\psi_\beta$. We refer to this transformation as a *generalized rotation of the state vector* in Hilbert space, the word "generalized" indicating that the rotation may involve stretching or contraction of the components as well as pure rotation; in particular, the generalized rotation usually does not conserve the norm of the state vector.   The matrix element $\psi_\alpha{}^\dagger\Omega\psi_\beta = (\psi_\alpha,\Omega\psi_\beta)$ is

[1] R. Courant and D. Hilbert, "Methods of Mathematical Physics," vol. I, p. 55 (Interscience, New York, 1953); P. R. Halmos, "Introduction to Hilbert Space," chap. I (Chelsea, New York, 1957).

then the inner product of the state vectors ψ_α and $\Omega\psi_\beta$. It is easily seen to be independent of the representation.

DIRAC'S BRA AND KET NOTATION

The transformation theory developed in this section can be put into extremely compact form by making use of a notation invented by Dirac.[1] We describe a state function or state vector, whether it be represented by ψ_α, a_α, or b_α, by a *ket* or *ket vector* $|\alpha\rangle$, and the hermitian adjoint state $\psi_\alpha{}^\dagger$, $a_\alpha{}^\dagger$, or $b_\alpha{}^\dagger$ by a *bra* or *bra vector* $\langle\alpha|$. The inner product of two state vectors is written

$$\psi_\alpha{}^\dagger\psi_\beta = \langle\alpha|\beta\rangle$$

and is called a bracket expression, which is a number. The first three and last three letters of *bracket* provide the names for the two kinds of state vectors.

Operation on a ket vector from the left with Ω produces another ket vector

$$\Omega|\beta\rangle = |\beta'\rangle \tag{23.27}$$

and operation on a bra vector from the right with Ω produces another bra vector

$$\langle\alpha|\Omega = \langle\alpha''|$$

The matrix element of Ω between states α and β is a number and can be written in any of the equal forms

$$\Omega_{\alpha\beta} = \int\psi_\alpha^*(\mathbf{r})\Omega\psi_\beta(\mathbf{r})\,d^3r = \int[\Omega^\dagger\psi_\alpha(\mathbf{r})]^*\psi_\beta(\mathbf{r})\,d^3r$$
$$= (\psi_\alpha,\Omega\psi_\beta) = (\Omega^\dagger\psi_\alpha,\psi_\beta)$$
$$= \langle\alpha|\beta'\rangle = \langle\alpha''|\beta\rangle = \langle\alpha|\Omega|\beta\rangle \tag{23.28}$$

of which the first and last are the most commonly used notations. The matrix elements of the hermitian adjoint operator $\Omega^\dagger$ are given in accordance with Eq. (22.15) by

$$(\Omega^\dagger)_{\beta\alpha} = \Omega_{\alpha\beta}^* = \langle\beta|\Omega^\dagger|\alpha\rangle = \langle\alpha|\Omega|\beta\rangle^*$$

A particular example of Eqs. (23.27) and (23.28) is that in which Ω is the unit operator:

$$\langle\alpha|1|\beta\rangle = \langle\alpha|\beta\rangle$$

This equation can be used to obtain a bracket expression for the unitary matrix W from (23.5) by identifying ψ_α with u_k and ψ_β with v_μ:

$$w_{k\mu} = \langle k|\mu\rangle = \langle\mu|k\rangle^* \tag{23.29}$$

We are now in a position to rewrite the principal equations of this

---

[1] P. A. M. Dirac, "The Principles of Quantum Mechanics," 4th ed., sec. 6 (Oxford, New York, 1958).

section in Dirac notation.   Our three representations will be specified by the three complete sets of kets $|k\rangle$, $|\mu\rangle$, and $|\mathbf{r}\rangle$.   Just as $|k\rangle$ is an energy eigenstate with eigenvalue E_k, and $|\mu\rangle$ is an Ω eigenstate with eigenvalue ω_μ, so $|\mathbf{r}\rangle$ is a coordinate eigenstate with eigenvalue $\mathbf{r}$ (compare with Chap. 3, Prob. 2).   Then, in analogy with (23.28), Eq. (23.16) may be written in the forms

$$\langle k|\mathbf{r}\rangle = u_k^*(\mathbf{r}) \qquad \text{and} \qquad \langle \mathbf{r}|k\rangle = u_k(\mathbf{r}) \tag{23.30}$$

Similarly, we may write

$$\langle \mu|\mathbf{r}\rangle = v_\mu^*(\mathbf{r}) \qquad \text{and} \qquad \langle \mathbf{r}|\mu\rangle = v_\mu(\mathbf{r}) \tag{23.31}$$

Again, identifying ψ_α with u_k, we obtain

$$\psi_\alpha(\mathbf{r}) = \langle \mathbf{r}|\alpha\rangle \qquad a_{\alpha k} = \langle k|\alpha\rangle \qquad b_{\alpha\mu} = \langle \mu|\alpha\rangle \tag{23.32}$$

A summation convention will be employed such that any state symbol that appears twice in a given expression (once in the ket and once in the bra position) is assumed to be summed over a complete orthonormal set of states; thus the symbol S_μ will be omitted from expressions of the form

$$S_\mu \, \cdots \, |\mu\rangle\langle\mu| \, \cdots \tag{23.33}$$

The rewritten equations below are numbered with primes of their original numbers.

$$\Omega|\mu\rangle = \omega_\mu|\mu\rangle \qquad \text{or} \qquad \langle \mathbf{r}|\Omega|\mathbf{r}'\rangle\langle \mathbf{r}'|\mu\rangle = \omega_\mu\langle \mathbf{r}|\mu\rangle \tag{23.3$'$}$$

$$|\mu\rangle = |k\rangle\langle k|\mu\rangle \qquad \text{or} \qquad \langle \mathbf{r}|\mu\rangle = \langle \mathbf{r}|k\rangle\langle k|\mu\rangle \tag{23.4$'$}$$

$$\langle k|\mu\rangle = \langle k|\mathbf{r}\rangle\langle \mathbf{r}|\mu\rangle \tag{23.5$'$}$$

$$|k\rangle = |\mu\rangle\langle \mu|k\rangle \qquad \text{or} \qquad \langle \mathbf{r}|k\rangle = \langle \mathbf{r}|\mu\rangle\langle \mu|k\rangle \tag{23.6$'$}$$

$$\langle k|\mu\rangle\langle \mu|l\rangle = \langle k|\mathbf{r}\rangle\langle \mathbf{r}|l\rangle = \langle k|l\rangle \tag{23.7$'$}$$

$$\langle \mathbf{r}|\mu\rangle\langle \mu|\mathbf{r}'\rangle = \langle \mathbf{r}|\mathbf{r}'\rangle \tag{23.8$'$}$$

$$\langle \mu|k\rangle\langle k|\nu\rangle = \langle \mu|\nu\rangle \tag{23.9$'$}$$

$$\langle k|H|l\rangle = E_k\langle k|l\rangle \tag{23.10$'$}$$

$$\langle k|\mu\rangle\langle \mu|H|\nu\rangle\langle \nu|l\rangle = \langle k|H|l\rangle \tag{23.12$'$}$$

$$\langle \mathbf{r}|H|\mathbf{r}'\rangle\langle \mathbf{r}'|k\rangle = \langle \mathbf{r}|l\rangle\langle l|H|k\rangle \tag{23.15$'$}$$

$$\langle \mu|\mathbf{r}\rangle\langle \mathbf{r}|H|\mathbf{r}'\rangle\langle \mathbf{r}'|\nu\rangle = \langle \mu|H|\nu\rangle \tag{23.17$'$}$$

$$\langle k|\mu\rangle = \langle k|\mathbf{r}\rangle\langle \mathbf{r}|\mu\rangle \tag{23.18$'$}$$

$$\langle \mathbf{r}|\alpha\rangle = \langle \mathbf{r}|k\rangle\langle k|\alpha\rangle \tag{23.22$'$}$$

$$\langle k|\alpha\rangle = \langle k|\mathbf{r}\rangle\langle \mathbf{r}|\alpha\rangle \tag{23.23$'$}$$

$$\langle \mathbf{r}|\alpha\rangle = \langle \mathbf{r}|\mu\rangle\langle \mu|\alpha\rangle \qquad \text{and} \qquad \langle \mu|\alpha\rangle = \langle \mu|\mathbf{r}\rangle\langle \mathbf{r}|\alpha\rangle \tag{23.25$'$}$$

$$\langle \alpha|\beta\rangle = \langle \alpha|\mathbf{r}\rangle\langle \mathbf{r}|\beta\rangle \tag{23.26$'$}$$

With the exception of Eqs. (23.3′) and (23.10′), which are eigenvalue equations for Ω and H, respectively, all these equations have one property in common. If we assume that a repeated state symbol (k, μ, or $\mathbf{r}$), which is understood to be summed over a complete orthonormal set of states as in (23.33), is equivalent to the unit operator, these equations become trivial identities. For example, each of the two sides of Eq. (23.15′) becomes equal to $\langle \mathbf{r}|H|k \rangle$, since $|\mathbf{r}'\rangle\langle \mathbf{r}'|$ and $|l\rangle\langle l|$ may be replaced by unit operators on the left and right sides, respectively. This replacement is evidently equivalent to the use of the closure property of any complete orthonormal set of functions. Conversely, unit operators can always be inserted, as in going from the left to the right side of (23.4′). The simplest proof of the correctness of these assumptions is the observation that the removal or insertion of such repeated state symbols always leads to valid equations.

Note that an insertion can also be made between two operators, for example,

$$\Omega\Gamma = \Omega|k\rangle\langle k|\Gamma \tag{23.34}$$

PROJECTION OPERATORS

Consider the equation

$$|\alpha\rangle = S_\mu|\mu\rangle\langle\mu|\alpha\rangle = S_\mu P_\mu|\alpha\rangle \tag{23.35}$$

where the operator P_μ is defined by

$$P_\mu \equiv |\mu\rangle\langle\mu| \tag{23.36}$$

for a single state μ, that is, without the generalized summation. It is clear from the first of Eqs. (23.3′) that $P_\mu|\alpha\rangle$ is an eigenstate of Ω with eigenvalue ω_μ. Thus an arbitrary ket $|\alpha\rangle$ can be written as a generalized sum of eigenstates of any operator Ω through Eq. (23.35). The operator P_μ is called a *projection operator*, since it projects out of $|\alpha\rangle$ the part that is a particular eigenstate of Ω.

Suppose now that Ω has only two distinct eigenvalues ω_1 and ω_2, with a great deal of degeneracy. An example might be the parity operator, with eigenvalues ± 1, or a component of the spin angular momentum of a spin $\frac{1}{2}$ particle, with eigenvalues $\pm\frac{1}{2}\hbar$ (see the next chapter). In such a situation it is sometimes desirable to write any state $|\alpha\rangle$ as a sum of two parts, each of which is an eigenstate of Ω with the eigenvalues ω_1 and ω_2. This can be accomplished by defining projection operators through the equations

$$P_i \equiv S_{\mu=\mu_i}P_\mu \tag{23.37}$$

with $i = 1, 2$, instead of through (23.36). Then $P_i|\alpha\rangle$ is an eigenstate of Ω with eigenvalue ω_i.   It is easily verified that

$$P_1 = \frac{\Omega - \omega_2}{\omega_1 - \omega_2} \qquad \text{and} \qquad P_2 = \frac{\Omega - \omega_1}{\omega_2 - \omega_1} \tag{23.38}$$

and that

$$\sum_i P_i = 1 \qquad P_i P_j = \delta_{ij} P_i \tag{23.39}$$

Equations (23.38) can be generalized to the situation in which Ω has more than two distinct eigenvalues.   With the definition (23.37), we now have

$$P_i = \prod_{j \neq i} \frac{\Omega - \omega_j}{\omega_i - \omega_j} \tag{23.40}$$

and Eqs. (23.39) are still valid.

Since Ω is hermitian, its eigenvalues ω_μ are real, and the P_μ and P_i are evidently hermitian.   Finally, it is easy to see that tr $(P_\mu) = 1$ if $|\mu\rangle$ is a normalized eigenstate that corresponds to a discrete eigenvalue.   In this case tr (P_i) is equal to the number of linearly independent eigenstates of Ω that have eigenvalue ω_i; hence it is equal to the dimensionality of the Hilbert subspace that corresponds to ω_i.

We shall have occasion to discuss projection operators further in Sec. 42.

PHYSICAL MEANING OF MATRIX ELEMENTS

We have seen that the diagonal matrix elements of an operator that is in diagonal form are just the eigenvalues of that operator.   Comparison with the work of Sec. 7 shows that, if the operator is not in diagonal form, the diagonal matrix elements are the expectation values of operators for states that are normalized.   More generally, $\langle\alpha|\Omega|\alpha\rangle/\langle\alpha|\alpha\rangle$ is the expectation value of the operator for the state represented by the normalizable ket $|\alpha\rangle$.

Thus far we have no simple interpretation for off-diagonal matrix elements such as $\langle\alpha|\Omega|\beta\rangle$.   We shall see in Chap. 8 that, among other things, they are related to the probabilities for transitions between pairs of states.

24□EQUATIONS OF MOTION

The transformation theory developed in the preceding section makes no reference to dynamics; it deals with the description of a physical system at one instant of time.   This description involves three kinds of objects. First, there are those which specify the state of the system at a particular time.   These may be written as state functions $\psi_\alpha(\mathbf{r})$; as column matrices

ψ_α, a_α, or b_α; as Hilbert space vectors; or as kets $|\alpha\rangle$. To each of these there corresponds a hermitian adjoint quantity such as $\psi_\alpha{}^\dagger$ or $\langle\alpha|$. Second, there are unitary transformations, which may be written as rectangular matrices such as U, the elements of which are bracket expressions $\langle k|\mathbf{r}\rangle$. These effect changes from one representation to another. From the Hilbert-space point of view, they rotate axes without changing the state vectors, so that a particular state vector is referred to a different set of axes. Third, there are dynamical variables, such as Ω, which may be written as operators or as square matrices. The elements of these matrices can be calculated with respect to a particular set of axes in Hilbert space, and a unitary matrix transforms their values from one set of axes or representation to another. Thus U transforms Ω from the coordinate representation $\langle\mathbf{r}|\Omega|\mathbf{r}'\rangle$ to the energy representation $\langle k|\Omega|l\rangle$, just as it transforms $|\alpha\rangle$ from the coordinate representation $\langle\mathbf{r}|\alpha\rangle$ to the energy representation $\langle k|\alpha\rangle$.

Alternatively, the matrix elements of Ω can be calculated with respect to particular state vectors ψ_α, which need not be members of a complete set. These matrix elements are the inner products $(\psi_\alpha, \Omega\psi_\beta) = \langle\alpha|\Omega|\beta\rangle$ and are invariant with respect to unitary transformations; that is, their numerical values do not depend on the choice of the representation (choice of axes in Hilbert space). The result of operation with Ω on a ket $|\beta\rangle$ is a new ket $\Omega|\beta\rangle$, which is related to $|\beta\rangle$ through a generalized rotation of the state vector in Hilbert space. If $|\beta\rangle$ happens to be an eigenstate $|\mu\rangle$ of Ω, then the "rotation" consists merely in multiplying the state vector by ω_μ without changing its direction.

A distinction must be made between rotations of axes in Hilbert space without change of the state vectors, which are produced by unitary transformations, and generalized rotations of state vectors without change of the axes, which are produced by dynamical variables.

We consider in this section the way in which a physical system changes from one instant of time to another. As we shall see, this time dependence may be variously viewed as a change in the state vectors, in the dynamical variables, or in both. It turns out that there is one particular point of view that puts the equations of motion in a form very similar to that of the classical equations of motion in their hamiltonian formulation. This similarity suggests a rather general method for inferring quantum equations that agree in the appropriate limit with the classical equations for the same system.

SCHRÖDINGER PICTURE

We take as our starting point the time-dependent Schrödinger equation (6.16) and write it in terms of a time-dependent ket $|\alpha_S(t)\rangle$ and the hamiltonian H:

$$i\hbar \frac{d}{dt} |\alpha_S(t)\rangle = H|\alpha_S(t)\rangle \tag{24.1}$$

The total time derivative is used here since the dependence of the ket on coordinate or other variables does not appear explicitly. The subscript S refers to the ket as viewed in the *Schrödinger picture*, according to which it varies in time in conformity with the ordinary differential equation (24.1). The hermitian adjoint equation of motion is

$$-i\hbar \frac{d}{dt} \langle \alpha_S(t)| = \langle \alpha_S(t)|H^\dagger = \langle \alpha_S(t)|H \tag{24.2}$$

since H is hermitian.

The solutions of the differential equations (24.1) and (24.2) are easily found if H is independent of the time, which we assume to be the case:

$$|\alpha_S(t)\rangle = e^{-iHt/\hbar}|\alpha_S(0)\rangle \qquad \langle \alpha_S(t)| = \langle \alpha_S(0)|e^{iHt/\hbar} \tag{24.3}$$

That the differential equations follow from Eqs. (24.3) may be verified by expanding the exponentials in power series and differentiating term by term.

The operator $e^{-iHt/\hbar}$ is an infinite sum of powers of H, each of which is a dynamical variable that can be written as an operator or a square matrix. Thus the series as a whole is also a dynamical variable. In this particular case, it is easily seen to be unitary since H is hermitian. However, it is essential to remember that $e^{-iHt/\hbar}$ is not a unitary transformation in the same sense as U, V, or W. It does not transform from one representation to another (rotation of axes in Hilbert space); rather it changes the ket $|\alpha_S(0)\rangle$ into the ket $|\alpha_S(t)\rangle$ and so performs a generalized rotation of the state vector in Hilbert space. However, since $e^{-iHt/\hbar}$ is unitary, the norm of the ket is unchanged, and the generalized rotation in this case is a pure rotation.

The time rate of change of the matrix element of a dynamical variable Ω_S in the Schrödinger picture is easily found with the help of Eqs. (24.1) and (24.2):

$$\frac{d}{dt}\langle \alpha_S(t)|\Omega_S|\beta_S(t)\rangle = \left[\frac{d}{dt}\langle \alpha_S(t)|\right]\Omega_S|\beta_S(t)\rangle$$

$$+ \left\langle \alpha_S(t)\left|\frac{\partial\Omega_S}{\partial t}\right|\beta_S(t)\right\rangle + \left\langle \alpha_S(t)\left|\Omega_S\left[\frac{d}{dt}\right|\beta_S(t)\right\rangle\right]$$

$$= \left\langle \alpha_S(t)\left|\frac{\partial\Omega_S}{\partial t}\right|\beta_S(t)\right\rangle + \frac{1}{i\hbar}\langle \alpha_S(t)|(\Omega_S H - H\Omega_S)|\beta_S(t)\rangle \tag{24.4}$$

The first term on the right side is that part of the change in the matrix element that arises from any explicit dependence that Ω_S may have on the time, and the second term is that caused by the change in time of the state vectors. The operator that appears in this second term is called a *commutator bracket*, which is defined by

$$[A,B] \equiv AB - BA \tag{24.5}$$

Note that, in accordance with the definitions of Sec. 22, the commutator bracket has no meaning unless both matrices are square and have their rows and columns labeled in the same way.

An interesting special case of Eq. (24.4) is that in which Ω_S commutes with H and has no explicit dependence on the time. Then the right side is zero, and all matrix elements of Ω_S are constant in time. Such a dynamical variable is said to be a *constant of the motion*.

HEISENBERG PICTURE

Substitution of Eqs. (24.3) into (24.4) gives

$$\frac{d}{dt} \langle \alpha_S(0)|e^{iHt/\hbar}\Omega_S e^{-iHt/\hbar}|\beta_S(0)\rangle = \left\langle \alpha_S(0) \left| e^{iHt/\hbar} \frac{\partial \Omega_S}{\partial t} e^{-iHt/\hbar} \right| \beta_S(0) \right\rangle$$

$$+ \frac{1}{i\hbar} \langle \alpha_S(0)|[e^{iHt/\hbar}\Omega_S e^{-iHt/\hbar},H]|\beta_S(0)\rangle \tag{24.6}$$

where use has been made of the fact that H commutes with $e^{\pm iHt/\hbar}$. It is convenient to define time-independent state vectors through

$$|\alpha_H(t)\rangle \equiv |\alpha_S(0)\rangle = e^{iHt/\hbar}|\alpha_S(t)\rangle \tag{24.7}$$

and time-dependent dynamical variables through

$$\Omega_H \equiv e^{iHt/\hbar}\Omega_S e^{-iHt/\hbar} \tag{24.8}$$

Unless Ω_S commutes with H, Ω_H depends on t even if Ω_S has no explicit time dependence. The subscript H denotes the *Heisenberg picture*. The time $t = 0$ at which the kets and operators in the Schrödinger picture are the same as those in the Heisenberg picture is, of course, arbitrary and is chosen for convenience. If this time were $t = t_0$, then $e^{\pm iHt/\hbar}$ would be replaced by $e^{\pm iH(t-t_0)/\hbar}$.

Since $|\alpha_H(t)\rangle$ does not depend on the time, the explicit mention of t may be omitted. Further, the time derivative on the left side of Eq. (24.6) can be taken inside the matrix element, so that the equation reads

$$\left\langle \alpha_H \left| \frac{d}{dt} \Omega_H \right| \beta_H \right\rangle = \left\langle \alpha_H \left| \frac{\partial \Omega_H}{\partial t} \right| \beta_H \right\rangle + \frac{1}{i\hbar} \langle \alpha_H|[\Omega_H,H]|\beta_H\rangle \tag{24.9}$$

where in accordance with (24.8) we have defined

$$\frac{\partial \Omega_H}{\partial t} \equiv \left(\frac{\partial \Omega}{\partial t}\right)_H = e^{iHt/\hbar} \frac{\partial \Omega_S}{\partial t} e^{-iHt/\hbar}$$

Since Eq. (24.9) is valid for an arbitrary bra and an arbitrary ket, it must be valid for the operators themselves. We are thus led to the equation of motion as viewed in the Heisenberg picture:

$$\frac{d\Omega_H}{dt} = \frac{\partial \Omega_H}{\partial t} + \frac{1}{i\hbar} [\Omega_H, H] \tag{24.10}$$

This equation, which also follows directly from differentiation of Eq. (24.8), is the one that is most similar to the corresponding classical equation of motion, as we shall see below. It should be noted from Eq. (24.8) that H is the same in the Schrödinger and Heisenberg pictures.

We thus see that the description of the change in time of a physical system may be viewed in two contrasting ways. In the Schrödinger picture, the dynamical variables are constant in time (except for a possible explicit time dependence) and the state vectors vary in accordance with Eq. (24.1). In the Heisenberg picture the state vectors are constant in time and the dynamical variables vary in accordance with Eq. (24.10). The transformation from one picture to the other is made with the help of the unitary dynamical variables $e^{\pm iHt/\hbar}$ in accordance with Eqs. (24.7) and (24.8).

We have deliberately avoided referring to these "pictures" as "representations," as is sometimes done, since we wish to reserve the term "representation" for designation of the choice of axes in Hilbert space or, equivalently, the choice of the complete orthonormal set of functions, with respect to which the states and dynamical variables are specified. In this connection it is important to note that Eqs. (24.1), (24.7), (24.8), and (24.10) have the same form in all representations, as is easily shown. On the other hand, we use the term "transformation" in connection with the change from one picture to the other, since it is accomplished by means of a unitary operator. Because of this, all norms and inner products of state vectors are independent of the picture and constant in time, as well as independent of the representation.

INTERACTION PICTURE

The discussion of the two preceding subsections shows that neither the state vectors alone nor the dynamical variables alone are central for the description of the development of a physical system in time. Both can be altered by means of the unitary transformation $e^{-iHt/\hbar}$, and the two pictures thus obtained are equally valid. The quantities that are not altered are the matrix elements of dynamical variables calculated for pairs of states, such as $\langle \alpha | \Omega | \beta \rangle$. These provide the essential physical content of the theory, since eigenvalues, expectation values, and transition probabilities can be obtained from them. It is apparent that any unitary transformation, whether or not it depends on the time, may be applied to both states and dynamical variables, without affecting the values of the matrix elements. Thus an arbitrarily large number of different pictures, as well as of different representations, can be found.

An especially useful third picture can be specified by dividing the hamiltonian into two parts,

$$H = H_0 + H' \tag{24.11}$$

such that H_0 does not depend explicitly on the time and also has a simple structure. For example, H_0 might be the kinetic energy and H' the potential energy. Or H_0 might be the hamiltonian for a relatively simple potential such as the coulomb field and H' some additional interaction such as an external electromagnetic field. In the latter case it is often of interest to permit H' to depend explicitly on the time, and so we shall admit this possibility in what follows. Since H, H_0, and H' do not in general commute with each other, subscripts must be used to distinguish between them in the various pictures.

We define the *interaction picture* by the equations

$$\begin{aligned} |\alpha_I(t)\rangle &\equiv e^{iH_0 st/\hbar}|\alpha_S(t)\rangle \\ \Omega_I(t) &\equiv e^{iH_0 st/\hbar}\Omega_S e^{-iH_0 st/\hbar} \end{aligned} \tag{24.12}$$

so that the interaction and Heisenberg pictures are the same when $H' = 0$. We know from earlier work that $H_H = H_S$, and the second of Eqs. (24.12) shows that $H_{0I} = H_{0S}$. In general, $H_I \neq H_S$, $H_{0H} \neq H_{0S}$, and H'_S, H'_H, and H'_I are all different. Differentiation of the first of Eqs. (24.12) gives for the equation of motion of $|\alpha_I(t)\rangle$

$$\begin{aligned} i\hbar \frac{d}{dt}|\alpha_I(t)\rangle &= -H_{0S}e^{iH_0 st/\hbar}|\alpha_S(t)\rangle + i\hbar e^{iH_0 st/\hbar}\frac{d}{dt}|\alpha_S(t)\rangle \\ &= -H_{0S}|\alpha_I(t)\rangle + e^{iH_0 st/\hbar}H_S e^{-iH_0 st/\hbar}|\alpha_I(t)\rangle \\ &= e^{iH_0 st/\hbar}H'_S e^{-iH_0 st/\hbar}|\alpha_I(t)\rangle \\ &= H'_I|\alpha_I(t)\rangle \end{aligned} \tag{24.13}$$

where use has been made of Eqs. (24.1), (24.11), and the second of Eqs. (24.12). In similar fashion, differentiation of the second of Eqs. (24.12) gives for the equation of motion of $\Omega_I(t)$

$$\frac{d\Omega_I}{dt} = \frac{\partial\Omega_I}{\partial t} + \frac{1}{i\hbar}[\Omega_I, H_{0S}] = \frac{\partial\Omega_I}{\partial t} + \frac{1}{i\hbar}[\Omega_I, H_{0I}] \tag{24.14}$$

What the interaction picture accomplishes is to assign part of the time dependence to the state vectors and part to the dynamical variables, instead of having one constant and the other with the time dependence caused by the full hamiltonian. In this picture the state vectors change in accordance with H' and the dynamical variables in accordance with H_0; note the resemblance between Eqs. (24.1) and (24.13) on the one hand, and between Eqs. (24.10) and (24.14) on the other. This is useful if H' is a small disturbance or *perturbation*, since then the dynamical variables have their unperturbed forms and the state functions are nearly constant in time (see Sec. 35).

ENERGY REPRESENTATION

The energy representation is specified by the kets $|k\rangle$, which are eigenstates of the full hamiltonian H with eigenvalues E_k. Equation (24.1) then shows that in the Schrödinger picture the time-dependent ket $|k_S(t)\rangle$ satisfies the equation

$$i\hbar \frac{d}{dt} |k_S(t)\rangle = H|k_S(t)\rangle = E_k|k_S(t)\rangle$$

which integrates to

$$|k_S(t)\rangle = |k_S(0)\rangle e^{-iE_k t/\hbar} \tag{24.15}$$

This is in agreement with Eq. (8.3). Equation (24.15) and its adjoint can be used to find the time dependence of the matrix elements in the Schrödinger picture of an operator that has no explicit time dependence:

$$\langle k_S(t)|\Omega_S|l_S(t)\rangle = \langle k_S(0)|\Omega_S|l_S(0)\rangle e^{i(E_k - E_l)t/\hbar} \tag{24.16}$$

It is easily verified explicitly that this is equal to the matrix element $\langle k_H|\Omega_H|l_H\rangle$ in the Heisenberg picture, as it must be.

Equation (24.16) shows that off-diagonal matrix elements in the energy representation oscillate in time with frequencies that are proportional to the energy differences between the stationary states, in accordance with Bohr's frequency condition (see Sec. 2). This is consistent with the remark at the end of Sec. 23 that these matrix elements are related to the transition probabilities between states. It also follows from Eq. (24.16) that diagonal matrix elements or expectation values in the energy representation are constant in time for operators that have no explicit time dependence.

CLASSICAL LAGRANGIAN AND HAMILTONIAN EQUATIONS OF MOTION

In order to bring out the similarity between Eq. (24.10) and the corresponding classical equation, we review briefly the structure of classical hamiltonian theory. The equations of motion of a conservative dynamical system that has f degrees of freedom may be derived from a *lagrangian* function $L(q_1, \ldots, q_f, \dot{q}_1, \ldots, \dot{q}_f, t)$ of the coordinates q_i, the velocities

$\dot{q}_i \equiv dq_i/dt$, and the time, by means of a variational principle:[1]

$$\delta \int_{t_1}^{t_2} L \, dt = 0 \qquad \delta q_i(t_1) = \delta q_i(t_2) = 0 \qquad (24.17)$$

The resulting lagrangian equations are

$$\frac{d}{dt}\left(\frac{\partial L}{\partial \dot{q}_i}\right) - \frac{\partial L}{\partial q_i} = 0 \qquad i = 1 \cdots f \qquad (24.18)$$

If now we define a *momentum canonically conjugate* to q_i as $p_i \equiv \partial L/\partial \dot{q}_i$, and a *hamiltonian* function of the coordinates and momenta as

$$H(q_1 \cdots q_f, p_1 \cdots p_f, t) = \sum_{i=1}^{f} p_i \dot{q}_i - L \qquad (24.19)$$

variation of H leads to the hamiltonian equations of motion

$$\dot{q}_i = \frac{\partial H}{\partial p_i} \qquad \dot{p}_i = -\frac{\partial H}{\partial q_i} \qquad i = 1 \cdots f \qquad (24.20)$$

The time dependence of any function of the coordinates, momenta, and the time, calculated along a moving phase point, is

$$\frac{d}{dt} F(q_1 \cdots q_f, p_1 \cdots p_f, t) = \frac{\partial F}{\partial t} + \sum_{i=1}^{f} \left(\frac{\partial F}{\partial q_i} \dot{q}_i + \frac{\partial F}{\partial p_i} \dot{p}_i\right)$$

$$= \frac{\partial F}{\partial t} + \sum_{i=1}^{f} \left(\frac{\partial F}{\partial q_i} \frac{\partial H}{\partial p_i} - \frac{\partial H}{\partial q_i} \frac{\partial F}{\partial p_i}\right)$$

on making use of the hamiltonian equations (24.20). The *Poisson bracket* $\{A,B\}$ of any two functions of the coordinates and momenta is defined as

$$\{A,B\} \equiv \sum_{i=1}^{f} \left(\frac{\partial A}{\partial q_i} \frac{\partial B}{\partial p_i} - \frac{\partial B}{\partial q_i} \frac{\partial A}{\partial p_i}\right) \qquad (24.21)$$

In terms of the Poisson bracket, the equation of motion for the function F of the dynamical variables becomes

$$\frac{dF}{dt} = \frac{\partial F}{\partial t} + \{F,H\} \qquad (24.22)$$

[1] E. T. Whittaker, "Analytical Dynamics," 3d ed., secs. 99, 109 (Cambridge, London, 1927); H. C. Corben and P. Stehle, "Classical Mechanics," secs. 26, 63 (Wiley, New York, 1950); H. Goldstein, "Classical Mechanics," chaps. 2, 7 (Addison-Wesley, Reading, Mass., 1950); A. Katz, "Classical Mechanics, Quantum Mechanics, Field Theory," chap. 1 (Academic, New York, 1965).

The left side of Eq. (24.22) is the total time derivative of F along a moving phase point. The first term on the right side takes into account the explicit time dependence of F, and the last term is the change in F arising from the motion of the phase point at which F is evaluated.

POISSON BRACKETS AND COMMUTATOR BRACKETS

The strong resemblance between Eqs. (24.10) and (24.22) suggests that quantum analogs of the classical equations of motion can be found in general by substituting the commutator bracket divided by $i\hbar$ for the Poisson bracket,

$$\{A,B\} \to \frac{1}{i\hbar} [A,B] \tag{24.23}$$

and working with the Heisenberg picture.

There are two observations that lend support to this suggestion. The first concerns the classical conditions for a contact transformation from one set of canonical variables q_i, p_i to another Q_i, P_i:[1]

$$\{Q_i,P_j\} = \delta_{ij} \qquad \{Q_i,Q_j\} = 0 \qquad \{P_i,P_j\} = 0 \tag{24.24}$$

where the Poisson brackets are calculated with respect to the original variables q_i, p_i. We saw in Sec. 6 that a successful transition from classical to quantum theory could be made by substituting the differential operator $-i\hbar(\partial/\partial x)$ for p_x, etc. The commutator of x and p_x can then be found by letting it operate on an arbitrary function $g(\mathbf{r})$ of the coordinates.

$$(xp_x - p_x x)g(\mathbf{r}) = -i\hbar x \frac{\partial g}{\partial x} + i\hbar \frac{\partial}{\partial x} (xg) = i\hbar g(\mathbf{r}) \tag{24.25}$$

Since $g(\mathbf{r})$ is arbitrary, this and the other commutators may be written as operator equations:

$$
\begin{aligned}
xp_x - p_x x &= -i\hbar \left(x \frac{\partial}{\partial x} - \frac{\partial}{\partial x} x \right) = i\hbar \\
xp_y - p_y x &= -i\hbar \left(x \frac{\partial}{\partial y} - \frac{\partial}{\partial y} x \right) = 0 \\
xy - yx &= 0 \qquad p_x p_y - p_y p_x = 0 \qquad \text{etc.}
\end{aligned}
\tag{24.26}
$$

These are in agreement with the classical equations (24.24) when the substitution (24.23) is made.

The second observation is that the algebraic properties of the commutator brackets are identical with those of the Poisson brackets. It is

[1] Whittaker, *op. cit.*, pp. 300, 307; Corben and Stehle, *op. cit.*, chaps. 11–13; Goldstein, *op. cit.*, chap. 8; Katz, *loc. cit.*

readily verified from the definition (24.21) that

$$\{A,B\} = -\{B,A\} \qquad \{A,c\} = 0 \qquad \text{where } c \text{ is a number}$$

$$\{(A_1 + A_2), B\} = \{A_1,B\} + \{A_2,B\}$$

$$\{A_1 A_2,B\} = \{A_1,B\}A_2 + A_1\{A_2,B\} \tag{24.27}$$

$$\{A,\{B,C\}\} + \{B,\{C,A\}\} + \{C,\{A,B\}\} = 0$$

The order of possibly noncommuting factors has not been altered. Dirac[1] has shown that the form of the quantum analog of the Poisson bracket is determined by Eqs. (24.27) to be the right side of (24.23); the constant $\hbar$ is, of course, arbitrary so far as this discussion is concerned (see also Prob. 9).

QUANTIZATION OF A CLASSICAL SYSTEM

We now have available a plausible procedure for finding a quantum system that reduces to any specified classical system in the correspondence principle or classical limit. We simply write the classical hamiltonian equations in terms of Poisson brackets and replace the Poisson brackets with commutator brackets in accordance with (24.23). The classical equation of motion (24.22) then becomes the quantum equation (24.10), which states how the dynamical variables in the Heisenberg picture change with time. Similarly, the classical relations (24.24) become[2]

$$[q_i,p_j] = i\hbar\delta_{ij} \qquad [q_i,q_j] = 0 \qquad [p_i,p_j] = 0 \tag{24.28}$$

These *quantum conditions* are generalizations of Eqs. (24.26) and are easily seen to be valid in any of the pictures discussed earlier in this section. Thus the Heisenberg picture need be specified only for the equations of motion; we shall assume that this is the case throughout the remainder of this section, and the subscript H will be omitted.

Two precautions are necessary in applying this quantization procedure. First, the coordinates and momenta must be expressed in cartesian coordinates. Second, ambiguities in the order of noncommuting factors are usually resolved by taking a symmetric average of the various possible orders. These precautions are illustrated in the following example.

It is important to realize that there is no unique way of making the transition from classical to quantum mechanics. Terms can always be added to the quantum equations of motion that vanish in the classical or correspondence-principle limit. On the other hand, if the classical behavior of a system is known, certain restrictions are placed on its quan-

---

[1] Dirac, *op. cit.*, sec. 21.

[2] Note that the derivation of Eq. (12.7) then shows that for *any* pair of canonical variables $\Delta q_i \cdot \Delta p_i \geq \frac{1}{2}\hbar$.

tum equations. The present procedure generally yields the simplest quantum system that has the correct classical limit. This simplest system may omit interesting aspects of the true situation; thus the intrinsic spin and magnetic moment that some charged particles actually possess do not appear in the example treated below.

MOTION OF A PARTICLE IN AN ELECTROMAGNETIC FIELD

As an example of the foregoing quantization procedure, we consider the problem of the motion of a charged mass point in a general external electromagnetic field. The classical hamiltonian, expressed in terms of the canonical variables $\mathbf{r}$, $\mathbf{p}$ and the electromagnetic potentials $\mathbf{A}(\mathbf{r},t)$, $\phi(\mathbf{r},t)$, is[1]

$$H = \frac{1}{2m}\left(\mathbf{p} - \frac{e}{c}\mathbf{A}\right)^2 + e\phi \qquad (24.29)$$

where e is the charge on the particle and c is the speed of light; the electric and magnetic field strengths are given in terms of the potentials by

$$\mathbf{E} = -\frac{1}{c}\frac{\partial \mathbf{A}}{\partial t} - \boldsymbol{\nabla}\phi \qquad \mathbf{H} = \boldsymbol{\nabla} \times \mathbf{A} \qquad (24.30)$$

The quantum conditions (24.28) in cartesian coordinates are

$$[x,p_x] = [y,p_y] = [z,p_z] = i\hbar \qquad (24.31)$$

with other pairs of coordinate and momentum components commuting. We now use Eq. (24.10), with the expression (24.29) for H and the relations (24.31), to calculate expressions for the particle velocity $d\mathbf{r}/dt$ and acceleration $d^2\mathbf{r}/dt^2$, for comparison with the corresponding classical expressions.

EVALUATION OF COMMUTATOR BRACKETS

In order to facilitate evaluation of some of the commutator brackets that arise from substitution into (24.10), we derive a few elementary results. Any two functions of $\mathbf{r}$ commute with each other, since all components of $\mathbf{r}$ commute with each other. It follows from (24.31) that

$$x^2 p_x - p_x x^2 = x(p_x x + i\hbar) - p_x x^2$$
$$= (p_x x + i\hbar)x + i\hbar x - p_x x^2 = 2i\hbar x$$

It is readily shown by induction that

$$x^n p_x - p_x x^n = n i\hbar x^{n-1} \qquad (24.32)$$

[1] J. H. Van Vleck, "The Theory of Electric and Magnetic Susceptibilities," pp. 7, 20 (Oxford, New York, 1932). Gaussian units are used in the present book.

It follows from (24.32) that for any function $f(\mathbf{r})$ that can be expressed as a power series in x, y, z, the relation

$$[f(\mathbf{r}),p_x] = f(\mathbf{r})p_x - p_x f(\mathbf{r}) = i\hbar \frac{\partial}{\partial x} f(\mathbf{r}) \tag{24.33}$$

is valid.[1] Equation (24.33) can also be established for more general functions than power series by making use of the representation of p_x as $-i\hbar(\partial/\partial x)$, as in (24.25); if we operate with the left side of (24.33) on an arbitrary function $g(\mathbf{r})$, we obtain

$$[f(\mathbf{r}),p_x]g(\mathbf{r}) = -i\hbar \left[f(\mathbf{r}) \frac{\partial}{\partial x} - \frac{\partial}{\partial x} f(\mathbf{r}) \right] g(\mathbf{r}) = g(\mathbf{r}) \left[i\hbar \frac{\partial}{\partial x} f(\mathbf{r}) \right]$$

which is equivalent to the operator equality (24.33) since $g(\mathbf{r})$ is arbitrary. By repeated application of (24.33) it is easily shown that

$$f(\mathbf{r})p_x^2 - p_x^2 f(\mathbf{r}) = i\hbar \left(p_x \frac{\partial f}{\partial x} + \frac{\partial f}{\partial x} p_x \right) = 2i\hbar \frac{\partial f}{\partial x} p_x + \hbar^2 \frac{\partial^2 f}{\partial x^2} \tag{24.34}$$

VELOCITY AND ACCELERATION OF A CHARGED PARTICLE

The hamiltonian (24.29) may now be written, with the help of (24.33),

$$H = \frac{\mathbf{p}^2}{2m} - \frac{e}{2mc} (\mathbf{p} \cdot \mathbf{A} + \mathbf{A} \cdot \mathbf{p}) + \frac{e^2}{2mc^2} \mathbf{A}^2 + e\phi$$

$$= \frac{\mathbf{p}^2}{2m} - \frac{e}{mc} \mathbf{A} \cdot \mathbf{p} + \frac{ie\hbar}{2mc} \nabla \cdot \mathbf{A} + \frac{e^2}{2mc^2} \mathbf{A}^2 + e\phi \tag{24.35}$$

The time derivative of a component of $\mathbf{r}$ is then easily shown from (24.10) to be

$$\frac{dx}{dt} = \frac{1}{m} \left(p_x - \frac{e}{c} A_x \right) \tag{24.36}$$

in agreement with the classical relation between the velocity and momentum of a particle in the presence of an electromagnetic field.

The calculation of a component of the acceleration of the particle

$$\frac{d^2x}{dt^2} = \frac{1}{m} \left(\frac{dp_x}{dt} - \frac{e}{c} \frac{dA_x}{dt} \right)$$

$$= \frac{1}{i\hbar m} [p_x,H] - \frac{e}{mc} \frac{\partial A_x}{\partial t} - \frac{e}{i\hbar mc} [A_x,H]$$

[1] This corresponds to the classical relation $\{f(\mathbf{r}),p_x\} = \partial f(\mathbf{r})/\partial x$ [compare with Eq. (24.23)].

is straightforward but rather tedious. The result may be written

$$
\frac{d^2x}{dt^2} = -\frac{e}{m}\left(\frac{1}{c}\frac{\partial A_x}{\partial t} + \frac{\partial \phi}{\partial x}\right) + \frac{e}{2m^2c}\left[\left(p_y - \frac{e}{c}A_y\right)\left(\frac{\partial A_y}{\partial x} - \frac{\partial A_x}{\partial y}\right)\right.
$$
$$
+ \left(\frac{\partial A_y}{\partial x} - \frac{\partial A_x}{\partial y}\right)\left(p_y - \frac{e}{c}A_y\right)\right] - \frac{e}{2m^2c}\left[\left(p_z - \frac{e}{c}A_z\right)\left(\frac{\partial A_x}{\partial z} - \frac{\partial A_z}{\partial x}\right)\right.
$$
$$
\left. + \left(\frac{\partial A_x}{\partial z} - \frac{\partial A_z}{\partial x}\right)\left(p_z - \frac{e}{c}A_z\right)\right] \quad (24.37)
$$

THE LORENTZ FORCE

Equation (24.37), with the similar y- and z-component equations, can be written as a single vector equation for the "force":

$$
m\frac{d^2\mathbf{r}}{dt^2} = e\left(-\frac{1}{c}\frac{\partial \mathbf{A}}{\partial t} - \nabla\phi\right)
$$
$$
+ \frac{1}{2}\frac{e}{c}\left[\frac{1}{m}\left(\mathbf{p} - \frac{e}{c}\mathbf{A}\right)\times(\nabla\times\mathbf{A}) - (\nabla\times\mathbf{A})\times\frac{1}{m}\left(\mathbf{p} - \frac{e}{c}\mathbf{A}\right)\right]
$$
$$
= e\mathbf{E} + \frac{1}{2}\frac{e}{c}\left(\frac{d\mathbf{r}}{dt}\times\mathbf{H} - \mathbf{H}\times\frac{d\mathbf{r}}{dt}\right) \quad (24.38)
$$

where use has been made of Eqs. (24.30) and (24.36). Equation (24.38) is in agreement with the corresponding classical expression

$$
e\mathbf{E} + \frac{e}{c}(\mathbf{v}\times\mathbf{H})
$$

where $\mathbf{v} = d\mathbf{r}/dt$ is the velocity of the particle, if we take a symmetric average of the two terms $\mathbf{v}\times\mathbf{H}$ and $-\mathbf{H}\times\mathbf{v}$. These are identical classically but differ in quantum mechanics since the $\mathbf{v}$ given by (24.36) does not commute with $\mathbf{H}$; also, although their sum is hermitian, the separate terms are not.

Equation (24.38) includes a generalization of Ehrenfest's theorem, which was discussed in Sec. 7. If we consider a diagonal element, the left side is the product of the mass and the second time derivative of the expectation value of the position vector of the particle, since the Heisenberg-picture kets are independent of t. The right side is the expectation value of the Lorentz force acting on the charge of the particle. Thus (24.38) states that a wave packet moves like a classical particle if it is sufficiently well localized so that the electromagnetic fields change by a negligible amount over its dimensions. This result can also be obtained by the method of Sec. 7 when, in accordance with (24.1) and (24.35), the Schrödinger-picture wave equation is taken to be

$$
i\hbar\frac{\partial \psi}{\partial t} = \left(-\frac{\hbar^2}{2m}\nabla^2 + \frac{ie\hbar}{mc}\mathbf{A}\cdot\nabla + \frac{ie\hbar}{2mc}\nabla\cdot\mathbf{A} + \frac{e^2}{2mc^2}\mathbf{A}^2 + e\phi\right)\psi
$$
$$
(24.39)
$$

VIRIAL THEOREM

A proof of the virial theorem in quantum mechanics can be given in analogy with the corresponding proof in classical mechanics. In the latter, the starting point is the time average of the time derivative of the quantity $\mathbf{r} \cdot \mathbf{p}$, which is zero for a periodic system. The analogous quantity in quantum mechanics is the time derivative of the expectation value of $\mathbf{r} \cdot \mathbf{p}$, or the diagonal matrix element of the commutator of $\mathbf{r} \cdot \mathbf{p}$ and H in the energy representation, which is also zero.

$$\frac{d}{dt} \langle \mathbf{r} \cdot \mathbf{p} \rangle = \frac{1}{i\hbar} \langle [(\mathbf{r} \cdot \mathbf{p}),H] \rangle = 0$$

$$[(\mathbf{r} \cdot \mathbf{p}),H] = \left[(xp_x + yp_y + zp_z), \frac{p_x{}^2 + p_y{}^2 + p_z{}^2}{2m} + V(x,y,z) \right]$$

$$= \frac{i\hbar}{m} (p_x{}^2 + p_y{}^2 + p_z{}^2) - i\hbar \left(x \frac{\partial V}{\partial x} + y \frac{\partial V}{\partial y} + z \frac{\partial V}{\partial z} \right)$$

$$= 2i\hbar T - i\hbar(\mathbf{r} \cdot \boldsymbol{\nabla} V)$$

where T is the kinetic energy. We thus conclude that

$$2\langle T \rangle = \langle \mathbf{r} \cdot \boldsymbol{\nabla} V \rangle \tag{24.40}$$

Note that it is immaterial whether we start with $\mathbf{r} \cdot \mathbf{p}$ or $\mathbf{p} \cdot \mathbf{r}$, since the difference between them is a constant and hence commutes with H.

If V is spherically symmetric and proportional to r^n, and the expectation values exist, Eq. (24.40) shows that $2\langle T \rangle = n\langle V \rangle$. The case $n = -1$ is in agreement with the result of Prob. 13, Chap. 4, and the case $n = 2$ is in agreement with the results of Sec. 13.

25☐MATRIX THEORY OF THE HARMONIC OSCILLATOR

The linear harmonic oscillator was discussed from the point of view of the Schrödinger equation in Sec. 13. This system can also be treated by manipulating the matrix equations directly. The hamiltonian is the one-dimensional form of Eq. (23.2), with $V(x) = \frac{1}{2}Kx^2$:

$$H = \frac{p^2}{2m} + \frac{1}{2}Kx^2 \tag{25.1}$$

where x and p are hermitian since they are physically measurable dynamical variables. The quantum condition is

$$xp - px = i\hbar \tag{25.2}$$

No further information is needed to obtain the energy eigenvalues and eigenfunctions.[1]

[1] Dirac, *op. cit.*, sec. 34.

ENERGY REPRESENTATION

We work at first in the energy representation, in which H is diagonal. Equation (25.1) may be written in Dirac notation as

$$\langle k|H|l\rangle = E_k\langle k|l\rangle = \frac{1}{2m}\langle k|p|j\rangle\langle j|p|l\rangle + \tfrac{1}{2}K\langle k|x|j\rangle\langle j|x|l\rangle \tag{25.3}$$

where the summation symbol S_j has been omitted as in Eq. (23.33). Now

$$\langle j|p|l\rangle = \langle l|p^\dagger|j\rangle^* = \langle l|p|j\rangle^*$$

since p is hermitian, and a similar expression holds for the matrix elements of x. Thus, for the diagonal elements of Eq. (25.3), the right side is a sum of squares of absolute values of matrix elements and hence is non-negative. An energy eigenvalue E_k can be zero only if the matrix elements $\langle k|p|j\rangle$ and $\langle k|x|j\rangle$ are zero for all j. However, this would be inconsistent with the kth diagonal matrix element of Eq. (25.2). We conclude, then, that all the energy eigenvalues are positive.

As a next step, we calculate the commutator bracket of x and of p with H:

$$xH - Hx = \frac{i\hbar}{m}p \qquad pH - Hp = -i\hbar Kx \tag{25.4}$$

Equations of this type are generally useful if the representation is chosen so that one of the factors in the commutator is diagonal, since then a difference between two eigenvalues appears when a matrix element is taken. Thus the first of Eqs. (25.4) becomes

$$\langle k|x|j\rangle\langle j|H|l\rangle - \langle k|H|j\rangle\langle j|x|l\rangle = (E_l - E_k)\langle k|x|l\rangle = \frac{i\hbar}{m}\langle k|p|l\rangle \tag{25.5}$$

In similar fashion, the second of Eqs. (25.4) becomes

$$(E_l - E_k)\langle k|p|l\rangle = -i\hbar K\langle k|x|l\rangle \tag{25.6}$$

It follows, on elimination of $\langle k|x|l\rangle$ from Eqs. (25.5) and (25.6), that either $\langle k|x|l\rangle = \langle k|p|l\rangle = 0$ or

$$E_l - E_k = \pm\hbar\left(\frac{K}{m}\right)^{\frac{1}{2}} = \pm\hbar\omega_c \tag{25.7}$$

where, as in Sec. 13, ω_c is the angular frequency of the corresponding classical harmonic oscillator. If we were to rule out the first possibility, the energy eigenvalues would all differ from each other by integer multiples of $\hbar\omega_c$. It is then possible to show, as will be done below, that these eigenvalues are equal to $(n + \tfrac{1}{2})\hbar\omega_c$, where n is a positive integer or zero. If we try to exploit the first possibility in order to bring in states with different energy eigenvalues, we see that the matrices that represent x and p are identically zero for the new states and so again are inconsistent with Eq. (25.2). Thus the only possible states are those whose energy eigenvalues differ by integer multiples of $\hbar\omega_c$.

RAISING AND LOWERING OPERATORS

Equations (25.5) and (25.6) can also be combined in a different way by multiplying the first by $-im\omega_c$ and adding it to the second. The result is

$$(E_l - E_k - \hbar\omega_c)\langle k|(p - im\omega_c x)|l\rangle = 0$$

Thus $\langle k|(p - im\omega_c x)|l\rangle$ fails to vanish only when $E_k = E_l - \hbar\omega_c$. This means that the result of operating with $p - im\omega_c x$ on the ket $|l\rangle$ is some multiple of the ket $|k\rangle$, which has an energy lower by $\hbar\omega_c$. In similar fashion, it is easily seen that the hermitian adjoint operator $p + im\omega_c x$ raises the energy of any state by $\hbar\omega_c$. Repeated application of the energy-lowering operator to any ket will ultimately lead to a difficulty, since the energy must be positive, unless there is a lowest energy eigenstate $|0\rangle$ such that

$$(p - im\omega_c x)|0\rangle = 0 \tag{25.8}$$

The lowest energy eigenvalue can be found from Eq. (25.8) by operating on it from the left with $p + im\omega_c x$. The result is

$$(p + im\omega_c x)(p - im\omega_c x)|0\rangle = [p^2 + m^2\omega_c^2 x^2 + im\omega_c(xp - px)]|0\rangle$$
$$= (p^2 + m^2\omega_c^2 x^2 - m\hbar\omega_c)|0\rangle = 2m(H - \tfrac{1}{2}\hbar\omega_c)|0\rangle = 0$$

Thus $|0\rangle$ is an eigenstate of H with the eigenvalue $\tfrac{1}{2}\hbar\omega_c$. Application of the energy-raising operator $p + im\omega_c x$ to $|0\rangle$ gives a multiple of the ket $|1\rangle$ that has energy $\tfrac{3}{2}\hbar\omega_c$. Further application generates an infinite sequence of eigenstates that are conveniently labeled $|n\rangle$, with energy eigenvalues

$$E_n = (n + \tfrac{1}{2})\hbar\omega_c \qquad n = 0, 1, 2, \ldots \tag{25.9}$$

This is in agreement with Eq. (13.8).

It is often convenient to put the energy-raising and -lowering operators in dimensionless form by multiplying them with $-i(2m\hbar\omega_c)^{-\frac{1}{2}}$ and $i(2m\hbar\omega_c)^{-\frac{1}{2}}$, respectively. We call the *raising* and *lowering operators* obtained in this way $a^\dagger$ and a, respectively. It is easily seen that

$$aa^\dagger = \frac{H}{\hbar\omega_c} + \frac{1}{2} \qquad a^\dagger a = \frac{H}{\hbar\omega_c} - \frac{1}{2}$$

Thus a and $a^\dagger$ satisfy the commutation relation

$$aa^\dagger - a^\dagger a = 1 \tag{25.10}$$

and H may be written in terms of them as

$$H = (a^\dagger a + \tfrac{1}{2})\hbar\omega_c \tag{25.11}$$

It follows from Eqs. (25.9) and (25.11) that the eigenvalues of $a^\dagger a$ are the positive integers and zero; for this reason $a^\dagger a$ is often called the *number operator*. This result is a direct consequence of the commutation relation (25.10) and requires no other information. The fact that the eigenvalues of $a^\dagger a$, when a is any operator that satisfies Eq. (25.10), are the positive integers and zero is useful in connection with the quantization of wave fields (see Chap. 14). The operators $a^\dagger$ and a appear there *ab initio*, rather than as combinations of x and p, and have the physical significance of respectively increasing and decreasing the number of particles represented by the field. They are therefore called *creation* and *destruction operators*. In the same context, the number operator $a^\dagger a$ specifies the number of particles present in an eigenstate of the field.

MATRICES FOR a, x, AND p

The only nonvanishing matrix elements of a are $\langle n - 1|a|n\rangle$, which we call λ_n. Similarly, the only nonvanishing matrix elements of $a^\dagger$ are $\langle n|a^\dagger|n - 1\rangle$; because of Eq. (22.13), these are equal to λ_n^*. Then a diagonal matrix element of $a^\dagger a$ is

$$\langle n|a^\dagger a|n\rangle = \langle n|a^\dagger|n'\rangle\langle n'|a|n\rangle = |\lambda_n|^2$$

where a summation over the complete set n' is implied. Since this diagonal element is equal to n, λ_n is equal to $n^{\frac{1}{2}}$ except for a possible multiplying phase factor of unit magnitude, which we can choose to be unity. Thus the matrices for a and $a^\dagger$ are

$$a = \begin{bmatrix} 0 & 1 & 0 & 0 \\ 0 & 0 & 2^{\frac{1}{2}} & 0 \\ 0 & 0 & 0 & 3^{\frac{1}{2}} \\ 0 & 0 & 0 & 0 \\ & & & & \cdot \\ & & & & & \cdot \\ & & & & & & \cdot \end{bmatrix} \qquad a^\dagger = \begin{bmatrix} 0 & 0 & 0 & 0 \\ 1 & 0 & 0 & 0 \\ 0 & 2^{\frac{1}{2}} & 0 & 0 \\ 0 & 0 & 3^{\frac{1}{2}} & 0 \\ & & & & \cdot \\ & & & & & \cdot \\ & & & & & & \cdot \end{bmatrix} \tag{25.12}$$

The product $a^\dagger a$ can be formed from these matrices; it is diagonal with eigenvalues $0, 1, 2, \ldots$, as expected.

The expressions for a and $a^\dagger$ in terms of x and p are readily solved back to give

$$x = \left(\frac{\hbar}{2m\omega_c}\right)^{\frac{1}{2}} (a^\dagger + a) \qquad p = i\left(\frac{m\hbar\omega_c}{2}\right)^{\frac{1}{2}} (a^\dagger - a) \tag{25.13}$$

Explicit matrices for x and p are easily found from Eqs. (25.12) and (25.13). Each has nonvanishing elements that border the principal diagonal on both sides, and they are in agreement with Eqs. (13.18).

COORDINATE REPRESENTATION

The ket $|0\rangle$ can be found in the coordinate representation $\langle x|0\rangle$ by solving Eq. (25.8) in that representation. We have

$$\langle x|(p - im\omega_c x)|0\rangle = \langle x|(p - im\omega_c x)|x'\rangle\langle x'|0\rangle = 0$$

where

$$\langle x|p|x'\rangle = -i\hbar \frac{d}{dx} \delta(x - x') \qquad \text{and} \qquad \langle x|x|x'\rangle = x \delta(x - x')$$

so that

$$(-i\hbar \frac{d}{dx} - im\omega_c x)\langle x|0\rangle = 0$$

This has the solution

$$\langle x|0\rangle = A_0 e^{-(m\omega_c/2\hbar)x^2} \tag{25.14}$$

where A_0 is an arbitrary constant. The normalization requirement

$$\langle 0|x\rangle\langle x|0\rangle \equiv \int_{-\infty}^{\infty} |\langle x|0\rangle|^2 \, dx = 1$$

shows that $A_0 = (m\omega_c/\pi\hbar)^{\frac{1}{4}} = \alpha^{\frac{1}{2}}/\pi^{\frac{1}{4}}$, in agreement with Eq. (13.19) when α is defined as in Eq. (13.3).

As remarked above, repeated application of the energy-raising operator $p + im\omega_c x$ to $\langle x|0\rangle$ generates all the (unnormalized) eigenstates $\langle x|n\rangle$. It is easily verified that for an arbitrary function $g(x)$

$$(p + im\omega_c x)g(x) = -i\hbar \left(\frac{d}{dx} - \frac{m\omega_c}{\hbar} x \right) g(x)$$

$$= -i\hbar e^{m\omega_c x^2/2\hbar} \frac{d}{dx} [e^{-m\omega_c x^2/2\hbar} g(x)] \tag{25.15}$$

A second application of $p + im\omega_c x$ gives

$$(p + im\omega_c x)^2 g(x) = -i\hbar e^{m\omega_c x^2/2\hbar} \frac{d}{dx} \{e^{-m\omega_c x^2/2\hbar}[(p + im\omega_c x)g(x)]\}$$

which on substitution from Eq. (25.15) becomes

$$(-i\hbar)^2 e^{m\omega_c x^2/2\hbar} \frac{d^2}{dx^2} [e^{-m\omega_c x^2/2\hbar} g(x)]$$

The induction to $(p + im\omega_c x)^n g(x)$ is evident.   Thus, when $g(x)$ is chosen to have the form (25.14), we obtain

$$\langle x|n\rangle = A_n e^{m\omega_c x^2/2\hbar} \frac{d^n}{dx^n} e^{-m\omega_c x^2/\hbar} \tag{25.16}$$

where A_n is a normalization constant.   Equation (25.16) is in agreement with Eqs. (13.12) and (13.13).

PROBLEMS

1. Assume that any hermitian matrix can be diagonalized by a unitary matrix. From this, show that the necessary and sufficient condition that two hermitian matrices can be diagonalized by the same unitary transformation is that they commute.

2. Show that a nonsingular matrix of finite rank must be square.   Also show that in this case the equation $AA^{-1} = 1$ implies the equation $A^{-1}A = 1$.

3. Show that det $(e^A) = e^{\text{tr}(A)}$. State the conditions on A that must be assumed in your proof.

4. Find two matrices A and B that satisfy the following equations:

$$A^2 = O \qquad AA^\dagger + A^\dagger A = 1 \qquad B = A^\dagger A$$

where O is the null matrix and 1 is the unit matrix.   Show that $B^2 = B$.   Obtain explicit expressions for A and B in a representation in which B is diagonal, assuming that it is nondegenerate.   Can A be diagonalized in any representation?

5. Find three matrices A, B, and C that satisfy the following equations:

$$A^2 = B^2 = C^2 = 1 \qquad AB + BA = BC + CB = CA + AC = O$$

where 1 is the unit matrix and O is the null matrix.   Obtain explicit expressions for all three matrices in a representation in which A is diagonal, assuming that it is nondegenerate.

6. Find three matrices A, B, and C that satisfy the following equations:

$$A^2 = B^2 = C^2 = 1 \qquad BC - CB = iA$$

where 1 is the unit matrix.   Show that $AB + BA = AC + CA = O$, where O is the null matrix.   Obtain explicit expressions for all three matrices in a representation in which A is diagonal, assuming that it is nondegenerate.

7. If A and B are any two square matrices of the same rank and $C \equiv [B,A]$, show that

$$e^{A+B} = e^A e^B e^{\frac{1}{2}C}$$

provided that $[C,A] = [C,B] = 0$.

8. If $H = p^2/2\mu + V(x)$ for one-dimensional motion of a particle, and $V(x)$ can be expressed as a power series in x, show by purely matrix methods that

$$\frac{dx}{dt} = \frac{p}{\mu} \qquad \frac{dp}{dt} = -\frac{dV}{dx}$$

where x and p are in the Heisenberg picture.

9. $A(x,p)$ and $B(x,p)$ can be expressed as power series in x and p, and $[x,p] = i\hbar$. Show by purely matrix methods that

$$\lim_{\hbar \to 0} \frac{1}{i\hbar} [A,B] = \{A,B\}$$

where the right side is the Poisson bracket calculated as if x and p were classical variables.

10.   The hamiltonian $H = \mathbf{p}^2/2\mu + V(\mathbf{r})$ has a set of eigenkets $|k\rangle$ with eigenvalues E_k.   Show that, if $|l\rangle$ is any ket that has a discrete eigenvalue,

$$S_k(E_k - E_l)|\langle k|x|l\rangle|^2 = \frac{\hbar^2}{2\mu}$$

where x is a cartesian component of $\mathbf{r}$.   As a byproduct of your solution, give a matrix proof of Prob. 9, Chap. 3.

11.   The hamiltonian for the harmonic oscillator may be written in the coordinate representation as

$$\langle x|H|x'\rangle = -\frac{\hbar^2}{2m} \frac{d^2}{dx^2} \delta(x - x') + \tfrac{1}{2}Kx^2 \delta(x - x')$$

Transform H into the momentum representation, and find the p-representation wave functions that correspond to the x-representation wave functions given in Eq. (13.13) or (25.16).

12.   Show that the matrix for x obtained from Eqs. (25.12) and (25.13) is in agreement with Eqs. (13.18), and that Eq. (25.16) is in agreement with Eqs. (13.12) and (13.13).

7

Symmetry in
Quantum Mechanics

Symmetry is a fundamental attribute of the natural world that enables
an investigator to study particular aspects of physical systems by themselves. For example, the assumption that space is homogeneous, or
possesses translational symmetry, leads to the conclusion that the linear
momentum of a closed isolated system does not change as the system
moves. This makes it possible to study separately the motion of the
center of mass and the internal motion of the system. In similar fashion,
the assumption that space is isotropic, or possesses rotational symmetry,
means that the total angular momentum of such a system is constant.
Connections of this kind between symmetry properties and conservation
laws have been used earlier in this book without developing an elaborate
formalism, as in the reduction of the Schrödinger equation for the hydrogen atom from seven independent variables to one (Sec. 16). However,
a systematic treatment is useful in solving more complicated problems.
More important, the unified view of symmetry that results provides a
deeper insight into the structure of physics.

   In this chapter we consider first the *geometrical symmetries* that may
be associated with the displacements of a physical system in space and

time, with its rotation and inversion in space, and with the reversal of the sense of progression of time.   We then discuss the *dynamical symmetries* that lead to the unexpected degeneracies of the energy levels of the hydrogen atom and the isotropic harmonic oscillator.   Several other symmetries that are of interest in physics are omitted, notably those that relate to molecules, crystals, and relativity.   Although we shall consider mainly a single particle, or equivalently a pair of particles in the center-of-mass system, many of the results obtained can be extended to several interacting particles provided that the symmetries apply to all coordinates of all particles.   For identical particles there is also an additional permutation symmetry, which will be discussed in Sec. 40.

26□SPACE AND TIME DISPLACEMENTS

We shall work entirely in the Schrödinger picture.   As our first symmetry operation, we consider the displacement in space of a physical system in a state represented by the ket $|\alpha\rangle$ or the wave function $\psi_\alpha(\mathbf{r})$.   The displacement is through a vector ϱ and changes the ket $|\alpha\rangle$ into the ket $|\alpha'\rangle$ or changes the wave function $\psi_\alpha(\mathbf{r})$ into the wave function $\psi_{\alpha'}(\mathbf{r})$.   This means that

$$\psi_{\alpha'}(\mathbf{r} + \varrho) = \psi_\alpha(\mathbf{r}) \tag{26.1}$$

As an example of (26.1), we note that, if $\psi_\alpha(\mathbf{r})$ is a wave packet that has its maximum value when its argument $\mathbf{r}$ is equal to $\mathbf{r}_0$, then $\psi_{\alpha'}(\mathbf{r})$ is a wave packet of the same shape that has its maximum value when its argument $\mathbf{r}$ is equal to $\mathbf{r}_0 + \varrho$.   Thus $\psi_{\alpha'}$ has its maximum displaced by ϱ with respect to the maximum of ψ_α.

What we have just described is usually called the *active* point of view, in which the coordinate system is unchanged and the state function is displaced.   The completely equivalent *passive* point of view consists in leaving the state function unchanged but referring it to a coordinate system that is displaced by the vector $-\varrho$ with respect to the original coordinate system.   For the situations discussed in this book, the active point of view seems to be more appropriate physically, and we shall use it consistently.   However, it should be noted that most treatments of homogeneous Lorentz transformations make use of the passive point of view, which seems more suitable when relative motion (rather than relative displacement) is being considered; the same physical system is then viewed by observers who are moving with respect to each other.

UNITARY DISPLACEMENT OPERATOR

Two kinds of transformations were discussed in Secs. 23 and 24.   The first kind, of which U, V, and W are examples, are unitary transformations from one representation to another that rotate axes in Hilbert space without change in the state vectors. The second kind, of which Ω and $e^{-iHt/\hbar}$ are examples, are dynamical variables that produce generalized rotations of the state vectors in Hilbert space without change in the axes. We now wish to find a transformation of the second kind that changes the ket $|\alpha\rangle$ into the ket $|\alpha'\rangle$; since the norm of the ket should not be affected by displacement, the corresponding operator is expected to be unitary, and this will be shown by explicit construction. We call this operator $U_r(\varrho)$, where the subscript denotes a displacement in space and the argument is the vector displacement interval [in contrast with $U_t(\tau)$ considered below, which is the operator for displacement in time through the interval τ].

We thus have

$$U_r(\varrho)|\alpha\rangle = |\alpha'\rangle \qquad \text{or} \qquad U_r(\varrho)\psi_\alpha(\mathbf{r}) = \psi_{\alpha'}(\mathbf{r}) \tag{26.2}$$

The second of Eqs. (26.2) makes use of the coordinate representation of the state vector; together with Eq. (26.1) it becomes

$$U_r(\varrho)\psi_\alpha(\mathbf{r}) = \psi_\alpha(\mathbf{r} - \varrho) \tag{26.3}$$

In evaluating $\psi_\alpha(\mathbf{r} - \varrho)$ it is convenient to choose the coordinate axes at first so that the x axis is in the direction of the vector ϱ. Then a Taylor's series expansion gives

$$\psi_\alpha(\mathbf{r} - \varrho) = \psi_\alpha(x - \rho, y, z) = \psi_\alpha(x,y,z) - \rho\frac{\partial}{\partial x}\psi_\alpha(x,y,z)$$
$$+ \frac{\rho^2}{2!}\frac{\partial^2}{\partial x^2}\psi_\alpha(x,y,z) - \cdots$$

The right side may be written in the form

$$e^{-\rho(\partial/\partial x)}\psi_\alpha(x,y,z)$$

For a general choice of coordinate axes, $\rho(\partial/\partial x)$ may be replaced by $\varrho \cdot \nabla$, so that we obtain

$$\psi_\alpha(\mathbf{r} - \varrho) = \exp(-\varrho \cdot \nabla)\psi_\alpha(\mathbf{r}) = \exp\left(\frac{-i\varrho \cdot \mathbf{p}}{\hbar}\right)\psi_\alpha(\mathbf{r})$$

where the momentum operator $\mathbf{p} = -i\hbar\nabla$ has been introduced. Thus if we choose

$$U_r(\varrho) = \exp\frac{-i\varrho \cdot \mathbf{p}}{\hbar} \tag{26.4}$$

Eq. (26.3) is valid for all state vectors. Further, since the operator ∇, which is defined only in the coordinate representation, has been replaced by $i\mathbf{p}/\hbar$, Eq. (26.4) is valid in all representations. It is easily verified that $U_r(\varrho)$ is unitary, since ϱ is real and $\mathbf{p}$ is hermitian.

EQUATION OF MOTION

A physical system in a state represented by any ket $|\alpha(t)\rangle$ at a particular time t can always be displaced in space through the vector ϱ by making use of Eqs. (26.2) and (26.4).[1] However it need not be true that the kets $|\alpha'(t)\rangle$ obtained in this way at different times will represent a possible motion of the system. In other words, if $|\alpha(t)\rangle$ obeys the Schrödinger equation of motion (24.1), it may or may not be true that $|\alpha'(t)\rangle = U_r(\varrho)|\alpha(t)\rangle$ also obeys this equation. In order to see whether or not this is the case, we calculate the time derivative of $|\alpha'(t)\rangle$:

$$i\hbar \frac{d}{dt}|\alpha'(t)\rangle = i\hbar U_r(\varrho)\frac{d}{dt}|\alpha(t)\rangle = U_r(\varrho)H|\alpha(t)\rangle$$

$$= U_r(\varrho)HU_r{}^\dagger(\varrho)|\alpha'(t)\rangle$$

This agrees with Eq. (24.1) if and only if

$$U_r(\varrho)HU_r{}^\dagger(\varrho) = H \qquad \text{or} \qquad [U_r(\varrho),H] = 0 \tag{26.5}$$

If ϱ is allowed to be any vector, Eq. (26.5) is valid only if $\mathbf{p}$ commutes with H. Then, in accordance with the discussion of Eq. (24.4), the momentum operator is a constant of the motion. It also follows from Sec. 22 that $\mathbf{p}$ and H can be diagonalized simultaneously, so that a single state can have well-defined eigenvalues for both momentum and energy.

Th: s we have shown that a physical system that can be displaced in space and still be a possible physical system can be characterized by a constant and well-defined value of the momentum, as well as of the energy. Such a system is said to possess space-displacement *symmetry* or space-displacement *invariance*. This result is reasonable, since a particle can be space-displacement symmetric or invariant only if no force acts on it, in which case its momentum is constant. A free electron possesses this symmetry, whereas the electron in a hydrogen atom does not. In the latter case, displacement of the wave function yields a wave packet that retains its form only momentarily.

SYMMETRY AND DEGENERACY

An important aspect of symmetry has to do with its relation to the degeneracy of energy eigenvalues. Suppose that a ket $|\alpha\rangle$ represents an energy eigenstate of a system, so that $H|\alpha\rangle = E_\alpha|\alpha\rangle$, and that there is some operator Ω that commutes with H. Then it is easily seen that $\Omega|\alpha\rangle$ is also an eigenstate of H with the same energy eigenvalue E_α. Thus, if $\Omega|\alpha\rangle$ is linearly independent of $|\alpha\rangle$, this energy eigenvalue is degenerate.

[1] The subscript S that denotes the Schrödinger picture is omitted here, since only this picture will be used throughout this chapter.

Since a space-displaced state is generally linearly independent of the original state, space-displacement symmetry (for which $\Omega = \mathbf{p}$) gives rise to energy degeneracy of momentum eigenfunctions. This is not a new result, since we know that the energy of a free particle depends only on the magnitude, not the direction, of its momentum. An exceptional situation arises when the state is constant in space, since then the space-displaced state is not linearly independent. Such a state has zero momentum and is nondegenerate.

Energy degeneracy associated with a geometrical symmetry such as space displacement is usually easy to identify. In Sec. 30 we shall consider two less obvious examples, of dynamical rather than geometrical symmetry, where there is also degeneracy. The problem then is to find the operator Ω, analogous to $\mathbf{p}$ above, that commutes with the hamiltonian and hence defines the symmetry.

MATRIX ELEMENTS FOR DISPLACED STATES

A matrix element of a dynamical variable Ω can be calculated for any pair of states and compared with the matrix element of the same operator when the states are displaced. The first matrix element is $\langle \alpha | \Omega | \beta \rangle$, and the second is

$$\langle \alpha' | \Omega | \beta' \rangle = \langle \alpha | U_r{}^\dagger(\varrho) \Omega U_r(\varrho) | \beta \rangle$$

It is apparent that matrix elements of any function of the momentum operator are unchanged when the states are displaced. On the other hand, if Ω is the coordinate operator $\mathbf{r}$, it can be shown that

$$U_r{}^\dagger(\varrho) \mathbf{r} U_r(\varrho) = \mathbf{r} + \varrho \tag{26.6}$$

Thus the matrix elements of $\mathbf{r}$ for the displaced states are equal to the corresponding matrix elements of $\mathbf{r} + \varrho$ for the original states, as expected.

THE GROUP CONCEPT

The branch of mathematics that is appropriate for a full treatment of symmetry is the theory of groups. Although we shall make essentially no use of the formal aspects of group theory in this book, it is often convenient to refer to some of its ideas and terminology. We therefore give a few basic definitions here.[1]

[1] For fuller discussions of symmetry and group theory, see E. P. Wigner, "Group Theory" (Academic, New York, 1959), especially chaps. 15, 20, and 26; M. Hamermesh, "Group Theory and Its Applications to Physical Problems" (Addison-Wesley, Reading, Mass., 1962), especially chap. 8; A. Messiah, "Quantum Mechanics," vol. II, chap. XV and App. D (North Holland Publishing Company, Amsterdam,

A set of objects $a, b, c, \ldots$ form a *group* if a process can be defined that enables us to combine any two of the objects, such as a and b, to form an object ab, and if the following conditions are satisfied.

1. All results of combination, such as ab, are members of the group.
2. The group contains an identity or unit member e that has the properties $ae = ea = a$, where a is any member of the group.
3. Each member a has an inverse a^{-1}, also in the group, such that $a^{-1}a = aa^{-1} = e$.
4. Group combination is associative, so that $(ab)c = a(bc)$.

The members of the group are called *elements*, and the combination process is often called *multiplication*, even though it may not be related to arithmetic or matrix multiplication. For example, the integers 0, $\pm 1, \pm 2, \ldots$ form a group if the combination process is ordinary arithmetic addition; in this case the identity or unit element e is the number 0.

A group is *abelian* if multiplication is commutative, so that $ab = ba$ for all pairs of elements. A group is *continuous* if its elements can be labeled by one or more continuously varying parameters. It is *continuously connected* if a continuous variation of the group parameters leads from any element to any other. A continuous group is *compact* if every infinite sequence of elements of the group has a limit element that is also in the group. Two groups are said to be *isomorphic* to each other if there is a unique one-to-one correspondence between elements of the two groups such that products of corresponding elements correspond to each other. If a group is isomorphic to another group, the elements of which are matrices, the latter is said to be a *matrix representation* of the former.

It is easily established that all displacement vectors ϱ form an abelian, continuously connected, three-parameter, noncompact group, for which the multiplication process is vector addition. Also, the operators $U_r(\varrho)$ form a group that is isomorphic to the group of displacement vectors. In this case the multiplication process is successive operation and in the case of a matrix representation of the operators is matrix multiplication.

1962); M. Tinkham, "Group Theory and Quantum Mechanics" (McGraw-Hill, New York, 1964), especially chap. 5; M. L. Goldberger and K. M. Watson, "Collision Theory," chap. 2 (Wiley, New York, 1964); P. Roman, "Advanced Quantum Theory," chap. 5 and App. 2 (Addison-Wesley, Reading, Mass., 1965); H. J. Lipkin, "Lie Groups for Pedestrians" (North Holland Publishing Company, Amsterdam, 1965); R. Hermann, "Lie Groups for Physicists" (Benjamin, New York, 1966); A. Katz, "Classical Mechanics, Quantum Mechanics, Field Theory," chap. 2 (Academic, New York, 1965).

TIME DISPLACEMENT

We consider next the displacement of a state represented by the ket $|\alpha(t)\rangle$ in time through the interval τ, which changes it into the ket $|\alpha'(t)\rangle$. In analogy with Eq. (26.1), this means that

$$|\alpha'(t + \tau)\rangle = |\alpha(t)\rangle \qquad (26.7)$$

As in the first of Eqs. (26.2), we define an operator $U_t(\tau)$ that produces a generalized rotation of the ket $|\alpha(t)\rangle$ into the ket $|\alpha'(t)\rangle$:

$$U_t(\tau)|\alpha(t)\rangle = |\alpha'(t)\rangle \qquad (26.8)$$

Combination of Eqs. (26.7) and (26.8) gives

$$U_t(\tau)|\alpha(t)\rangle = |\alpha(t - \tau)\rangle \qquad (26.9)$$

The right side of Eq. (26.9) can be reduced, in analogy with Eq. (26.3), to give

$$|\alpha(t - \tau)\rangle = e^{-\tau d/dt}|\alpha(t)\rangle \qquad (26.10)$$

Since our kets are being viewed in the Schrödinger picture, Eq. (24.1) enables us to replace $(d/dt)|\alpha(t)\rangle$ by $(i\hbar)^{-1}H|\alpha(t)\rangle$. However, $(d^2/dt^2)|\alpha(t)\rangle$ can be replaced by $(i\hbar)^{-2}H^2|\alpha(t)\rangle$ only if H is independent of the time, and a similar remark applies to the higher time derivatives that appear in Eq. (26.10). As in Sec. 24, we assume that H is constant and obtain

$$U_t(\tau) = e^{i\tau H/\hbar} \qquad (26.11)$$

Equation (26.11) is a valid expression for the time-displacement operator if it is applied to any ket that represents a physical state, that is, any ket that satisfies the Schrödinger equation (24.1). Since $U_t(\tau)$ commutes with H, it is easily seen that the time-displaced ket $|\alpha'(t)\rangle$ given by Eq. (26.8) also obeys the Schrödinger equation. Thus the assumption that the hamiltonian or energy operator is a constant leads to the conclusion that a physical system can be displaced in time and still be a physical system. Such a system is said to possess time-displacement symmetry or invariance.

Although intuitively obvious, it is slightly more difficult to show that if H depends on the time the system does not possess time-displacement symmetry. In this case the expression for $U_t(\tau)$ is somewhat more complicated than Eq. (26.11). However, it is enough to consider the case in which τ is infinitesimally small and only terms of first order in τ are retained. Then $U_t(\tau)$ is given approximately by $1 + i\tau H(t)/\hbar$ and evidently depends on t as well as on τ. Then, in order to see whether or not $|\alpha'(t)\rangle$ satisfies the Schrödinger equation, we calculate its time derivative from Eq. (26.8):

$$i\hbar \frac{d}{dt} |\alpha'(t)\rangle \approx -\tau \frac{dH}{dt} |\alpha(t)\rangle + U_t(\tau) H(t) |\alpha(t)\rangle$$

To first order in τ, the right side is equal to

$$-\tau \frac{dH}{dt} |\alpha'(t)\rangle + H(t) |\alpha'(t)\rangle$$

so that $|\alpha'(t)\rangle$ does not obey the Schrödinger equation. In other words, if the hamiltonian changes with time, the time-displaced system finds itself in an altered environment and hence will not develop properly in time.

In the case in which H is constant, it might at first be thought that there is a contradiction between the first of Eqs. (24.3),

$$|\alpha(t)\rangle = e^{-iHt/\hbar} |\alpha(0)\rangle$$

and Eq. (26.8), which with the help of (26.11) reads

$$|\alpha'(t)\rangle = e^{i\tau H/\hbar} |\alpha(t)\rangle$$

That they actually agree may be seen by setting $t = -\tau$ in the first equation and $t = 0$ in the second, in which case they become

$$|\alpha(-\tau)\rangle = e^{i\tau H/\hbar} |\alpha(0)\rangle \qquad \text{and} \qquad |\alpha'(0)\rangle = e^{i\tau H/\hbar} |\alpha(0)\rangle$$

respectively. Equation (26.7) with $t = -\tau$ then shows that the left sides are equal. This may be put into words by saying that $|\alpha'(t)\rangle$ has the structure at $t = \tau$ that $|\alpha(t)\rangle$ has at $t = 0$ and hence may be obtained from $|\alpha(\tau)\rangle$ by letting it develop backward in time from τ to 0 in accordance with Eq. (24.3).

27☐ROTATION, ANGULAR MOMENTUM, AND UNITARY GROUPS

As our next symmetry operation we consider the rotation in space of a physical system in a state represented by the ket $|\alpha\rangle$ or the wave function $\psi_\alpha(\mathbf{r})$. We describe a rotation by a linear operator R, which is so defined that any vector $\mathbf{r}$ is rotated into the vector $R\mathbf{r}$. The rotation changes the ket $|\alpha\rangle$ into the ket $|\alpha'\rangle$ or changes the wave function $\psi_\alpha(\mathbf{r})$ into the wave function $\psi_{\alpha'}(\mathbf{r})$. In analogy with Eq. (26.1), this means that

$$\psi_{\alpha'}(R\mathbf{r}) = \psi_\alpha(\mathbf{r}) \tag{27.1}$$

PROPER ROTATION GROUP

Each rotation operator may conveniently be represented by a 3×3 matrix. We write the rectangular components of an arbitrary vector $\mathbf{r}$

and the rotated vector $\mathbf{r}_R$ as column matrices, so that the equation $\mathbf{r}_R = R\mathbf{r}$ is written as the matrix equation

$$\begin{bmatrix} x_R \\ y_R \\ z_R \end{bmatrix} = \begin{bmatrix} R_{xx} & R_{xy} & R_{xz} \\ R_{yx} & R_{yy} & R_{yz} \\ R_{zx} & R_{zy} & R_{zz} \end{bmatrix} \begin{bmatrix} x \\ y \\ z \end{bmatrix} \tag{27.2}$$

The requirement that the components of $\mathbf{r}_R$ be real when the components of $\mathbf{r}$ are real means that the elements of the matrix R are real. Further, the requirement that the scalar product of any two vectors be unchanged when both vectors are subjected to the same rotation can be used to show that R is orthonormal: the three rows of R are orthonormal to each other, the three columns of R are orthonormal to each other; also, the determinant of R is equal to ± 1. We shall consider in this section only *proper rotations*, for which the determinant is equal to $+1$. Since the determinant is not zero, the inverse transformation R^{-1} exists and has the property $\mathbf{r} = R^{-1}\mathbf{r}_R$. It can also be shown that R^{-1} is the transpose of R: $(R^{-1})_{ij} = R_{ji}$, where $i, j = x, y, z$. Finally, since there are six independent constraints on the nine matrix elements R_{ij}, all rotations can be described by three continuously varying parameters.

The matrices R satisfy all the requirements of a group. The combination process is matrix multiplication, which is associative. Multiplication of two matrices with the above properties leads to a third with the same properties. The matrix δ_{ij} is the identity element, and each R has an inverse. An example is easily devised which shows that rotations do not in general commute, so that the group is not abelian. Thus the matrices R form a continuously connected, three-parameter group that is easily seen to be compact. This group is designated $O(3)$, the *orthogonal group* in three dimensions, which is the set of all 3×3 real orthonormal matrices with determinant equal to $+1$.

A continuously connected group in which the parameters of the product of two elements are continuous, differentiable functions of the parameters of the elements is called a *Lie group*. The space- and time-displacement groups are noncompact Lie groups, and the rotation group is a compact Lie group. The Lorentz group has three parameters to describe rotations and three more parameters to describe velocity changes. It is a six-parameter Lie group that is, however, noncompact, since there is no transformation that corresponds to the limiting value c of the velocity change in any direction.

GEOMETRICAL ISOMORPHISM

Each matrix R corresponds to a physical rotation. Hence it can be represented by a vector $\boldsymbol{\phi}$ whose direction is the axis about which rotation occurs (always assumed to be in the clockwise direction when looking out from the origin along $\boldsymbol{\phi}$), and whose magnitude is the angle of rotation in radians. The endpoints of the vectors that represent all possible rotations fill a sphere of radius π; diametrically opposite points on the surface of this sphere represent the same rotation. The process by which two vector endpoints within the sphere are combined to form a third point in the sphere is complicated when described in terms of the coordinates of the first two points but can be determined by putting the three points into one-to-one correspondence with two of the R's and their matrix product. Thus such points in a sphere of radius π form a group that is isomorphic to the rotation group.[1] It is, however, more of pictorial than of calculational value, since the weight function for the group space is not constant.

This geometrical isomorphism can be used to show that the rotation group, although continuously connected, is not *simply connected*. This means that the group parameters may be varied along more than one continuous path leading from any element to any other, so that these paths are not continuously deformable into each other. In the present case there are two distinct paths. One of them goes from element R_1 to element R_2 entirely within the sphere. The other goes from R_1 to the surface of the sphere, reappears at the diametrically opposite point, and then goes to R_2. A path that makes two jumps between diametrically opposite surface points can be reduced to the first kind of path, and so on. Thus the rotation group is *doubly connected*.

INFINITESIMAL ROTATIONS

A great deal can be learned about the structure of a Lie group from a study of the elements that are infinitesimally close to the identity element. As might be expected, this is much simpler than a study of the full group. If the vector $\boldsymbol{\phi}$ is of infinitesimal length and only quantities of first order in $\boldsymbol{\phi}$ are retained, the relation $\mathbf{r}_R = R\mathbf{r}$ may be written

$$\mathbf{r}_R \approx \mathbf{r} + \boldsymbol{\phi} \times \mathbf{r} \tag{27.3}$$

Combination of Eqs. (27.2) and (27.3) shows that

$$R \approx \begin{bmatrix} 1 & -\phi_z & \phi_y \\ \phi_z & 1 & -\phi_x \\ -\phi_y & \phi_x & 1 \end{bmatrix} \tag{27.4}$$

We now wish to find a transformation $U_R(\boldsymbol{\phi})$ that changes the ket $|\alpha\rangle$ into the ket $|\alpha'\rangle$ or changes the wave function $\psi_\alpha(\mathbf{r})$ into the wave function $\psi_{\alpha'}(\mathbf{r})$:

$$U_R(\boldsymbol{\phi})\psi_\alpha(\mathbf{r}) = \psi_{\alpha'}(\mathbf{r}) \tag{27.5}$$

---

[1] Wigner, *op. cit.*, pp. 90, 249.

Combination of Eqs. (27.1) and (27.5) gives

$$U_R(\phi)\psi_\alpha(\mathbf{r}) = \psi_\alpha(R^{-1}\mathbf{r})$$
$$\approx \psi_\alpha(\mathbf{r} - \phi \times \mathbf{r})$$
$$\approx \psi_\alpha(\mathbf{r}) - (\phi \times \mathbf{r}) \cdot \nabla\psi_\alpha(\mathbf{r})$$
$$= \psi_\alpha(\mathbf{r}) - \frac{i}{\hbar}(\phi \times \mathbf{r}) \cdot \mathbf{p}\psi_\alpha(\mathbf{r})$$

in analogy with the derivation of Eq. (26.4). We may thus put

$$U_R(\phi) \approx 1 - \frac{i}{\hbar}\phi \cdot \mathbf{L} \tag{27.6}$$

where in accordance with Eqs. (14.19)

$$\mathbf{L} = \mathbf{r} \times \mathbf{p} \tag{27.7}$$

is the operator for the angular momentum of the particle about the origin.

The three operators L_x, L_y, and L_z are called the *generators* of the infinitesimal rotations about the three coordinate axes through the angles ϕ_x, ϕ_y, and ϕ_z, respectively, in accordance with Eq. (27.6). In similar fashion, the infinitesimal forms of Eqs. (26.4) and (26.11) show that $\mathbf{p}$ and $-H$ are the generators of the infinitesimal displacements in space and time, respectively. The fact that the components of $\mathbf{p}$ commute with each other leads directly to the conclusion that the space-displacement group is abelian. On the other hand, the components of $\mathbf{L}$ do not commute with each other and so the rotation group is not abelian.

The equation of motion of the rotated ket $|\alpha'\rangle$ can be found in exact analogy with the discussion preceding Eq. (26.5). The condition that the system possess rotational symmetry or invariance is that $U_R(\phi)$ commute with H for all ϕ or that the generators L_x, L_y, and L_z commute with H. This last means that the angular momentum $\mathbf{L}$ is a constant of the motion, as is expected for a system that possesses rotational symmetry. It also means that there is energy degeneracy if $\mathbf{L}|\alpha\rangle$ is linearly independent of $|\alpha\rangle$.

SPIN OF A VECTOR PARTICLE

The fact that the generators of infinitesimal symmetry transformations are equal to recognizable dynamical variables in the simple situations thus far considered suggests that they be used to define dynamical variables in more complicated situations. As an example, we now consider a particle possessing internal degrees of freedom that can be related to an intrinsic *spin angular momentum*. The particle is assumed to be described by a vector wave function $\boldsymbol{\psi}_\alpha(\mathbf{r})$ instead of by a scalar wave function $\psi_\alpha(\mathbf{r})$ such as has been considered thus far. Further, we assume that, when the state is rotated, not only does $\mathbf{r}$ change into $R\mathbf{r}$ but also ψ_α changes into $R\psi_\alpha$. Thus Eq. (27.1) becomes

$$\psi_{\alpha'}(R\mathbf{r}) = R\psi_\alpha(\mathbf{r}) \tag{27.8}$$

In similar fashion Eq. (27.5) becomes

$$U_R(\phi)\psi_\alpha(\mathbf{r}) = \psi_{\alpha'}(\mathbf{r}) \tag{27.9}$$

where $U_R(\phi)$ is now a tensor operator since it changes the vectorial character of ψ_α. Combination of Eqs. (27.8) and (27.9) gives to first order in ϕ

$$
\begin{aligned}
U_R(\phi)\psi_\alpha(\mathbf{r}) &= R\psi_\alpha(R^{-1}\mathbf{r}) \\
&\approx \psi_\alpha(R^{-1}\mathbf{r}) + \phi \times \psi_\alpha(R^{-1}\mathbf{r}) \\
&\approx \psi_\alpha(\mathbf{r} - \phi \times \mathbf{r}) + \phi \times \psi_\alpha(\mathbf{r}) \\
&\approx \psi_\alpha(\mathbf{r}) - \frac{i}{\hbar}(\phi \cdot \mathbf{L})\psi_\alpha(\mathbf{r}) + \phi \times \psi_\alpha(\mathbf{r})
\end{aligned}
\tag{27.10}
$$

The tensorial character of $U_R(\phi)$ is most conveniently exhibited by writing it as a 3×3 matrix that multiplies the vector ψ_α to produce the vector $\psi_{\alpha'}$, in analogy with Eq. (27.2). The first two terms on the right side of Eq. (27.10) are then proportional to the unit matrix. Comparison of Eqs. (27.3) and (27.4) shows that the third term may be written in the form

$$\phi \times \psi_\alpha(\mathbf{r}) = -\frac{i}{\hbar}(\phi \cdot \mathbf{S})\psi_\alpha(\mathbf{r})$$

where the components of $\mathbf{S}$ are the following 3×3 matrices:

$$
S_x = i\hbar \begin{bmatrix} 0 & 0 & 0 \\ 0 & 0 & -1 \\ 0 & 1 & 0 \end{bmatrix} \qquad
S_y = i\hbar \begin{bmatrix} 0 & 0 & 1 \\ 0 & 0 & 0 \\ -1 & 0 & 0 \end{bmatrix}
$$

$$
S_z = i\hbar \begin{bmatrix} 0 & -1 & 0 \\ 1 & 0 & 0 \\ 0 & 0 & 0 \end{bmatrix}
\tag{27.11}
$$

With this definition of $\mathbf{S}$ the infinitesimal rotation transformation is

$$U_R(\phi) \approx 1 - \frac{i}{\hbar}\phi \cdot (\mathbf{L} + \mathbf{S}) \tag{27.12}$$

The generators of the infinitesimal rotations are the three components of the vector

$$\mathbf{J} = \mathbf{L} + \mathbf{S} \tag{27.13}$$

which we identify with the total angular momentum of the particle. The orbital angular momentum operator is $\mathbf{L}$, and it acts only on the $\mathbf{r}$ dependence of $\psi_\alpha(\mathbf{r})$ without affecting its components. The operator $\mathbf{S}$ is called the *spin angular momentum*, and it rearranges the components of $\psi_\alpha(\mathbf{r})$ without affecting its $\mathbf{r}$ dependence. Thus $\mathbf{L}$ and $\mathbf{S}$ commute with each other. It often happens that $\mathbf{L}$ and $\mathbf{S}$ do not separately commute with H, whereas $\mathbf{J}$ does. Physically this means that the hamiltonian contains terms that couple spin and orbital angular momentum to each other but not to the surroundings.

It was found in Eq. (14.22) that the possible eigenvalues of $\mathbf{L}^2 = L_x{}^2 + L_y{}^2 + L_z{}^2$ are $l(l+1)\hbar^2$, where l is a positive integer or zero and is called the *orbital angular momentum quantum number*. Direct substitution from the matrices (27.11) shows that $\mathbf{S}^2 = S_x{}^2 + S_y{}^2 + S_z{}^2$ is equal to $2\hbar^2$ times the unit matrix. This corresponds to $l = 1$ in the orbital case, so that the particle carries spin angular momentum $\hbar$. This conclusion derives from the assumed vectorial transformation property of the infinitesimal elements of a Lie group determine the main characteristics of the structure of the entire group, since in effect they specify how the group elements may be integrated to a finite distance from the identity element.[1]

COMMUTATION RELATIONS FOR THE GENERATORS

It was remarked above that the components of $\mathbf{L}$ do not commute with each other, and so the rotation group is not abelian. More generally, it can be shown that the commutation relations between the generators of the infinitesimal elements of a Lie group determine the main characteristics of the structure of the entire group, since in effect they specify how the group elements may be integrated to a finite distance from the identity element.[1]

The commutation relations between the components of $\mathbf{L}$ are readily found from Eq. (27.7) and the quantum conditions (24.26). The results are

$$[L_x,L_y] = i\hbar L_z \qquad [L_y,L_z] = i\hbar L_x \qquad [L_z,L_x] = i\hbar L_y \qquad (27.14)$$

Direct substitution from Eqs. (27.11) shows that the components of $\mathbf{S}$ satisfy the same relations. Then, since $\mathbf{L}$ and $\mathbf{S}$ commute with each other, the components of $\mathbf{J}$ also satisfy Eqs. (27.14). These three equations are often written in the equivalent form

$$\mathbf{J} \times \mathbf{J} = i\hbar\mathbf{J} \qquad\qquad (27.15)$$

The relations (27.15) have been established only for the total angular momentum of spin zero (scalar) and spin one (vector) particles. Nevertheless we adopt them as the defining equations for the angular momentum and for the rotation group generators in the general case. The generators of a Lie group form the basis of a *Lie algebra;* this algebra is

[1] Wigner, *op. cit.*

closed in the sense that the commutator of any pair of generators is a linear combination of the generators. Our next task will be to solve the algebraic relations (27.15) in order to obtain explicit matrices for the J's and hence for the infinitesimal elements of the group.

Once the $\mathbf{J}$ matrices are known, it is an easy matter to extend the infinitesimal rotation operators given by Eqs. (27.12) and (27.13) to finite rotations. Suppose we wish to find $U_R(\phi)$ for some finite rotation ϕ. We choose coordinate axes so that one of them, say the x axis, is along ϕ. Then the effect of a small increase in the magnitude of ϕ, from ϕ to $\phi + \Delta\phi$, is to follow the finite rotation $U_R(\phi)$ by the infinitesimal rotation $1 - (i/\hbar) \Delta\phi J_x$, to give

$$U_R(\phi + \Delta\phi) \approx \left(1 - \frac{i}{\hbar} \Delta\phi J_x\right) U_R(\phi)$$

Thus $U_R(\phi)$ satisfies the differential equation

$$\frac{dU_R(\phi)}{d\phi} = -\frac{i}{\hbar} J_x U_R(\phi)$$

together with the boundary condition $U_R(0) = 1$. This equation is readily integrated to give

$$U_R(\phi) = e^{-i\phi J_x/\hbar}$$

Since no restriction was involved in the choice of the x axis for ϕ, we obtain

$$U_R(\phi) = \exp \frac{-i\phi \cdot \mathbf{J}}{\hbar} \tag{27.16}$$

as the operator for finite rotations.

CHOICE OF A REPRESENTATION

We now solve Eqs. (27.15) of the Lie algebra in a manner similar to that used for the harmonic oscillator in Sec. 25. We have three hermitian dynamical variables, J_x, J_y, and J_z, no one of which commutes with any other. Thus not more than one of them can be made diagonal. However we can construct $\mathbf{J}^2$ from them, and it is easily seen that it commutes with each component of $\mathbf{J}$. In analogy with the energy representation in the oscillator problem, we now choose a representation in which $\mathbf{J}^2$ and one of the components, say J_z, are diagonal.

Just as in the oscillator problem it was more convenient to work with $p \pm im\omega_c x$ than with x and p, so it proves to be more convenient now to work with $J_x \pm iJ_y$ than with J_x and J_y. We therefore define the nonhermitian operators

$$J_+ = J_x + iJ_y \qquad J_- = J_x - iJ_y \tag{27.17}$$

which are hermitian adjoints of each other and play a role similar to the raising and lowering operators in the oscillator problem. It is evident that $J_\pm$ commute with $\mathbf{J}^2$, and the other commutation relations become

$$[J_z,J_+] = \hbar J_+ \qquad [J_z,J_-] = -\hbar J_- \qquad [J_+,J_-] = 2\hbar J_z \qquad (27.18)$$

We label the rows and the columns of our representation with a pair of numbers j and m. It is convenient to choose the eigenvalues of J_z to be equal to $m\hbar$, where m is a set of dimensionless real numbers. However, the relation between j and the eigenvalues of $\mathbf{J}^2$ will be left open for the present; these eigenvalues will be written $f(j)\hbar^2$, where $f(j)$ is a dimensionless function of j. In our representation, then, the matrices for $\mathbf{J}^2$ and J_z are

$$\langle jm|\mathbf{J}^2|j'm'\rangle = f(j)\hbar^2\,\delta_{jj'}\,\delta_{mm'} \qquad \langle jm|J_z|j'm'\rangle = m\hbar\,\delta_{jj'}\,\delta_{mm'} \quad (27.19)$$

Further, since $J_\pm$ commute with $\mathbf{J}^2$, they are diagonal in j although not in m.

The first of Eqs. (27.18) may be written in this representation as

$$\langle jm|J_z|j'm'\rangle\langle j'm'|J_+|j''m''\rangle - \langle jm|J_+|j'm'\rangle\langle j'm'|J_z|j''m''\rangle$$
$$= \hbar\langle jm|J_+|j''m''\rangle$$

where the summation symbols for j' and m' have not been written explicitly. Both sides of this equation vanish unless $f(j) = f(j') = f(j'')$. We then obtain, with the help of the second of Eqs. (27.19),

$$(m - m'' - 1)\langle jm|J_+|jm''\rangle = 0 \qquad (27.20)$$

Thus $\langle jm|J_+|jm''\rangle$ fails to vanish only when $m = m'' + 1$. This means that the result of operating with J_+ on the ket $|jm''\rangle$ is some multiple of the ket $|j, m'' + 1\rangle$, so that J_+ is a raising operator on the eigenvalues of J_z. In similar fashion, the second of Eqs. (27.18) leads to

$$(m - m'' + 1)\langle jm|J_-|jm''\rangle = 0 \qquad (27.21)$$

so that J_- is a lowering operator.

We can thus write the nonvanishing matrix elements of J_+ and its hermitian adjoint J_- in the forms

$$\langle j, m + 1|J_+|jm\rangle = \lambda_m\hbar \qquad \langle jm|J_-|j, m + 1\rangle = \lambda_m^*\hbar \qquad (27.22)$$

Substitution of the matrix elements (27.22) into the third of Eqs. (27.18) shows that the off-diagonal elements vanish on both sides, and a typical diagonal element is

$$|\lambda_{m-1}|^2 - |\lambda_m|^2 = 2m \qquad (27.23)$$

It should be noted that λ_m may depend on j as well as on m.

VALUES OF m, $f(j)$, AND λ_m

Equation (27.23) is a first-order linear difference equation in $|\lambda_m|^2$, and its general solution has one arbitrary constant:

$$|\lambda_m|^2 = C - m(m + 1) \qquad (27.24)$$

Now $|\lambda_m|^2$ is necessarily positive or zero, and yet the right side of (27.24) evidently attains negative values for sufficiently large positive and negative values of m. This does not cause difficulty if there are two values m_1 and m_2 of m for which $\lambda_m = 0$ and if these two values differ from each other by an integer. If this is the case, the series of m values in which successive terms differ by unity can terminate at both ends without $|\lambda_m|^2$ becoming negative. Equation (27.20) can be satisfied at the upper end ($m = m_1$) by having $\langle j, m_1 + 1|J_+|jm_1\rangle = 0$ rather than by having an eigenvalue of J_z greater than $m_1\hbar$. Similarly, Eq. (27.21) can be satisfied at the lower end ($m = m_2$) by having $\langle jm_2|J_-|j, m_2 + 1\rangle = 0$ rather than by having an eigenvalue of J_z less than $(m_2 + 1)\hbar$. $|\lambda_m|^2$ is evidently nonnegative for m values that range from $m_2 + 1$ up to m_1, inclusive.

We thus have a finite series of values of m ranging from m_1 down to $m_2 + 1$ by unit steps, where m_1 and m_2 are the larger and smaller roots of the quadratic equation $C - m(m + 1) = 0$:

$$m_1 = -\tfrac{1}{2} + \tfrac{1}{2}(1 + 4C)^{\frac{1}{2}} \qquad m_2 = -\tfrac{1}{2} - \tfrac{1}{2}(1 + 4C)^{\frac{1}{2}}$$

Since $m_2 + 1$ is equal to $-m_1$, the series of m values ranges from m_1 to $-m_1$ by unit steps, which means that $2m_1$ must be a positive integer or zero. Thus m_1 is restricted to the series of values $0, \tfrac{1}{2}, 1, \tfrac{3}{2}, \ldots$ and $C = m_1(m_1 + 1)$.

In order to evaluate $f(j)$, we calculate the jm diagonal matrix element of $\mathbf{J}^2 = \tfrac{1}{2}(J_+J_- + J_-J_+) + J_z^2$. The result is

$$f(j)\hbar^2 = \tfrac{1}{2}|\lambda_{m-1}|^2\hbar^2 + \tfrac{1}{2}|\lambda_m|^2\hbar^2 + m^2\hbar^2$$
$$= C\hbar^2 = m_1(m_1 + 1)\hbar^2$$

where use has been made of Eq. (27.24). We rename m_1, which is the largest value of m for a given series, and call it j, so that the eigenvalues of $\mathbf{J}^2$ are $j(j + 1)\hbar^2$, where j is zero or a positive integer or half an odd integer. For each value of j, there are $2j + 1$ values of m that range by integer steps from j to $-j$. The nonvanishing matrix elements of the raising and lowering operators are obtained from Eqs. (27.22) and (27.24) and may be written in various equivalent ways:

$$\langle j, m + 1|J_+|jm\rangle = [j(j + 1) - m(m + 1)]^{\frac{1}{2}}\hbar$$
$$= [(j - m)(j + m + 1)]^{\frac{1}{2}}\hbar$$
$$\langle j, m - 1|J_-|jm\rangle = [j(j + 1) - m(m - 1)]^{\frac{1}{2}}\hbar$$
$$= [(j + m)(j - m + 1)]^{\frac{1}{2}}\hbar \qquad (27.25)$$
$$J_z|jm\rangle = m\hbar|jm\rangle$$
$$J_\pm|jm\rangle = [j(j + 1) - m(m \pm 1)]^{\frac{1}{2}}\hbar|j, m \pm 1\rangle$$

An arbitrary phase factor has been set equal to unity, in conformity with the usual convention.

ANGULAR MOMENTUM MATRICES

Our choice of a representation in which $\mathbf{J}^2$ and J_z are diagonal has led to discrete sequences of values for the corresponding labels j and m. The infinite matrices thus obtained are most conveniently handled by breaking them up into an infinite set of finite matrices, each of which is characterized by a particular value of j and has $2j + 1$ rows and columns.

For $j = 0$, $\mathbf{J}^2$ and the components of $\mathbf{J}$ are all represented by null matrices of unit rank: $[0]$. The matrices for the next three values of j are obtained by using Eqs. (27.17) and (27.25):

$j = \frac{1}{2}$:

$$J_x = \tfrac{1}{2}\hbar \begin{bmatrix} 0 & 1 \\ 1 & 0 \end{bmatrix} \qquad J_y = \tfrac{1}{2}\hbar \begin{bmatrix} 0 & -i \\ i & 0 \end{bmatrix}$$

$$J_z = \tfrac{1}{2}\hbar \begin{bmatrix} 1 & 0 \\ 0 & -1 \end{bmatrix} \qquad \mathbf{J}^2 = \tfrac{3}{4}\hbar^2 \begin{bmatrix} 1 & 0 \\ 0 & 1 \end{bmatrix}$$

$j = 1$:

$$J_x = \frac{\hbar}{\sqrt{2}} \begin{bmatrix} 0 & 1 & 0 \\ 1 & 0 & 1 \\ 0 & 1 & 0 \end{bmatrix} \qquad J_y = \frac{\hbar}{\sqrt{2}} \begin{bmatrix} 0 & -i & 0 \\ i & 0 & -i \\ 0 & i & 0 \end{bmatrix}$$

$$J_z = \hbar \begin{bmatrix} 1 & 0 & 0 \\ 0 & 0 & 0 \\ 0 & 0 & -1 \end{bmatrix} \qquad \mathbf{J}^2 = 2\hbar^2 \begin{bmatrix} 1 & 0 & 0 \\ 0 & 1 & 0 \\ 0 & 0 & 1 \end{bmatrix}$$

$$(27.26)$$

$j = \frac{3}{2}$:

$$J_x = \tfrac{1}{2}\hbar \begin{bmatrix} 0 & \sqrt{3} & 0 & 0 \\ \sqrt{3} & 0 & 2 & 0 \\ 0 & 2 & 0 & \sqrt{3} \\ 0 & 0 & \sqrt{3} & 0 \end{bmatrix}$$

$$J_y = \tfrac{1}{2}\hbar \begin{bmatrix} 0 & -i\sqrt{3} & 0 & 0 \\ i\sqrt{3} & 0 & -2i & 0 \\ 0 & 2i & 0 & -i\sqrt{3} \\ 0 & 0 & i\sqrt{3} & 0 \end{bmatrix}$$

$$J_z = \tfrac{1}{2}\hbar \begin{bmatrix} 3 & 0 & 0 & 0 \\ 0 & 1 & 0 & 0 \\ 0 & 0 & -1 & 0 \\ 0 & 0 & 0 & -3 \end{bmatrix} \qquad \mathbf{J}^2 = \tfrac{15}{4}\hbar^2 \begin{bmatrix} 1 & 0 & 0 & 0 \\ 0 & 1 & 0 & 0 \\ 0 & 0 & 1 & 0 \\ 0 & 0 & 0 & 1 \end{bmatrix}$$

CONNECTION WITH SPHERICAL HARMONICS

Comparison of the foregoing results with those of Sec. 14 suggests a close connection between the angular momentum matrices, for which $j = l$ is an integer, and the spherical harmonics $Y_{lm}(\theta,\phi)$ defined in Eq. (14.16). The eigenvalue equations (14.22) and (14.23) are consistent with the diagonal forms of the $\mathbf{J}^2$ and J_z matrices, respectively. Further, the $L_\pm$ can be expressed as differential operators with the help of Eqs. (14.20):

$$
\begin{aligned}
L_+ &= L_x + iL_y = \hbar e^{i\phi}\left(\frac{\partial}{\partial\theta} + i\cot\theta\,\frac{\partial}{\partial\phi}\right) \\
L_- &= L_x - iL_y = \hbar e^{-i\phi}\left(-\frac{\partial}{\partial\theta} + i\cot\theta\,\frac{\partial}{\partial\phi}\right)
\end{aligned}
\tag{27.27}
$$

It is then possible, by using the properties of the spherical harmonics discussed in Sec. 14, to show that

$$
\begin{aligned}
L_+Y_{lm}(\theta,\phi) &= [l(l+1) - m(m+1)]^{\frac{1}{2}}\hbar Y_{l,m+1}(\theta,\phi) \\
L_-Y_{lm}(\theta,\phi) &= [l(l+1) - m(m-1)]^{\frac{1}{2}}\hbar Y_{l,m-1}(\theta,\phi)
\end{aligned}
\tag{27.28}
$$

as would be expected from Eqs. (27.25).

It is apparent that the spherical harmonics can be regarded as constituting a unitary transformation from the angular momentum to the angular coordinate representation, in accordance with the transformation theory developed in Sec. 23:

$$
Y_{lm}(\theta,\phi) = \langle\theta\phi|lm\rangle
\tag{27.29}
$$

In using Eq. (27.29), it must be remembered that the weight function $\sin\theta$ is to be included whenever an angular coordinate integration is performed.

SPIN ANGULAR MOMENTUM

Since the orbital angular momentum $\mathbf{L} = \mathbf{r} \times \mathbf{p}$ is expressed in terms of the coordinates and momenta, the quantity $\mathbf{L}^2$ is not in general a constant of the motion. Thus the quantum number l need not be well defined and cannot be used to characterize a particle except in very restricted circumstances. It is, however, possible to have an angular momentum $\mathbf{S}$ that satisfies the fundamental commutation relations (27.15) and such that $\mathbf{S}^2$ commutes with all dynamical variables; a necessary condition is that $\mathbf{S}$ not be expressed in terms of $\mathbf{r}$ and $\mathbf{p}$. Then $\mathbf{S}^2$ is strictly a constant of the motion and can be replaced by the number $s(s+1)\hbar^2$, where s is an integer or half an odd integer. We have already seen an example of such an intrinsic spin angular momentum, in which a vector wave function was found to have $s = 1$. As expected, this wave function has $2s + 1 = 3$ components, and the spin matrices (27.11) are essentially the same as the matrices in (27.26) that correspond to $j = 1$. The second set of matrices may be obtained from the first by a unitary transformation that merely has the effect of regrouping the components of the vector wave function (see Prob. 7).

It is found experimentally that electrons, protons, neutrons, neutrinos, and μ mesons (muons) each have $s = \frac{1}{2}$, photons have $s = 1$, and π mesons (pions) have $s = 0$. There are also other shorter-lived particles and aggregates of particles that are characterized by definite values of the spin angular momentum.[1]

COVERING GROUP

The angular momentum matrices that correspond to half-odd-integer values of j cannot represent pure orbital angular momenta and so can appear in nature only in connection with spin. A particle or system that has $j = \frac{1}{2}, \frac{3}{2}, \ldots$ has the following interesting property. Suppose that a state of such a system is rotated through 2π radians. For convenience we choose the axis of rotation to be the z axis and calculate the rotation operator from Eq. (27.16):

$$U_R(2\pi) = e^{-2\pi i J_z/\hbar}$$

Since the J_z matrices given in Eqs. (27.26) are diagonal, $U_R(2\pi)$ is also diagonal and has eigenvalues $e^{-2\pi i m}$, where m is half an odd integer. Thus $U_R(2\pi)$ is equal to -1 times the unit matrix. It is easily seen that this result applies to rotation of 2π radians about any axis, since the component of $\mathbf{J}$ in that direction can always be chosen to be diagonal.

We conclude that rotation of a half-odd-integer spin particle through 2π radians changes the sign of its state function. An integer spin particle is unchanged by a 2π rotation, whereas a half-odd-integer spin particle requires a 4π rotation to return to itself. Since $s = \frac{1}{2}$ particles actually occur in nature, this result cannot be dismissed as a mathematical curiosity. That there is no conflict with experience follows from the fact that the wave function itself is not a directly measurable quantity. Rather, bilinear combinations of the wave functions appear in the results of measurements, and these do not change sign on 2π rotation.

We see then that half of the matrices that can be used to represent $\mathbf{J}$ or $U_R(\phi)$ are double-valued with respect to the vectors ϕ. This suggests that these representations could be made single-valued by distinguishing between ϕ's that differ by a 2π rotation, for example, by enlarging the

---

[1] See, for example, K. Nishijima, "Fundamental Particles" (Benjamin, New York, 1964); S. Gasiorowicz, "Elementary Particle Physics," pt. III (Wiley, New York, 1966); A. H. Rosenfeld, A. Barbaro-Galtieri, W. J. Podolsky, L. R. Price, P. Soding, C. G. Wohl, M. Roos, and W. J. Willis, *Rev. Mod. Phys.* **39**, 1 (1967).

sphere of radius π that contains the endpoints of these vectors into a sphere of radius 2π. As before, the weight function for the group space is not constant throughout the sphere. This provides a geometrical isomorphism to a new group, which has twice as many elements as the rotation group. Although the rotation group is doubly connected, the new group is seen to be simply connected since the entire surface of the sphere of radius 2π corresponds to a single element of the group. This new group is called the *universal covering group*, or simply the *covering group*, of the rotation group. It is said to be *homomorphic* onto the rotation group since to each element of the covering group there corresponds one and only one element of the rotation group, to each element of the rotation group there corresponds at least one element (actually two) of the covering group, and there is a correspondence with respect to group multiplication.[1]

UNITARY AND SPECIAL UNITARY GROUPS IN TWO DIMENSIONS

The lowest-rank nontrivial representation of the generators of the rotation group are the first three matrices of Eqs. (27.26), which we write in the form

$$\mathbf{J} = \tfrac{1}{2}\hbar\boldsymbol{\sigma}$$

$$\sigma_x = \begin{bmatrix} 0 & 1 \\ 1 & 0 \end{bmatrix} \qquad \sigma_y = \begin{bmatrix} 0 & -i \\ i & 0 \end{bmatrix} \qquad \sigma_z = \begin{bmatrix} 1 & 0 \\ 0 & -1 \end{bmatrix} \qquad (27.30)$$

The σ's are called the *Pauli spin matrices*, since they were first discovered in connection with electron spin.[2] The $U_R(\boldsymbol{\phi})$ generated in accordance with Eqs. (27.16) and (27.30) have two rows and columns and are double-valued with respect to the vectors $\boldsymbol{\phi}$, so that the Pauli matrices generate a representation of the covering group. It is apparent that, since $\mathbf{J}$ is hermitian, $U_R(\boldsymbol{\phi})$ is unitary.

It is easily seen that the set of all unitary matrices with two rows and columns form a group for which the combination process is matrix multiplication. This is the *unitary group* in two dimensions, designated $U(2)$. However, this group is larger than the group of matrices $U_R(\boldsymbol{\phi})$ constructed from (27.16) and (27.30) with all real vectors $\boldsymbol{\phi}$, since the matrices that appear in the exponent of $U_R(\boldsymbol{\phi})$ have zero trace. Now, from Eq. (22.22),

$$\det\left(e^A\right) = e^{\operatorname{tr}(A)} \qquad (27.31)$$

Since the trace of each component of $\boldsymbol{\sigma}$ is zero, the $U_R(\boldsymbol{\phi})$ have unit determinant. Thus the covering group is what is called the *special*

---

[1] Wigner, *op. cit.*, p. 249.

[2] W. Pauli, *Z. Physik* **43**, 601 (1927); electron spin is discussed more fully in Sec. 41.

unitary group or the *unitary unimodular group* in two dimensions, designated $SU(2)$, which is the group of all 2×2 unitary matrices with determinant equal to $+1$. These matrices do in fact form a group since the unimodular property is preserved in matrix multiplication.

THE GROUPS $U(n)$ **AND** $SU(n)$

A unitary matrix that has n rows and columns can be written in the form

$$U = e^{iH} \tag{27.32}$$

where H is a hermitian matrix that has n rows and columns. All such matrices U clearly form a group, designated $U(n)$, for which the combination process is matrix multiplication. The diagonal matrix elements of H are real, and the off-diagonal elements symmetrically located with respect to the principal diagonal are complex conjugates of each other. Thus H, and hence also U, is characterized by n^2 independent parameters. The group $U(n)$ is easily seen to be a continuously connected, n^2-parameter, compact Lie group.

The trace of any hermitian matrix is real, and the determinant of any unitary matrix is a complex number of unit magnitude, so that in accordance with Eqs. (27.31) and (27.32)

$$\operatorname{tr}(H) = \alpha \qquad \det(U) = e^{i\alpha} \qquad \alpha \text{ real} \tag{27.33}$$

Thus if the determinant of U is required to be equal to $+1$, a single constraint is placed on the n^2 parameters, since then $\alpha = 0 \pmod{2\pi}$. These matrices also form a continuously connected, compact Lie group. It is designated $SU(n)$ and has $n^2 - 1$ parameters. Every member of $SU(n)$ is clearly a member of $U(n)$, but the converse is not true. $SU(n)$ is therefore said to be a *subgroup* of $U(n)$.

We denote a typical member of $SU(n)$ by U_0, where

$$U_0 = e^{iH_0} \qquad \operatorname{tr}(H_0) = 0 \qquad \det(U_0) = 1 \tag{27.34}$$

Then from a typical member of $U(n)$, characterized by Eqs. (27.32) and (27.33), we may construct a corresponding matrix U_0 such that

$$H = H_0 + \frac{\alpha}{n}\mathbf{1} \qquad U = (e^{i\alpha/n}\mathbf{1})U_0 = U_0(e^{i\alpha/n}\mathbf{1})$$

where $\mathbf{1}$ is the n-dimensional unit matrix, and U_0 and H_0 are related by (27.34). The numbers $e^{i\alpha/n}$ are 1×1 unitary matrices that constitute the group $U(1)$, and the $n \times n$ matrices $e^{i\alpha/n}\mathbf{1}$ evidently form an n-dimensional matrix representation of $U(1)$. Thus any member of $U(n)$ can be written as a matrix product of appropriate members of $U(1)$ and $SU(n)$.

It is not difficult to see that $U(n)$ is a subgroup of $U(m)$, and $SU(n)$ is a subgroup of $SU(m)$, provided that $n < m$. Any member U of $U(n)$ can be expanded to an $m \times m$ unitary matrix by adding rows and columns in the following way:

$$\begin{bmatrix} U & O \\ O & 1 \end{bmatrix} \tag{27.35}$$

Here 1 is the unit matrix with $m - n$ rows and columns, and O is a rectangular null matrix. The corresponding hermitian matrix H can be expanded in a similar fashion to

$$\begin{bmatrix} H & O \\ O & O \end{bmatrix} \tag{27.36}$$

where clearly (27.35) and (27.36) are related by Eq. (27.32). Thus a particular subset of the matrices of $U(m)$ constitute a matrix representation of $U(n)$, and similarly for $SU(m)$ and $SU(n)$.

GENERATORS OF $U(n)$ AND $SU(n)$

The generators of any Lie group are defined in terms of the group elements that are infinitesimally close to the unit element, in analogy with Eq. (27.6). Thus, if the group has s parameters, the s generators λ_j specify an infinitesimal element of the group in terms of s infinitesimal real parameters ϕ_j:

$$1 + i \sum_{j=1}^{s} \phi_j \lambda_j$$

For $U(n)$, the generators may be taken to be any n^2 linearly independent hermitian matrices with n rows and columns. Since i times the commutator of any pair of these is also hermitian, it can be expressed as a linear combination of the generators. Hence the Lie algebra of $U(n)$ is closed. In the same way, the generators of $SU(n)$ may be taken to be any $n^2 - 1$ linearly independent traceless hermitian matrices with n rows and columns. Again, i times the commutator of any pair of these is also hermitian and traceless, and so the algebra is closed.

In the case $n = 2$, the special unitary group has $2^2 - 1 = 3$ parameters, which may be taken to be the three components of the real vector ϕ. A convenient choice for the three generators is that defined by Eqs. (27.30), which is consistent with the commutation relations (27.15). It is apparent that no two of the three generators commute with each other. The *rank* of a group is defined to be the maximum number of mutually commuting generators, so that $SU(2)$ is of rank 1.

We found earlier in this section that a particular representation of a Lie algebra, and hence of the group generated by the algebra, is conveniently specified by choosing as many operators to be diagonal as possible. Thus we started with the $O(3)$ algebra, defined by the commutation relations (27.14) or (27.15), and chose a representation in which the commuting operators J_z and $\mathbf{J}^2$ are diagonal, as in (27.19). Solution of Eqs. (27.15) then led to half-odd-integer as well as to integer values of j and hence to the recognition that the covering group of $O(3)$ is $SU(2)$. In this way the operator $\mathbf{J}^2$, constructed from the generators, played an essential role in determining the representations.

According to a theorem of Racah,[1] the number of independent operators that can be constructed from the generators, like $\mathbf{J}^2$ above, and that commute with all the generators of a Lie group, is equal to the rank of the group. It was first recognized by Casimir[2] that one such operator can always be formed by taking a suitable bilinear combination of the generators; they are therefore called *Casimir operators*. Since $SU(2)$ is of rank 1, its only Casimir operator is $\mathbf{J}^2$.

THE $SU(3)$ GROUP

The special unitary group in three dimensions has $3^2 - 1 = 8$ generators, $\lambda_1, \ldots, \lambda_8$, which may be chosen in many convenient ways. Since $SU(2)$ is a useful subgroup of $SU(3)$, we specify those three generators of $SU(3)$ that are also generators of $SU(2)$ by expanding the Pauli matrices (27.30) from two to three rows and columns in accordance with (27.36).

$$\lambda_1 = \begin{bmatrix} 0 & 1 & 0 \\ 1 & 0 & 0 \\ 0 & 0 & 0 \end{bmatrix} \qquad \lambda_2 = \begin{bmatrix} 0 & -i & 0 \\ i & 0 & 0 \\ 0 & 0 & 0 \end{bmatrix} \qquad \lambda_3 = \begin{bmatrix} 1 & 0 & 0 \\ 0 & -1 & 0 \\ 0 & 0 & 0 \end{bmatrix}$$

$$(27.37)$$

These first three of the eight λ's evidently satisfy the same commutation relations as the σ's; the relations may be written

$$[\sigma_i, \sigma_j] = 2i \sum_k \epsilon_{ijk}\sigma_k \qquad i, j, k = x, y, z \text{ or } 1, 2, 3 \qquad (27.38)$$

where ϵ_{ijk} is the fully antisymmetric Kronecker symbol whose only nonvanishing values are

$$\epsilon_{123} = \epsilon_{231} = \epsilon_{312} = -\epsilon_{132} = -\epsilon_{321} = -\epsilon_{213} = 1 \qquad (27.39)$$

---

[1] G. Racah, *Rend. Lincei* **8**, 108 (1950); "Group Theory and Spectroscopy," CERN preprint 61-8, 1961 (reprint of 1951 lectures at Institute for Advanced Study, Princeton, N.J.).

[2] H. B. G. Casimir, *Proc. Roy. Soc. Amsterdam* **34**, 844 (1931).

The remaining five λ's may still be chosen in many ways. However, since the principal application of the $SU(3)$ algebra is to the classification of elementary particles, we follow the notation adopted in that connection:[1]

$$\lambda_4 = \begin{bmatrix} 0 & 0 & 1 \\ 0 & 0 & 0 \\ 1 & 0 & 0 \end{bmatrix} \qquad \lambda_5 = \begin{bmatrix} 0 & 0 & -i \\ 0 & 0 & 0 \\ i & 0 & 0 \end{bmatrix} \qquad \lambda_6 = \begin{bmatrix} 0 & 0 & 0 \\ 0 & 0 & 1 \\ 0 & 1 & 0 \end{bmatrix}$$

(27.40)

$$\lambda_7 = \begin{bmatrix} 0 & 0 & 0 \\ 0 & 0 & -i \\ 0 & i & 0 \end{bmatrix} \qquad \lambda_8 = \frac{1}{\sqrt{3}} \begin{bmatrix} 1 & 0 & 0 \\ 0 & 1 & 0 \\ 0 & 0 & -2 \end{bmatrix}$$

It is easily verified that the analog of Eq. (27.38) is

$$[\lambda_i, \lambda_j] = 2i \sum_k f_{ijk} \lambda_k \qquad i, j, k = 1, \ldots, 8 \qquad (27.41)$$

where f_{ijk} is fully antisymmetric, so that it changes sign when any two of its indices are interchanged. The only nonvanishing values of f_{ijk} are permutations of the following:

$$f_{123} = 1 \qquad f_{147} = f_{165} = f_{246} = f_{257} = f_{345} = f_{376} = \tfrac{1}{2} \qquad (27.42)$$
$$f_{458} = f_{678} = \tfrac{1}{2}\sqrt{3}$$

Thus f_{123} is equal to the ϵ_{123} given by (27.39), as expected.

There are at most two of the eight generators that commute with each other, λ_8 and one of the first three λ's in the present notation, so that $SU(3)$ is of rank 2. Thus there are two Casimir operators that commute with all the λ's. One of these is

$$C = \sum_{i=1}^{8} \lambda_i^2 \qquad (27.43)$$

and the other is a rather complicated sum of trilinear products of the λ's.[2] It is important to note that the relation $[C, \lambda_i] = 0$ must be established from the operator equations (27.41) to (27.43) and not from the particular matrix representation of the λ's given by (27.37) and (27.40).

REPRESENTATION IN TERMS OF COORDINATES AND MOMENTA

It was noted earlier that the orbital angular momentum operators (27.7) satisfy the commutation relations (27.14) for the generators of $O(3)$ or $SU(2)$, provided that the components of $\mathbf{r}$ and $\mathbf{p}$ satisfy the quantum

[1] M. Gell-Mann and Y. Ne'eman, "The Eightfold Way" (Benjamin, New York, 1964).
[2] J. J. de Swart, *Rev. Mod. Phys.* **35**, 916 (1963).

conditions given.   Thus we would expect to be able to identify three of the eight generators of $SU(3)$ with the components of **L**.   Once this is done, it is reasonable to expect that the other five generators can also be represented in terms of coordinates and momenta.   Since there are five of them, it is natural to attempt to associate them with the five components of some quadrupole tensor.[1]   We are led in this way to consider the following eight quantities as possible representations of the eight generators of $SU(3)$:

$$L_x = yp_z - zp_y \qquad L_y = zp_x - xp_z \qquad L_z = xp_y - yp_x$$
$$Q_{xy} = \alpha xy + \beta p_x p_y \qquad Q_{yz} = \alpha yz + \beta p_y p_z \qquad Q_{zx} = \alpha zx + \beta p_z p_x$$
$$\text{(27.44)}$$

$$Q_0 = \frac{\alpha}{2\sqrt{3}}(x^2 + y^2 - 2z^2) + \frac{\beta}{2\sqrt{3}}(p_x{}^2 + p_y{}^2 - 2p_z{}^2)$$

$$Q_1 = \frac{\alpha}{2}(x^2 - y^2) + \frac{\beta}{2}(p_x{}^2 - p_y{}^2)$$

where α and β are some dimensional real numbers.

The 28 commutators of these eight operators are readily worked out and may then be compared with the commutators of the eight λ's, given in Eqs. (27.41) and (27.42).   It might at first be thought reasonable to identify L_x, L_y, and L_z with multiples of λ_1, λ_2, and λ_3, respectively, and the commutation relations (27.38) admit of this possibility.   However, it then turns out to be impossible to find linear combinations of the λ's that correspond to the five Q's.   The reason for this derives from the difference between the way in which $SU(2)$ is a subgroup of $SU(3)$ and the way in which $O(3)$ is a subgroup of $SU(3)$.[2]   The Pauli matrices (27.30), which are the generators of $SU(2)$, were expanded from two to three rows and columns to yield the first three λ's given in (27.37).   On the other hand, $O(3)$ is a subgroup of $SU(3)$ for the reason that the rotation matrix R, given in Eq. (27.2), is a 3×3 real orthonormal matrix with determinant equal to unity and hence a special case of a 3×3 unitary unimodular matrix.   It is clearly impossible to find a representation of the typical infinitesimal rotation (27.4) that is of the form (27.37), since the third rows and third columns of the latter all consist of zeros.   This conclusion is not surprising when it is remembered that λ_1, λ_2, λ_3 generate the $j = \frac{1}{2}$ representation of $SU(2)$, whereas only integer j representations can be expressed in terms of coordinates and momenta.

[1] J. P. Elliott, *Proc. Roy. Soc.* (*London*) **A245,** 128 (1958).

[2] H. J. Lipkin, "Lie Groups for Pedestrians," sec. 4.2 (North Holland Publishing Company, Amsterdam, 1965).

The proper identification is obtained by writing (27.4) in a form like (27.6):

$$R \approx 1 - \frac{i}{\hbar}(\phi \cdot \mathbf{L}) \qquad \phi \text{ infinitesimal}$$

It then follows from comparison with (27.37) and (27.40) that

$$L_x = \hbar\lambda_7 \qquad L_y = -\hbar\lambda_5 \qquad L_z = \hbar\lambda_2 \qquad\qquad (27.45)$$

The remaining identifications are obtained by comparing the commutation relations of the L's and Q's with those of the λ's:

$$Q_{xy} = \hbar\sqrt{\alpha\beta}\,\lambda_1 \qquad Q_{yz} = \hbar\sqrt{\alpha\beta}\,\lambda_6 \qquad Q_{zx} = \hbar\sqrt{\alpha\beta}\,\lambda_4$$

$$Q_0 = \hbar\sqrt{\alpha\beta}\,\lambda_8 \qquad Q_1 = \hbar\sqrt{\alpha\beta}\,\lambda_3 \quad (27.46)$$

The Casimir operator (27.43) is, in this representation,

$$C = \hbar^{-2}\mathbf{L}^2 + (\hbar^2\alpha\beta)^{-1}(Q_{xy}{}^2 + Q_{yz}{}^2 + Q_{zx}{}^2 + Q_0{}^2 + Q_1{}^2)$$

$$= -3 + (3\hbar^2)^{-1}\left[\left(\frac{\alpha}{\beta}\right)^{\frac{1}{2}}\mathbf{r}^2 + \left(\frac{\beta}{\alpha}\right)^{\frac{1}{2}}\mathbf{p}^2\right]^2 \quad (27.47)$$

We return in Sec. 30 to this coordinate-momentum representation of $SU(3)$, in connection with the three-dimensional isotropic harmonic oscillator.

28□COMBINATION OF ANGULAR MOMENTUM STATES AND TENSOR OPERATORS

A central problem of the old quantum theory was the combination of the angular momenta associated with two parts of a system (such as the orbital angular momenta of two electrons in an atom, or the spin and orbital angular momenta of the same electron) to form the angular momentum of the whole system. The vector model solved this problem with an addition rule: The magnitude of the sum of two angular momentum vectors can have any value ranging from the sum of their magnitudes (parallel case) to the difference of their magnitudes (antiparallel case), by integer steps. This is called the *triangle rule*, since the magnitudes of the two angular momenta and their resultant must form a closed triangle (which may have zero area). The vector model also states that the sum of the z components of the angular momenta equals that of their resultant.

Both of these rules are valid in quantum mechanics as well. We show first that they apply to those linear combinations of products of eigenstates of two commuting angular momentum operators that are eigenstates of the total angular momentum. The same kind of addition formula is then shown to hold for products of rotation or tensor operators and for the state produced when a tensor operator acts on an angular momentum eigenstate.

It is apparent that any number of angular momentum eigenstates and tensor operators can be combined by taking them two at a time in accordance with the methods developed in this section. However, analogous procedures have also been worked out for the direct combination of three or more angular momentum eigenstates.[1]

EIGENVALUES OF THE TOTAL ANGULAR MOMENTUM

We start with two commuting angular momentum operators J_1 and J_2; all components of J_1 commute with all components of J_2, and J_1 and J_2 separately satisfy the commutation relations (27.15). The orthonormal eigenstates of $J_1{}^2$ and J_{1z} are $|j_1m_1\rangle$, and J_2 has no effect on them. Similarly, $|j_2m_2\rangle$ are orthonormal eigenstates of $J_2{}^2$ and J_{2z}, and J_1 has no effect on them. This representation is specified by the orthonormal set of kets $|j_1m_1j_2m_2\rangle$, each of which is a product of the kets $|j_1m_1\rangle$ and $|j_2m_2\rangle$; any other parameters that may be needed to specify the kets can be ignored in what follows.

Since J_1 and J_2 commute, the total angular momentum $J = J_1 + J_2$ also satisfies Eq. (27.15). The orthonormal eigenstates of J^2 and J_z are $|jm\rangle$ and specify a second representation. We wish to find the unitary transformation (rotation of axes in Hilbert space) that changes from one of these representations to the other. It is, however, unnecessary to deal with the entire infinite-dimensional Hilbert space at once. Instead, we consider the subspace for which j_1 and j_2 have definite values; its dimensionality is $(2j_1 + 1)(2j_2 + 1)$. With this restriction, the kets of the first representation may be denoted simply $|m_1m_2\rangle$, and our object is to find the unitary transformation $\langle m_1m_2|jm\rangle$. Then in analogy with the first of Eqs. (23.4'), we have

$$|jm\rangle = |m_1m_2\rangle\langle m_1m_2|jm\rangle \tag{28.1}$$

where summations over m_1 from $-j_1$ to j_1 and over m_2 from $-j_2$ to j_2 are implied.

Since $J_z = J_{1z} + J_{2z}$, it is apparent that $\langle m_1m_2|jm\rangle$ is zero unless $m = m_1 + m_2$. This immediately gives the second vector-model rule mentioned at the beginning of this section. It also follows that the largest value of m is $j_1 + j_2$ and that this value occurs only once, when $m_1 = j_1$ and $m_2 = j_2$. This shows that the largest value of j is $j_1 + j_2$ and that there is only one such state. The next largest value of m is $j_1 + j_2 - 1$, and this occurs twice: when $m_1 = j_1$ and $m_2 = j_2 - 1$, and

---

[1] See, for example, A. R. Edmonds, "Angular Momentum in Quantum Mechanics," chap. 6 (Princeton, Princeton, N.J., 1957).

when $m_1 = j_1 - 1$ and $m_2 = j_2$ (provided that neither j_1 nor j_2 is zero). One of the two linearly independent combinations of these two states must be associated with the new state for which $j = j_1 + j_2$, since for that j value there must be values of m ranging from $j_1 + j_2$ to $-j_1 - j_2$ by integer steps. The other combination cannot be associated with this or a larger j, since the larger m values that would then also be present actually are not. Therefore the second combination is associated with $j = j_1 + j_2 - 1$, and there is only one state with this j value. By an extension of this argument we can see that each j value, ranging from $j_1 + j_2$ to $|j_1 - j_2|$ by integer steps, appears just once. This establishes the triangle rule of the vector model.

Each j value of the new representation has associated with it $2j + 1$ linearly independent combinations of the original eigenstates. Thus the number of $|jm\rangle$ eigenstates is

$$\sum_{j = |j_1 - j_2|}^{j_1 + j_2} (2j + 1)$$

which is equal to $(2j_1 + 1)(2j_2 + 1)$, as expected.

CLEBSCH–GORDAN COEFFICIENTS

The elements of the unitary matrix $\langle m_1 m_2 | jm \rangle$ are the coefficients of the expansion of the eigenstates $|jm\rangle$ in terms of the eigenstates $|m_1 m_2\rangle$, in accordance with Eq. (28.1). They are called *Clebsch-Gordan, Wigner,* or *vector-coupling coefficients.* The inverse expansion to (28.1) is

$$|m_1 m_2\rangle = |jm\rangle\langle jm | m_1 m_2\rangle$$

where summations over m from $-j$ to j and over j from $|j_1 - j_2|$ to $j_1 + j_2$ are implied. The unitary character of the transformation matrix is expressed through the analogs of Eqs. (23.9′) and (23.29):

$$\langle m_1 m_2 | jm \rangle \langle jm | m_1' m_2' \rangle = \langle m_1 m_2 | m_1' m_2' \rangle$$
$$\langle jm | m_1 m_2 \rangle \langle m_1 m_2 | j'm' \rangle = \langle jm | j'm' \rangle \qquad (28.2)$$
$$\langle jm | m_1 m_2 \rangle = \langle m_1 m_2 | jm \rangle^*$$

The right sides of the first two of Eqs. (28.2) are unit matrices (products of Kronecker δ symbols). We shall follow the usual convention and choose the matrix elements to be real, so that the asterisk may be removed on the right side of the third of Eqs. (28.2).

It is possible to obtain explicit formulas for the Clebsch-Gordan coefficients.[1] However, they are sufficiently complicated so that it is generally simpler either to construct the coefficients as needed in particular

---

[1] Edmonds, *op. cit.,* pp. 44–45.

cases or to refer to published tables.[1]   In what follows we first derive
two recursion relations and then construct some simple cases.

RECURSION RELATIONS

We apply the angular momentum raising operator J_+ defined by Eq.
(27.17) to the left side of Eq. (28.1), and the equal operator $J_{1+} + J_{2+}$
to the right side.   On making use of the first of Eqs. (27.25) and dividing
by $\hbar$, we obtain

$$[j(j + 1) - m(m + 1)]^{\frac{1}{2}}|j, m + 1\rangle$$
$$= \{[j_1(j_1 + 1) - m_1(m_1 + 1)]^{\frac{1}{2}}|m_1 + 1, m_2\rangle +$$
$$[j_2(j_2 + 1) - m_2(m_2 + 1)]^{\frac{1}{2}}|m_1, m_2 + 1\rangle\}\langle m_1 m_2|jm\rangle$$

We can now substitute for $|j, m + 1\rangle$ on the left side from Eq. (28.1).
On the right side we note that the summation over m_1 may be replaced
by a summation over $m_1' = m_1 + 1$ in the first term; it is easily seen that
the summation range of m_1' can also be taken to be $-j_1$ to j_1.   Similarly,
the summation over m_2 may be replaced by the same summation over
$m_2 + 1$ in the second term on the right side.   Since the kets $|m_1 m_2\rangle$ are
orthonormal, we can then equate their coefficients on the two sides to
obtain

$$[j(j + 1) - m(m + 1)]^{\frac{1}{2}}\langle m_1 m_2|j, m + 1\rangle$$
$$= [j_1(j_1 + 1) - m_1(m_1 - 1)]^{\frac{1}{2}}\langle m_1 - 1, m_2|jm\rangle$$
$$+ [j_2(j_2 + 1) - m_2(m_2 - 1)]^{\frac{1}{2}}\langle m_1, m_2 - 1|jm\rangle \quad (28.3)$$

This procedure may be repeated, starting with J_- instead of J_+.
The result is

$$[j(j + 1) - m(m - 1)]^{\frac{1}{2}}\langle m_1 m_2|j, m - 1\rangle$$
$$= [j_1(j_1 + 1) - m_1(m_1 + 1)]^{\frac{1}{2}}\langle m_1 + 1, m_2|jm\rangle$$
$$+ [j_2(j_2 + 1) - m_2(m_2 + 1)]^{\frac{1}{2}}\langle m_1, m_2 + 1|jm\rangle \quad (28.4)$$

CONSTRUCTION PROCEDURE

The matrix $\langle m_1 m_2|jm\rangle$ has $(2j_1 + 1)(2j_2 + 1)$ rows and columns but
breaks up into disconnected submatrices in accordance with the value
of $m = m_1 + m_2$.   Thus there will be a 1×1 submatrix for which
$m = j_1 + j_2$ and $j = j_1 + j_2$.   Then there will be a 2×2 submatrix for
which $m = j_1 + j_2 - 1$ and j is either $j_1 + j_2$ or $j_1 + j_2 - 1$.   The rank

[1] A list of tables published prior to 1957 is given by Edmonds, *op. cit.*, p. 50; see also
M. Rotenberg, R. Bivins, N. Metropolis, and J. K. Wooten, Jr., "The 3-j and 6-j
Symbols" (Technology Press, Cambridge, Mass., 1959).   Rosenfeld et al., *op. cit.*,
give the matrices for several values of j_1 and j_2 in condensed form on a detachable
wallet card.

of these submatrices at first increases by unity from one to the next until a maximum rank is reached and maintained for one or more submatrices; thereafter it decreases by unity until the last 1×1 submatrix has $m = -j_1 - j_2$ and $j = j_1 + j_2$. Each of these submatrices is unitary, so that the first 1×1 submatrix is a number of unit magnitude, which we choose by convention to be $+1$:

$$\langle j_1 j_2 | j_1 + j_2, j_1 + j_2 \rangle = 1 \tag{28.5}$$

We next use Eq. (28.4) with $m_1 = j_1$, $m_2 = j_2 - 1$, $j = j_1 + j_2$, and $m = j_1 + j_2$. The first term on the right side is zero, and we obtain

$$\langle j_1, j_2 - 1 | j_1 + j_2, j_1 + j_2 - 1 \rangle = \left(\frac{j_2}{j_1 + j_2} \right)^{\frac{1}{2}} \tag{28.6}$$

when use is made of (28.5). Similar use of Eq. (28.4) with $m_1 = j_1 - 1$, $m_2 = j_2$, $j = j_1 + j_2$, and $m = j_1 + j_2$ gives

$$\langle j_1 - 1, j_2 | j_1 + j_2, j_1 + j_2 - 1 \rangle = \left(\frac{j_1}{j_1 + j_2} \right)^{\frac{1}{2}} \tag{28.7}$$

Equations (28.6) and (28.7) give the half of the 2×2 submatrix of $\langle m_1 m_2 | jm \rangle$ for which $m = j_1 + j_2 - 1$ and $j = j_1 + j_2$. The other half, for which $m = j_1 + j_2 - 1$ and $j = j_1 + j_2 - 1$, is obtained by making use of the second orthonormality relation (28.2). There is, however, an arbitrary multiplying factor of unit magnitude, which we choose so that

$$\langle j_1, j_2 - 1 | j_1 + j_2 - 1, j_1 + j_2 - 1 \rangle = \left(\frac{j_1}{j_1 + j_2} \right)^{\frac{1}{2}}$$

$$\langle j_1 - 1, j_2 | j_1 + j_2 - 1, j_1 + j_2 - 1 \rangle = -\left(\frac{j_2}{j_1 + j_2} \right)^{\frac{1}{2}} \tag{28.8}$$

The convention here is that the first matrix element, which has the form $\langle j_1, j - j_1 | jj \rangle$, is real and positive.

The next submatrix may be obtained in similar fashion. Substitution of Eqs. (28.6) and (28.7) into the right side of (28.4) gives

$$\langle j_1, j_2 - 2 | j_1 + j_2, j_1 + j_2 - 2 \rangle$$

$$= \left[\frac{j_2(2j_2 - 1)}{(j_1 + j_2)(2j_1 + 2j_2 - 1)} \right]^{\frac{1}{2}}$$

$$\langle j_1 - 1, j_2 - 1 | j_1 + j_2, j_1 + j_2 - 2 \rangle$$

$$= \left[\frac{4j_1 j_2}{(j_1 + j_2)(2j_1 + 2j_2 - 1)} \right]^{\frac{1}{2}} \tag{28.9}$$

$$\langle j_1 - 2, j_2 | j_1 + j_2, j_1 + j_2 - 2 \rangle$$

$$= \left[\frac{j_1(2j_1 - 1)}{(j_1 + j_2)(2j_1 + 2j_2 - 1)} \right]^{\frac{1}{2}}$$

In the same way, Eqs. (28.4) and (28.8) lead to

$$\langle j_1, j_2 - 2 | j_1 + j_2 - 1, j_1 + j_2 - 2 \rangle$$
$$= \left[\frac{j_1(2j_2 - 1)}{(j_1 + j_2)(j_1 + j_2 - 1)} \right]^{\frac{1}{2}}$$

$$\langle j_1 - 1, j_2 - 1 | j_1 + j_2 - 1, j_1 + j_2 - 2 \rangle$$
$$= \frac{j_1 - j_2}{[(j_1 + j_2)(j_1 + j_2 - 1)]^{\frac{1}{2}}} \qquad (28.10)$$

$$\langle j_1 - 2, j_2 | j_1 + j_2 - 1, j_1 + j_2 - 2 \rangle$$
$$= - \left[\frac{j_2(2j_1 - 1)}{(j_1 + j_2)(j_1 + j_2 - 1)} \right]^{\frac{1}{2}}$$

We again use the second of Eqs. (28.2) to obtain a normalized set of coefficients that are orthogonal to (28.9) and (28.10). As with Eqs. (28.8), we choose the arbitrary phase factor so that the first of the following coefficients is real and positive:

$$\langle j_1, j_2 - 2 | j_1 + j_2 - 2, j_1 + j_2 - 2 \rangle$$
$$= \left[\frac{j_1(2j_1 - 1)}{(j_1 + j_2 - 1)(2j_1 + 2j_2 - 1)} \right]^{\frac{1}{2}}$$

$$\langle j_1 - 1, j_2 - 1 | j_1 + j_2 - 2, j_1 + j_2 - 2 \rangle$$
$$= - \left[\frac{(2j_1 - 1)(2j_2 - 1)}{(j_1 + j_2 - 1)(2j_1 + 2j_2 - 1)} \right]^{\frac{1}{2}} \qquad (28.11)$$

$$\langle j_1 - 2, j_2 | j_1 + j_2 - 2, j_1 + j_2 - 2 \rangle$$
$$= \left[\frac{j_2(2j_2 - 1)}{(j_1 + j_2 - 1)(2j_1 + 2j_2 - 1)} \right]^{\frac{1}{2}}$$

The only difficult part of the foregoing construction procedure is the use of orthogonality, which becomes progressively more complicated as the rank of the submatrix increases. However, it need be employed only once for each submatrix, and it is easier to work out an example with particular numerical values for j_1 and j_2 than the general case just considered. It should be noted that the first recursion relation (28.3) can also be used to construct the Clebsch-Gordan coefficients if we start at the other end with the 1×1 submatrix that has $m = -j_1 - j_2$ and $j = j_1 + j_2$.

SOME PARTICULAR COEFFICIENTS

The detachable wallet card referred to earlier contains condensed tables of Clebsch-Gordan coefficients for the seven cases

$$j_1: \quad \tfrac{1}{2} \quad 1 \quad 1 \quad \tfrac{3}{2} \quad \tfrac{3}{2} \quad 2 \quad 2$$
$$j_2: \quad \tfrac{1}{2} \quad \tfrac{1}{2} \quad 1 \quad \tfrac{1}{2} \quad 1 \quad \tfrac{1}{2} \quad 1$$

The first three of these are reproduced below, written in full. In each case the rows of the matrix are labeled by $(m_1 m_2)$ and the columns by $\begin{pmatrix} j \\ m \end{pmatrix}$.

All the matrix elements outside the dotted lines are equal to zero. It is easily verified that Eqs. (28.5) through (28.11) are in agreement with these matrices.

$j_1 = \tfrac{1}{2} \qquad j_2 = \tfrac{1}{2}:$

$$
\begin{array}{cc}
 & \begin{array}{cccc} 1 & 1 & 0 & 1 \\ 1 & 0 & 0 & -1 \end{array} \\
\begin{array}{cc}
\tfrac{1}{2} & \tfrac{1}{2} \\[2pt]
\tfrac{1}{2} & -\tfrac{1}{2} \\[2pt]
-\tfrac{1}{2} & \tfrac{1}{2} \\[2pt]
-\tfrac{1}{2} & -\tfrac{1}{2}
\end{array}
&
\left[
\begin{array}{cccc}
1 & & & \\
& \sqrt{\tfrac{1}{2}} & \sqrt{\tfrac{1}{2}} & \\
& \sqrt{\tfrac{1}{2}} & -\sqrt{\tfrac{1}{2}} & \\
& & & 1
\end{array}
\right]
\end{array}
\tag{28.12}
$$

$j_1 = 1 \qquad j_2 = \tfrac{1}{2}:$

$$
\begin{array}{cc}
 & \begin{array}{cccccc}
 \tfrac{3}{2} & \tfrac{3}{2} & \tfrac{1}{2} & \tfrac{3}{2} & \tfrac{1}{2} & \tfrac{3}{2} \\
 \tfrac{3}{2} & \tfrac{1}{2} & \tfrac{1}{2} & -\tfrac{1}{2} & -\tfrac{1}{2} & -\tfrac{3}{2}
 \end{array} \\
\begin{array}{cc}
1 & \tfrac{1}{2} \\[2pt]
1 & -\tfrac{1}{2} \\[2pt]
0 & \tfrac{1}{2} \\[2pt]
0 & -\tfrac{1}{2} \\[2pt]
-1 & \tfrac{1}{2} \\[2pt]
-1 & -\tfrac{1}{2}
\end{array}
&
\left[
\begin{array}{cccccc}
1 & & & & & \\
& \sqrt{\tfrac{1}{3}} & \sqrt{\tfrac{2}{3}} & & & \\
& \sqrt{\tfrac{2}{3}} & -\sqrt{\tfrac{1}{3}} & & & \\
& & & \sqrt{\tfrac{2}{3}} & \sqrt{\tfrac{1}{3}} & \\
& & & \sqrt{\tfrac{1}{3}} & -\sqrt{\tfrac{2}{3}} & \\
& & & & & 1
\end{array}
\right]
\end{array}
\tag{28.13}
$$

$j_1 = 1 \qquad j_2 = 1:$

$$
\begin{array}{cc}
 & \begin{array}{ccccccccc}
 2 & 2 & 1 & 2 & 1 & 0 & 2 & 1 & 2 \\
 2 & 1 & 1 & 0 & 0 & 0 & -1 & -1 & -2
 \end{array} \\
\begin{array}{cc}
1 & 1 \\[2pt]
1 & 0 \\[2pt]
0 & 1 \\[2pt]
1 & -1 \\[2pt]
0 & 0 \\[2pt]
-1 & 1 \\[2pt]
0 & -1 \\[2pt]
-1 & 0 \\[2pt]
-1 & -1
\end{array}
&
\left[
\begin{array}{ccccccccc}
1 & & & & & & & & \\
& \sqrt{\tfrac{1}{2}} & \sqrt{\tfrac{1}{2}} & & & & & & \\
& \sqrt{\tfrac{1}{2}} & -\sqrt{\tfrac{1}{2}} & & & & & & \\
& & & \sqrt{\tfrac{1}{6}} & \sqrt{\tfrac{1}{2}} & \sqrt{\tfrac{1}{3}} & & & \\
& & & \sqrt{\tfrac{2}{3}} & 0 & -\sqrt{\tfrac{1}{3}} & & & \\
& & & \sqrt{\tfrac{1}{6}} & -\sqrt{\tfrac{1}{2}} & \sqrt{\tfrac{1}{3}} & & & \\
& & & & & & \sqrt{\tfrac{1}{2}} & \sqrt{\tfrac{1}{2}} & \\
& & & & & & \sqrt{\tfrac{1}{2}} & -\sqrt{\tfrac{1}{2}} & \\
& & & & & & & & 1
\end{array}
\right]
\end{array}
\tag{28.14}
$$

MATRIX ELEMENTS FOR ROTATED STATES

In Sec. 26, a comparison was made between a matrix element of a dynamical variable Ω, calculated for any pair of states, and the matrix element of
the same operator when the states are displaced. Equation (26.6)
showed in particular that the matrix elements of $\mathbf{r}$ for states displaced
through the vector $\boldsymbol{\varrho}$ are equal to the corresponding matrix elements of
$\mathbf{r} + \boldsymbol{\varrho}$ for the original states. In similar fashion, Prob. 5 shows that the
matrix elements of $\mathbf{r}$ for states rotated through the infinitesimal vector $\boldsymbol{\varphi}$
are equal to the corresponding matrix elements of $\mathbf{r} + \boldsymbol{\varphi} \times \mathbf{r}$ for the
original states.

We can thus use the analog of Eq. (26.6) to define an infinitesimally
rotated operator Ω_R as

$$\Omega_R = U_R{}^\dagger(\boldsymbol{\varphi})\Omega U_R(\boldsymbol{\varphi}) \approx \Omega + \frac{i}{\hbar}[(\boldsymbol{\varphi} \cdot \mathbf{J}),\Omega] \qquad (28.15)$$

where use has been made of Eqs. (27.12) and (27.13). The matrix
elements of Ω for rotated states are equal to the corresponding matrix
elements of Ω_R for the original states. It follows that the rotation properties of any operator are determined by its commutator with the angular
momentum. For example, a *scalar operator* is one that has the same
matrix elements for rotated states as for the original states, or one for
which $\Omega_R = \Omega$. For such an operator $[\mathbf{J},\Omega] = 0$. As another example, a
vector operator is one for which Eq. (28.15) leads to a relation of the same
form that (27.3) has for the vector $\mathbf{r}$. Thus Prob. 6 shows that $\mathbf{J}_R \approx$
$\mathbf{J} + \boldsymbol{\varphi} \times \mathbf{J}$, so that angular momentum is also a vector operator, as
expected.

IRREDUCIBLE TENSOR OPERATORS

Operators with rotation properties of higher order than scalars and vectors
can also be constructed. For example, two vector operators $\mathbf{A}$ and $\mathbf{B}$ can
be combined to form a nine-component *tensor operator* A_iB_j, where
$i, j = x, y, z$. This is not a convenient form with which to work, any
more than it is in classical physics; it is customary to use instead the
scalar product, the vector product or antisymmetric tensor of second rank,
and the traceless symmetric tensor of second rank, which have one, three,
and five independent components, respectively. The latter can be shown
to have the rotation properties of the spherical harmonics $Y_{lm}(\theta,\boldsymbol{\varphi})$ with
$l = 0, 1$, and 2, respectively; they are examples of *irreducible tensor operators*, so called because they have the simplest transformation properties.[1]

As remarked in connection with Eq. (28.15), the commutator with
$\mathbf{J}$ determines the rotation properties of an operator. In order to relate

[1] For further discussion, see U. Fano and G. Racah, "Irreducible Tensorial Sets"
(Academic, New York, 1959).

these to the spherical harmonics $Y_{lm}(\theta,\phi)$, we operate with $\mathbf{J}$ on $Y_{lm}(\theta,\phi)f(\theta,\phi)$, where $f(\theta,\phi)$ is an arbitrary function of the angles.[1] The third of Eqs. (14.20) expresses J_z as the differential operator $-i\hbar(\partial/\partial\phi)$, so that

$$J_z[Y_{lm}(\theta,\phi)f(\theta,\phi)] = f(\theta,\phi)J_zY_{lm}(\theta,\phi) + Y_{lm}(\theta,\phi)J_zf(\theta,\phi)$$

The first term on the right is $m\hbar Y_{lm}(\theta,\phi)f(\theta,\phi)$, so that

$$[J_z,Y_{lm}(\theta,\phi)]f(\theta,\phi) = m\hbar Y_{lm}(\theta,\phi)f(\theta,\phi)$$

Since $f(\theta,\phi)$ is arbitrary, we obtain the commutation relation

$$[J_z,Y_{lm}] = m\hbar Y_{lm} \tag{28.16}$$

In similar fashion, Eqs. (27.27) and (27.28) can be used to obtain

$$\begin{aligned}[J_+,Y_{lm}] &= [l(l+1) - m(m+1)]^{\frac{1}{2}}\hbar Y_{l,m+1} \\ [J_-,Y_{lm}] &= [l(l+1) - m(m-1)]^{\frac{1}{2}}\hbar Y_{l,m-1}\end{aligned} \tag{28.17}$$

In analogy with the preceding paragraph, we now *define* an irreducible tensor operator $\mathbf{T}(k)$, where $k = 0, \frac{1}{2}, 1, \frac{3}{2}, \ldots$, to be a set of $2k+1$ operators $T(k,q)$, where $q = k, k-1, \ldots, -k$, that have commutators with $\mathbf{J}$ similar to those in Eqs. (28.16) and (28.17), where l or j is replaced by k and m is replaced by q:

$$\begin{aligned}[J_z, T(k,q)] &= q\hbar T(k,q) \\ [J_+, T(k,q)] &= [k(k+1) - q(q+1)]^{\frac{1}{2}}\hbar T(k, q+1) \\ [J_-, T(k,q)] &= [k(k+1) - q(q-1)]^{\frac{1}{2}}\hbar T(k, q-1)\end{aligned} \tag{28.18}$$

The importance of these operators derives from the fact that many dynamical variables of physical interest can be expressed in this form. For example, the 2^l electric or magnetic multipole moment operator is an irreducible tensor operator with $k = l$.

PRODUCT OF TENSOR OPERATORS

The close similarity between Eqs. (27.25) and (27.28) on the one hand, and Eqs. (28.18) on the other, suggests that irreducible tensor operators can be combined in accordance with the same rule as angular momentum eigenstates. Some such rule is needed, since we have seen that the product of two vector operators is reducible.

We therefore try to adapt Eq. (28.1) to this purpose. Its analog is

$$T(k,q) = \sum T_1(k_1,q_1)T_2(k_2,q_2)\langle q_1q_2|kq\rangle \tag{28.19}$$

[1] This is the method employed in deriving Eq. (24.34).

where the Clebsch-Gordan coefficient $\langle q_1 q_2 | k q \rangle$ corresponds to $j_1 = k_1$ and $j_2 = k_2$; the summation is over q_1 from $-k_1$ to k_1 and over q_2 from $-k_2$ to k_2. As before, we apply J_z, J_+, and J_- in succession. However, in developing recursion relations from (28.1), we could apply $\mathbf{J}$ to the left side and $\mathbf{J}_1 + \mathbf{J}_2$ to the right side. The analogous procedure here derives from the identity

$$[\mathbf{J}, T_1 T_2] = [\mathbf{J}, T_1] T_2 + T_1 [\mathbf{J}, T_2] \tag{28.20}$$

Thus if the commutator with J_z is taken with both sides of (28.19) we obtain

$$
\begin{aligned}
[J_z, T(k,q)] &= \sum \{ [J_z, T_1(k_1,q_1)] T_2(k_2,q_2) \\
&\qquad + T_1(k_1,q_1)[J_z, T_2(k_2,q_2)] \} \langle q_1 q_2 | k q \rangle \\
&= \sum (q_1 + q_2) \hbar T_1(k_1,q_1) T_2(k_2,q_2) \langle q_1 q_2 | k q \rangle \\
&= q \hbar T(k,q)
\end{aligned}
$$

where use has been made of the first of Eqs. (28.18) applied to T_1 and T_2 separately and of the fact that $\langle q_1 q_2 | k q \rangle$ is zero unless $q = q_1 + q_2$. Thus $T(k,q)$ as defined by (28.19) also satisfies the first of Eqs. (28.18).

Next we take the commutator of (28.19) with J_+:

$$
\begin{aligned}
[J_+, T(k,q)] &= \sum \{ [k_1(k_1 + 1) - q_1(q_1 + 1)]^{\frac{1}{2}} \hbar T_1(k_1, q_1 + 1) T_2(k_2,q_2) \\
&\quad + [k_2(k_2 + 1) - q_2(q_2 + 1)]^{\frac{1}{2}} \hbar T_1(k_1,q_1) T_2(k_2, q_2 + 1) \} \langle q_1 q_2 | k q \rangle
\end{aligned}
$$

where use has been made of the second of Eqs. (28.18) applied to T_1 and T_2 separately. Now, just as in deriving Eq. (28.3), the summation over q_1 in the first term may be replaced by a summation over $q_1' = q_1 + 1$, with the same range for q_1' from $-k_1$ to k_1. With similar treatment of the second term, we obtain

$$
\begin{aligned}
&[J_+, T(k,q)] = \\
&\sum \{ [k_1(k_1 + 1) - q_1'(q_1' - 1)]^{\frac{1}{2}} \hbar T_1(k_1,q_1') T_2(k_2,q_2) \langle q_1' - 1, q_2 | k q \rangle + \\
&\qquad [k_2(k_2 + 1) - q_2'(q_2' - 1)]^{\frac{1}{2}} \hbar T_1(k_1,q_1) T_2(k_2,q_2') \langle q_1, q_2' - 1 | k q \rangle \}
\end{aligned}
$$

We may now drop the primes and use the recursion relation (28.3) to simplify the right side:

$$
\begin{aligned}
&[J_+, T(k,q)] \\
&\qquad = \sum [k(k + 1) - q(q + 1)]^{\frac{1}{2}} \hbar T_1(k_1,q_1) T_2(k_2,q_2) \langle q_1 q_2 | k, q + 1 \rangle
\end{aligned}
$$

Then substitution from (28.19) with q replaced by $q + 1$ shows that $T(k,q)$ satisfies the second of the commutation relations (28.18). In similar fashion, the commutator of (28.19) with J_- shows that $T(q,k)$ satisfies the third of Eqs. (28.18).

We have thus shown that the $2k + 1$ operators $T(k,q)$ defined by Eq. (28.19) constitute an irreducible tensor operator. The expansion (28.19) can also be inverted by making use of the orthonormality relations (28.2) to give the explicit reduction of a product of two irreducible tensors if the $T(k,q)$ are known:

$$T_1(k_1,q_1) T_2(k_2,q_2) = \sum T(k,q)\langle kq|q_1q_2\rangle = \sum T(k,q)\langle q_1q_2|kq\rangle \qquad (28.21)$$

The summation here is over q from $-k$ to k, and then over k from $|k_1 - k_2|$ to $k_1 + k_2$; the last expression follows from the third of Eqs. (28.2) since the Clebsch-Gordan coefficients are real.

COMBINATION OF OPERATOR AND EIGENSTATE

Finally, we can find the analog of Eqs. (28.1) and (28.19) when one of the factors on the right is an irreducible tensor operator and the other is an angular momentum eigenstate:

$$|jm\rangle = \sum T_1(k_1,q_1)|j_2m_2\rangle\langle q_1m_2|jm\rangle \qquad (28.22)$$

The Clebsch-Gordan coefficient $\langle q_1m_2|jm\rangle$ corresponds to $j_1 = k_1$ and j_2; the summation is over q_1 from $-k_1$ to k_1 and over m_2 from $-j_2$ to j_2. Two matters of notation are worthy of comment in connection with this equation. First, we have used subscripts 1 and 2 so that they correspond respectively to the first tensor operator on the right side of (28.19) and to the second eigenfunction on the right side of (28.1). Second, we have, as before, omitted all reference to the parameters other than angular momentum quantum numbers which may be needed to specify the states. The existence of these other parameters is implied and would in general cause the radial dependence, for example, of the ket $|jm\rangle$ to be different from that of the ket $|j_2m_2\rangle$.

The identity analogous to (28.20) that is needed here is

$$\mathbf{J}T_1|j_2m_2\rangle = [\mathbf{J},T_1]|j_2m_2\rangle + T_1\mathbf{J}|j_2m_2\rangle$$

The algebra proceeds exactly as in the preceding subsection and leads to the conclusion that the set of kets $|jm\rangle$ defined by Eq. (28.22) for a particular j and all m between $-j$ and j are angular momentum eigenstates since they satisfy equations like (27.25) and (27.28). However, they are not normalized, since it is not in general true that $\langle jm|jm\rangle = 1$. On the other hand, the fact that the $|jm\rangle$ satisfy homogeneous equations like (27.28) shows that their normalization does not depend on m, although it will in general depend on j, and also on k_1, j_2, and the form of the tensor operator $\mathbf{T}_1$.

WIGNER–ECKART THEOREM

The series expansion of $|jm\rangle$ in terms of $T_1(k_1,q_1)|j_2m_2\rangle$, given in Eq. (28.22), can be inverted by making use of the orthonormality of the

Clebsch-Gordan coefficients:

$$T_1(k_1,q_1)|j_2m_2\rangle = \sum |jm\rangle\langle jm|q_1m_2\rangle = \sum |jm\rangle\langle q_1m_2|jm\rangle \qquad (28.23)$$

The summations are over m from $-j$ to j and over j from $|k_1 - j_2|$ to $k_1 + j_2$; as with Eq. (28.21), use has been made of the third of Eqs. (28.2) and the reality of the Clebsch-Gordan coefficients to arrive at the last expression.

We may now multiply Eq. (28.23) through from the left with a bra $\langle j'm'|$, which may depend on the other parameters in a different way than $|jm\rangle$. On making use of the orthogonality relation

$$\langle j'm'|jm\rangle = 0 \qquad \text{unless} \qquad j = j' \text{ and } m = m'$$

we obtain

$$\langle j'm'|T_1(k_1,q_1)|j_2m_2\rangle = N(j',k_1,j_2,T_1)\langle q_1m_2|j'm'\rangle$$

$N \equiv \langle j'm'|j'm'\rangle$ is the normalization factor mentioned at the end of the preceding subsection, which is independent of m'. We drop the primes and write N in a form that agrees with the standard convention:[1]

$$\langle jm|T_1(k_1,q_1)|j_2m_2\rangle = (-1)^{k_1-j_2+j}(2j+1)^{-\frac{1}{2}}\langle j||T_1(k_1)||j_2\rangle\langle q_1m_2|jm\rangle$$
$$(28.24)$$

Equation (28.24) embodies the *Wigner-Eckart theorem*.[2] It states that the matrix element of an irreducible tensor operator between angular momentum eigenstates depends on the three m values (q_1, m_2, and m) only through the Clebsch-Gordan coefficient $\langle q_1m_2|jm\rangle$ that corresponds to $j_1 = k_1$ and j_2. This is not a surprising result, since these three m values determine the orientation of the operator and the two states with respect to the coordinate system and hence should influence the value of the matrix element only through a geometrical factor (the Clebsch-Gordan coefficient). The physical properties of the matrix element are contained in the factor $\langle j||T_1(k_1)||j_2\rangle$, which is called the *reduced* or *double-bar matrix element*. It depends on the magnitudes of the three angular momenta (k_1, j_2, and j) associated with the operator and the two states, on the form of the tensor operator T_1, and on the other parameters that are needed to specify the two states.

This factorization of the matrix elements of tensor operators greatly simplifies their calculation. Since k_1 is an integer for physical operators, it is simplest to calculate the reduced matrix element from Eq. (28.24) with $q_1 = 0$ and with $m_2 = m = 0$ or $m_2 = m = \frac{1}{2}$ as appropriate. Matrix elements for other combinations of q_1, m_2, and m are then readily obtained.

[1] Edmonds, *op. cit.*, p. 75.

[2] Wigner, *op. cit.*, p. 245; C. Eckart, *Rev. Mod. Phys.* **2**, 305 (1930).

Among the most important consequences of the Wigner-Eckart theorem are two conditions under which matrix elements of tensor operators necessarily vanish. The appearance of the Clebsch-Gordan coefficient shows that the matrix element is zero unless $m = q_1 + m_2$ and unless k_1, j_2, and j satisfy the triangle rule. As an example, the latter condition shows that a system in a state with total angular momentum j cannot have a nonvanishing expectation value (diagonal matrix element) for the 2^l electric or magnetic multipole moment operator unless $l \leq 2j$. Thus a particle with spin zero cannot possess a magnetic dipole moment, and a particle with spin $\frac{1}{2}$ cannot possess an electric quadrupole moment.

29☐SPACE INVERSION AND TIME REVERSAL

Parity has appeared earlier in this book in connection with both the one-dimensional (Sec. 9) and three-dimensional (Sec. 14) Schrödinger equations. So long as the potential energy is unchanged when the coordinate **r** is replaced by $-\mathbf{r}$, the energy eigenfunctions can be chosen either to remain unchanged or to change sign when **r** changes sign, that is, to have either even or odd parity. We start this section by applying the general approach of Sec. 26 to the relation between parity and the symmetry operation of space inversion ($\mathbf{r} \rightarrow -\mathbf{r}$).

We then consider the symmetry operation of time reversal. The classical equations of motion for particles that move under the influence of conservative forces are symmetric when the sense of progression of time is reversed, since they involve second time derivatives. It is to be expected that the corresponding quantum equations also possess time-reversal symmetry. However, the fact that the Schrödinger equation is of first order in the time derivative whereas the newtonian equations are of second order introduces new and physically interesting features into the treatment of the quantum situation.[1]

SPACE INVERSION

The matrix, analogous to R defined in Eq. (27.2), that produces an inversion is

$$I = \begin{bmatrix} -1 & 0 & 0 \\ 0 & -1 & 0 \\ 0 & 0 & -1 \end{bmatrix}$$

so that $I\mathbf{r} = -\mathbf{r}$. It is apparent that I is real and orthonormal, but its determinant is equal to -1 so that it is not a proper rotation. Any 3×3 real orthonormal matrix with determinant equal to -1 can be

[1] For a classical discussion of some aspects of space inversion and time reversal, see L. I. Schiff, *Physics* **1**, 209 (1965).

written as a product of I and a proper rotation. The unit matrix and I by themselves form a *discrete* group with two elements, such that $I^2 = 1$.

The inversion of a physical system in a state represented by the ket $|\alpha\rangle$ or the wave function $\psi_\alpha(\mathbf{r})$ changes it into a state represented by $|\alpha'\rangle$ or $\psi_{\alpha'}(\mathbf{r})$. The relation between the two states is assumed to be

$$\psi_{\alpha'}(I\mathbf{r}) = \omega\psi_\alpha(\mathbf{r}) \tag{29.1}$$

where ω is a number to be discussed below. The introduction of this number into (29.1) and its absence from the corresponding equations (26.1), (26.7), (27.1), and (27.8) are consequences of the discrete nature of the inversion group as contrasted with the continuous nature of the displacement and rotation groups. Any such number introduced into the earlier equations would have to depend continuously on ϱ, τ, or ϕ, as the case may be, and approach unity as these parameters approach zero since $|\alpha'\rangle = |\alpha\rangle$ in the limit; it can then be shown not to have any physical consequences.

UNITARY INVERSION OPERATOR

The unitary inversion operator U_I is defined by

$$U_I|\alpha\rangle = |\alpha'\rangle \qquad \text{or} \qquad U_I\psi_\alpha(\mathbf{r}) = \psi_{\alpha'}(\mathbf{r}) \tag{29.2}$$

Substitution of (29.1) into the second of Eqs. (29.2), followed by another operation with U_I, gives

$$U_I\psi_\alpha(\mathbf{r}) = \omega\psi_\alpha(-\mathbf{r}) \qquad U_I^2\psi_\alpha(\mathbf{r}) = \omega^2\psi_\alpha(\mathbf{r}) \tag{29.3}$$

Two inversions bring the coordinate space into itself, so that U_I^2 is expected to bring a state into itself. In such a situation, the state cannot change its norm, although it may be multiplied by a phase factor of unit magnitude. Thus ω^2 is a number of unit magnitude, from which it follows that ω is also. It is also true that ω must be the same for all states that can be superposed with each other, that is, for all states that can be used to describe the same system of particles. For example, if

$$\psi(\mathbf{r}) = \sum_\alpha a_\alpha\psi_\alpha(\mathbf{r})$$

where the a_α are some set of numerical coefficients, then

$$U_I\psi(\mathbf{r}) = \sum_\alpha \omega_\alpha a_\alpha\psi_\alpha(-\mathbf{r})$$

which will, in general, be a different state from $\omega\psi(-\mathbf{r})$ unless the ω_α are all the same.

We shall assume that ω has a definite value for each kind of particle. We have already noted near the end of Sec. 27 that a 2π rotation of an integer spin particle leaves its state function unchanged, and we expect that this is also true for two space inversions. Thus $\omega^2 = 1$, and $\omega = \pm 1$. For half-odd-integer spin particles, we note from Eq. (28.1) that products of pairs of them can be superposed to give states of integer angular momentum. Thus we expect that ω^2 for a half-odd-integer spin particle can be equal to the possible values of ω for an integer spin particle. These are ± 1, so that a half-odd-integer spin particle can have $\omega = \pm 1$, $\pm i$.

INTRINSIC PARITY

The experimental determination of ω for various particles involves their mutual interactions.[1] In particular, it is found that a π^0 meson (neutral pion), which has zero spin, disintegrates into two photons, so that its *intrinsic parity* can be found relative to that of the electromagnetic field, and corresponds to $\omega = -1$; this assumes that the parity of the system is conserved during the decay process. The neutral pion is therefore said to have odd intrinsic parity, or to be a *pseudoscalar* particle; this is in contrast with a spin zero particle with $\omega = +1$ (should such exist), which would be called a *scalar* particle. The intrinsic parity of the $\pi^\pm$ mesons (charged pions), which also have zero spin, cannot be found relative to that of the electromagnetic field, since conservation of electric charge prevents their decay into photons. However, charged pions can be created or destroyed through interactions of nucleons (protons and neutrons), and so their intrinsic parity can be found relative to that of the nucleons, again if parity conservation during the interaction is assumed. Conventional usage assigns even parity to the nucleons and odd parity to the pions.

INVERTED STATES AND OPERATORS

The equation of motion of an inverted state can be found in the same manner as for a displaced state at the beginning of Sec. 26. As expected from analogy with Eq. (26.5), it is found that if a particular ket obeys the Schrödinger equation the inverted ket does also, provided that $[U_I, H] = 0$. In this case H and U_I can be diagonalized simultaneously, so that the energy eigenstates can be chosen to have well-defined parities. Further, if $|\alpha\rangle$ and $U_I|\alpha\rangle$ are linearly independent, there must be energy degeneracy.

In analogy with the discussion of Eq. (26.6), the matrix elements of a dynamical variable Ω for inverted states are equal to the corresponding matrix elements of $U_I^\dagger \Omega U_I$ for the original states. Since U_I is defined

---

[1] C. N. Yang and J. Tiomno, *Phys. Rev.* **79**, 495 (1950); G. C. Wick, A. S. Wightman, and E. P. Wigner, *Phys. Rev.* **88**, 101 (1952); K. Nishijima, "Fundamental Particles," p. 41 (Benjamin, New York, 1964).

to be unitary, multiplication of the first of Eqs. (29.3) from the left by $U_I{}^\dagger$ gives

$$\psi_\alpha(\mathbf{r}) = \omega U_I{}^\dagger \psi_\alpha(-\mathbf{r}) \qquad \text{or} \qquad U_I{}^\dagger \psi_\alpha(\mathbf{r}) = \omega^{-1}\psi_\alpha(-\mathbf{r})$$

We can then evaluate $U_I{}^\dagger \mathbf{r} U_I$ by allowing it to operate on an arbitrary state $\psi_\alpha(\mathbf{r})$:

$$U_I{}^\dagger \mathbf{r} U_I \psi_\alpha(\mathbf{r}) = U_I{}^\dagger \mathbf{r} \omega \psi_\alpha(-\mathbf{r}) = \omega^{-1}\omega(-\mathbf{r})\psi_\alpha(\mathbf{r})$$

so that

$$U_I{}^\dagger \mathbf{r} U_I = -\mathbf{r} \tag{29.4}$$

In similar fashion, since $\mathbf{p} = -i\hbar\boldsymbol{\nabla}$ and $\mathbf{L} = \mathbf{r} \times \mathbf{p}$, it is easily seen that

$$U_I{}^\dagger \mathbf{p} U_I = -\mathbf{p} \qquad U_I{}^\dagger \mathbf{L} U_I = \mathbf{L} \tag{29.5}$$

Since U_I affects the space coordinates but not the spin, we expect that it commutes with $\mathbf{S}$ and hence also with $\mathbf{J} = \mathbf{L} + \mathbf{S}$, so that

$$U_I{}^\dagger \mathbf{S} U_I = \mathbf{S} \qquad U_I{}^\dagger \mathbf{J} U_I = \mathbf{J} \tag{29.6}$$

Equations (29.4) to (29.6) are in agreement with what would be expected classically from the space-inversion properties of coordinates, momenta, and angular momenta. Coordinates and momenta are examples of what is called a *vector* or a *polar vector*, and an angular momentum is an *axial vector* or a *pseudovector*.

TIME REVERSAL[1]

The reversal in time of a state represented by the ket $|\alpha\rangle$ or the wave function ψ_α changes it into the ket $|\alpha'\rangle$ or the wave function $\psi_{\alpha'}$ that develops in accordance with the opposite sense of progression of time. For this new state the signs of all linear and angular momenta are reversed but other quantities are unchanged. Time reversal is effected by a time-independent operator T such that

$$T|\alpha\rangle = |\alpha'\rangle \qquad \text{or} \qquad T\psi_\alpha = \psi_{\alpha'} \tag{29.7}$$

We shall assume in what follows that T is a symmetry operation for closed isolated physical systems; at present all experimental evidence is consistent with this assumption.   This means that if $|k\rangle$ or u_k represents an eigenstate of the hamiltonian (which is constant in time) with energy eigenvalue E_k, then $T|k\rangle$ or Tu_k also represents an eigenstate with the same eigenvalue.

[1] Time reversal was introduced into quantum mechanics by E. P. Wigner, *Göttinger Nachr.* **31**, 546 (1932).   See also E. P. Wigner, "Group Theory," chap. 26 (Academic, New York, 1959).

At some particular time, say $t = 0$, the wave function ψ_α can be expanded in terms of the energy eigenfunctions u_k in accordance with Eq. (23.22):

$$\psi_\alpha = S_k a_{\alpha k} u_k \tag{29.8}$$

We now consider two pairs of operations that can be performed on ψ_α that are expected to lead to the same physical state. In the first case we allow the state to propagate to time t and then reverse it. In the second case we reverse it at $t = 0$ and then allow the reversed state to propagate with the opposite sense of progression of time, that is, to time $-t$. With the first pair of operations, propagation to time t takes the wave function (29.8) into

$$S_k a_{\alpha k} e^{-iE_k t/\hbar} u_k$$

If now we tentatively assume that T is a linear operator (which we shall immediately see leads to a contradiction), time reversal gives

$$S_k a_{\alpha k} e^{-iE_k t/\hbar} T u_k \tag{29.9}$$

With the second pair of operations, time reversal at $t = 0$ takes the wave function (29.8) into

$$S_k a_{\alpha k} T u_k$$

Since the energy eigenvalue of $T u_k$ is E_k, propagation to time $-t$ then gives

$$S_k a_{\alpha k} e^{iE_k t/\hbar} T u_k \tag{29.10}$$

It is apparent that, in general, the wave functions (29.9) and (29.10) are not multiples of each other, as they must be if they are to represent the same physical state. Thus T cannot be a linear operator.

ANTILINEAR OPERATORS

The foregoing contradiction is clearly connected somehow with the operation of complex conjugation. This is not surprising, since a change in the sign of t in the Schrödinger equation for ψ_α changes it into the equation for ψ_α^*, provided that H is real and independent of the time. Therefore, instead of assuming that T is a linear operator with the property

$$T(a_1\psi_1 + a_2\psi_2) = a_1 T\psi_1 + a_2 T\psi_2$$

we try the assumption that T has the property

$$T(a_1\psi_1 + a_2\psi_2) = a_1^* T\psi_1 + a_2^* T\psi_2 \tag{29.11}$$

Such an operator is said to be *antilinear*. With the assumption (29.11) for T, the two states (29.9) and (29.10) both become

$$S_k a_{\alpha k}^* e^{iE_k t/\hbar} T u_k$$

and the contradiction disappears.

Application of T to both sides of the Schrödinger equation

$$i\hbar \frac{\partial \psi_\alpha}{\partial t} = H\psi_\alpha$$

gives

$$-i\hbar \frac{\partial(T\psi_\alpha)}{\partial t} = TH\psi_\alpha$$

Thus if T commutes with the hamiltonian, so that

$$[T,H] = 0 \tag{29.12}$$

then $T\psi_\alpha$ satisfies the Schrödinger equation with t replaced by $-t$, as would be expected. It also follows from (29.12) that Tu_k is an energy eigenfunction with eigenvalue E_k, as assumed above. Thus the condition that T is a symmetry operation is that Eq. (29.12) be satisfied. The situation here is no different from that with the unitary symmetry operations discussed earlier, for example, in connection with Eq. (26.5).

ANTIUNITARY OPERATORS

An antilinear operator can be expressed as the product of a linear operator and the complex-conjugation operator K, which is defined by

$$K\psi = \psi^*$$

for an arbitrary function ψ. We note that $K^2 = 1$. An especially useful class of antilinear operators consists of those for which the linear operator that multiplies K is unitary; such operators are called *antiunitary*. It is apparent that K itself is antilinear and also antiunitary. It is easily shown (Prob. 15) that the inner product of two state functions is changed into its complex conjugate when the states are operated on with the same antiunitary operator. The same argument shows that the norm of a state is unchanged since it is real. It is plausible to expect that the norms of states and the absolute magnitudes of the inner products of pairs of states are unchanged by time reversal. We therefore assume that T is antiunitary and write it in the form

$$T = UK \tag{29.13}$$

where U is unitary.

If H is complex, as with the optical-model potential considered in Sec. 20, the condition (29.12) requires that U transform H^* into H:

$UH^*U^\dagger = H$. There is, in general, no unitary operator that has this property, so that the physical system represented by a complex hamiltonian is not time-reversal invariant.[1] This is to be expected, since the absorption of particles by a complex potential specifies a particular sense of progression of time, as shown in Eq. (20.1). The situation here is roughly analogous to friction in classical particle motion or viscosity in classical hydrodynamics, which introduces forces that change sign when the velocity changes sign, thus destroying time-reversal invariance. Both the complex potential in quantum mechanics and friction or viscosity in classical mechanics provide simple phenomenological descriptions of much more complicated situations and do not of themselves imply a lack of time-reversal invariance at a more elementary level.

T FOR A ZERO SPIN PARTICLE

We now obtain an explicit expression for T such that for the time-reversed state the signs of all linear and angular momenta are reversed but other quantities are unchanged. The simplest case is a spin zero particle in which a state is represented by a one-component wave function. Operation on some ψ_α with the coordinate produces a new state which we call ψ_β: $\mathbf{r}\psi_\alpha = \psi_\beta$. If the sign of $\mathbf{r}$ is not to change on time reversal, we expect this relation to hold also for the time-reversed states; that is, if $\psi_{\alpha'} = T\psi_\alpha$ and $\psi_{\beta'} = T\psi_\beta$, then $\mathbf{r}\psi_{\alpha'} = \psi_{\beta'}$. It then follows that

$$\mathbf{r}T\psi_\alpha = \mathbf{r}\psi_{\alpha'} = \psi_{\beta'} = T\psi_\beta = T\mathbf{r}\psi_\alpha$$

Since ψ_α is an arbitrary state, we have that

$$\mathbf{r}T = T\mathbf{r} \tag{29.14}$$

Operation on ψ_α with the momentum produces a new state which we call ψ_γ: $\mathbf{p}\psi_\alpha = \psi_\gamma$. If now the sign of $\mathbf{p}$ is to change on time reversal, we expect to have for the time-reversed states $\mathbf{p}\psi_{\alpha'} = -\psi_{\gamma'}$. We then have

$$\mathbf{p}T\psi_\alpha = \mathbf{p}\psi_{\alpha'} = -\psi_{\gamma'} = -T\psi_\gamma = -T\mathbf{p}\psi_\alpha$$

so that

$$\mathbf{p}T = -T\mathbf{p} \tag{29.15}$$

In similar fashion, since $\mathbf{L} = \mathbf{r} \times \mathbf{p}$,

$$\mathbf{L}T = -T\mathbf{L} \tag{29.16}$$

In the coordinate representation, $\mathbf{r}$ is a real operator and $\mathbf{p} = -i\hbar\nabla$ is a pure imaginary operator. The simplest choice for T that satisfies

---

[1] Note that, in spite of this, the reciprocity theorem (20.16) is valid in this situation.

Eqs. (29.14) to (29.16) is then

$$U = 1 \qquad T = K \tag{29.17}$$

This conclusion evidently depends on the choice of representation. Thus if we use the momentum representation, in which ψ_α is a function of $\mathbf{p}$ rather than of $\mathbf{r}$, then $\mathbf{p}$ is a real multiplicative operator and $\mathbf{r}$ is pure imaginary, for example, $x = i\hbar(\partial/\partial p_x)$. In this case Eq. (29.13) is still valid, but U is now the operator that replaces $\mathbf{p}$ by $-\mathbf{p}$: $U\psi_\alpha(\mathbf{p}) = \psi_\alpha(-\mathbf{p})$. We shall always work in the coordinate representation, since this is most familiar and is also convenient.

T FOR A NONZERO SPIN PARTICLE

For a particle with spin, we expect in analogy with Eq. (29.16) that

$$\mathbf{S}T = -T\mathbf{S} \qquad \text{and} \qquad \mathbf{J}T = -T\mathbf{J} \tag{29.18}$$

Since the explicit form of T depends on the representation, we must choose a specific set of $\mathbf{S}$ matrices when $s \neq 0$, in addition to the earlier choice of the coordinate representation. We have already seen (see Prob. 7) that the $s = 1$ spin matrices (27.11) and the $j = 1$ matrices in (27.26) differ only by a unitary transformation, so that they correspond to different choices of representation. When dealing with spin, we shall for definiteness always work in the representation specified by Eqs. (27.26).

It then follows that $\mathbf{r}$, S_x, and S_z are real operators, and $\mathbf{p}$, $\mathbf{L}$, and S_y are pure imaginary operators. Thus if T were equal to K, Eqs. (29.14) to (29.16) and the S_y equation in (29.18) would be satisfied but the S_x and S_z equations would not be. We must therefore choose U so that it commutes with $\mathbf{r}$, $\mathbf{p}$, $\mathbf{L}$, and S_y and so that

$$S_x U = -U S_x \qquad \text{and} \qquad S_z U = -U S_z \tag{29.19}$$

Thus U may be any unitary operator that is a function only of S_y and that satisfies Eqs. (29.19).

We know from Eq. (27.16) that the unitary operator $\exp(-i\boldsymbol{\phi}\cdot\mathbf{J}/\hbar)$ rotates a state through the vector angle $\boldsymbol{\phi}$. Also, through Eq. (28.15), it transforms an operator into the same operator rotated through $\boldsymbol{\phi}$. In similar fashion, the unitary operator $\exp(-i\boldsymbol{\phi}\cdot\mathbf{S}/\hbar)$ transforms any operator function of $\mathbf{S}$ into the same function in which the argument is the result of rotating $\mathbf{S}$ through $\boldsymbol{\phi}$. In particular, $e^{-i\pi S_y/\hbar}$ is a unitary transformation that rotates $\mathbf{S}$ through π radians about the y axis and hence transforms S_x into $-S_x$ and S_z into $-S_z$. We may therefore put

$$T = e^{-i\pi S_y/\hbar}K \tag{29.20}$$

That this T has the desired properties is shown explicitly in Prob. 16.

For a spin $\frac{1}{2}$ particle, Eq. (29.20) takes the particularly simple form[1]

$$T = -i\sigma_y K \qquad \text{where} \qquad \sigma_y = \begin{bmatrix} 0 & -i \\ i & 0 \end{bmatrix} \qquad (29.21)$$

SYSTEMS OF SEVERAL PARTICLES

When several particles are present, T may be constructed by multiplying together the U's that correspond to each particle and then multiplying this product into K:

$$T = e^{-i\pi S_{1y}/\hbar} \cdots e^{-i\pi S_{ny}/\hbar} K \qquad (29.22)$$

The order of factors in the product of exponentials is unimportant since each operates only on the state of that particle; thus they all commute with each other, and T satisfies the first of Eqs. (29.18) for each $\mathbf{S}$.

Since each S_y is pure imaginary, each exponential in (29.22) is real and hence commutes with K. Then, since $K^2 = 1$, we see that

$$T^2 = e^{-2i\pi S_{1y}/\hbar} \cdots e^{-2i\pi S_{ny}/\hbar}$$

Each of these exponentials is a rotation through 2π radians. According to the discussion in Sec. 27, it is equal to $+1$ for an integer spin particle and -1 for a half-odd-integer spin particle. Thus T^2 is equal to $+1$ or -1 according as the total number of half-odd-integer spin particles in the system is even or odd.

As remarked below Eq. (29.12), if u_k is an energy eigenfunction, Tu_k is also an energy eigenfunction with the same eigenvalue. We suppose at first that there is no degeneracy. Then Tu_k represents the same state as u_k, so that $Tu_k = cu_k$, where c is some number, and

$$T^2 u_k = Tcu_k = c^* Tu_k = |c|^2 u_k$$

If $T^2 = +1$, then $|c|^2 = 1$, which is a possible situation. But if $T^2 = -1$, there is no number c, which means that there must be some degeneracy. In this case, u_k and Tu_k are orthogonal, as may be seen in the following way. It is shown in Prob. 15 that $(T\psi_1, T\psi_2) = (\psi_2, \psi_1)$. If we choose $\psi_1 = Tu_k$ and $\psi_2 = u_k$, this relation becomes $(T^2 u_k, Tu_k) = (u_k, Tu_k)$. Since $T^2 = -1$, the left side is the negative of the right side, so that both sides are zero and Tu_k is orthogonal to u_k. Thus for every u_k there is a distinct Tu_k that is degenerate with it, so that the overall degeneracy is even.

For a crystal of low symmetry, each atom is in an unsymmetrical environment, and one would not normally expect any degeneracy for the states of the electrons in that atom. These electrons are moving in the

[1] σ_y is one of the three Pauli spin matrices defined in Eq. (27.30), which are discussed more fully in Sec. 41.

static electric field produced by the rest of the crystal, which can be represented by a term $\sum_i e\phi(\mathbf{r}_i)$ in the hamiltonian, as in Eq. (24.29), where $\mathbf{r}_i$ is the coordinate of the ith electron of the atom. Such a term evidently does not destroy the time-reversal invariance of the rest of the hamiltonian that describes the atom. Then if the number of electrons per atom is odd, $T^2 = -1$ and there must be at least a twofold degeneracy; this is called *Kramers degeneracy*.[1] The degeneracy is removed if the crystal is placed in an external magnetic field $\mathbf{H}$. As we shall see later (Sec. 48), the magnetic effects associated with the orbital motion and spin of each electron cause interaction terms to appear in the hamiltonian that are proportional to $\mathbf{L} \cdot \mathbf{H}$ and $\mathbf{S} \cdot \mathbf{H}$. Equations (29.16) and (29.18) then show that the hamiltonian is no longer time-reversal invariant. Thus the magnetic field produces a splitting of the energy levels if the number of electrons per atom of the crystal is odd. It should be noted that this situation is not in contradiction with the assumption, stated just below Eq. (29.7), that T is a symmetry operation for closed isolated physical systems. An external magnetic field is, by definition, imposed from outside the system under consideration; the degeneracy is removed because we have assumed implicitly that the currents producing the field $\mathbf{H}$ are not reversed by T.

REALITY OF EIGENFUNCTIONS

Let us consider a system that has no spin or in which the spin is not significant. Then $U = 1$ and $T = K$ in the coordinate representation. Further, we suppose that there is an operator Ω that commutes with K and that has nondegenerate eigenvalues ω_μ: $\Omega v_\mu = \omega_\mu v_\mu$. Then $K v_\mu$ represents the same state as v_μ, so that $K v_\mu = v_\mu^* = c v_\mu$, where c is some number. If now we write v_μ as the sum of its real and imaginary parts, $v_\mu = w_\mu + i z_\mu$, where w_μ and z_μ are real functions, then

$$w_\mu - i z_\mu = c(w_\mu + i z_\mu) \qquad \text{or} \qquad (1 - c)w_\mu = i(1 + c)z_\mu$$

This means that w_μ and z_μ are multiples of each other, so that v_μ is real except for a possible complex multiplying coefficient. In particular, all nondegenerate energy eigenfunctions are real in this sense if the system is time-reversal invariant.

The foregoing argument can sometimes be extended to the case in which there is degeneracy. An interesting example is provided by a real hamiltonian that contains an arbitrary spherically symmetric potential, so that

$$[H, \mathbf{L}^2] = 0 \qquad [K, H] = 0 \qquad [K, \mathbf{L}^2] = 0$$

[1] H. A. Kramers, *Koninkl. Ned. Akad. Wetenschap., Proc.* **33**, 959 (1930).

Eigenfunctions v_{klm} labeled by an energy eigenvalue E_k and an orbital angular momentum quantum number l are still degenerate with respect to the magnetic quantum number m. However the operator associated with m, $L_z = -i\hbar(\partial/\partial\phi)$, is pure imaginary and, in accordance with Eq. (29.16), does not commute with K. Thus we cannot argue, as was done in the preceding paragraph, that $Kv_{klm} = cv_{klm}$ so that v_{klm} is real; in actuality it is not real in general since it is proportional to the spherical harmonic $Y_{lm}(\theta,\phi)$, which is complex for $m \neq 0$.

If, however, we restrict our attention to the case $m = 0$, we are dealing only with eigenfunctions of L_z that have the eigenvalue zero. It then follows from the relation $L_z K = -KL_z$ that K times an eigenfunction of L_z is still an eigenfunction of L_z with eigenvalue zero. Thus if there is no additional degeneracy, we can be sure that those eigenfunctions v_{kl0} of H and $\mathbf{L}^2$ that have $m = 0$ are all real in the sense used above. These are just the eigenfunctions used in the scattering theory of Secs. 19 and 20. As expected, the phase shifts δ_l are real or complex according as the hamiltonian is or is not time-reversal invariant.[1]

30□DYNAMICAL SYMMETRY

We have seen in Sec. 26 that symmetry and degeneracy are associated with each other. For example, a system that possesses space-displacement symmetry is usually degenerate with respect to the direction of the momentum vector $\mathbf{p}$, an exception arising when $\mathbf{p} = 0$. Similarly, a system that possesses rotational symmetry is usually degenerate with respect to the direction of the angular momentum vector $\mathbf{J}$, that is, with respect to the eigenvalue of a particular component such as J_z. Again, the case $\mathbf{J} = 0$ is exceptional. In the cases of the discrete symmetries of space inversion and time reversal, degeneracy is less common, since the transformed states are more likely to be the same as the original states.

It was pointed out in Chap. 4 that the hydrogen atom (Sec. 16) and the isotropic harmonic oscillator (Prob. 12) have additional degeneracy beyond that associated with rotational symmetry. As remarked there, this is to be expected whenever the wave equation can be solved in more than one way, in different coordinate systems or in a single coordinate system oriented in different ways. From our present point of view, we also expect these degeneracies to be associated with some symmetry, which evidently is not of the geometrical type considered thus far in this chapter. We call such symmetries *dynamical*, since they arise from particular forms of the force law. In the two relatively simple cases con-

[1] For an extension of the methods of this subsection to systems in which spin is significant, see R. G. Sachs, "Nuclear Theory," App. 3 (Addison-Wesley, Reading, Mass., 1953).

sidered in this section, the existence and general nature of the dynamical symmetry can be inferred from the corresponding classical system, in much the same way as with geometrical symmetries.   This is not possible in general; indeed, many situations of physical interest have no classical analogs.

CLASSICAL KEPLER PROBLEM

The classical hamiltonian for the Kepler problem in relative coordinates is

$$H = \frac{\mathbf{p}^2}{2\mu} - \frac{\kappa}{r} \tag{30.1}$$

where μ is the reduced mass and κ is a positive quantity.   For the hydrogen atom, comparison with Sec. 16 shows that $\kappa = Ze^2$.   A particular solution of the classical orbit problem is an ellipse with semimajor axis a that is equal to half the distance from perihelion P to aphelion A (Fig. 25), and with eccentricity e that is equal to $(a^2 - b^2)^{\frac{1}{2}}/a$, where b is the semiminor axis.

Since H is independent of the time, the total energy E is a constant of the motion.   Also, since H possesses rotational symmetry, the orbital angular momentum $\mathbf{L} = \mathbf{r} \times \mathbf{p}$ is a constant of the motion.   Both of these statements are easily established from Eq. (24.22) and require calculation of some Poisson brackets.   It is not difficult to show that

$$E = -\frac{\kappa}{2a} \qquad \text{and} \qquad L^2 = \mu\kappa a(1 - e^2) \tag{30.2}$$

$\mathbf{L}$ is evidently an axial vector that is perpendicular to the plane of the orbit.

The rotational symmetry of H is enough to cause the orbit to lie in some plane through O, but it is not enough to require the orbit to be closed. A small deviation of the potential energy from the newtonian form $V(r) = -(\kappa/r)$ causes the major axis PA of the ellipse to precess slowly, so that the orbit is not closed.   This suggests that there is some quantity, other than H and $\mathbf{L}$, that is a constant of the motion and that can be used to characterize the orientation of the major axis in the orbital plane.   We

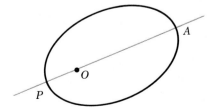

Fig. 25   Classical Kepler orbit with the center of attraction at a focus O of the ellipse.

thus look for a constant vector $\mathbf{M}$, which we expect to lie along the major axis, pointing from O to P or from O to A.

Such a vector has been known for a long time and is called the *Lenz vector* or the *Runge-Lenz vector*.[1]   We write it in the form

$$\mathbf{M} = \frac{\mathbf{p} \times \mathbf{L}}{\mu} - \frac{\kappa}{r}\mathbf{r} \tag{30.3}$$

It is easily seen to be a constant of the motion, to have magnitude κe, and to be directed from O to P.   The following relations are independent of the particular choice of the orbital parameters a and e:

$$\mathbf{L} \cdot \mathbf{M} = 0 \qquad \mathbf{M}^2 = \frac{2H}{\mu}\mathbf{L}^2 + \kappa^2 \tag{30.4}$$

HYDROGEN ATOM

In order to treat the hydrogen atom, the foregoing quantities must be translated into quantum mechanics.   This has already been done for $\mathbf{r}$, $\mathbf{p}$, and $\mathbf{L}$.   For $\mathbf{M}$, we note that $\mathbf{p} \times \mathbf{L}$ is not equal to $-\mathbf{L} \times \mathbf{p}$, so that Eq. (30.3) does not define a hermitian quantity.   We therefore redefine $\mathbf{M}$ as a symmetric average:

$$\mathbf{M} = \frac{1}{2\mu}(\mathbf{p} \times \mathbf{L} - \mathbf{L} \times \mathbf{p}) - \frac{\kappa}{r}\mathbf{r} \tag{30.5}$$

It can then be shown from the commutation relations for $\mathbf{r}$ and $\mathbf{p}$, after a considerable amount of computation, that

$$[\mathbf{M},H] = 0 \qquad \mathbf{L} \cdot \mathbf{M} = \mathbf{M} \cdot \mathbf{L} = 0$$
$$\mathbf{M}^2 = \frac{2H}{\mu}(\mathbf{L}^2 + \hbar^2) + \kappa^2 \tag{30.6}$$

These are the quantum-mechanical analogs of the constancy of $\mathbf{M}$ and of Eqs. (30.4).

Equations (30.5) and (30.6) were used by Pauli[2] to find the energy levels of the hydrogen atom, independently of and simultaneously with Schrödinger's[3] treatment on the basis of the wave equation that was discussed in Sec. 16.   Pauli's approach is equivalent to regarding the three components of $\mathbf{M}$ as generators of some infinitesimal transformations, in much the same way that the three components of $\mathbf{L}$ were regarded in Sec. 27 as generators of infinitesimal rotations about the three axes.   We thus proceed by working out the algebra of the six generators $\mathbf{L}$, $\mathbf{M}$, which consists of 15 commutation relations.   Three of these have already been

[1] C. Runge, "Vektoranalysis," vol. 1, p. 70 (S. Hirzel, Leipzig, 1919); W. Lenz, *Z. Physik* **24**, 197 (1924).

[2] W. Pauli, *Z. Physik* **36**, 336 (1926).

[3] E. Schrödinger, *Ann. Physik* **79**, 361 (1926).

given in Eqs. (27.14) and are cyclic permutations of

$$[L_x, L_y] = i\hbar L_z \tag{30.7}$$

Nine more are cyclic permutations of

$$[M_x, L_x] = 0 \qquad [M_x, L_y] = i\hbar M_z \qquad [M_x, L_z] = -i\hbar M_y \tag{30.8}$$

The last three are much more difficult to calculate and are cyclic permutations of

$$[M_x, M_y] = -\frac{2i\hbar}{\mu} H L_z \tag{30.9}$$

The **L** by themselves constitute the closed algebra (30.7) and, as we have seen in Sec. 27, generate the group $O(3)$. The **L** and **M** together, however, do not form a closed algebra since, although Eqs. (30.8) involve only **L** and **M**, Eq. (30.9) brings in H as well. However, since H is independent of the time and commutes with **L** and **M**, we can work in a subspace of the Hilbert space that corresponds to a particular energy eigenvalue E of the hamiltonian H. Then H may be replaced in Eq. (30.9) by E, which for bound states is a negative quantity. It is convenient now to replace **M** by

$$\mathbf{M}' \equiv \left(-\frac{\mu}{2E}\right)^{\frac{1}{2}} \mathbf{M} \tag{30.10}$$

The commutation relations (30.8) hold as well for $\mathbf{M}'$, and (30.9) is replaced by

$$[M'_x, M'_y] = i\hbar L_z \tag{30.11}$$

THE $O(4)$ GROUP

The six generators **L**, $\mathbf{M}'$ constitute a closed algebra, which can be identified with a known algebra in the following way. We relabel the coordinate vector $\mathbf{r} = (x,y,z)$ and the momentum vector $\mathbf{p} = (p_x, p_y, p_z)$ as

$$\mathbf{r} = (r_1, r_2, r_3) \qquad \text{and} \qquad \mathbf{p} = (p_1, p_2, p_3)$$

and relabel the angular momentum vector $\mathbf{L} = (L_x, L_y, L_z)$ accordingly as

$$\mathbf{L} = (L_{23}, L_{31}, L_{12})$$

We thus have

$$L_{ij} = r_i p_j - r_j p_i \qquad [r_i, p_j] = i\hbar \delta_{ij} \tag{30.12}$$

where $i, j = 1, 2, 3$. We now extend Eqs. (30.12) to $i, j = 1, 2, 3, 4$ by inventing fourth coordinate and momentum components r_4 and p_4 such that

$$M'_x = L_{14} \qquad M'_y = L_{24} \qquad M'_z = L_{34} \tag{30.13}$$

It is easily verified that Eqs. (30.12) and (30.13) lead to the commutation relations (30.7), (30.8), and (30.11).

The six generators L_{ij} obviously constitute the generalization of the three generators $\mathbf{L}$ from three to four dimensions. The group that they generate can be shown to be the proper rotation group or orthogonal group in four dimensions, designated $O(4)$, which is the set of all 4×4 real orthonormal matrices with determinant equal to $+1$. This evidently does not represent a geometrical symmetry of the hydrogen atom, since the fourth components r_4 and p_4 are fictitious and cannot be identified with dynamical variables. For this reason, $O(4)$ is said to describe a dynamical symmetry of the hydrogen atom. It does, of course, contain the geometrical symmetry $O(3)$ as a subgroup.

It is important to note that the $O(4)$ generators were obtained by restricting our considerations to bound states. For continuum states, E is positive, and the sign inside the square root of (30.10) must be changed in order for $\mathbf{M'}$ to be hermitian. Then the sign on the right side of Eq. (30.11) is changed, and the identifications (30.12) and (30.13) are no longer valid. It turns out that the dynamical symmetry group in this case is isomorphic to the group of Lorentz transformations in one time and three space dimensions, rather than to the group of rotations in four space dimensions.[1]

ENERGY LEVELS OF HYDROGEN

The energy eigenvalues can now be found with practically no further effort. We define two quantities

$$\mathbf{I} = \tfrac{1}{2}(\mathbf{L} + \mathbf{M'}) \qquad \mathbf{K} = \tfrac{1}{2}(\mathbf{L} - \mathbf{M'}) \tag{30.14}$$

which are easily seen to satisfy the commutation relations

$$[I_x, I_y] = i\hbar I_z \quad \text{etc.} \qquad [K_x, K_y] = i\hbar K_z \quad \text{etc.}$$
$$[\mathbf{I}, \mathbf{K}] = 0 \qquad\qquad [\mathbf{I}, H] = [\mathbf{K}, H] = 0 \tag{30.15}$$

Thus $\mathbf{I}$ and $\mathbf{K}$ each constitute an $O(3)$ or $SU(2)$ algebra, and we see at once that the possible eigenvalues are

$$\mathbf{I}^2 = i(i+1)\hbar^2 \qquad \mathbf{K}^2 = k(k+1)\hbar^2 \qquad i, k = 0, \tfrac{1}{2}, 1, \ldots \tag{30.16}$$

It is easily seen from the commutation relations (30.15) that the $O(4)$ group is of rank 2. Thus there are two Casimir operators, which may evidently be chosen to be

$$\mathbf{I}^2 = \tfrac{1}{4}(\mathbf{L} + \mathbf{M'})^2 \qquad \text{and} \qquad \mathbf{K}^2 = \tfrac{1}{4}(\mathbf{L} - \mathbf{M'})^2$$

[1] V. Fock, Z. Physik **98**, 145 (1935); V. Bargmann, Z. Physik **99**, 576 (1936); M. Bander and C. Itzykson, Rev. Mod. Phys. **38**, 330, 346 (1966).

Alternatively, they may be chosen to be the sum and difference of $\mathbf{I}^2$ and $\mathbf{K}^2$:

$$C = \mathbf{I}^2 + \mathbf{K}^2 = \tfrac{1}{2}(\mathbf{L}^2 + \mathbf{M}'^2) \qquad \text{and} \qquad C' = \mathbf{I}^2 - \mathbf{K}^2 = \mathbf{L} \cdot \mathbf{M}' \tag{30.17}$$

The second of Eqs. (30.6) shows that $C' = 0$, so that we are dealing only with that part of $O(4)$ for which $\mathbf{I}^2 = \mathbf{K}^2$. Thus $i = k$, and the possible values of the first Casimir operator are

$$C = 2k(k + 1)\hbar^2 \qquad k = 0, \tfrac{1}{2}, 1, \ldots \tag{30.18}$$

The third of Eqs. (30.6), together with (30.10) and (30.17), then gives

$$C = \frac{1}{2} \left(\mathbf{L}^2 - \frac{\mu}{2E} \mathbf{M}^2 \right) = -\frac{\mu \kappa^2}{4E} - \tfrac{1}{2}\hbar^2$$

With the expression (30.18) for C, we obtain

$$E = -\frac{\mu \kappa^2}{2\hbar^2(2k + 1)^2} \tag{30.19}$$

Equation (30.19) agrees with the wave equation result (16.15) if we remember that $\kappa = Ze^2$ and make the natural identification $n = 2k + 1$, which gives n the sequence of values $1, 2, 3, \ldots$.

It is important to note that there is no objection to using half-odd-integer values for i and k in (30.16). The only physical restriction is that $\mathbf{L}^2 = l(l + 1)\hbar^2$ have only integer values of l. But, since $\mathbf{L} = \mathbf{I} + \mathbf{K}$ from (30.14), the triangle rule of Sec. 28 shows that l can have any value ranging from $i + k = 2k = n - 1$ down to $|i - k| = 0$, by integer steps. Thus l not only is restricted to integer values but has the correct range of values with respect to the total quantum number n. The degeneracy of this energy level is also given correctly since I_z and K_z can each have $2k + 1 = n$ independent eigenvalues, and there are therefore n^2 possible states altogether.

Finally we note that, as discussed in connection with Eq. (29.5), $\mathbf{L}$ is an axial vector and does not change sign on space inversion. In similar fashion, it is apparent that $\mathbf{M}$ defined by (30.5) is a polar vector, which does change sign. Thus we expect that states defined by the symmetry generators $\mathbf{L}$ and $\mathbf{M}$ need not have well-defined parity. This is actually the case, since states of even and odd l are degenerate in the hydrogen atom.

CLASSICAL ISOTROPIC OSCILLATOR

The three-dimensional isotropic harmonic oscillator is described by the hamiltonian

$$H = \frac{\mathbf{p}^2}{2m} + \tfrac{1}{2}K\mathbf{r}^2 \tag{30.20}$$

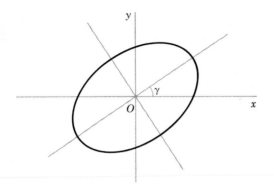

Fig. 26 Classical harmonic-oscillator orbit with the center of attraction at the center O of the ellipse.

This is the generalization of the linear harmonic oscillator discussed in Sec. 13, for the case in which the force constant is the same in all directions. A particular solution of the classical orbit problem is an ellipse with semimajor axis a and semiminor axis b, which has its major axis oriented so as to make an angle γ with the x axis (Fig. 26). As in the Kepler problem, H and $\mathbf{L}$ are constants of the motion, with values given by

$$E = \tfrac{1}{2}K(a^2 + b^2) \qquad \text{and} \qquad \mathbf{L}^2 = mKa^2b^2$$

The fact that the orbit is closed again suggests that there is some other constant of the motion that can be used to characterize the orientation angle γ. There is, however, a striking difference between Figs. 25 and 26. In the Kepler problem, the center of attraction O is at a focus of the ellipse, whereas in the oscillator problem it is at the center. Thus the two directions OA and OP along the major axis are not equivalent in the Kepler orbit, and the minor axis is not a symmetry element. In contrast, both directions along the major axis and both directions along the minor axis are equally good symmetry elements in the oscillator orbit. Thus we expect that the additional constant of the motion is not a vector, as in the Kepler problem, but rather a quadrupole tensor.

We define the components of the quadrupole tensor as in the last five of Eqs. (27.44). Computation of the appropriate Poisson brackets then shows that the Q's are constants if and only if we choose α and β such that $\alpha/\beta = mK$. For the orbit shown in Fig. 26, the Q's then have the values

$$Q_{xy} = \tfrac{1}{2}\alpha(a^2 - b^2)\sin 2\gamma \qquad Q_{yz} = Q_{zx} = 0$$

$$Q_0 = \frac{\alpha}{2\sqrt{3}}(a^2 + b^2) \qquad Q_1 = \tfrac{1}{2}\alpha(a^2 - b^2)\cos 2\gamma$$

As expected from Fig. 26, the components of the quadrupole tensor are unchanged if γ is replaced by $\gamma + \pi$, and also if a and b are interchanged and γ is replaced by $\gamma \pm \tfrac{1}{2}\pi$.

QUANTUM ISOTROPIC OSCILLATOR

Since the quantum problem separates in cartesian coordinates, the solution is easily found in terms of those given in Sec. 13. The energy levels are

$$E_n = (n + \tfrac{3}{2})\hbar \left(\frac{K}{m}\right)^{\frac{1}{2}} \qquad n = n_x + n_y + n_z$$

$$n_x, n_y, n_z = 0, 1, 2, \ldots \quad (30.21)$$

The degeneracy of E_n is easily seen to be $\tfrac{1}{2}(n + 1)(n + 2)$, and the parity of this state is even or odd according as n is even or odd. Thus the only possible l values are n, $n - 2$, . . . down to 1 or 0, and it can be shown that each l occurs just once.

Comparison with the work of Sec. 27 shows that the dynamical symmetry group is $SU(3)$.[1] Since we require that $\alpha/\beta = mK$, the Casimir operator (27.47) is related to the square of the hamiltonian (30.20):

$$C = -3 + \frac{4m}{3\hbar^2 K} H^2 \qquad (30.22)$$

Substitution of the expression (30.21) for the nth eigenvalue of H into (30.22) gives

$$C = \tfrac{4}{3}(n^2 + 3n)$$

Since $SU(3)$ is of rank 2, there are two Casimir operators; they can be expressed in terms of two parameters, λ and μ, which take on the values 0, 1, 2, ... The general expression for the first Casimir operator (27.47) in terms of these parameters is[2]

$$C = \tfrac{4}{3}(\lambda^2 + \lambda\mu + \mu^2 + 3\lambda + 3\mu)$$

Thus only the representations of $SU(3)$ with $(\lambda,\mu) = (n,0)$ are realized by the isotropic oscillator. The situation here is somewhat analogous to that in the hydrogen atom, where only the representations of $O(4)$ with $i = k$ are realized.

In contrast with the hydrogen atom, we have seen that there is no parity mixing in the isotropic oscillator, since the l values in each degenerate state are either all even or all odd. This is to be expected since all eight of the generators, the three components of $\mathbf{L}$ and the five Q's, are unchanged in sign on space inversion.

The connection between the isotropic oscillator and $SU(3)$ can also be made through the raising and lowering operators, $a^\dagger$ and a, defined in Sec. 25. There are now three of each, one pair associated with each of the three coordinates. The commutation relation (25.10) and the

[1] J. M. Jauch and E. L. Hill, *Phys. Rev.* **57,** 641 (1940).

[2] Lipkin, *op. cit.,* p. 126; his definition of C differs from that used here by a factor 4.

hamiltonian (25.11) become

$$[a_i, a_j^\dagger] = \delta_{ij} \qquad \text{and} \qquad H = \left(\sum_{i=1}^{3} a_i^\dagger a_i + \frac{3}{2} \right) \hbar \omega_c$$

where $i, j = x, y, z$.   Then the algebra of the nine operators $a_i^\dagger a_j$ is that of the generators of $U(3)$; linear combinations of these can be found that are equal to H and the eight generators of $SU(3)$.[1]

PROBLEMS

1.   Show that Eq. (26.6) is valid, making use of the form (26.4) for $U_r(\varrho)$ and the commutation relations for the components of **r** and **p**.

2.   Make use of the invariance of the scalar product of any two vectors under rotations, in order to show that the rows and columns of the rotation matrix R are respectively orthonormal to each other.   Show also that the transpose of R is equal to the inverse of R and that the determinant of R is equal to ± 1.

3.   Show that the three commutation relations (27.14) are valid, making use of the form (27.7) for **L** and the commutation relations for the components of **r** and **p**.

4.   Show that the three matrices **S** defined in Eqs. (27.11) satisfy the relations **S** $\times$ **S** $= i\hbar$**S**.   Show also that $\mathbf{S}^2 = 2\hbar^2$.

5.   Show that the matrix elements of **r** for states that are rotated through the infinitesimal vector $\boldsymbol{\phi}$ are equal to the corresponding matrix elements of $\mathbf{r}_R = \mathbf{r} + \boldsymbol{\phi} \times \mathbf{r}$ for the original states.

6.   Show that the matrix elements of **J** for states that are rotated through the infinitesimal vector $\boldsymbol{\phi}$ are equal to the corresponding matrix elements of $\mathbf{J}_R = \mathbf{J} + \boldsymbol{\phi} \times \mathbf{J}$ for the original states.

7.   Show that the eigenvalues of S_z given in (27.11) are the same as those of J_z given in (27.26) for $j = 1$.   Then find the most general unitary matrix that transforms S_z into J_z: $US_z U^\dagger = J_z$.   Choose the arbitrary parameters in U so that it also transforms S_x into J_x and S_y into J_y.   Into what does this U transform the vector wave function ψ_α of Eq. (27.8)?

8.   Establish Eq. (27.28) by using the definitions (27.27) and the properties of the spherical harmonics given in Sec. 14.

9.   Obtain an explicit expression for $U_R(\boldsymbol{\phi}) = \exp(-i\boldsymbol{\phi} \cdot \mathbf{J}/\hbar)$ in the form of a 2×2 matrix when **J** is given by Eq. (27.26) with $j = \frac{1}{2}$.   Let the vector $\boldsymbol{\phi}$ have the magnitude ϕ and the polar angles θ and φ.   Show explicitly that your matrix for $U_R(\boldsymbol{\phi})$ is unitary and that it is equal to -1 when $\phi = 2\pi$.

10.   Show that the matrices λ_j $(j = 1, \ldots, 8)$ defined by Eqs. (27.37) and (27.40) satisfy the commutation relations (27.41) and (27.42).   Then use these commutation relations (*not* the original matrix representation of the λ_j) to show that each λ_j commutes with the Casimir operator C defined by Eq. (27.43).

11.   Show that the 28 commutators of the eight operators (27.44), computed from the commutation relations between the components of **r** and **p**, agree with the commutators of the λ_j when the identifications (27.45) and (27.46) are adopted.

[1] For fuller discussion, see J. P. Elliott, *Proc. Roy. Soc. (London)* **A245**, 128 (1958); Lipkin, *op. cit.*, chap. 4.

12. Use the methods and formulas of Sec. 28 to calculate the matrix of Clebsch-Gordan coefficients in the case $j_1 = \frac{3}{2}$, $j_2 = \frac{1}{2}$. Compare your results with the wallet card.

13. A deuteron has spin 1. Use the Wigner-Eckart theorem to find the ratios of the expectation values of the electric quadrupole moment operator $Q(2,0)$ for the three orientations of the deuteron: $m = 1, 0, -1$.

14. Show that the momentum inversion operator U defined after Eq. (29.17), that has the property $U\psi_\alpha(\mathbf{p}) = \psi_\alpha(-\mathbf{p})$, is unitary.

15. Show that, if $\psi_{\alpha'} = T\psi_\alpha$ and $\psi_{\beta'} = T\psi_\beta$, then $(\psi_{\alpha'},\psi_{\beta'}) = (\psi_\alpha,\psi_\beta)^* = (\psi_\beta,\psi_\alpha)$. From this, show that the norm of a state vector is unchanged by time reversal.

16. Show *explicitly* that $U = e^{-i\pi S_y/\hbar}$ satisfies the two equations (29.19). Make use of the commutation properties of S_y and the operators $S_\pm \equiv S_z \pm iS_x$.

17. Show by direct expansion that, for $s = \frac{1}{2}$, $e^{-i\pi S_y/\hbar} = -i\sigma_y$.

18. Show by a general argument that $T^2 = \pm 1$. Make use of the form $T = UK$ and of the fact that two successive time reversals take a state into itself so that T^2 is a multiple of the unit matrix. Do not make use of the particular form for T given in Eq. (29.20).

19. A charged particle with spin operator $\mathbf{S}$ is assumed to possess an electric dipole moment operator $\mu\mathbf{S}$, where μ is a numerical constant, so that the hamiltonian for this particle in any electric field $\mathbf{E}$ contains the interaction term $-\mu\mathbf{S} \cdot \mathbf{E}$. Show that neither space inversion nor time reversal is a symmetry operation for this particle moving in a spherically symmetric electrostatic potential $\phi(r)$, even when no external electric field is present.

20. Find the lowest energy eigenfunction of the hydrogen atom in the coordinate representation, starting from the work of Sec. 30. Proceed by finding the analog of Eq. (25.8) for the lowest state of the linear oscillator; then solve it in analogy with Eq. (25.14).

8
Approximation Methods for Bound States

In quantum mechanics, as in classical mechanics, there are relatively few systems of physical interest for which the equations of motion can be solved exactly. Approximation methods are therefore expected to play an important part in virtually all applications of the theory. This enhances rather than diminishes the importance of those problems for which exact solutions can be found since, as was pointed out at the beginning of Chaps. 4 and 5, exact solutions are often useful as starting points for approximate calculations. They may also help to establish limits of validity for various approximation methods.

In this chapter and the next we develop several approximation methods and apply them to illustrative problems. It is convenient to divide the methods into two groups according as they deal with bound states (considered in this chapter) or with scattering states (considered in Chap. 9).

31□STATIONARY PERTURBATION THEORY

The stationary perturbation theory[1] is concerned with finding the changes in the discrete energy levels and eigenfunctions of a system when a small disturbance is applied. It is assumed from the outset that the hamiltonian H in the Schrödinger wave equation can be written as the sum of two parts. One of these parts, H_0, is of sufficiently simple structure that its Schrödinger equation can be solved, and the other part H' is small enough so that it can be regarded as a *perturbation* on H_0. It is convenient to retain our old symbols u_k and E_k for the supposedly known orthonormal eigenfunctions and eigenvalues of the *unperturbed* hamiltonian H_0 and to use ψ and W for the perturbed stationary wave function and energy level:

$$H\psi = W\psi \qquad H = H_0 + H' \qquad H_0 u_k = E_k u_k \qquad (31.1)$$

NONDEGENERATE CASE

The assumption that H' is small suggests that we expand the perturbed eigenfunction and eigenvalue as power series in H'. This is most conveniently accomplished in terms of a parameter λ, such that the zero, first, etc., powers of λ correspond to the zero, first, etc., orders of the perturbation calculation. We replace H' by $\lambda H'$ and express ψ and W as power series in λ. We assume that these two series are continuous analytic functions of λ for λ between zero and one, although the results obtained often have the usefulness of an asymptotic series even when this is not the case. The different orders of the perturbation approximation are then given by the coefficients of corresponding powers of λ. In the final results, λ is set equal to 1.

The perturbed wave function and energy level are written

$$\begin{aligned}
\psi &= \psi_0 + \lambda\psi_1 + \lambda^2\psi_2 + \lambda^3\psi_3 + \cdots \\
W &= W_0 + \lambda W_1 + \lambda^2 W_2 + \lambda^3 W_3 + \cdots
\end{aligned} \qquad (31.2)$$

and are substituted into the wave equation to give

$$\begin{aligned}
(H_0 + \lambda H')(\psi_0 + \lambda\psi_1 + \cdots) \\
= (W_0 + \lambda W_1 + \cdots)(\psi_0 + \lambda\psi_1 + \cdots) \quad (31.3)
\end{aligned}$$

Since Eq. (31.3) is supposed to be valid for a continuous range of λ, we can equate the coefficients of equal powers of λ on both sides to obtain a series of equations that represent successively higher orders of the perturbation.

$$\begin{aligned}
(H_0 - W_0)\psi_0 &= 0 \\
(H_0 - W_0)\psi_1 &= (W_1 - H')\psi_0 \\
(H_0 - W_0)\psi_2 &= (W_1 - H')\psi_1 + W_2\psi_0 \\
(H_0 - W_0)\psi_3 &= (W_1 - H')\psi_2 + W_2\psi_1 + W_3\psi_0 \qquad \text{etc.}
\end{aligned} \qquad (31.4)$$

[1] E. Schrödinger, *Ann. Physik* **80,** 437 (1926).

The first of Eqs. (31.4) means that ψ_0 is any one of the unperturbed eigenfunctions, as expected.   We therefore put

$$\psi_0 = u_m \qquad W_0 = E_m \tag{31.5}$$

This state u_m is discrete, since we are dealing with the perturbation of a bound state.   It is assumed to be nondegenerate as well, although others of the unperturbed eigenfunctions may be degenerate or continuously distributed in energy.   The case in which the unperturbed state ψ_0 is degenerate is considered later in this section.

Two general comments can be made in regard to Eqs. (31.4).[1]   First, any of the functions ψ_s can have an arbitrary multiple of ψ_0 added to it without affecting the value of the left side and hence without otherwise affecting the determination of ψ_s in terms of lower-order functions.   We choose this arbitrary multiple in such a way that

$$(\psi_0, \psi_s) = 0 \qquad s > 0 \tag{31.6}$$

Second, the inner product of ψ_0 and the left side of each of Eqs. (31.4) is seen to be zero when use is made of (23.21) or (23.28).   Thus the inner product of ψ_0 and the right side is zero in each case, and it follows with the help of Eqs. (31.5) and (31.6) that

$$W_s = \frac{(\psi_0, H'\psi_{s-1})}{(\psi_0, \psi_0)} = (u_m, H'\psi_{s-1}) \qquad s > 0 \tag{31.7}$$

We see that the calculation of W to a given order in H' requires knowledge of ψ only to the next lower order.[2]

FIRST–ORDER PERTURBATION

Equation (31.7) with $s = 1$ shows that

$$W_1 = (u_m, H'u_m) = \langle m|H'|m \rangle \tag{31.8}$$

which is the expectation value of H' for the unperturbed state m.

It is convenient to calculate ψ_1 by expanding it in terms of the u_n:

$$\psi_1 = S_n a_n^{(1)} u_n \tag{31.9}$$

where S, defined at the beginning of Sec. 23, denotes a summation over the discrete set together with an integration over the continuous set of eigenfunctions.   Substitution of (31.9) into the second of Eqs. (31.4) gives

$$S_n a_n^{(1)} (H_0 - E_m) u_n = (W_1 - H') u_m$$

[1] P.-O. Löwdin, *J. Math. Phys.*, **6,** 1341 (1965).

[2] It can also be shown from Eqs. (31.4) and (31.6) that knowledge of all the ψ's up to ψ_s is sufficient to determine all the W's up to W_{2s+1}.   P.-O. Löwdin, *J. Molec. Spectr.* **13,** 326 (1964); see also Prob. 14.

where $a_m{}^{(1)} = 0$ because of (31.6).   We replace $H_0 u_n$ by $E_n u_n$, multiply by u_k^*, and integrate over all space, making use of the orthonormality of the u's:

$$a_k{}^{(1)} = \frac{\langle k|H'|m\rangle}{E_m - E_k} \qquad k \neq m \tag{31.10}$$

SECOND-ORDER PERTURBATION

Equation (31.7) with $s = 2$, together with Eqs. (31.9) and (31.10), gives

$$W_2 = S_n' a_n{}^{(1)}\langle m|H'|n\rangle = S_n' \frac{\langle m|H'|n\rangle\langle n|H'|m\rangle}{E_m - E_n}$$

$$= S_n' \frac{|\langle m|H'|n\rangle|^2}{E_m - E_n} \tag{31.11}$$

where the prime on S_n' denotes the omission of the term $n = m$ from the summation and integration over n.   The last step in (31.11) follows since it is assumed that H' is hermitian.

We calculate ψ_2 by again expanding in terms of the u_n:

$$\psi_2 = S_n' a_n{}^{(2)} u_n \qquad a_m{}^{(2)} = 0 \tag{31.12}$$

and substituting into the third of Eqs. (31.4) to obtain

$$S_n' a_n{}^{(2)}(H_0 - E_m)u_n = S_n' a_n{}^{(1)}(W_1 - H')u_n + W_2 u_m$$

As before, we replace $H_0 u_n$ by $E_n u_n$, multiply by u_k^*, and integrate:

$$a_k{}^{(2)}(E_k - E_m) = a_k{}^{(1)}W_1 - S_n' a_n{}^{(1)}\langle k|H'|n\rangle \qquad k \neq m$$

This gives, with the help of (31.8) and (31.10),

$$a_k{}^{(2)} = S_n' \frac{\langle k|H'|n\rangle\langle n|H'|m\rangle}{(E_m - E_k)(E_m - E_n)} - \frac{\langle k|H'|m\rangle\langle m|H'|m\rangle}{(E_m - E_k)^2} \tag{31.13}$$

Equations (31.2) and (31.8) to (31.13), with $\lambda = 1$, give the energy and wave function to second order in H':

$$W = E_m + \langle m|H'|m\rangle + S_n' \frac{|\langle m|H'|n\rangle^2}{E_m - E_n}$$

$$\psi = u_m + S_k' u_k \left[\frac{\langle k|H'|m\rangle}{E_m - E_k}\left(1 - \frac{\langle m|H'|m\rangle}{E_m - E_k}\right) \right.$$

$$\left. + S_n' \frac{\langle k|H'|n\rangle\langle n|H'|m\rangle}{(E_m - E_k)(E_m - E_n)} \right] \tag{31.14}$$

The primes again denote omission of $k = m$ or $n = m$, as the case may be.

It is important to note that this ψ is not normalized, since

$$(\psi,\psi) = 1 + S'_k \frac{|\langle k|H'|m\rangle|^2}{(E_m - E_k)^2}$$

to second order in H'. This occurred because of the arbitrary imposition of the condition (31.6). Other choices for (ψ_0,ψ_s) would lead to expressions for ψ that differ from (31.14) only by a multiplicative complex number; they would not affect the expression for W.

PERTURBATION OF AN OSCILLATOR

As a simple example of the application of the first- and second-order perturbation theory to a nondegenerate state, we consider the perturbation of the mth energy level of the linear harmonic oscillator of Secs. 13 and 25 by an additional energy $H' = \frac{1}{2}bx^2$. The unperturbed hamiltonian is $H_0 = p^2/2\mu + \frac{1}{2}Kx^2$ (the mass is denoted by μ to avoid confusion with the quantum number m); the unperturbed eigenfunctions $u_m(x)$ given by Eq. (13.13) correspond to the eigenvalues $E_m = (m + \frac{1}{2})\hbar(K/\mu)^{\frac{1}{2}}$, where $m = 0, 1, 2, \ldots$. This example is evidently a trivial one since the perturbed eigenfunctions and eigenvalues are given simply by replacing K by $K + b$ in $u_m(x)$ and E_m; it is nevertheless instructive.

We require the matrix elements of x^2 between various pairs of harmonic-oscillator wave functions. They may be obtained with the help of the generating function (13.10) for the Hermite polynomials, as in Prob. 3 of Chap. 4, or more simply by matrix multiplication using the definition (22.3) and the expressions for $\langle n|x|m\rangle$ given in Eq. (13.18) or in Eqs. (25.12) and (25.13). We readily obtain

$$\langle n|x^2|m\rangle = \begin{cases} (2\alpha^2)^{-1}[(m + 1)(m + 2)]^{\frac{1}{2}} & n = m + 2 \\ (2\alpha^2)^{-1}(2m + 1) & n = m \\ (2\alpha^2)^{-1}[m(m - 1)]^{\frac{1}{2}} & n = m - 2 \\ 0 & \text{otherwise} \end{cases}$$

where $\alpha = (\mu K/\hbar^2)^{\frac{1}{4}}$. Substitution into the first of Eqs. (31.14) then gives for the energy to second order

$$W = (m + \frac{1}{2})\hbar\left(\frac{K}{\mu}\right)^{\frac{1}{2}}\left(1 + \frac{b}{2K} - \frac{b^2}{8K^2}\right)$$

in agreement with the expansion of $(m + \frac{1}{2})\hbar[(K + b)/\mu]^{\frac{1}{2}}$ to second order in b.

DEGENERATE CASE

The discussion thus far has assumed that the initial state $\psi_0 = u_m$ is nondegenerate, although others of the unperturbed eigenfunctions may be degenerate. Suppose now that there are two states, u_m and u_l, that have the same unperturbed energy. Then Eq. (31.10) causes difficulty when $k = l$ unless it happens that $\langle l|H'|m\rangle = 0$. We consider first the case in which $\langle l|H'|m\rangle \neq 0$, so that the results obtained above cannot be valid.

The initial state is not specified by its unperturbed energy; the state may be u_m or u_l or any linear combination of them. Let us suppose that the perturbation H' removes the degeneracy in some order, so that for finite λ there are two states that have different energies. We assumed earlier that ψ and W are continuous analytic functions of λ as $\lambda \to 0$; thus each of the two states approaches a definite linear combination of u_m and u_l when $\lambda = 0$. If we happen to choose one of these two linear combinations as the initial state, the perturbation expansion can be carried through without difficulty. If, however, we start with any other linear combination, there is a discontinuous change at $\lambda = 0$, so that the expansions (31.2) are not valid there and the method developed above breaks down. Out of the infinite number of orthonormal pairs of linear combinations of u_m and u_l, the particular pair that we require will depend on H'. For example, if H' is the perturbation produced by an external electric or magnetic field, the pair we want will depend not only on which kind of field is present but also on its direction.

In order to find this pair, we write in place of Eq. (31.5)

$$\psi_0 = a_m u_m + a_l u_l \qquad W_0 = E_m = E_l$$

We then substitute this ψ_0 into the right side of the second of Eqs. (31.4) and take the inner product of this equation successively with u_m and u_l:

$$(\langle m|H'|m\rangle - W_1)a_m + \langle m|H'|l\rangle a_l = 0$$
$$\langle l|H'|m\rangle a_m + (\langle l|H'|l\rangle - W_1)a_l = 0 \qquad (31.15)$$

These homogeneous algebraic equations can be solved for a_m and a_l if and only if the determinant of their coefficients vanishes. We thus obtain a secular equation of just the type encountered in connection with Eq. (22.21); in the present situation it is a quadratic equation for W_1. The two solutions of this equation are

$$W_1 = \tfrac{1}{2}(\langle m|H'|m\rangle + \langle l|H'|l\rangle)$$
$$\pm \tfrac{1}{2}[(\langle m|H'|m\rangle - \langle l|H'|l\rangle)^2 + 4|\langle m|H'|l\rangle|^2]^{\frac{1}{2}} \quad (31.16)$$

Since the diagonal matrix elements of the hermitian operator H' are real, both values of W_1 are real. They are equal if and only if

$$\langle m|H'|m\rangle = \langle l|H'|l\rangle \qquad \text{and} \qquad \langle m|H'|l\rangle = 0 \qquad (31.17)$$

In this case we say that the degeneracy is not removed in first order; then a_m and a_l evidently cannot be determined from the first-order calculation.

On the other hand, if either or both of Eqs. (31.17) are not satisfied, the two values of W_1 calculated from (31.16) are distinct, and each can be used in turn to calculate a_m and a_l from Eqs. (31.15). We thus obtain the desired pair of linear combinations of the unperturbed states u_m and u_l. Next we take the inner product of u_k with the second of Eqs. (31.4), where $k \neq m,\ l$, and make use of (31.9) to obtain

$$a_k{}^{(1)}(E_k - E_m) = - \langle k|H'|m\rangle a_m - \langle k|H'|l\rangle a_l \qquad (31.18)$$

This gives $a_k{}^{(1)}$ for $k \neq m,\ l$, and Eq. (31.6) with $s = 1$ is satisfied if we assume that $a_m{}^{(1)} = a_l{}^{(1)} = 0$. The calculation can then be carried to higher order just as in the nondegenerate situation considered earlier.

REMOVAL OF DEGENERACY IN SECOND ORDER[1]

If the two values of W_1 obtained in the preceding subsection are the same, we must go to second order in order to remove the degeneracy. The inner product of the third of Eqs. (31.4) with u_m and u_l yields

$$S_n'\langle m|H'|n\rangle a_n{}^{(1)} - W_2 a_m = 0 \qquad S_n'\langle l|H'|n\rangle a_n{}^{(1)} - W_2 a_l = 0$$
$$(31.19)$$

The prime on S_n' now denotes the omission of both of the terms $n = m$ and $n = l$ from the summation and integration over n, since we again assume on the basis of Eq. (31.6) that $a_m{}^{(1)} = a_l{}^{(1)} = 0$. Substitution of $a_n{}^{(1)}$ from (31.18) into (31.19) gives a pair of homogeneous algebraic equations for a_m and a_l:

$$\left(S_n' \frac{|\langle m|H'|n\rangle|^2}{E_m - E_n} - W_2 \right) a_m + S_n' \frac{\langle m|H'|n\rangle\langle n|H'|l\rangle}{E_m - E_n} a_l = 0$$
$$S_n' \frac{\langle l|H'|n\rangle\langle n|H'|m\rangle}{E_m - E_n} a_m + \left(S_n' \frac{|\langle l|H'|n\rangle|^2}{E_m - E_n} - W_2 \right) a_l = 0$$
$$(31.20)$$

The secular equation associated with Eqs. (31.20) yields solutions for W_2 that are of the same general form as (31.16). The analogs of Eqs. (31.17) are

$$S_n' \frac{|\langle m|H'|n\rangle|^2}{E_m - E_n} = S_n' \frac{|\langle l|H'|n\rangle|^2}{E_m - E_n}$$

$$\text{and} \qquad S_n' \frac{\langle m|H'|n\rangle\langle n|H'|l\rangle}{E_m - E_n} = 0 \qquad (31.21)$$

Unless both of these equations are satisfied, the degeneracy is removed in second order.

The close analogy between the sums that appear in Eqs. (31.20) and (31.21) and the matrix elements that appear in Eqs. (31.15) and (31.17) leads to the former often being referred to as *second-order matrix elements*.

[1] J. H. Van Vleck, *Phys. Rev.* **33**, 467 (1929), Sec. 4.

A necessary and sufficient condition that degeneracy is removed in any given order is then either that the diagonal matrix elements of H' for the two degenerate unperturbed states are unequal [so that the first of Eqs. (31.17) or (31.21) is not valid] or that the off-diagonal matrix element of H' between these states fails to vanish [so that the second of Eqs. (31.17) or (31.21) is not valid].

So far as the latter situation is concerned, a sufficient condition that the degeneracy is removed in first order is that the perturbation H' *connects* the initial degenerate states u_m and u_l in first order, so that $\langle m|H'|l \rangle$ fails to vanish. Similarly, the degeneracy is removed in second order if the perturbation connects the initial states in second order, so that there are one or more other states u_n such that $\langle m|H'|n \rangle$ and $\langle l|H'|n \rangle$ both fail to vanish.

It is not difficult to show that all the foregoing work can be generalized to the removal of degeneracy in higher order and also to the case in which the initial state is more than doubly degenerate.

ZEEMAN EFFECT WITHOUT ELECTRON SPIN

The change in the energy levels of an atom caused by a uniform external magnetic field is called the *Zeeman effect*. We now consider the change of first order in the field strength H for a hydrogen atom. For simplicity, the interaction between the magnetic moment associated with the electron spin and the magnetic field will be neglected, although in actuality it is of the same order of magnitude as the term we calculate. The effect of electron spin will be included in Sec. 48.

A constant magnetic field can be represented by the vector potential

$$\mathbf{A} = \tfrac{1}{2}\mathsf{H} \times \mathbf{r} \tag{31.22}$$

since $\mathsf{H} = \nabla \times \mathbf{A}$. The divergence of (31.22) is zero, so that the terms involving $\mathbf{A}$ that appear in the hamiltonian (24.39) for an electron of charge $-e$ and reduced mass μ are

$$-\frac{ie\hbar}{\mu c}\mathbf{A} \cdot \nabla + \frac{e^2}{2\mu c^2}\mathbf{A}^2 = \frac{e}{2\mu c}(\mathsf{H} \times \mathbf{r}) \cdot \mathbf{p} + \frac{e^2}{8\mu c^2}(\mathsf{H} \times \mathbf{r}) \cdot (\mathsf{H} \times \mathbf{r})$$

$$= \frac{e}{2\mu c}\mathsf{H} \cdot \mathbf{L} + \frac{e^2}{8\mu c^2}\mathsf{H}^2 r^2 \sin^2 \theta \tag{31.23}$$

where $\mathbf{L} = \mathbf{r} \times \mathbf{p}$, θ is the angle between $\mathbf{r}$ and H, and e is a positive quantity. Since we wish to work only to first order in H, we can put

$$H' = \frac{e}{2\mu c}\mathsf{H} \cdot \mathbf{L} \tag{31.24}$$

The energy eigenfunctions of the unperturbed hydrogen atom are usually chosen to be eigenstates of $\mathbf{L}_z$, with eigenvalues $m\hbar$, where m is the magnetic quantum number introduced in Sec. 14. However, this is a sensible choice only if the magnetic field is in the z direction, since then Eq. (31.8) becomes

$$W_1 = \langle m|H'|m \rangle = \frac{e}{2\mu c} Hm\hbar \qquad (31.25)$$

and the degeneracy of the $2l + 1$ states of given n and l is removed in first order. On the other hand, if the magnetic field is not in the z direction, the states labeled by m are not a suitable starting point for the degenerate-perturbation calculation. This provides an example of the remark at the end of the paragraph above Eqs. (31.15) that the unperturbed initial states must be chosen with the direction of the perturbing field in mind.

FIRST-ORDER STARK EFFECT IN HYDROGEN

The change in the energy levels of an atom caused by a uniform external electric field of strength E is called the *Stark effect*. Calculation of the change of first order in E in the case of a hydrogen atom is somewhat more complicated than for a magnetic field. It is still desirable to choose the unperturbed initial states with the direction of the perturbing field in mind; as before, we take the z axis along the field and use eigenstates of L_z. However, there is now an additional complication from the fact that H', given by Eq. (31.26) below, is odd with respect to space inversion, so that the expectation value of H' is zero for all states that have definite parities.

The perturbation H' is now the extra energy of the nucleus and electron in the external field and is readily shown to be

$$H' = e\mathsf{E}z = e\mathsf{E}r \cos \theta \qquad (31.26)$$

where the polar axis and E are in the direction of positive z and e is again a positive quantity. The discussion of Sec. 14 showed that wave functions for any spherically symmetric potential energy, when expressed in spherical harmonics, have even or odd parity according as the azimuthal quantum number l is even or odd. Since the perturbation (31.26) is odd with respect to inversion, the only matrix elements of H' that fail to vanish are those for unperturbed states that have opposite parities. This shows that a nondegenerate state, such as the ground state ($n = 1$) of hydrogen which has even parity, has no first-order Stark effect.

The first excited state ($n = 2$) of hydrogen is fourfold degenerate; the quantum numbers l, m have the values (0,0), (1,0), (1,1), and (1,−1). We now show quite generally that nonvanishing off-diagonal matrix elements of H' exist only for states that have the same quantum number m. It is apparent from Eqs. (24.31) that z commutes with the z component of the orbital angular momentum $L_z = xp_y - yp_x$, so that $[L_z, H'] = 0$. The matrix element of this equation between states j and k in a representation in which L_z is diagonal is $(m_j - m_k)\hbar\langle j|H'|k\rangle = 0$, so that $\langle j|H'|k\rangle = 0$ unless $m_j = m_k$. Thus all 16 matrix elements of H' between the four degenerate unperturbed states given above are zero except for the off-diagonal elements between the first two (opposite parity) states.

PERTURBED ENERGY LEVELS

An extension of the discussion that led to Eq. (31.15) shows that the secular equation for the first-order Stark effect of the $n = 2$ state of hydrogen is

$$\begin{vmatrix} -W_1 & \langle 0,0|H'|1,0\rangle & 0 & 0 \\ \langle 1,0|H'|0,0\rangle & -W_1 & 0 & 0 \\ 0 & 0 & -W_1 & 0 \\ 0 & 0 & 0 & -W_1 \end{vmatrix} = 0 \qquad (31.27)$$

The nonvanishing matrix elements of H' are

$$\langle 1,0|H'|0,0\rangle = \langle 0,0|H'|1,0\rangle^* = e\mathsf{E}\int u_{210}^*(\mathbf{r})r\cos\theta\, u_{200}(\mathbf{r})\, d^3r$$

$$= \frac{e\mathsf{E}}{16{a_0}^4}\int_0^\infty \int_{-1}^1 r^4\left(2 - \frac{r}{a_0}\right) e^{-r/a_0}w^2\, dw\, dr$$

$$= -3e\mathsf{E}a_0$$

The four roots of Eq. (31.27) are 0, 0, $3e\mathsf{E}a_0$, and $-3e\mathsf{E}a_0$, so that half of the fourfold degeneracy is removed in first order. It is easily seen that the first two values of W_1 correspond to any two linearly independent combinations of u_{211} and $u_{2,1,-1}$ and that the third and fourth values correspond to $2^{-\frac{1}{2}}(u_{200} - u_{210})$ and $2^{-\frac{1}{2}}(u_{200} + u_{210})$, respectively. This means that a hydrogen atom in its first excited state behaves as though it has a permanent electric dipole moment of magnitude $3ea_0$ that can be oriented in three different ways: one state parallel to the external field, one state antiparallel to the field, and two states with zero component along the field.

OCCURRENCE OF PERMANENT ELECTRIC DIPOLE MOMENTS

It follows from the foregoing discussion that an atom can have a permanent electric dipole moment (energy change proportional to E) only when its unperturbed state is nondegenerate and does not have well-defined parity or is degenerate and contains components of opposite parities. On the other hand, any atom can have an induced electric dipole moment. This means that the dipole moment is proportional to E or that the energy of the atom in the external electric field is proportional to E^2.   In accordance with Eq. (31.11), a second-order perturbation energy of this type is expected for any system.

The discussion of Sec. 29 shows that if the unitary space-inversion operator U_I commutes with the hamiltonian for any system, the energy eigenstates can be chosen to have well-defined parities.   With the exception of the weak interactions, which among other things are responsible for radioactive beta decay, all known hamiltonians commute with U_I. Then it is expected that an atom or nucleus in its ground state will at most possess an extremely small permanent electric dipole moment ($\lesssim e \times 10^{-20}$ cm) that might arise from the weak interactions.   Thus far, none has been found experimentally.

It is also possible, as in the case of the hydrogen atom, that unperturbed degenerate states of opposite parities can give rise to a permanent electric dipole moment.   However, this occurs only in hydrogen because of a special dynamical symmetry (see Sec. 30) and even there does not occur for the ground state.   Such degeneracy could also occur accidentally but is then very improbable on statistical grounds.   In some molecules, however, there is a group of nearly degenerate rotational states of both parities.   If these energy levels are closely spaced in comparison either with the thermal energy of the molecule or with the energy associated with the applied electric field, they can give rise to a permanent electric dipole moment.[1]   In this case the direction of the dipole is related to a figure axis of the molecule; the dipole would, for example, be along the line joining the two atoms in an unsymmetrical molecule such as hydrogen chloride.

In the systems considered thus far, the electric dipole moment is either along the applied electric field (hydrogen atom in an excited state) or along a molecular figure axis (hydrogen chloride).   For an elementary particle or a nucleus, it is reasonable to assume that the ground state is nondegenerate and that the only figure axis is that defined by the spin operator S.   Then the electric dipole moment operator must be proportional to S.   This means that, for such a particle moving in a static, spherically symmetric electrostatic potential $\phi(r)$, the hamiltonian contains a term of the form $\mu S \cdot \nabla\phi$, where μ is a numerical constant.   Thus even in this environment neither space inversion nor time reversal is a symmetry operation (see Prob. 19, Chap. 7).   An extension of this argument shows that although a particle or nucleus may possess an electric charge, magnetic dipole moment, electric quadrupole moment, etc., it cannot possess a magnetic monopole, electric dipole moment, magnetic quadrupole moment, etc., if either or both of space inversion and time reversal are symmetry operations.   This supplements the remark at

[1] J. H. Van Vleck, "The Theory of Electric and Magnetic Susceptibilities," p. 154 (footnote 28), sec. 48, (Oxford, New York, 1932).

the end of Sec. 28 which relates allowed multipole moments to the total angular momentum quantum number.

32☐THE VARIATION METHOD

The variation method can be used for the approximate determination of the lowest or ground-state energy level of a system when there is no closely related problem that is capable of exact solution, so that the perturbation method is inapplicable. It can also be applied to systems that are described by a nonseparable Schrödinger equation, in which case numerical solutions are extremely arduous and the WKB method (Sec. 34) cannot be used.

EXPECTATION VALUE OF THE ENERGY

It was shown in Sec. 10 that, if an arbitrary normalized function ψ is expanded in energy eigenfunctions

$$\psi = \sum_E A_E u_E \qquad \text{where} \qquad H u_E = E u_E \qquad (32.1)$$

and the u_E form a complete orthonormal set, the expectation value of H for the function ψ is given by

$$\langle H \rangle = \int \psi^* H \psi \, d\tau = \sum_E E |A_E|^2 \qquad (32.2)$$

where the integration is extended over the entire range of all the coordinates of the system. It is assumed for convenience in Eqs. (32.1) and (32.2) that the energy eigenvalues are all discrete; this can be accomplished by enclosing the system in a box (Sec. 10), or the summation can be replaced by the symbol S (Sec. 23).

A useful inequality can be derived from Eq. (32.2) by replacing each eigenvalue E in the summation on the right side by the lowest eigenvalue E_0:

$$\langle H \rangle \geq \sum_E E_0 |A_E|^2 = E_0 \sum_E |A_E|^2 \qquad (32.3)$$

Since $\sum_E |A_E|^2 = 1$ for a normalized function ψ, as was shown in Sec. 10, (32.3) yields the inequality

$$E_0 \leq \int \psi^* H \psi \, d\tau \qquad (32.4)$$

In the event that ψ is not normalized, (32.4) evidently can be rewritten as

$$E_0 \leq \frac{\int \psi^* H \psi \, d\tau}{\int |\psi|^2 \, d\tau} \qquad (32.5)$$

The variation method[1] consists in evaluating the integrals on the right side of (32.4) or (32.5) with a *trial function* ψ that depends on a number of parameters and varying these parameters until the expectation value of the energy is a minimum. The result is an upper limit for the ground-state energy of the system, which is likely to be close if the form of the trial function resembles that of the eigenfunction (see Prob. 5). Thus it is important to make use of any available information or physical intuition in choosing the trial function.[2]

APPLICATION TO EXCITED STATES

The variation method can also be used to obtain an upper limit for one of the higher energy levels if the trial function is orthogonal to the eigenfunctions of all the lower states. Suppose that the energy levels are arranged in an ascending series: $E_0, E_1, E_2, \ldots$. Then, if ψ is orthogonal to u_{E_i} for $i = 0, 1, \ldots, n$, it is easily seen from (32.1) that the corresponding expansion coefficients A_{E_i} are all zero. An inequality can be derived from (32.2) by replacing each eigenvalue E in the summation on the right by E_{n+1}, with the result that the expectation value of the energy is an upper limit on this eigenvalue.

The trial function $\psi - u_{E_0} \int u_{E_0}^* \psi \, d\tau$ is evidently orthogonal to u_{E_0} so that, if the lowest eigenfunction is known either from an exact solution or to a sufficiently good approximation from a variation calculation, an upper limit for the energy of the first excited state can be computed. Trial functions that are orthogonal to any number of known eigenfunctions are easily found in this way.

It is sometimes possible to divide the energy eigenfunctions into groups such that any member of one group is orthogonal to any member of any other group. Suppose that there is a hermitian operator F that commutes with H $(FH - HF = 0)$; then, from a theorem of Sec. 22, F and H can be diagonalized simultaneously and have common eigenfunctions. Now any two eigenfunctions of F that correspond to different eigenvalues are orthogonal to each other.[3] Thus a trial function that is constructed entirely from eigenfunctions of F that correspond to a given eigenvalue is orthogonal to all other eigenfunctions that correspond to

[1] The method was originally applied by Lord Rayleigh in 1873 to the computation of the vibration frequencies of mechanical systems: "Theory of Sound," 2d rev. ed., vol. 1, sec. 88 (Macmillan, London, 1937; reprinted by Dover, New York). See also W. Ritz, *J. Reine Angew. Math.* **135**, 1 (1908); P. M. Morse and H. Feshbach, "Methods of Theoretical Physics," sec. 9.4 (McGraw-Hill, New York, 1953).

[2] For an extension of this method that brackets several of the lowest eigenvalues, see J. K. L. MacDonald, *Phys. Rev.* **43**, 830 (1933). Lower bounds have been studied by P.-O. Löwdin, *Phys. Rev.* **139**, A357 (1965), who also gives references to earlier work.

[3] This is shown explicitly in Eq. (10.4) for the energy operator, and the proof given there is easily extended to any hermitian operator.

different eigenvalues of F, and will provide an upper limit for the lowest energy eigenvalue that is associated with this eigenvalue of F. The foregoing results are useful when the operator F is one whose eigenfunctions are easily recognizable by some simple property, such as, for example, the symmetry in case F is the angular momentum or the parity. Then a trial function with angular dependence corresponding to a particular angular momentum, or with a particular parity, can easily be written and gives an upper limit for the lowest energy level that has this angular momentum or parity.

GROUND STATE OF HELIUM

As a first example, we use the variation method with a simple trial function to obtain an upper limit for the energy of the ground state of the helium atom. The helium atom consists of a nucleus of charge $+2e$ surrounded by two electrons; from Eq. (16.1) we find that its hamiltonian is (neglecting the motion of the nucleus)

$$H = -\frac{\hbar^2}{2m}(\nabla_1^2 + \nabla_2^2) - 2e^2\left(\frac{1}{r_1} + \frac{1}{r_2}\right) + \frac{e^2}{r_{12}} \tag{32.6}$$

where $\mathbf{r}_1$ and $\mathbf{r}_2$ are the position vectors of the two electrons with respect to the nucleus as origin, and $r_{12} = |\mathbf{r}_1 - \mathbf{r}_2|$ is the distance between the two electrons.

If the interaction energy e^2/r_{12} between the two electrons were not present, the ground-state eigenfunction of H would be the product of two normalized hydrogenic wave functions $u_{100}(\mathbf{r}_1)u_{100}(\mathbf{r}_2)$ given in Eq. (16.24):

$$\psi(\mathbf{r}_1,\mathbf{r}_2) = \frac{Z^3}{\pi a_0^3} e^{-(Z/a_0)(r_1+r_2)} \tag{32.7}$$

with $Z = 2$. We shall use (32.7) as a trial function and permit Z to be the variation parameter so that it is not necessarily equal to 2.

It follows from Prob. 13, Chap. 4, that the expectation values of the kinetic and potential energies for the ground state of a hydrogen atom are $e^2/2a_0$ and $-e^2/a_0$, respectively; the corresponding hydrogen wave function is $(\pi a_0^3)^{-\frac{1}{2}}e^{-r/a_0}$. The expectation value of either of the kinetic-energy operators in (32.6) for the function (32.7) is obtained most easily by noting that operation with the laplacian gives a result that is inversely proportional to the square of the length scale of the wave function; since the scale of (32.7) is smaller than that of the hydrogen wave function by a factor of Z, the expectation value of each of the kinetic-energy operators is $e^2Z^2/2a_0$. Similarly, the factors $1/r$ make the expectation values of the nuclear potential-energy operators inversely proportional to the length scale; there is also an additional factor 2 from the nuclear charge, so that each one is $-2e^2Z/a_0$.

ELECTRON INTERACTION ENERGY

The expectation value of the interaction energy between the electrons is

$$\iint \psi^*(\mathbf{r}_1,\mathbf{r}_2) \frac{e^2}{r_{12}} \psi(\mathbf{r}_1,\mathbf{r}_2) \, d^3r_1 \, d^3r_2$$

$$= \left(\frac{Z^3}{\pi a_0^3}\right)^2 e^2 \iint \frac{1}{r_{12}} e^{-(2Z/a_0)(r_1+r_2)} \, d^3r_1 \, d^3r_2 \quad (32.8)$$

This integral is most easily evaluated by regarding it as the mutual electrostatic energy of two overlapping, spherically symmetric, charge distributions, in which case simplifications from the theory of electrostatics can be introduced.

A more general way of performing the integration, which can also be used for wave functions that are not spherically symmetric, consists in expanding $1/r_{12}$ in spherical harmonics.

$$\frac{1}{r_{12}} = \frac{1}{r_1} \sum_{l=0}^{\infty} \left(\frac{r_2}{r_1}\right)^l P_l(\cos\theta) \qquad r_1 > r_2$$

$$\frac{1}{r_{12}} = \frac{1}{r_2} \sum_{l=0}^{\infty} \left(\frac{r_1}{r_2}\right)^l P_l(\cos\theta) \qquad r_1 < r_2$$

$$(32.9)$$

where θ is the angle between $\mathbf{r}_1$ and $\mathbf{r}_2$, $\cos\theta = \cos\theta_1 \cos\theta_2 + \sin\theta_1 \cdot \sin\theta_2 \cos(\phi_1 - \phi_2)$, and θ_1, ϕ_1 and θ_2, ϕ_2 are the polar angles of the vectors $\mathbf{r}_1$ and $\mathbf{r}_2$, respectively.[1] It can be shown[2] that

$$P_l(\cos\theta) = P_l(\cos\theta_1)P_l(\cos\theta_2)$$

$$+ 2 \sum_{m=1}^{l} \frac{(l-m)!}{(l+m)!} P_l^m(\cos\theta_1)P_l^m(\cos\theta_2) \cos m(\phi_1 - \phi_2) \quad (32.10)$$

When (32.9) and (32.10) are substituted into (32.8) and use is made of the orthogonality of the spherical harmonics, the integration over the polar angles of $\mathbf{r}_1$ causes all terms to vanish except that for which l and m are zero. The integral on the right side of (32.8) becomes

$$(4\pi)^2 \int_0^{\infty} \left(\int_0^{r_1} \frac{1}{r_1} e^{-(2Z/a_0)(r_1+r_2)} r_2^2 \, dr_2 + \int_{r_1}^{\infty} \frac{1}{r_2} e^{-(2Z/a_0)(r_1+r_2)} r_2^2 \, dr_2\right) r_1^2 \, dr_1$$

which can be evaluated as $5\pi^2 a_0^5/8Z^5$. Thus the electron interaction energy has the expectation value $5e^2Z/8a_0$.

[1] Equations (32.9) follow at once from the generating function (14.10) for the Legendre polynomials; the expression for $\cos\theta$ is simply obtained from the scalar product of the vectors $\mathbf{r}_1$ and $\mathbf{r}_2$ in rectangular coordinates.

[2] E. T. Whittaker and G. N. Watson, "A Course of Modern Analysis," 4th ed., p. 328 (Cambridge, London, 1935).

VARIATION OF THE PARAMETER Z

We now have the result that the expectation value of the hamiltonian (32.6) for the trial function (32.7) is

$$\langle H \rangle = \frac{e^2 Z^2}{a_0} - \frac{4e^2 Z}{a_0} + \frac{5e^2 Z}{8a_0} = \frac{e^2}{a_0}(Z^2 - \tfrac{27}{8}Z)$$

Differentiation with respect to Z shows that this is a minimum when $Z = \tfrac{27}{16} = 1.69$. Thus the lowest upper limit for the ground-state energy of the helium atom obtainable with this trial function is

$$-(\tfrac{27}{16})^2 \frac{e^2}{a_0} = -2.85 \frac{e^2}{a_0}$$

The experimental value for the minimum energy required to remove both electrons from a helium atom is $2.904 e^2/a_0$, so that our limit is about 1.9 percent high. The most careful variation calculation of the ground-state energy of helium gives a result in excellent agreement with experiment[1] and provides an important verification of the theory of quantum mechanics.

The result that hydrogenic wave functions give the best energy value when $Z = \tfrac{27}{16}$ rather than 2 indicates that each electron screens the nucleus from the other electron, the effective nuclear charge being reduced by $\tfrac{5}{16}$ of an electronic charge.

If the electron interaction term e^2/r_{12} is regarded as a perturbation, the first-order perturbation energy is given by $\langle H \rangle$ with $Z = 2$ and is $-2.75 e^2/a_0$, which is 5.3 percent above the experimental value. It is apparent that, in general, the first-order perturbation calculation is equivalent to a nonoptimal variation calculation.

VAN DER WAALS INTERACTION

As our second example of the application of the variation method, we calculate the van der Waals (long-range) interaction between two hydrogen atoms in their ground states. It is convenient to consider this problem first by means of the perturbation theory, since it is then easier to see that the leading term in the energy at great separation distances varies inversely as the sixth power of this distance. Also, it turns out that the perturbation theory and the variation method provide opposite limits for the coefficient of this term.

We assume that the nuclei of the two hydrogen atoms, A and B, are fixed in space a distance R apart and that the z axis is chosen parallel to the line through A and B. Then if $\mathbf{r}_1$ is the vector displacement of electron 1 from nucleus A and $\mathbf{r}_2$ is the vector displacement of electron 2

[1] E. A. Hylleraas, Z. Physik **65,** 209 (1930). J. Sucher and H. M. Foley, Phys. Rev. **95,** 966 (1954), discuss a number of corrections and give references to more recent work.

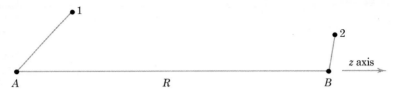

Fig. 27   Two hydrogen atoms, with nuclei at A and B separated by a distance R, have electrons at 1 and 2; their interaction is given by H' in Eq. (32.11).

from nucleus B (see Fig. 27), the hamiltonian for the two electrons can be written

$$H = H_0 + H'$$

$$H_0 = -\frac{\hbar^2}{2m}\left(\nabla_1{}^2 + \nabla_2{}^2\right) - \frac{e^2}{r_1} - \frac{e^2}{r_2}$$

(32.11)

$$H' = \frac{e^2}{R} + \frac{e^2}{r_{12}} - \frac{e^2}{r_{1B}} - \frac{e^2}{r_{2A}}$$

The unperturbed hamiltonian H_0 has the solution

$$u_0(\mathbf{r}_1,\mathbf{r}_2) = u_{100}(\mathbf{r}_1)u_{100}(\mathbf{r}_2)$$

for two noninteracting hydrogen atoms in their ground states. We regard the interaction terms H' as a perturbation; this is equivalent to assuming that $R \gg a_0$.

Since we are interested in the leading term in the interaction energy when R is large, we expand H' in powers of $1/R$ and keep the lowest terms.

$$H' = \frac{e^2}{R}\left\{1 + \left[1 + \frac{2(z_2 - z_1)}{R}\right.\right.$$
$$\left. + \frac{(x_2 - x_1)^2 + (y_2 - y_1)^2 + (z_2 - z_1)^2}{R^2}\right]^{-\frac{1}{2}}$$
$$\left. - \left(1 - \frac{2z_1}{R} + \frac{r_1{}^2}{R^2}\right)^{-\frac{1}{2}} - \left(1 + \frac{2z_2}{R} + \frac{r_2{}^2}{R^2}\right)^{-\frac{1}{2}}\right\}$$

$$\approx \frac{e^2}{R^3}(x_1x_2 + y_1y_2 - 2z_1z_2)$$

(32.12)

The last term is the interaction energy of two electric dipoles that correspond to the instantaneous configurations of the two atoms.[1]

It is apparent at once that the expectation value of the leading

[1] The neglected terms in the expansion (32.12) that vary like $1/R^4$ are the dipole-quadrupole interaction; the $1/R^5$ terms are the quadrupole-quadrupole interaction, etc.

term in H' for the state $u_0(\mathbf{r}_1,\mathbf{r}_2)$ is zero, since u_0 is an even function of $\mathbf{r}_1$ and $\mathbf{r}_2$ and H' is an odd function of $\mathbf{r}_1$ and $\mathbf{r}_2$ separately. It can also be shown that all the neglected higher terms in H' have zero expectation value for u_0, since these terms can be expressed as spherical harmonics of order different from zero. Thus the leading term in the interaction energy is the second-order perturbation of the dipole-dipole term, which is proportional to H'^2 and hence varies like $1/R^6$.[1]

PERTURBATION CALCULATION

From Eq. (31.11), the second-order change in the energy of the two hydrogen atoms is

$$W(R) = S'_n \frac{|\langle 0|H'|n\rangle|^2}{E_0 - E_n} \tag{32.13}$$

where the index n refers to all states of the pair of unperturbed hydrogen atoms (including dissociated states), and the ground state u_0 is excluded from the generalized summation. It is apparent that $W(R)$ is negative, since $E_0 < E_n$ and the numerator of each term in (32.13) is positive. We thus conclude that the interaction is attractive and proportional to $1/R^6$, when R is large; both of these conclusions can be shown to be valid for any pair of atoms that are in nondegenerate, spherically symmetric ground states.

We can obtain an upper limit on the positive quantity $-W(R)$ by replacing each E_n in (32.13) by the energy E_{n*} of the lowest excited state of the two hydrogen atoms for which $\langle 0|H'|n^*\rangle$ is different from zero.[2] Then the denominator can be taken outside of the summation, which can be evaluated as a matrix product:

$$S'_n|\langle 0|H'|n\rangle|^2 = S_n\langle 0|H'|n\rangle\langle n|H'|0\rangle - (\langle 0|H'|0\rangle)^2$$
$$= \langle 0|H'^2|0\rangle - (\langle 0|H'|0\rangle)^2$$

Since we have seen that $\langle 0|H'|0\rangle = 0$, we have that

$$- W(R) \le \frac{\langle 0|H'^2|0\rangle}{E_{n*} - E_0} \tag{32.14}$$

The state n^* is that in which both atoms are excited to states of principal quantum number 2, so that $E_0 = -2(e^2/2a_0)$, $E_{n*} = -2(e^2/8a_0)$, and $E_{n*} - E_0 = 3e^2/4a_0$. From (32.12) we have

$$H'^2 = \frac{e^4}{R^6} (x_1{}^2x_2{}^2 + y_1{}^2y_2{}^2 + 4z_1{}^2z_2{}^2 + 2x_1x_2y_1y_2 - \cdots) \tag{32.15}$$

[1] F. London, Z. Physik **63**, 245 (1930).

[2] A. Unsöld, Z. Physik **43**, 563 (1927).

The expectation value of the cross-product terms like $x_1x_2y_1y_2$ is zero since these terms are odd functions of one of the cartesian components of $\mathbf{r}_1$ or $\mathbf{r}_2$. The first three terms in the parenthesis of (32.15) each lead to a product of two identical factors that are equal to

$$\int x^2 |u_{100}(\mathbf{r})|^2 \, d^3r = \tfrac{1}{3} \int r^2 |u_{100}(\mathbf{r})|^2 \, d^3r$$

$$= \frac{1}{3\pi a_0{}^3} \int_0^\infty r^2 e^{-2r/a_0} 4\pi r^2 \, dr = a_0{}^2$$

so that $\langle 0|H'^2|0\rangle = 6e^4 a_0{}^4/R^6$. Substitution into (37.14) gives

$$W(R) \geq -\frac{8e^2 a_0{}^5}{R^6} \tag{32.16}$$

VARIATION CALCULATION

An upper limit on $W(R)$ can always be obtained by the variation method. It is apparent, however, that some judgment must be used in the choice of the trial function ψ; thus, if ψ does not depend on R, the dependence of the expectation value of the energy on R will be like that of H', that is, $1/R^3$. An upper limit with this R dependence is of no value to us, since what we want to determine is a limit on the coefficient of the $1/R^6$ interaction. A useful choice for ψ will be one in which there is a term proportional to H', since there will then be terms in the expectation value that are proportional to H'^2 and hence vary like $1/R^6$.

We choose for the trial function

$$\psi(\mathbf{r}_1, \mathbf{r}_2) = u_{100}(\mathbf{r}_1) u_{100}(\mathbf{r}_2)(1 + AH')$$

where A is to be the variation parameter. Since this ψ is not normalized, we use (32.5) rather than (32.4) and obtain

$$E_0 + W(R) \leq \frac{\int\int u_0(1 + AH')(H_0 + H')u_0(1 + AH') \, d^3r_1 \, d^3r_2}{\int\int u_0{}^2(1 + AH')^2 \, d^3r_1 \, d^3r_2} \tag{32.17}$$

where again u_0 is the product of the ground-state hydrogen wave functions, and A is assumed to be real. The right side of (32.17) can be written

$$\frac{E_0 + 2A\langle 0|H'^2|0\rangle + A^2\langle 0|H'H_0H'|0\rangle}{1 + A^2\langle 0|H'^2|0\rangle} \tag{32.18}$$

since u_0 is a normalized eigenfunction of H_0 with the eigenvalue

$$E_0 = -e^2/a_0$$

and $\langle 0|H'|0\rangle = \langle 0|H'^3|0\rangle = 0$. It is easily seen that $\langle 0|H'H_0H'|0\rangle$ is a sum of squares of factors of the form $\int u_{100}(\mathbf{r})xH_0xu_{100}(\mathbf{r}) \, d^3r$; this can be shown by direct computation to be zero.

Since we are interested only in terms of order H'^2, we expand the denominator of (32.18) to obtain

$$(E_0 + 2A\langle 0|H'^2|0\rangle)(1 + A^2\langle 0|H'^2|0\rangle)^{-1}$$
$$\approx E_0 + (2A - E_0 A^2)\langle 0|H'^2|0\rangle \quad (32.19)$$

If we remember that E_0 is negative, we find that (32.19) has a minimum with respect to variation of A when $A = 1/E_0$, in which case (32.17) becomes

$$E_0 + W(R) \leq E_0 + \frac{\langle 0|H'^2|0\rangle}{E_0} = E_0 - \frac{6e^2 a_0{}^5}{R^6} \quad (32.20)$$

Thus in (32.16) and (32.20) we have both upper and lower limits on the interaction energy:

$$-\frac{8e^2 a_0{}^5}{R^6} \leq W(R) \leq -\frac{6e^2 a_0{}^5}{R^6} \quad (32.21)$$

More careful variation calculations have shown that the numerical coefficient in $W(R)$ is very nearly 6.50.[1]

33□ALTERNATIVE TREATMENT OF THE PERTURBATION SERIES

We have seen in Sec. 32 how the expression (31.11) for the second-order perturbed energy can give a useful limit even when the generalized summation S cannot be carried out. In some situations, however, closed-form expressions for W_2 and ψ_1, both of which otherwise involve infinite summations, can be obtained. We illustrate this first with the problem of the second-order Stark effect of a hydrogen atom in its ground state and then generalize the procedure to a wider class of situations.

SECOND–ORDER STARK EFFECT IN HYDROGEN

The ground state of a hydrogen atom is nondegenerate, and the first-order perturbed energy in a uniform external electric field is zero. Our problem then is to calculate Eq. (31.11):

$$W_2 = S_n' \frac{|\langle 0|H'|n\rangle|^2}{E_0 - E_n} \quad (33.1)$$

[1] See L. Pauling and E. B. Wilson, Jr., "Introduction to Quantum Mechanics," sec. 47a (McGraw-Hill, New York, 1935). The result (32.21) is not strictly correct, since H' in (32.12) included only the static dipole-dipole interaction between the two atoms. In reality, there is also an effect of retardation, which arises from the finite speed of propagation of the electromagnetic interaction between the two dipoles. This causes $W(R)$ to fall off like $-1/R^7$ when R is large in comparison with the electromagnetic wavelength associated with an atomic transition frequency: $R \gg \hbar c a_0/e^2 = 137 a_0$. At such large distances the interaction is uninterestingly small, so that (32.21) actually provides useful limits on $W(R)$. See H. B. G. Casimir and D. Polder, *Phys. Rev.* **73**, 360 (1948).

The ground state ket $|0\rangle$ in the coordinate representation is

$$\langle \mathbf{r}|0\rangle = u_{100}(\mathbf{r}) = (\pi a_0{}^3)^{-\frac{1}{2}} e^{-r/a_0},$$

and $E_0 = -e^2/2a_0$. Equation (33.1) and the variation method are used in Prob. 9 to obtain lower and upper bounds, respectively, for W_2.

Instead of working directly with Eq. (33.1), we shall first find ψ_1 by solving the second of Eqs. (31.4) subject to the condition (31.6), and then make use of (31.7).[1] With H' given by (31.26), $W_1 = 0$, and the second of Eqs. (31.4) is an inhomogeneous differential equation for ψ_1:

$$\left(-\frac{\hbar^2}{2\mu} \nabla^2 - \frac{e^2}{r} - E_0 \right) \psi_1 = -e\mathsf{E}r \cos\theta\, u_{100} \tag{33.2}$$

We show first that the only angle dependence of ψ_1 is through a multiplying factor $\cos\theta$. One way of seeing this is to expand ψ_1 as a series of functions of r times spherical harmonics in θ, ϕ and to note that each term is an eigenfunction of the angular part of ∇^2. Then the left side of (33.2) is a similar series of spherical harmonics, and the only term we wish to retain is that which has the same angular dependence as the right side: $Y_{10}(\theta,\phi)$ or $\cos\theta$. An alternative way of seeing the same thing is to note that ψ_1 given by (31.9) is a sum over only those unperturbed states u_n for which $a_n{}^{(1)}$ fails to vanish; in accordance with (31.10), this means that u_n is proportional to $\cos\theta$ since the unperturbed state is spherically symmetrical. Thus each term in the series for ψ_1 is proportional to $\cos\theta$, and hence ψ_1 is also.

We can thus write

$$\psi_1(\mathbf{r}) = f(r) \cos\theta \tag{33.3}$$

and Eq. (31.6) is automatically satisfied. Substitution of (33.3) into (33.2) gives

$$\frac{d^2 f}{dr^2} + \frac{2}{r}\frac{df}{dr} - \frac{2}{r^2}f + \frac{2}{a_0 r}f - \frac{1}{a_0{}^2}f = \frac{2\mathsf{E}}{ea_0(\pi a_0{}^3)^{\frac{1}{2}}} re^{-r/a_0} \tag{33.4}$$

The solution of Eq. (33.4) is expected to have the form of a power series in r multiplied by e^{-r/a_0}; further, the series is expected to start with the first or higher power of r, since otherwise (33.3) will be singular at the origin. It turns out that the series terminates after two terms, so that the solution of (33.4) is

$$f(r) = -(\pi a_0{}^3)^{-\frac{1}{2}} \frac{\mathsf{E}}{e} (a_0 r + \tfrac{1}{2}r^2)e^{-r/a_0} \tag{33.5}$$

[1] This approach appears to have been first published by M. Kotani, "Quantum Mechanics," vol. I, p. 127 (Yuwanami Book Co., Tokyo, 1951).

as may be verified by substitution. Thus the wave function that is correct through first order in E is

$$(\pi a_0{}^3)^{-\frac{1}{2}}e^{-r/a_0}\left[1 - \frac{\mathsf{E}}{e}(a_0 r + \tfrac{1}{2}r^2)\cos\theta \right] \tag{33.6}$$

Substitution of the expression for ψ_1 obtained from Eqs. (33.3) and (33.5) into (31.7) gives for the second-order perturbed energy

$$W_2 = e\mathsf{E}(\pi a_0{}^3)^{-\frac{1}{2}}\!\int r\cos^2\theta f(r)e^{-r/a_0}\,d^3r$$

$$= -\frac{4\mathsf{E}^2}{3a_0{}^3}\int_0^\infty (a_0 r^4 + \tfrac{1}{2}r^5)e^{-2r/a_0}\,dr$$

$$= -\frac{9}{4}\mathsf{E}^2 a_0{}^3 \tag{33.7}$$

This expression for the second-order Stark effect was first obtained by separation of the wave equation in parabolic coordinates.[1]

POLARIZABILITY OF HYDROGEN

It was remarked at the end of Sec. 31 that the second-order Stark effect could be interpreted in terms of an induced electric dipole moment. This induced moment is proportional to the applied electric field and in the same direction, and the ratio α of dipole moment to field strength is called the *polarizability*. It is easily seen that these conditions hold exactly for a charged isotropic harmonic oscillator and that the energy change in this case is $-\frac{1}{2}\alpha\mathsf{E}^2$ (Prob. 1). For a general system, in which the energy change is not exactly proportional to E^2, it is still true that

$$W_2 = -\tfrac{1}{2}\alpha\mathsf{E}^2 \tag{33.8}$$

Comparison of Eqs. (33.7) and (33.8) shows that

$$\alpha = \tfrac{9}{2}a_0{}^3 \tag{33.9}$$

for a hydrogen atom its ground state (see Prob. 12).

[1] G. Wentzel, *Z. Physik* **38**, 518 (1926); I. Waller, *Z. Physik* **38**, 635 (1926); P. S. Epstein, *Phys. Rev.* **28**, 695 (1926). The general expression for the first- and second-order Stark effect with nuclear charge Z, in terms of the parabolic quantum numbers of Sec. 16, is $\frac{3}{2}n(n_1 - n_2)(e\mathsf{E}a_0/Z) - (\mathsf{E}^2 a_0{}^3/16Z^4)n^4[17n^2 - 3(n_1 - n_2)^2 - 9m^2 + 19]$. It should be noted that such a series in powers of E cannot converge since, strictly speaking, the system has no bound states. This is so because the electron of a hydrogen atom placed in a uniform electric field can gain enough energy by moving in the direction $-\mathsf{E}$ to compensate for its binding energy. In other words, the electron can tunnel through the potential barrier created by the nuclear coulomb field and the external electric field, as discussed in Sec. 17. The rate of spontaneous dissociation for a hydrogen atom in an electric field was calculated by J. R. Oppenheimer, *Phys. Rev.* **31**, 66 (1928), and is exceedingly small for fields of laboratory strength. Even though the series for the perturbed energy in powers of E does not converge, it is useful for ordinary field strengths.

METHOD OF DALGARNO AND LEWIS

The foregoing procedure can be generalized in the following way.[1] We start with Eq. (31.11), which is applicable to the ground state of any system since in all known cases this state is nondegenerate:

$$W_2 = S'_n \frac{\langle 0|H'|n\rangle\langle n|H'|0\rangle}{E_0 - E_n} \tag{33.10}$$

Suppose now that an operator F can be found such that

$$\frac{\langle n|H'|0\rangle}{E_0 - E_n} = \langle n|F|0\rangle \tag{33.11}$$

for all states n other than the ground state. Substitution into (33.10) then gives

$$W_2 = S'_n\langle 0|H'|n\rangle\langle n|F|0\rangle = \langle 0|H'F|0\rangle - \langle 0|H'|0\rangle\langle 0|F|0\rangle \tag{33.12}$$

where the term $n = 0$ has first been added in to make the summation complete and then subtracted out. Thus, if F can be found, the evaluation of W_2 is greatly simplified, since only integrals over the unperturbed ground-state wave function need be evaluated.

Equation (33.11) can be written as

$$\langle n|H'|0\rangle = (E_0 - E_n)\langle n|F|0\rangle = \langle n|[F,H_0]|0\rangle$$

which is evidently valid if F satisfies the operator equation

$$[F,H_0] = H' + C$$

where C is any constant. However, this last equation is unnecessarily general; it is enough that F satisfy the much simpler equation

$$[F,H_0]|0\rangle = H'|0\rangle + C|0\rangle \tag{33.13}$$

from which it follows that $C = -\langle 0|H'|0\rangle$.

We now define a new ket $|1\rangle$, which is the result of operating on $|0\rangle$ with F. Then Eq. (33.13) may be written

$$(E_0 - H_0)|1\rangle = H'|0\rangle - \langle 0|H'|0\rangle|0\rangle \qquad \text{where} \qquad |1\rangle \equiv F|0\rangle \tag{33.14}$$

The ket $|1\rangle$ can evidently have an arbitrary multiple of $|0\rangle$ added to it; we choose this multiple so that $\langle 0|1\rangle = 0$. If now Eq. (33.14), which is an inhomogeneous differential equation, can be solved for $|1\rangle$, the second-order perturbed energy (33.12) can be written in terms of it as

$$W_2 = \langle 0|H'|1\rangle \tag{33.15}$$

---

[1] A. Dalgarno and J. T. Lewis, *Proc. Roy. Soc. (London)* **A233,** 70 (1955); C. Schwartz, *Ann. Phys. (N.Y.)* **6,** 156 (1959).

In similar fashion the series (31.9) for ψ_1 can be written in closed form:

$$\psi_1 = S_n' \frac{|n\rangle\langle n|H'|0\rangle}{E_0 - E_n} = S_n'|n\rangle\langle n|F|0\rangle$$

$$= F|0\rangle - |0\rangle\langle 0|F|0\rangle = |1\rangle \qquad (33.16)$$

It is apparent that Eqs. (33.15) and (33.16) are consistent with Eq. (31.7), as of course they must be.

The Dalgarno-Lewis method thus replaces the evaluation of the infinite summation (31.9) by the solution of the inhomogeneous differential equation (33.14). The latter procedure may be much simpler even when it cannot be done in closed form, as with (33.4).

THIRD-ORDER PERTURBED ENERGY

The ket $|1\rangle = F|0\rangle$ is all that is needed to find the third-order perturbed energy W_3. We make use of Eqs. (31.7), (31.12), (31.13), and the complex conjugate of (33.11) to write

$$W_3 = (u_0, H'\psi_2)$$

$$= S_k' \frac{\langle 0|H'|k\rangle}{E_0 - E_k}\left(S_n' \frac{\langle k|H'|n\rangle\langle n|H'|0\rangle}{E_0 - E_n} - \frac{\langle k|H'|0\rangle\langle 0|H'|0\rangle}{E_0 - E_k}\right)$$

$$= S_k'\langle 0|F^\dagger|k\rangle(S_n'\langle k|H'|n\rangle\langle n|F|0\rangle - \langle k|F|0\rangle\langle 0|H'|0\rangle)$$

$$= \langle 0|F^\dagger H'F|0\rangle - \langle 0|F^\dagger|0\rangle\langle 0|H'F|0\rangle - \langle 0|F^\dagger H'|0\rangle\langle 0|F|0\rangle$$

$$\quad - \langle 0|F^\dagger F|0\rangle\langle 0|H'|0\rangle + 2\langle 0|F^\dagger|0\rangle\langle 0|H'|0\rangle\langle 0|F|0\rangle$$

$$= \langle 1|H'|1\rangle - \langle 1|1\rangle\langle 0|H'|0\rangle \qquad (33.17)$$

since $\langle 0|1\rangle = 0$. We thus obtain a closed expression for W_3 as well.[1]

INTERACTION OF A HYDROGEN ATOM AND A POINT CHARGE

As an example of this method, we now calculate the change in energy of a hydrogen atom in its ground state when a point charge Ze is placed at a fixed distance R. The perturbation is

$$H' = \frac{Ze^2}{R} - \frac{Ze^2}{(R^2 + r^2 - 2Rr\cos\theta)^{\frac{1}{2}}}$$

$$= -\frac{Ze^2}{R}\sum_{l=1}^{\infty}\left(\frac{r}{R}\right)^l P_l(\cos\theta) \qquad (33.18)$$

provided that $R > r$ or, equivalently, that R is much greater than a_0.

---

[1] This result can also be obtained directly from Eqs. (31.4) and (31.6) as a special case of the formula derived in Prob. 14.

From the structure of Eq. (33.14), we expect that the coordinate representation of the ket $|1\rangle$ can be written in the form

$$\langle \mathbf{r}|1\rangle = \sum_{l=1}^{\infty} f_l(r)P_l(\cos\theta) \tag{33.19}$$

Substitution of (33.19) into (33.14) leads to the following differential equation for $f_l(r)$:

$$\frac{d^2f_l}{dr^2} + \frac{2}{r}\frac{df_l}{dr} - \frac{l(l+1)}{r^2}f_l + \frac{2}{a_0 r}f_l - \frac{1}{a_0^2}f_l = -\frac{2Z}{a_0 R^{l+1}(\pi a_0^3)^{\frac{1}{2}}}r^l e^{-r/a_0} \tag{33.20}$$

As expected, this agrees with Eq. (33.14) when we put $l=1$ and $\mathsf{E} = -Ze/R^2$.

A solution of Eq. (33.20) is easily found in analogy with (33.5) and again contains only two terms. Substitution into (33.19) gives

$$\langle \mathbf{r}|1\rangle = \sum_{l=1}^{\infty} \frac{Z}{R^{l+1}(\pi a_0^3)^{\frac{1}{2}}}\left(\frac{a_0 r^l}{l} + \frac{r^{l+1}}{l+1}\right)e^{-r/a_0}P_l(\cos\theta) \tag{33.21}$$

which, in accordance with (33.16), is equal to $\psi_1(\mathbf{r})$. Similarly, Eq. (33.15) shows that W_2 is given by

$$W_2 = \langle 0|H'|1\rangle = -Z^2 e^2 \sum_{l=1}^{\infty} \frac{(l+2)(2l+1)!}{l2^{2l+1}}\frac{a_0^{2l+1}}{R^{2l+2}} \tag{33.22}$$

Again, the leading term $(l=1)$ agrees with (33.7) when $\mathsf{E} = -Ze/R^2$.

It should be noted that, although Eq. (33.22) gives the first two terms of an asymptotic series in $1/R$ correctly, the third term, which is proportional to $1/R^8$, is dominated by the leading term of W_3. Equation (33.17) shows that $W_3 = \langle 1|H'|1\rangle$ in this case and that the leading term for large R is proportional to $1/R^7$ (see Prob. 15).[1]

34□THE WKB APPROXIMATION

In the development of quantum mechanics, the Bohr-Sommerfeld quantization rules of the old quantum theory (Sec. 2) occupy a position intermediate between classical and quantum mechanics. It is interesting that there is a method for the approximate treatment of the Schrödinger wave

[1] A. Dalgarno and A. L. Stewart, *Proc. Roy. Soc. (London)* **A238**, 276 (1956). It should be noted that, unlike the situation with the van der Waals interaction discussed in the preceding section, there is no correction arising from retardation in the present problem. This is because the only motion is that of a single electron in the electrostatic potential of two fixed charges.

equation that shows its connection with the quantization rules. It is based on an expansion of the wave function in powers of $\hbar$, which, although of a semiconvergent or asymptotic character, is nevertheless also useful for the approximate solution of quantum-mechanical problems in appropriate cases. This method is called the *Wentzel-Kramers-Brillouin* or *WKB approximation*, although the general mathematical technique had been used earlier by Liouville, Rayleigh, and Jeffreys.[1] It is applicable to situations in which the wave equation can be separated into one or more total differential equations, each of which involves a single independent variable.

CLASSICAL LIMIT

A solution $\psi(\mathbf{r},t)$ of the Schrödinger wave equation (6.16)

$$i\hbar \frac{\partial \psi}{\partial t} = -\frac{\hbar^2}{2\mu} \nabla^2 \psi + V(\mathbf{r})\psi$$

can be written in the form

$$\psi(\mathbf{r},t) = A \exp \frac{iW(\mathbf{r},t)}{\hbar}$$

in which case W satisfies the equation

$$\frac{\partial W}{\partial t} + \frac{1}{2\mu} (\nabla W)^2 + V - \frac{i\hbar}{2\mu} \nabla^2 W = 0 \qquad (34.1)$$

In the classical limit ($\hbar \to 0$), Eq. (34.1) is the same as Hamilton's partial differential equation for the principal function W:[2]

$$\frac{\partial W}{\partial t} + H(\mathbf{r},\mathbf{p}) = 0 \qquad \mathbf{p} = \nabla W$$

Since the momentum of the particle is the gradient of W, the possible trajectories are orthogonal to the surfaces of constant W and hence, in the classical limit, to the surfaces of constant phase of the wave function ψ.

---

[1] It is sometimes called the *BWK method*, the *classical approximation*, or the *phase integral method*. For the original work, see J. Liouville, *J. de Math.* **2**, 16, 418 (1837); Lord Rayleigh, *Proc. Roy. Soc. (London)* **A86**, 207 (1912); H. Jeffreys, *Proc. London Math. Soc.* (2)**23**, 428 (1923); G. Wentzel, *Z. Physik.* **38**, 518 (1926); H. A. Kramers, *Z. Physik.* **39**, 828 (1926); L. Brillouin, *Compt. Rend.* **183**, 24 (1926). For more recent developments, see E. C. Kemble, "The Fundamental Principles of Quantum Mechanics," sec. 21 (McGraw-Hill, New York, 1937); R. E Langer, *Phys. Rev.* **51**, 669 (1937); W. H. Furry, *Phys. Rev.* **71**, 360 (1947); S. C. Miller, Jr., and R. H. Good, Jr., *Phys. Rev.* **91**, 174 (1953). The treatment of this section resembles most closely those of Kramers and Langer.

[2] E. T. Whittaker, "Analytical Dynamics," 3d ed., sec. 142 (Cambridge, London, 1927); H. Goldstein, "Classical Mechanics," sec. 9-1 (Addison-Wesley, Reading, Mass., 1950).

Thus in this limit the rays associated with ψ (orthogonal trajectories to the surfaces of constant phase) are the possible paths of the classical particle.

If ψ is an energy eigenfunction $u(\mathbf{r})e^{-iEt/\hbar}$, W can be written

$$W(\mathbf{r},t) = S(\mathbf{r}) - Et$$

In this case, we have that

$$u(\mathbf{r}) = A \exp \frac{iS(\mathbf{r})}{\hbar} \qquad \frac{1}{2\mu} (\nabla S)^2 - [E - V(\mathbf{r})] - \frac{i\hbar}{2\mu} \nabla^2 S = 0 \tag{34.2}$$

The WKB method obtains the first two terms (one term beyond the classical expression) of an expansion of S in powers of $\hbar$, in the one-dimensional case.

APPROXIMATE SOLUTIONS

The basic equation that we consider is written in one of the forms

$$\frac{d^2u}{dx^2} + k^2(x)u = 0 \qquad k^2 > 0 \tag{34.3}$$

$$\frac{d^2u}{dx^2} - \kappa^2(x)u = 0 \qquad \kappa^2 > 0 \tag{34.4}$$

so that k and κ are always real. These are equivalent to the one-dimensional wave equation (8.5), if we put

$$k(x) = + \frac{1}{\hbar} \{2\mu[E - V(x)]\}^{\frac{1}{2}} \qquad \text{when } V(x) < E$$
$$\kappa(x) = + \frac{1}{\hbar} \{2\mu[V(x) - E]\}^{\frac{1}{2}} \qquad \text{when } V(x) > E \tag{34.5}$$

Equations (34.3) and (34.4) are also equivalent to the radial wave equation (19.2) if x is replaced by r, $V(r)$ is replaced by

$$V(r) + \frac{\hbar^2 l(l + 1)}{2\mu r^2}$$

and u is equal to r times the radial wave function.

We restrict our attention for the present to Eq. (34.3); we shall be able to generalize the resulting expression for $u(x)$ to obtain solutions of (34.4). We put

$$u(x) = Ae^{iS(x)/\hbar}$$

which on substitution into (34.3) gives the one-dimensional form of (34.2)

$$i\hbar S'' - S'^2 + \hbar^2 k^2 = 0 \tag{34.6}$$

where primes denote differentiation with respect to x.

We substitute an expansion of S in powers of $\hbar$ into (34.6) and equate equal powers of $\hbar$.

$$S = S_0 + \hbar S_1 + \cdots$$
$$-S_0'^2 + 2\mu(E - V) = 0$$
$$iS_0'' - 2S_0'S_1' = 0 \qquad \text{etc.}$$

Integration of these equations gives

$$S_0(x) = \pm\hbar \int^x k(x')\, dx' \qquad S_1(x) = \tfrac{1}{2}i \ln k(x)$$

where arbitrary constants of integration that can be absorbed in the coefficient A have been omitted. We thus obtain to this order of approximation

$$u(x) = Ak^{-\frac{1}{2}} \exp\left(\pm i \int^x k\, dx\right) \qquad V < E \qquad (34.7)$$

In similar fashion, the approximate solution of (34.4) is

$$u(x) = B\kappa^{-\frac{1}{2}} \exp\left(\pm \int^x \kappa\, dx\right) \qquad V > E \qquad (34.8)$$

ASYMPTOTIC NATURE OF THE SOLUTIONS

The accuracy of these WKB solutions can be gauged by comparing the magnitudes of the successive terms S_0 and $\hbar S_1$ in the series for S. Since S_0 is a monotonic increasing function of x so long as k does not vanish, the ratio $\hbar S_1/S_0$ is expected to be small if $\hbar S_1'/S_0'$ is small. We thus expect (34.7) to be useful in that part of the domain of x where

$$\left| \frac{\hbar S_1'}{S_0'} \right| = \left| \frac{k'}{2k^2} \right| \ll 1 \qquad (34.9)$$

The local de Broglie wavelength λ is $2\pi/k$, so that (34.9) can be written

$$\frac{\lambda}{4\pi} \left| \frac{dk}{dx} \right| \ll k$$

which means that the fractional change in k (or the wavelength) in the distance $\lambda/4\pi$ is small compared with unity. Thus the WKB solutions are useful when the potential energy changes so slowly that the momentum of the particle is sensibly constant over many wavelengths.

The same criterion is obtained for (34.8) if we now mean by the "wavelength" the distance in which the magnitude of u changes by a factor $e^{2\pi}$.

It is apparent that the condition (34.9) is violated near the turning points of the classical motion, where $V(x) = E$, k and κ are zero, and the "wavelength" is infinite. Thus the solutions (34.7) and (34.8) are asymptotically valid in the sense that they can be used several wavelengths from the nearest turning point if, as is usually the case, the wavelength there is slowly varying.

The asymptotic solutions are most useful if we know how to connect an oscillating solution like (34.7) to an exponential solution like (34.8) across a turning point. It is in this way, for example, that we apply boundary conditions and obtain energy eigenvalues. The derivation of such *connection formulas*, which we consider next, is of interest for this reason. However, it should be noted that many applications of the WKB approximation do not depend critically on the precise way in which the connections are made.

SOLUTION NEAR A TURNING POINT

The wave equations (34.3) and (34.4) are regular at a turning point, so that there is a solution that is analytic there and has asymptotic forms like (34.7) and (34.8). Such a solution usually cannot be written in closed form. The wave equation can, however, be modified slightly so that an exact solution that has the desired asymptotic forms can be obtained.

We can, without loss of generality, take the origin of x at a particular turning point; we also assume for the moment that $V(x) < E$ to the right of the turning point (positive x) and put $\xi(x) \equiv \int_0^x k \, dx$. Now if $k^2(x) = Cx^n$, where C is a positive constant, Eq. (34.3) is known to have the solutions

$$u(x) = A\xi^{\frac{1}{2}}k^{-\frac{1}{2}}J_{\pm m}(\xi) \qquad m = \frac{1}{n+2} \tag{34.10}$$

where J is a Bessel function; this can be verified by direct substitution. The asymptotic form of J is such (see below) that (34.10) agrees asymptotically with (34.7).

We therefore try to retain this form by rewriting (34.3) with an additional term $\theta(x)$ even when $k^2(x)$ is not a power of x:

$$\frac{d^2u}{dx^2} + (k^2 - \theta)u = 0 \tag{34.11}$$

Substitution of (34.10) into (34.11) shows that the new equation is satisfied if we define θ as

$$\theta(x) \equiv \frac{3k'^2}{4k^2} - \frac{k''}{2k} + (m^2 - \tfrac{1}{4})\frac{k^2}{\xi^2} \tag{34.12}$$

We expand k^2 as a power series in x:

$$k^2(x) = Cx^n(1 + ax + bx^2 + \cdots)$$

in which case θ can also be expanded in a series.   The $1/x^2$ and $1/x$ terms vanish, and the leading term is independent of x.

$$\theta(x) \xrightarrow[x \to 0]{} \frac{3(n+5)a^2}{2(n+4)(n+6)} - \frac{3b}{n+6} \tag{34.13}$$

We can now see that (34.11) is a good approximation to the actual wave equation (34.3). The similarity in structure between each of the three terms in (34.12) and the asymptotic accuracy criterion (34.9) indicates that $\theta \ll k^2$ in the asymptotic region if the WBK method can be used at all.   At and near the turning point, θ is not negligible in comparison with k^2, since θ is a constant and k^2 vanishes at $x = 0$.   However, (34.13) shows that $\theta(0)$ is quite small, being of second order in the deviation of k^2 from the simple form Cx^n.   Thus for potential functions $V(x)$ that are slowly varying, (34.10) is expected to be a good approximation to the actual solution of Eq. (34.3).

LINEAR TURNING POINT

We now specialize to the situation of greatest physical interest, in which $n = 1$.   A typical linear turning point is shown in Fig. 28; Eq. (34.3) is used in region 1 ($x > 0$), and Eq. (34.4) in region 2 ($x < 0$).   We put $\xi_1 \equiv \int_0^x k\,dx$, $\xi_2 \equiv \int_x^0 \kappa\,dx$, so that both ξ_1 and ξ_2 increase as x moves away from the turning point; this makes it easy to generalize the results to situations in which the regions 1 and 2 are interchanged.   The two independent solutions in each of the two regions are

$$\begin{aligned}
u_1^{\pm}(x) &= A_{\pm}\xi_1^{\frac{1}{2}}k^{-\frac{1}{2}}J_{\pm\frac{1}{3}}(\xi_1) \\
u_2^{\pm}(x) &= B_{\pm}\xi_2^{\frac{1}{2}}\kappa^{-\frac{1}{2}}I_{\pm\frac{1}{3}}(\xi_2)
\end{aligned} \tag{34.14}$$

It is evident that we must replace J by I, the Bessel function of imaginary argument, in region 2.

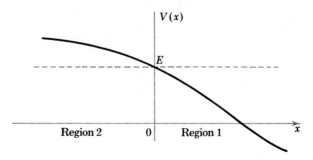

Fig. 28   A typical linear turning point, where $V(x) = E$ at $x = 0$; in region 1, $E > V(x)$, and in region 2, $E < V(x)$.

We require the leading terms of the power series expansions and of the asymptotic expansions for these functions[1]:

$$J_{\pm\frac{1}{3}}(\xi_1) \xrightarrow[x\to 0]{} \frac{(\frac{1}{2}\xi_1)^{\pm\frac{1}{3}}}{\Gamma(1 \pm \frac{1}{3})}$$

$$\xrightarrow[x\to\infty]{} (\tfrac{1}{2}\pi\xi_1)^{-\frac{1}{2}} \cos\left(\xi_1 \mp \frac{\pi}{6} - \frac{\pi}{4}\right) \tag{34.15}$$

$$I_{\pm\frac{1}{3}}(\xi_2) \xrightarrow[x\to 0]{} \frac{(\frac{1}{2}\xi_2)^{\pm\frac{1}{3}}}{\Gamma(1 \pm \frac{1}{3})}$$

$$\xrightarrow[x\to\infty]{} (2\pi\xi_2)^{-\frac{1}{2}} \left(e^{\xi_2} + e^{-\xi_2} \cdot e^{-(\frac{1}{2}\pm\frac{1}{3})\pi i}\right)$$

It is important to note that the term $e^{-\xi_2}$ in the asymptotic expansion for I can be retained only when a combination of solutions $I_{\pm\frac{1}{3}}$ is chosen such that the coefficient of e^{ξ_2} is zero. This is because other terms in the asymptotic expansion, such as e^{ξ_2}/ξ_2, have been neglected, and these are of larger order of magnitude than $e^{-\xi_2}$. The asymptotic nature of the WKB approximation is such that, if the term that increases exponentially away from the turning point is present, it is impossible to say whether or not the decreasing exponential term is also there.

CONNECTION AT THE TURNING POINT

The leading term in k^2 at $x = 0$ is Cx, so that $k \approx cx^{\frac{1}{2}}$, $\kappa \approx c|x|^{\frac{1}{2}}$, $\xi_1 \approx (2c/3)x^{\frac{3}{2}}$, $\xi_2 \approx (2c/3)|x|^{\frac{3}{2}}$, where $c = +C^{\frac{1}{2}}$. Then from (34.14) and (34.15) we obtain the behavior of the u's near $x = 0$:

$$u_1^+ \approx A_+ \frac{(\frac{2}{3})^{\frac{1}{3}}(\frac{1}{3}c)^{\frac{1}{3}}}{\Gamma(\frac{4}{3})} x \qquad\qquad u_1^- \approx A_- \frac{(\frac{2}{3})^{\frac{1}{3}}(\frac{1}{3}c)^{-\frac{1}{3}}}{\Gamma(\frac{2}{3})}$$

$$u_2^+ \approx B_+ \frac{(\frac{2}{3})^{\frac{1}{3}}(\frac{1}{3}c)^{\frac{1}{3}}}{\Gamma(\frac{4}{3})} |x| \qquad\qquad u_2^- \approx B_- \frac{(\frac{2}{3})^{\frac{1}{3}}(\frac{1}{3}c)^{-\frac{1}{3}}}{\Gamma(\frac{2}{3})}$$

It is apparent then that u_1^+ joins smoothly on to u_2^+ if $B_+ = -A_+$ and that u_1^- joins smoothly on to u_2^- if $B_- = A_-$.

These relations between the coefficients can be used to obtain asymptotic forms like (34.7) and (34.8) for the two independent solutions u^+ and u^- in the two regions (the arbitrary multiplying constants $A_\pm$ are omitted).

$$u^+ \xrightarrow[x\to+\infty]{} (\tfrac{1}{2}\pi k)^{-\frac{1}{2}} \cos\left(\xi_1 - \frac{5\pi}{12}\right)$$

$$\xrightarrow[x\to-\infty]{} - (2\pi\kappa)^{-\frac{1}{2}}(e^{\xi_2} + e^{-\xi_2-5\pi i/6})$$

$$u^- \xrightarrow[x\to+\infty]{} (\tfrac{1}{2}\pi k)^{-\frac{1}{2}} \cos\left(\xi_1 - \frac{\pi}{12}\right) \tag{34.16}$$

$$\xrightarrow[x\to-\infty]{} (2\pi\kappa)^{-\frac{1}{2}}(e^{\xi_2} + e^{-\xi_2-\pi i/6})$$

[1] Whittaker and Watson, *op. cit.*, chap. 17.

The asymptotic forms of any linear combination of u^+ and u^- can be found from Eqs. (34.16).

ASYMPTOTIC CONNECTION FORMULAS

Convenient connection formulas between the asymptotic WKB solutions in the two regions can be obtained by choosing suitable linear combinations of u^+ and u^-. Thus the combination $u^+ + u^-$ contains only the decreasing exponential and yields the first connection formula

$$\tfrac{1}{2}\kappa^{-\frac{1}{2}}e^{-\xi_2} \to k^{-\frac{1}{2}} \cos\,(\xi_1 - \tfrac{1}{4}\pi) \tag{34.17}$$

The arrow in (34.17) implies that the asymptotic solution in region 2 that appears on the left goes into the asymptotic solution in region 1 that appears on the right but that the converse is not necessarily true. This is because a small error in the phase of the cosine introduces the dominant increasing exponential in region 2.[1]

Another linear combination of u^+ and u^- can be found that gives the second connection formula

$$\sin\,\eta\,\kappa^{-\frac{1}{2}}e^{\xi_2} \leftarrow k^{-\frac{1}{2}} \cos\,(\xi_1 - \tfrac{1}{4}\pi + \eta) \tag{34.18}$$

where η is appreciably different from zero or an integer multiple of π. The arrow in (34.18) appears since the neglected decreasing exponential in region 2 alters the phase of the cosine in region 1 by an indeterminate amount if the connection is reversed.

ENERGY LEVELS OF A POTENTIAL WELL

We now give a simple example of the application of the WKB approximation that serves as a derivation of one of the Bohr-Sommerfeld quantization rules. We wish to find the energy levels of a particle moving in the one-dimensional potential well shown in Fig. 29. For any assumed energy level E, there are supposed to be just two turning points of the classical motion such that

$$V(x_1) = V(x_2) = E$$

The regions $x < x_1$ and $x > x_2$ are type 2 regions in which we know that u decreases away from the turning points in order to satisfy the boundary conditions at $\pm\,\infty$. Thus we have only the decreasing exponential WKB solution in these regions.

---

[1] The converse of (34.17) can be used in the following sense: If some parameter in the solution (such as the energy E) is varied continuously so that the phase of the cosine in region 1 passes through the value $-\tfrac{1}{4}\pi$, the increasing exponential in region 2 disappears for some indeterminate value of the phase close to $-\tfrac{1}{4}\pi$ and leaves only the decreasing exponential. This result is useful, for example, in treating the resonance scattering of alpha particles by a heavy nucleus.

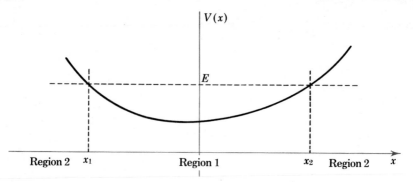

Fig. 29 Application of the WKB method to a potential trough; linear turning points occur at x_1 and x_2.

The connection formula (34.17) can be applied at the turning point x_1, which separates a type 2 region from the type 1 region $x_1 < x < x_2$. The only change is that the lower limit on the ξ_1 integral is changed from 0 to x_1, so that the solution to the right of the turning point is

$$k^{-\frac{1}{2}} \cos \left(\int_{x_1}^{x} k \, dx - \tfrac{1}{4}\pi \right) \tag{34.19}$$

apart from an arbitrary multiplying constant. The same connection formula can also be applied at x_2 by reversing the direction of the x axis and changing the fixed limit on the ξ integrals from 0 to x_2; the arrow in (34.17) still means that we go from a region 2 solution to a region 1 solution, but now the latter is to the left of the turning point and the former is to the right. We redefine $\xi_1 = \int_{x}^{x_2} k \, dx$, $\xi_2 = \int_{x_2}^{x} \kappa \, dx$ so that they still increase going away from the turning point, in which case (34.17) can be used without any modification. The solution to the left of this turning point is then $k^{-\frac{1}{2}} \cos \left(\int_{x}^{x_2} k \, dx - \tfrac{1}{4}\pi \right)$, which can be written

$$k^{-\frac{1}{2}} \cos \left(\int_{x_1}^{x} k \, dx - \tfrac{1}{4}\pi - \eta \right) \qquad \eta \equiv \int_{x_1}^{x_2} k \, dx - \tfrac{1}{2}\pi \tag{34.20}$$

As was the case in the qualitative discussion of discrete energy eigenvalues in Sec. 8, we obtain the energy levels of this system by requiring that the two solutions (34.19) and (34.20) join together smoothly in the interior of region 1. This evidently requires that η be zero or a positive integer multiple of π, since $\int_{x_1}^{x_2} k \, dx$ is necessarily positive. We can write the determining equation for the eigenvalues as

$$\int_{x_1}^{x_2} k \, dx = (n + \tfrac{1}{2})\pi \qquad n = 0, 1, 2, \ldots \tag{34.21}$$

Equation (34.21) is to be used for values of n up to the point at which E becomes so large that one or both of the turning points disappears.

A QUANTIZATION RULE

The expression (34.5) for k can be substituted into (34.21) to give one of the Bohr-Sommerfeld quantization rules of the old quantum theory:

$$2 \int_{x_1}^{x_2} \{2\mu[E - V(x)]\}^{\frac{1}{2}} dx = (n + \tfrac{1}{2})h \tag{34.22}$$

The left side of (34.22) is the integral around a complete cycle of the motion (from x_1 to x_2 and back to x_1) of the momentum $[2\mu(E - V)]^{\frac{1}{2}}$. The right side is the quantum value of the phase integral, with half-integer rather than integer quantum numbers.

It is easily seen from the form of the solution (34.20) that n is the number of nodes of the WKB wave function between the turning points. Since it is basic to the WKB method that we can develop asymptotic solutions like (34.7) only several wavelengths from each turning point, the approximation should be good only if the turning points are several wavelengths apart, or if n is large in comparison with unity. This confirms the earlier view that the WKB method is a semiclassical approximation, since it is expected to be most useful in the nearly classical limit of large quantum numbers.

Actually, the WKB approximation also gives quite good results for the low quantum states of many systems. For example, if we apply (34.22) to the harmonic oscillator $V(x) = \tfrac{1}{2}Kx^2$, it is known from the old quantum theory that the correct energy levels happen to be obtained for all quantum numbers (see Prob. 16).

SPECIAL BOUNDARY CONDITIONS

The boundary condition to be applied to a WKB solution at a perfectly rigid wall (V changes discontinuously to $+\infty$ at $x = x_0$) is that the wave function vanishes there. Thus if k (for a region of type 1) is slowly varying up to x_0 and other turning points are remote, the asymptotic solution can be used and has the form

$$k^{-\frac{1}{2}} \sin \left(\int_{x_0}^{x} k \, dx \right)$$

Similarly, for a finite potential step that is far from other turning points, the asymptotic WKB solutions can be used up to the point of discontinuity of V if k or κ is slowly varying. Then the magnitudes and slopes of the solutions on the two sides can be matched at this point.

As pointed out after Eq. (34.5), the WKB method can be applied to the radial wave equation for a spherically symmetric potential. When $l = 0$, the radial wave function must be finite at $r = 0$, and so u must vanish there. If k or κ is slowly varying there, the asymptotic solutions can be used; for example, if $E - V(r)$ is positive, finite, and slowly varying at and near $r = 0$, the solution is $k^{-\frac{1}{2}} \sin \left(\int_0^r k \, dr \right)$. When the effective potential energy is infinite at $r = 0$, either because V itself is infinite or because of the centrifugal-force contribution for $l \neq 0$, the situation is more complicated and requires further investigation.

TUNNELING THROUGH A BARRIER

Figure 30 shows a typical potential barrier, drawn as a function of the radial coordinate; as indicated below Eq. (34.5), the centrifugal term is included. In the type 2 region, the wave function is a real exponential of the form (34.8). Thus if $\int_{r_1}^{r_2} \kappa \, dr$ is appreciably larger than unity, the behavior of the solution is dominated by the large ratio of the wave function at the two turning points. We call the corresponding probability ratio, which is the square of the wave-function ratio, the *barrier penetration factor* P:

$$P = \exp \left[-2 \int_{r_1}^{r_2} \kappa(r) \, dr \right] \qquad \text{where}$$

$$\kappa(r) = +\frac{1}{\hbar} \left\{ 2\mu \left[V(r) + \frac{\hbar^2 l(l+1)}{2\mu r^2} - E \right] \right\}^{\frac{1}{2}} \qquad (34.23)$$

Tunneling through a square potential barrier, described at the end of Sec. 17, is a special case of this. It is easily seen that the dominant exponential factor in Eq. (17.8) is just the P given by (34.23).

In radioactive α decay, $V(r) = +ZZ'e^2/r$, where Z is the atomic number of the final nucleus, and $Z' = 2$. We assume that this expression

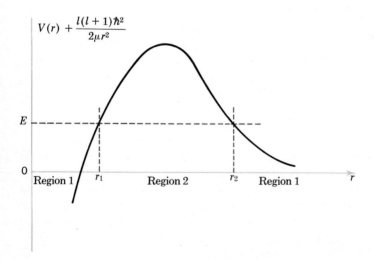

Fig. 30 Application of the WKB method to a potential barrier, with the radial coordinate as the independent variable.

for the potential is applicable only for $r > R$; within the nuclear radius R, strong attractive forces more than cancel the coulomb repulsion, so that $r_1 = R$. For $l = 0$, $r_2 = ZZ'e^2/E$, so that

$$\int_{r_1}^{r_2} \kappa(r) \, dr = \frac{(2\mu)^{\frac{1}{2}}}{\hbar} \int_R^{ZZ'e^2/E} \left(\frac{ZZ'e^2}{r} - E\right)^{\frac{1}{2}} dr$$

$$= \frac{\pi ZZ'e^2}{\hbar v}\left(1 - \frac{2}{\pi}\sin^{-1}\frac{1}{\gamma^{\frac{1}{2}}}\right) - \frac{\mu v R}{\hbar}(\gamma - 1)^{\frac{1}{2}} \qquad (34.24)$$

where $E = \frac{1}{2}\mu v^2$ and $\gamma \equiv ZZ'e^2/ER$ is the ratio of the coulomb-barrier height to the kinetic energy of the emerging α particle. Lifetimes for α decay are expected to be of the order of some characteristic time τ, divided by the P obtained from Eqs. (34.23) and (34.24). In this case, the wave function is much larger at r_1 than at r_2, and τ is roughly the period of oscillation of an α particle within the attractive nuclear potential of radius R. With $\tau \sim 10^{-21}$ sec and R somewhat less than 10^{-12} cm, a good fit with the observed Z and E dependence is obtained over a range of lifetimes of the order of a factor 10^{24}.

The barrier penetration factor also enters into the rate of nuclear reactions. In this case the wave function is much larger at r_2 than at r_1, and it is evident that P is in agreement with the Gamow factor, defined below Eq. (21.14), when $R = 0$.

As another example, we consider whether or not a zero-energy particle can be bound; this is of interest in connection with the work of Secs. 19 and 39. When $E = 0$,

$$\int_{r_1}^{r_2} \kappa(r) \, dr = \frac{(2\mu)^{\frac{1}{2}}}{\hbar} \int_{r_1}^{r_2} \left[V(r) + \frac{\hbar^2 l(l+1)}{2\mu r^2}\right]^{\frac{1}{2}} dr \qquad (34.25)$$

If $l = 0$ and $V(r)$ has a finite range, this integral is finite, and $P \neq 0$. Similarly, if $V(r)$ extends to infinity and falls off faster than $1/r^2$ for large r, the integral is finite when $r_2 = \infty$. On the other hand, if $l > 0$, (34.25) is infinite, and $P = 0$. Thus, as remarked near the end of Sec. 19, resonance at zero energy leads to a true bound state if l is not zero.

As pointed out earlier in this section, the applications of the WKB approximation made here do not depend critically on the precise way in which the connections across turning points are made. In the derivation of the quantization rule (34.22), only the number $\frac{1}{2}$ on the right side follows from the use of the connection formulas; the discussion of barrier penetration does not depend on them at all.

35□METHODS FOR TIME-DEPENDENT PROBLEMS

When the hamiltonian depends on the time, there are no stationary solutions of the Schrödinger equation. Thus our identification of a bound state with a discrete energy level and stationary eigenfunction must be modified. We consider in this section three ways in which this modification can be made, each of which corresponds to a particular kind of approximation. The *time-dependent perturbation theory*, which is sometimes called the *method of variation of constants*, assumes as in Sec. 31 that

$$H = H_0 + H' \qquad H_0 u_k = E_k u_k \qquad\qquad (35.1)$$

where H_0 is simple and H' is small. However, H' now depends on the time and has the effect of causing transitions between eigenstates of H_0 that would be stationary in the absence of H'. Alternatively, rather than decompose the hamiltonian in accordance with (35.1), the *abiabatic approximation* assumes that H contains parameters that change very slowly with time. Thus the system is expected to be described approximately by means of stationary eigenfunctions of the instantaneous hamiltonian. Finally, we consider the *sudden approximation*, in which H is constant in time except for a very short time interval in which it changes from one form to another.

TIME-DEPENDENT PERTURBATION THEORY[1]

We must now work with the time-dependent Schrödinger equation

$$i\hbar \frac{\partial \psi}{\partial t} = H\psi \qquad\qquad (35.2)$$

rather than with the first of Eqs. (31.1). Our procedure consists in expressing ψ as an expansion in the eigenfunctions $u_n e^{-iE_n t/\hbar}$ of the unperturbed time-dependent wave equation, where the expansion coefficients evidently depend on the time:

$$\psi = S_n a_n(t) u_n e^{-iE_n t/\hbar} \qquad\qquad (35.3)$$

Substitution of (35.3) into (35.2) gives

$$S_n i\hbar \dot{a}_n u_n e^{-iE_n t/\hbar} + S_n a_n E_n u_n e^{-iE_n t/\hbar} = S_n a_n (H_0 + H') u_n e^{-iE_n t/\hbar}$$

where the dot denotes differentiation with respect to the time.

We replace $H_0 u_n$ by $E_n u_n$ on the right side, multiply through on the left by u_k^*, and integrate over all space, making use of the orthonormality of the u's:

$$i\hbar \dot{a}_k e^{-iE_k t/\hbar} = S_n a_n e^{-iE_n t/\hbar} \langle k|H'|n \rangle$$

We define the Bohr (angular) frequency

$$\omega_{kn} \equiv \frac{E_k - E_n}{\hbar} \qquad\qquad (35.4)$$

---

[1] P. A. M. Dirac, *Proc. Roy. Soc.* (*London*) **A112**, 661 (1926); **A114**, 243 (1927).

and obtain

$$\dot{a}_k = (i\hbar)^{-1} S_n \langle k|H'|n\rangle a_n e^{i\omega_{kn}t} \tag{35.5}$$

The group of Eqs. (35.5) for all k is exactly equivalent to the Schrödinger equation (35.2).

INTERACTION PICTURE

Two kinds of changes have been made in going from (35.2) to (35.5). First, we have changed the *representation* from being specified in terms of the coordinates to being specified in terms of the unperturbed energy eigenvalues (see Sec. 23). Second, we have changed from the Schrödinger to the interaction *picture* (see Sec. 24). It is worth looking at these two changes in some detail. The Schrödinger-picture ket $|\alpha_S(t)\rangle$ corresponds to the wave function ψ and has the representation in terms of eigenvalues of the unperturbed hamiltonian H_0,

$$\langle k|\alpha_S(t)\rangle = (u_k, \psi) = a_k(t) e^{-iE_k t/\hbar} \tag{35.6}$$

where use has been made of Eq. (35.3). The interaction picture ket $|\alpha_I(t)\rangle$ may be found from the first of Eqs. (24.12); in the same representation it is

$$\langle k|\alpha_I(t)\rangle = \langle k|e^{iH_{0S}t/\hbar}|\alpha_S(t)\rangle = \langle k|e^{iH_{0S}t/\hbar}|n\rangle\langle n|\alpha_S(t)\rangle$$

where S_n is implied on the right side. The first bracket expression on the right side is simply $e^{iE_k t/\hbar}\langle k|n\rangle$, since H_{0S} is diagonal in this representation. Thus, with the help of (35.6), we find that

$$\langle k|\alpha_I(t)\rangle = a_k(t)$$

The perturbation that appears in (35.1) or (35.5) is given in the Schrödinger picture and thus should be designated H'_S. It may be found in the interaction picture from the second of Eqs. (24.12), which in our representation is

$$\langle k|H'_I|n\rangle = \langle k|e^{iH_{0S}t/\hbar}j\rangle\langle j|H'_S|l\rangle\langle l|e^{-iH_{0S}t/\hbar}|n\rangle$$
$$= e^{iE_k t/\hbar}\langle k|H'_S|n\rangle e^{-iE_n t/\hbar}$$
$$= \langle k|H'_S|n\rangle e^{i\omega_{kn}t}$$

Thus the equation of motion (24.13) for the ket in the interaction picture, expressed in the H_0 representation, is identical with Eq. (35.5).[1]

[1] Because this equation was first obtained by Dirac (*loc. cit.*) in connection with the time-dependent perturbation theory, the interaction picture is sometimes called the *Dirac picture*.

FIRST-ORDER PERTURBATION

We now return to Eq. (35.5), replace H' by $\lambda H'$, and express the a's as power series in λ:

$$a_n = a_n{}^{(0)} + \lambda a_n{}^{(1)} + \lambda^2 a_n{}^{(2)} + \cdots \tag{35.7}$$

As in Sec. 31, we assume that this series is a continuous analytic function of λ for λ between zero and one. We therefore substitute (35.7) into (35.5), equate coefficients of corresponding powers of λ, and set $\lambda = 1$ in the final results. The substitution yields the set of equations

$$\dot{a}_k{}^{(0)} = 0 \qquad \dot{a}_k{}^{(s+1)} = (i\hbar)^{-1} S_n \langle k|H'|n\rangle a_n{}^{(s)} e^{i\omega_{kn}t} \tag{35.8}$$

These can, in principle, be integrated successively to obtain approximate solutions to any desired order in the perturbation.

The first of Eqs. (35.8) shows that the zero-order coefficients $a_k{}^{(0)}$ are constant in time. Their values are the initial conditions of the problem and specify the state of the system before the perturbation is applied. We shall assume that all except one of the $a_k{}^{(0)}$ are zero, so that the system is initially in a definite unperturbed energy state.[1] The results that we shall obtain can easily be generalized to situations in which more than one of the zero-order coefficients are different from zero.

We thus put $a_k{}^{(0)} = \langle k|m\rangle = \delta_{km}$ or $\delta(k - m)$, according as the initial state m is one of a discrete or continuous set. Integration of the first-order equation gives

$$a_k{}^{(1)}(t) = (i\hbar)^{-1} \int_{-\infty}^{t} \langle k|H'(t')|m\rangle e^{i\omega_{km}t'} \, dt' \tag{35.9}$$

where the constant of integration is taken to be zero in order that $a_k{}^{(1)}$ be zero at $t = -\infty$ (before the perturbation is applied). If H' is of finite duration, the amplitude of a state u_k ($k \neq m$) after the perturbation has disappeared is proportional to the time Fourier component of the matrix element of the perturbation between this state and the initial state that corresponds to the angular frequency ω_{km} given in (35.4).

HARMONIC PERTURBATION

Equation (35.9) takes a particularly simple form if the perturbation H' depends harmonically on the time except for being turned on at one time and off at a later time. We call these two times 0 and t_0, respectively, and

---

[1] This need not conflict with the uncertainty relation (3.3), since the infinite lapse of time prior to the application of the perturbation makes it possible to determine the original energy of the system with arbitrarily great precision.

assume that we can write

$$\langle k|H'(t')|m\rangle = 2\langle k|H'|m\rangle \sin \omega t' \tag{35.10}$$

where $\langle k|H'|m\rangle$ is independent of the time and ω is defined to be positive. Substitution into (35.9) gives for the first-order amplitude at any time t at or after t_0

$$a_k^{(1)}(t \geq t_0) = -\frac{\langle k|H'|m\rangle}{i\hbar}\left(\frac{e^{i(\omega_{km}+\omega)t_0} - 1}{\omega_{km} + \omega} - \frac{e^{i(\omega_{km}-\omega)t_0} - 1}{\omega_{km} - \omega}\right) \tag{35.11}$$

The structure of Eq. (35.11) suggests that the amplitude is appreciable only when the denominator of one or the other of the two terms is practically zero. The first term is important when $\omega_{km} \approx -\omega$ or $E_k \approx E_m - \hbar\omega$, and the second term is important when $\omega_{km} \approx \omega$ or $E_k \approx E_m + \hbar\omega$. Thus the first-order effect of a perturbation that varies sinusoidally in the time with angular frequency ω is to transfer to or receive from the system on which it acts the Planck quantum of energy $\hbar\omega$.[1] This concept will be used to treat radiation processes in Chap. 11.

For the present, we specialize to a situation in which the initial state m is a discrete bound state and the final state k is one of a continuous set of dissociated states. Then $E_k > E_m$, and only the second term in (35.11) need be considered. The first-order probability of finding the system in the state k after the perturbation is removed is

$$|a_k^{(1)}(t \geq t_0)|^2 = \frac{4|\langle k|H'|m\rangle|^2 \sin^2 \frac{1}{2}(\omega_{km} - \omega)t_0}{\hbar^2(\omega_{km} - \omega)^2} \tag{35.12}$$

TRANSITION PROBABILITY

The factor $\sin^2 \frac{1}{2}(\omega_{km} - \omega)t_0/(\omega_{km} - \omega)^2$ is plotted in Fig. 31 as a function of $\omega_{km} - \omega$. The height of the main peak increases in proportion to t_0^2, and its breadth decreases inversely as t_0, so that the area under the curve is proportional to t_0. Thus if there is a group of states k that have energies nearly equal to $E_m + \hbar\omega$, and for which $\langle k|H'|m\rangle$ is roughly independent of k, the probability of finding the system in one or another of these states is proportional to t_0. This is the physically interesting situation, since what we wish to calculate eventually is a *transition probability per unit time*, w, and this implies that the probability that a transition has

---

[1] This is related to the reason for the insertion of the factor 2 on the right side of Eq. (35.10) in defining the time-independent matrix element $\langle k|H'|m\rangle$. A perturbation that is proportional to $\sin \omega t$ or to $\cos \omega t$ contains both time factors $e^{i\omega t}$ and $e^{-i\omega t}$ with equal amplitude. Since only the time factor $e^{-i\omega t}$ leads to transfer of energy from the perturbation to the unperturbed system, the insertion of the factor 2 ensures that the physically important matrix element of the perturbation is $\langle k|H'|m\rangle$ and not half this quantity.

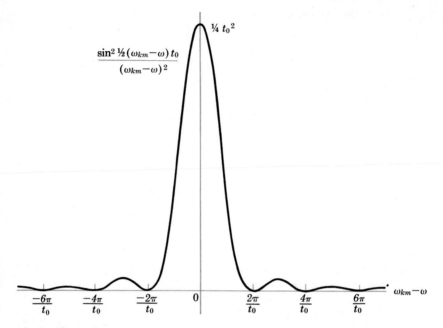

Fig. 31 The ordinate is proportional to the first-order perturbation probability of finding a system in a state of energy $E_k \equiv E_m + \hbar\omega_{km}$; the heights of the secondary peaks fall off like $1/(\omega_{km} - \omega)^2$.

taken place after the perturbation has been on for a time t_0 is proportional to t_0.[1]

The spread of energy of the final states to which transitions occur is connected with the uncertainty relation (3.3) in the following way. We can regard the perturbation H' as a device that measures the final energy of the system by transferring it to one of the states k. The time available for the measurement is t_0, so that the uncertainty in energy predicted by (3.3) is of order $\hbar/t_0$; this is in agreement with the breadth of the main peak in Fig. 31. It is interesting to note that conservation of energy, as expressed by the relation $E_k \approx E_m + \hbar\omega$ and suitably modified by the uncertainty principle, is an automatic consequence of the calculation and does not have to be inserted as a separate assumption.

The transition probability per unit time is given by integrating

---

[1] We assume that the total transition probability to all states k is small enough in comparison with unity so that the initial state m is not significantly depleted. This is equivalent to the original assumption that the perturbation is small, which means that for times t_0 of physical interest there is little change in the initial state. There can still be an effect of observable magnitude if a large number of independent systems receive identical treatment.

(35.12) over k and dividing by t_0:

$$w = \frac{1}{t_0} \int |a_k^{(1)}(t \geq t_0)|^2 \rho(k) \; dE_k \tag{35.13}$$

where $\rho(k) \; dE_k$ is the number of final states with energies between E_k and $E_k + dE_k$. The concept of an energy density $\rho(k)$ of final states is sensible, since we are considering the case in which the transition is to one or another of a continuous set of dissociated states. We now take advantage of the fact that the breadth of the main peak in Fig. 31 becomes small as t_0 becomes large, and we regard $\langle k|H'|m\rangle$ and $\rho(k)$ as quantities sufficiently independent of E_k so that they can be taken outside the integral in Eq. (35.13). We further simplify the integral by changing the integration variable from E_k to $x \equiv \frac{1}{2}(\omega_{km} - \omega)t_0$ and extending the limits on x to $\pm \infty$. Substitution of (35.12) into (35.13) then gives[1]

$$w = \frac{2\pi}{\hbar} \rho(k)|\langle k|H'|m\rangle|^2 \tag{35.14}$$

where we have made use of the result $\int_{-\infty}^{\infty} x^{-2} \sin^2 x \; dx = \pi$. This expression for w is independent of t_0, as expected.

There may be several different groups of final states $k_1, k_2, \ldots,$ all of which have about the same energy $E_m + \hbar\omega$ but for which the perturbation matrix elements $\langle k_i|H'|m\rangle$ and the densities of states $\rho(k_i)$, although nearly constant within each group, differ from one group to another. Then Eq. (35.14), with k replaced by k_i, gives the transition probability per unit time to the ith group.

It is apparent that the foregoing treatment fails to give a transition probability that is proportional to the time if the final as well as the initial state is discrete. In this case, Eq. (35.12) shows that $|a_k^{(1)}(t \geq t_0)|^2$ depends in a peculiar way on t_0 and on $\omega_{km} - \omega$. We return to this situation in Chap. 11 in connection with radiation processes.

IONIZATION OF A HYDROGEN ATOM

As an example of the first-order time-dependent perturbation theory, we now calculate the probability of ionization of a hydrogen atom initially in its ground state when it is placed in a harmonically time-varying electric field. We might, for instance, think of the atom as being placed between the plates of a capacitor to which an alternating voltage is applied. This is, of course, not a realistic situation, since the circular

---

[1] Equation (35.14) together with its analog for $\omega = 0$, which will be discussed in Sec. 37, is so useful that it was called "Golden Rule No. 2" by E. Fermi, "Nuclear Physics," p. 142 (University of Chicago Press, Chicago, 1950).

frequency $\omega/2\pi$ must exceed $\mu e^4/4\pi\hbar^3 = 3.6 \times 10^{15}$ cycles/sec in order for ionization to occur. However, the electric field produced by the capacitor can be regarded as a model for the field associated with a traveling electromagnetic wave that lies in the ultraviolet part of the spectrum.

The perturbation H' is given by Eq. (31.26), where in accordance with (35.10) we write

$$\mathsf{E}(t) = 2\mathsf{E}_0 \sin \omega t \tag{35.15}$$

The initial ground state of the hydrogen atom is obtained from Eqs. (16.24) with $Z = 1$:

$$u_m = u_{100}(\mathbf{r}) = (\pi a_0{}^3)^{-\frac{1}{2}} e^{-r/a_0} \tag{35.16}$$

The final states should correspond to the motion of a positive-energy electron in the coulomb field of the proton (scattering states). However, as suggested by the discussion in Sec. 21, these wave functions are rather complicated, and it is instructive to consider only the much simpler approximate situation in which the coulomb interaction is neglected after ionization has occurred. Then the final states are free-particle momentum eigenfunctions (plane waves). It is convenient to use box normalization, so that

$$u_k = L^{-\frac{3}{2}} \exp (i\mathbf{k} \cdot \mathbf{r}) \tag{35.17}$$

where $\hbar\mathbf{k}$ is the momentum of the ejected electron.

DENSITY OF FINAL STATES

The density of final states can be found from the permitted values of $\mathbf{k}$ in a box: $k_x = 2\pi n_x/L$, etc., where the n's are positive or negative integers or zero. Thus there are $(L/2\pi)^3 \, dk_x \, dk_y \, dk_z$ states in the range $dk_x \, dk_y \, dk_z$ of the propagation vector. Energy conservation gives $E_k = E_m + \hbar\omega$, or $\hbar^2 k^2/2\mu = -\mu e^4/2\hbar^2 + \hbar\omega$, so that the magnitude of $\mathbf{k}$ is fixed. The matrix element that appears in (35.14) will, however, depend on the direction of $\mathbf{k}$, and so it is reasonable to define groups of final states k_i each of which corresponds to an infinitesimal range of directions for the motion of the ejected electron. We therefore express the range of the propagation vector, which is given above in rectangular coordinates, in terms of spherical coordinates as $k^2 \, dk \sin \theta \, d\theta \, d\phi$, where θ, ϕ are the polar angles of $\mathbf{k}$ with respect to some direction which we take for convenience to be that of the electric field. Then $\rho(k) \, dE_k$ is equal to $(L/2\pi)^3 k^2 \, dk \sin \theta \, d\theta \, d\phi$, where dE_k and dk are related by differentiation of the equation $E_k = \hbar^2 k^2/2\mu$. We thus obtain

$$\rho(k) = \frac{\mu L^3}{8\pi^3 \hbar^2} k \sin \theta \, d\theta \, d\phi \tag{35.18}$$

IONIZATION PROBABILITY

The matrix element that is to be inserted into Eq. (35.14) is obtained from Eqs. (31.26), (35.10), and (35.15) and the initial and final wave functions (35.16) and (35.17).   The result is

$$\langle k|H'|m\rangle \; = \; eE_0(\pi a_0{}^3 L^3)^{-\frac{1}{2}} \!\int e^{-ikr\cos\theta'} r\cos\theta'' e^{-r/a_0}\, d^3r \qquad (35.19)$$

where θ' is the angle between $\mathbf{r}$ and $\mathbf{k}$, and θ'' is the angle between $\mathbf{r}$ and the electric field.   As remarked in the preceding subsection, we use θ to denote the angle between $\mathbf{k}$ and the electric field.   The integration over the direction of the vector $\mathbf{r}$ may be performed either using $\mathbf{k}$ as the polar axis (in which case θ'' must be expressed in terms of θ' and θ) or using the electric field direction as the polar axis (in which case θ' must be expressed in terms of θ'' and θ).   It is simpler to adopt the first procedure and put

$$\cos\theta'' \; = \; \cos\theta'\cos\theta + \sin\theta'\sin\theta\cos(\phi' - \chi)$$

Here θ', ϕ' are the polar angles of $\mathbf{r}$ with respect to $\mathbf{k}$ as polar axis, and θ, χ are the polar angles of the electric field direction with respect to $\mathbf{k}$, as in Fig. 32.

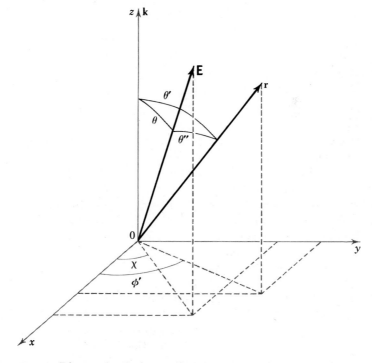

Fig. 32 Diagram for the integration of the matrix element (35.19).

We can now replace d^3r by $r^2\,dr\,d(\cos\theta')\,d\phi'$ in Eq. (35.19). The ϕ' integration causes the second term in the above expression for $\cos\theta''$ to vanish. The rest of the evaluation of the matrix element is straightforward and leads to

$$\langle k|H'|m\rangle = -\frac{32\pi ie\mathsf{E}_0ka_0{}^5\cos\theta}{(\pi a_0{}^3L^3)^{\frac{1}{2}}(1+k^2a_0{}^2)^3}$$

Substitution of this matrix element, together with the expression (35.18) for $\rho(k)$, into (35.14) gives for the probability per unit time that the electron of the hydrogen atom is ejected into the solid angle $\sin\theta\,d\theta\,d\phi$

$$w = \frac{256\mu k^3e^2\mathsf{E}_0{}^2a_0{}^7}{\pi\hbar^3(1+k^2a_0{}^2)^6}\cos^2\theta\,\sin\theta\,d\theta\,d\phi \tag{35.20}$$

The differential ionization probability per unit solid angle, $w/(\sin\theta\,d\theta\,d\phi)$, is proportional to $\cos^2\theta$. This is not surprising, since the probability amplitude is expected to be proportional to the component of the driving force in the direction of ejection, which is $e\mathsf{E}_0\cos\theta$. The dependence of w on ω is given most reliably when ω is large, since then k is also large, and the modification of the plane-wave final state by the coulomb field of the proton is expected to be least important. This may be seen from Eq. (21.13), which shows that, for large k or small n, $|u_c(0)|^2$ approaches $1/v$, which is the probability density at $r=0$ for a plane wave that is normalized to unit flux.

SECOND-ORDER PERTURBATION

It is a straightforward matter to substitute an expression like (35.11) into the right side of the second of Eqs. (35.8) and integrate the resulting equation for $\dot{a}_k{}^{(2)}$. Without going through the rather lengthy details of this calculation, it is not difficult to see that the second-order amplitude contains terms that are appreciable when ω_{km} is close to 2ω, -2ω, and 0. Terms of this type are physically plausible, since they correspond respectively to the absorption of two Planck quanta $\hbar\omega$ by the system, the emission of two quanta, and the absorption and emission of one quantum. Such two-quantum processes are expected from a second-order calculation in which the perturbation acts twice, in analogy with the one-quantum processes obtained as the result of the first-order calculation.

Unfortunately, however, the second-order amplitude also contains terms that are appreciable for other values of ω_{km}. A careful analysis shows that these unphysical terms arise from the earlier assumption that the perturbation (35.10) is turned on suddenly at $t=0$. The resulting discontinuity in the time derivative of the perturbation introduces Fourier components that are responsible for the secondary peaks in Fig. 31. In reality the perturbation will usually be turned on gradually during a time interval that will be much longer than $1/\omega$, so that the breadth of the Fourier transform of the perturbation, which has a maximum at ω, will be small in comparison with ω. Also, this time interval will be much shorter than the total time t_0 that the perturbation is on, in order that t_0 can be specified with reasonable accuracy. The sudden turning on of the perturbation does not cause serious difficulties in first order, since we were able to ignore the secondary peaks in Fig. 31 even though their heights fall off only as $1/(\omega_{km} - \omega)^2$. In second order, however, the effects are more marked and cannot be ignored; it is necessary then to turn the perturbation on slowly, and this complicates the calculation.

We shall not pursue this further here, but the problem will arise again in Sec. 37 in connection with collision theory. The case in which a sudden change in the hamiltonian of a system is an essential part of the physical situation, rather than merely a mathematical convenience as in the derivation of (35.11), is discussed toward the end of this section.

ADIABATIC APPROXIMATION[1]

It was remarked at the beginning of this section that methods can be developed for treating systems in which the time dependence of the hamiltonian is small, slowly varying, or rapidly varying; these correspond to the perturbation, adiabatic, and sudden approximations, respectively. In the adiabatic case, we expect on physical grounds that solutions of the Schrödinger equation can be approximated by means of stationary eigenfunctions of the instantaneous hamiltonian, so that a particular eigenfunction at one time goes over continuously into the corresponding eigenfunction at a later time. In other words, if the equation

$$H(t)u_n(t) = E_n(t)u_n(t) \tag{35.21}$$

can be solved at each instant of time, we expect that a system that is in a discrete nondegenerate state $u_m(0)$ with energy $E_m(0)$ at $t = 0$ is likely to be in the state $u_m(t)$ with energy $E_m(t)$ at time t, provided that $H(t)$ changes very slowly with time. Our objective is to estimate the extent to which this expectation is not fulfilled, so that other states appear in the expansion of ψ in terms of the u's.

The wave function ψ satisfies the time-dependent Schrödinger equation

$$i\hbar \frac{\partial \psi}{\partial t} = H(t)\psi \tag{35.22}$$

We proceed by expanding ψ in terms of the u's in the following way:

$$\psi = \sum_n a_n(t)u_n(t) \exp\left[(i\hbar)^{-1} \int_0^t E_n(t')\,dt' \right] \tag{35.23}$$

[1] M. Born and V. Fock, Z. Phys. **51**, 165 (1928).

where we assume that the u_n are orthonormal, discrete, and nondegenerate. Substitution into Eq. (35.22) gives

$$\sum_n \left[\dot{a}_n u_n + a_n \frac{\partial u_n}{\partial t} \right] \exp \left[(i\hbar)^{-1} \int_0^t E_n(t') \, dt' \right] = 0$$

where use has been made of (35.21). We multiply through on the left by u_k^* and integrate over all space to obtain

$$\dot{a}_k = - \sum_n a_n \langle k|\dot{n} \rangle \exp \left[(i\hbar)^{-1} \int_0^t (E_n - E_k) \, dt' \right]$$

$$\langle k|\dot{n} \rangle \equiv \int u_k^* \frac{\partial u_n}{\partial t} \, d^3r \quad (35.24)$$

An expression for $\langle k|\dot{n} \rangle$ can be found by differentiating Eq. (35.21) with respect to the time:

$$\frac{\partial H}{\partial t} u_n + H \frac{\partial u_n}{\partial t} = \frac{\partial E_n}{\partial t} u_n + E_n \frac{\partial u_n}{\partial t}$$

We multiply through on the left by u_k^*, where $k \neq n$, integrate over all space, and make use of Eqs. (23.21) and (35.21) to obtain

$$\left\langle k \left| \frac{\partial H}{\partial t} \right| n \right\rangle = (E_n - E_k) \langle k|\dot{n} \rangle \qquad k \neq n \quad (35.25)$$

CHOICE OF PHASES

We also require an expression for $\langle n|\dot{n} \rangle$. Differentiation of the equation $\langle n|n \rangle = 1$ with respect to time gives

$$\langle \dot{n}|n \rangle + \langle n|\dot{n} \rangle = 0$$

Since these two terms are complex conjugates of each other, each is purely imaginary, and we can write $\langle n|\dot{n} \rangle = i\alpha(t)$, where $\alpha(t)$ is real. We now change the phase of u_n by an amount $\gamma(t)$, which is permissible since the phases of the eigenfunctions are arbitrary at each instant of time. For the new eigenfunction $u_n' \equiv u_n e^{i\gamma(t)}$,

$$\langle n'|\dot{n}' \rangle = \langle n|\dot{n} \rangle + i\dot{\gamma} = i(\alpha + \dot{\gamma})$$

Thus the choice $\gamma(t) = - \int_0^t \alpha(t') \, dt'$ for the phase makes $\langle n'|\dot{n}' \rangle = 0$. In what follows, we assume that all phases have been chosen in this way and omit the primes.

Substitution of (35.25) into (35.24) then gives

$$\dot{a}_k = \sum_n' \frac{a_n}{\hbar \omega_{kn}} \left\langle k \left| \frac{\partial H}{\partial t} \right| n \right\rangle \exp \left[i \int_0^t \omega_{kn}(t') \, dt' \right] \quad (35.26)$$

where the prime on the summation indicates that the term $n = k$ is omitted. The group of Eqs. (35.26) for all k is exactly equivalent to the Schrödinger equation (35.22).

We can now estimate $\dot{a}_k$ by assuming that all quantities (a_n, ω_{kn}, u_n, $\partial H/\partial t$) that appear on the right side of (35.26), and which are expected to be slowly varying, are actually constant in time. If, further, we assume that the system is in the state m at $t = 0$, we can put $a_n = \delta_{nm}$. We thus obtain

$$\dot{a}_k \approx (\hbar\omega_{km})^{-1} \left\langle k \left| \frac{\partial H}{\partial t} \right| n \right\rangle e^{i\omega_{km}t} \qquad k \neq m$$

which is readily integrated to give

$$a_k(t) \approx (i\hbar\omega_{km}^2)^{-1} \left\langle k \left| \frac{\partial H}{\partial t} \right| n \right\rangle (e^{i\omega_{km}t} - 1) \qquad k \neq m \qquad (35.27)$$

With the above approximations, Eq. (35.27) shows that the probability amplitude for a state other than the initial state oscillates in time and shows no steady increase over long periods of time even though H changes by a finite amount. The magnitude of this amplitude after a long time is of the order of the ratio of the change in H during the Bohr period $2\pi/\omega_{km}$ to the energy difference $E_k - E_m$ between the states.

CONNECTION WITH PERTURBATION THEORY

An exceptional situation arises when the hamiltonian oscillates in time with a frequency nearly equal to one of the transition frequencies, say ω_{km}. This is a case of resonance, and we expect from the discussion of time-dependent perturbation theory earlier in this section that even a very small change in H can produce an appreciable amplitude a_k over long periods of time, so that (35.27) cannot be valid. The reason for the failure is that it is then no longer permissible to assume that the time dependence of $\partial H/\partial t$ can be neglected, so that the passage from (35.26) to (35.27) is not justified.

In order to consider this case in a way that permits comparison with the results of perturbation theory, we assume that only a small part of H oscillates in time with an angular frequency ω that is close to $|\omega_{km}|$:

$$H = H_0 + 2H' \sin \omega t \qquad \frac{\partial H}{\partial t} = 2\omega H' \cos \omega t$$

where H' is small compared with H_0 and both are constant in time. If the dependence of a_n, ω_{kn}, and u_n on time is neglected and we put $a_n = \delta_{nm}$ as before, Eq. (35.26) becomes

$$\dot{a}_k \approx \frac{\omega}{\hbar\omega_{km}} \langle k|H'|m \rangle (e^{i(\omega_{km}+\omega)t} + e^{i(\omega_{km}-\omega)t})$$

which is readily integrated to give

$$a_k(t) \approx \frac{\omega\langle k|H'|m\rangle}{i\hbar\omega_{km}} \left(\frac{e^{i(\omega_{km}+\omega)t} - 1}{\omega_{km} + \omega} + \frac{e^{i(\omega_{km}-\omega)t} - 1}{\omega_{km} - \omega} \right) \tag{35.28}$$

Equation (35.28) shows first that the adiabatic approximation breaks down for $\omega_{km} \approx \pm\omega$, since then (35.28) increases steadily with the time. It also shows that the perturbation result (35.11) is reproduced. If ω_{km} is close to $+\omega$, the first term in the parentheses can be neglected and we can replace ω/ω_{km} outside the parentheses by $+1$; if ω_{km} is close to $-\omega$, the second term in the parentheses can be neglected and we can replace ω/ω_{km} by -1.

DISCONTINUOUS CHANGE IN H

As an introduction to the sudden approximation, we consider first a situation in which the hamiltonian changes discontinuously from one form that is constant in time to another. Suppose that $H = H_0$ for $t < 0$ and $H = H_1$ for $t > 0$, where

$$H_0 u_n = E_n u_n \qquad H_1 v_\mu = E_\mu v_\mu$$

and the u's and v's are complete orthonormal sets of functions that are not necessarily discrete. The general solutions can be written

$$\begin{aligned} \psi &= S_n a_n u_n e^{-iE_n t/\hbar} & t &< 0 \\ \psi &= S_\mu b_\mu v_\mu e^{-iE_\mu t/\hbar} & t &> 0 \end{aligned} \tag{35.29}$$

where the a's and b's are independent of the time.

Since the wave equation (35.22) is of first order in the time, the wave function at each point in space must be a continuous function of the time at $t = 0$, although its time derivative is not. The b's are then readily expressed in terms of the a's by equating the two solutions (35.29) at $t = 0$, multiplying by a particular v^*, and integrating over the coordinates:

$$b_\mu = S_n a_n\langle \mu|n\rangle \tag{35.30}$$

If the system is initially in the state m, so that $a_n = \langle n|m\rangle$, Eq. (35.30) tells us that $b_\mu = \langle \mu|m\rangle$, and final states appear that do not have the same energy as the initial state. This is a consequence of the nonzero frequency Fourier components into which the suddenly changing hamiltonian can be resolved.

SUDDEN APPROXIMATION[1]

The sudden approximation consists in using Eq. (35.30) when the change in the hamiltonian occupies a very short but finite interval of time t_0. In order to make an estimate of the error introduced in this way, we

[1] W. Pauli, *Handbuch d. Physik* **24**, part 1, 164 (1933).

consider a problem that, although somewhat artificial, can easily be solved formally. Suppose that $H = H_0$ for $t < 0$, $H = H_1$ for $t > t_0$, and $H = H_i$ for $0 < t < t_0$. The intermediate hamiltonian, which is assumed to be constant in time, has a complete set of energy eigenfunctions:

$$H_i w_\kappa = E_\kappa w_\kappa$$

The true solution can be expanded in terms of the w's with constant coefficients:

$$\psi = S_\kappa c_\kappa w_\kappa e^{-iE_\kappa t/\hbar} \qquad 0 < t < t_0$$

The continuity condition at $t = 0$ gives $c_\kappa = S_n a_n \langle \kappa | n \rangle$, and the continuity condition at $t = t_0$ then gives

$$\begin{aligned} b_\mu &= S_\kappa c_\kappa \langle \mu | \kappa \rangle e^{-i(E_\kappa - E_\mu)t_0/\hbar} \\ &= S_n a_n S_\kappa \langle \mu | \kappa \rangle e^{-i(E_\kappa - E_\mu)t_0/\hbar} \langle \kappa | n \rangle \end{aligned} \qquad (35.31)$$

When $t_0 = 0$, the exponential is equal to unity, and an equation like (23.9′) shows that b_μ is given by (35.30), as it should be.

The sudden approximation is evidently best when t_0 is small. The exponential in (35.31) can then be expanded to give

$$b_\mu \approx S_n a_n S_\kappa \langle \mu | \kappa \rangle \left[1 - \frac{it_0}{\hbar} (E_\kappa - E_\mu) \right] \langle \kappa | n \rangle$$

which can be rewritten as

$$b_\mu \approx S_n a_n \langle \mu | \left[1 - \frac{it_0}{\hbar} (H_i - H_1) \right] | n \rangle \qquad (35.32)$$

by making use of the formalism of Sec. 23. Thus the error in the sudden approximation is proportional to t_0 for small t_0 and can be estimated in simple cases from Eq. (35.32). This equation can be generalized to a situation in which H_i depends on the time; in this case a result that is also correct to first order in t_0 is obtained by replacing $H_i t_0$ by $\int_0^{t_0} H_i \, dt$.

An interesting special case of Eq. (35.32) is that in which the initial and final hamiltonians are the same ($H_1 = H_0$) and the system is initially in a particular state m. We then obtain

$$b_k = \delta_{km} - \frac{it_0}{\hbar} \langle k | (H_i - H_0) | m \rangle$$

This can be used even when $H_i - H_0$ is not small in comparison with H_0, provided that t_0 is sufficiently small. On the other hand, the perturbation theory given earlier in this section is useful when $H_i - H_0 \ll H_0$ and t_0 is large.

DISTURBANCE OF AN OSCILLATOR

As a simple example of the application of the adiabatic and sudden approximations, we consider a linear harmonic oscillator in which the position of the equilibrium point $a(t)$ depends on the time. The hamiltonian for this system is

$$H(t) = -\frac{\hbar^2}{2m}\frac{\partial^2}{\partial x^2} + \tfrac{1}{2}K[x - a(t)]^2$$

The instantaneous energy eigenfunctions are the harmonic-oscillator wave functions (13.13) centered at the point $a(t)$, and the energy levels are unchanged:

$$u_n(x) = N_n H_n[\alpha(x - a)]e^{-\frac{1}{2}\alpha^2(x-a)^2} \qquad E_n = (n + \tfrac{1}{2})\hbar\omega_c$$

We suppose first that the equilibrium point moves slowly, and we investigate the circumstances under which the adiabatic approximation is applicable. If the oscillator is initially in its ground state $(n = 0)$, the time derivative of the hamiltonian $\partial H/\partial t = -K(x - a)\dot{a}$ has a nonvanishing matrix element only with the first excited state. With the help of (13.18) this is found to be

$$\left\langle 1 \left| \frac{\partial H}{\partial t} \right| 0 \right\rangle = -\frac{K\dot{a}}{\alpha\sqrt{2}} = -K\dot{a}\left(\frac{\hbar}{2}\right)^{\frac{1}{2}}(Km)^{-\frac{1}{4}}$$

Substitution into (35.27) shows that the coefficient of the time-dependent factor in the amplitude of the first excited state has the magnitude

$$\frac{K\dot{a}}{\hbar\omega_c^2}\frac{(\hbar/2)^{\frac{1}{2}}}{(Km)^{\frac{1}{4}}} = \frac{\dot{a}}{(2\hbar\omega_c/m)^{\frac{1}{2}}} \tag{35.33}$$

Equation (35.33) may be interpreted physically by noting that the denominator is of the order of the maximum speed of a hypothetical classical oscillator that has the zero-point energy. Thus the adiabatic approximation is good if the equilibrium point moves slowly in comparison with the classical-oscillator speed. It is not difficult to see that, for the nth excited state, the corresponding condition is that the equilibrium-point speed be small in comparison with $1/n$ times the corresponding classical-oscillator speed.

Application of the sudden approximation to an oscillator in its ground state gives for the probability amplitude of the nth state after displacement of the equilibrium point from $x = 0$ to $x = a$

$$\frac{\alpha^{\frac{1}{2}}}{\pi^{\frac{1}{4}}}\int_{-\infty}^{\infty} u_n^*(x - a)e^{-\frac{1}{2}\alpha^2 x^2}\,dx = \frac{\alpha^{\frac{1}{2}}}{\pi^{\frac{1}{4}}}\int_{-\infty}^{\infty} u_n^*(x)e^{-\frac{1}{2}\alpha^2(x+a)^2}\,dx \tag{35.34}$$

This integral is identical with the expression for A_n in Eq. (13.21), except for the sign of a, and has already been evaluated with the help of the generating function (13.10) for the Hermite polynomials. The earlier discussion (Sec. 13) shows that the states most likely to be excited are those that have a classical amplitude of oscillation that is of the order of the displacement a; this is in agreement with the corresponding classical result. Equation (35.32) can then be used to show that the sudden approximation is valid in this case if the time required to move the equilibrium point is small in comparison with $1/n_0$ times the classical-oscillator period, where n_0 is the quantum number of the state most likely to be excited.

PROBLEMS

1. A one-dimensional harmonic oscillator of charge e is perturbed by an electric field of strength E in the positive x direction. Calculate the change in each energy level to second order in the perturbation, and calculate the induced electric dipole moment. Show that this problem can be solved exactly, and compare the result with the perturbation approximation. Repeat the calculation for a three-dimensional isotropic oscillator. Show that, if the polarizability α of the oscillator is defined as the ratio of the induced electric dipole moment to E, the change in energy is exactly $-\frac{1}{2}\alpha\mathsf{E}^2$.

2. A one-dimensional harmonic oscillator is perturbed by an extra potential energy bx^3. Calculate the change in each energy level to second order in the perturbation.

3. Find the first-order Stark effect for a hydrogen atom in the state $n = 3$. Sketch the arrangement of the levels and state the quantum numbers associated with each.

4. A system that has three unperturbed states can be represented by the perturbed hamiltonian matrix

$$\begin{bmatrix} E_1 & 0 & a \\ 0 & E_1 & b \\ a^* & b^* & E_2 \end{bmatrix}$$

where $E_2 > E_1$. The quantities a and b are to be regarded as perturbations that are of the same order and are small compared with $E_2 - E_1$. Use the second-order non-degenerate perturbation theory to calculate the perturbed eigenvalues (is this procedure correct?). Then diagonalize the matrix to find the exact eigenvalues. Finally, use the second-order degenerate perturbation theory. Compare the three results obtained.

5. A trial function ψ differs from an eigenfunction u_E by a small amount, so that $\psi = u_E + \epsilon\psi_1$, where u_E and ψ_1 are normalized and $\epsilon \ll 1$. Show that $\langle H \rangle$ differs from E only by a term of order ϵ^2, and find this term.

6. If the first $n - 1$ eigenfunctions of a particular hamiltonian are known, write a formal expression for a variation-method trial function that could be used to get an upper limit on the nth energy level.

7. Find the next terms (of order R^{-4}) in the expansion of Eq. (32.12). Show that their diagonal matrix element for the unperturbed ground state vanishes, so that there is no inverse fourth-power contribution to the van der Waals interaction.

8. Use the first nonvanishing term in the series (32.13) to get a lower limit for $-W(R)$. Compare with that obtained from the variation calculation.

9. Use the combination of perturbation and variation methods employed in Sec. 32 in connection with the van der Waals interaction to obtain limits on the electric polarizability of a hydrogen atom in its ground state.

10. A particle of mass m is bound by the potential $V(r) = -V_0 e^{-r/a}$, where $\hbar^2/mV_0 a^2 = \frac{3}{4}$. Use the variation method with the trial function $e^{-\alpha r}$ to get a good limit on the lowest energy eigenvalue.

11. A hydrogen atom is placed in a uniform electric field of strength E. Use Eq. (33.6) to calculate the total electric field at the nucleus. Give a qualitative discussion of your answer in physical terms.

12. Make use of Eq. (33.6) to calculate the electric dipole moment induced in a hydrogen atom by a uniform electric field, and then find the polarizability. Show that the polarizability, electric field strength, and energy change are related by Eq. (33.8).

13. A hydrogen atom is placed in an electrostatic potential that has quadrupole symmetry. Make use of Eq. (33.21) to calculate the ratio of the strength of the total quadrupole potential in the infinitesimal neighborhood of the nucleus to the strength of the externally applied quadrupole potential.

14. Denote ψ_s in Eq. (31.2) by $|s\rangle$. Show from Eqs. (31.4) that

$$\langle s|H'|r\rangle = \sum_{q=0}^{s} \sum_{p=0}^{r} W_{q+p+1}\langle s-q|r-p\rangle$$

Use this formula to derive Eq. (33.17). (D. H. Smith, private communication.)

15. Calculate the leading term in the third-order perturbed energy of a hydrogen atom and a point charge Ze at a fixed distance R, for large R.

16. Show that the WKB approximation gives the correct energy eigenvalues for all states of the harmonic oscillator.

17. Apply the WKB method to the one-dimensional motion of a particle of mass m in a potential that equals $-V_0$ at $x = 0$, changes linearly with x until it vanishes at $x = \pm a$, and is zero for $|x| > a$. Find all the bound energy levels obtained in this approximation if $mV_0 a^2/\hbar^2 = 40$.

18. Use the WKB approximation to show that an attractive three-dimensional potential that falls off like r^{-n} for large r has an infinite number of bound states only if $n \leq 2$.

19. A hydrogen atom in its ground state is placed between the plates of a capacitor. field that has the time dependence $\mathsf{E} = 0$ for $t < 0$, $\mathsf{E} = \mathsf{E}_0 e^{-t/\tau}$ for $t > 0$. Find the first-order probability that the atom is in the $2S$ state (200) after a long time. What is the corresponding probability that it is in each of the $2P$ states?

20. Make use of Eq. (35.20) to calculate the total cross section for photoionization of a hydrogen atom by a photon of energy $\hbar\omega$. Show that the photon wavelength is large in comparison with the size of the atom if the photon energy is not much above threshold, so that the assumption of a spatially uniform electric field made in deriving (35.20) is appropriate to the photoionization problem. Show also that the effect of the magnetic field of the light wave can be neglected in comparison with that of the electric field.

21. Explain why Eq. (35.32) does not contain H_0 and H_1 in a symmetrical manner. Show also that $H_i t_0$ can be replaced by $\int_0^{t_0} H_i(t)\, dt$ if H_i depends on t, but only to first order.

22. Show that the remark below Eq. (35.33) about the excitation of the nth state in the adiabatic approximation is correct.

23. Show that the remark below Eq. (35.34) about the validity of the sudden approximation is correct.

24. A hydrogen nucleus of mass 3 is radioactive and changes into a helium nucleus of mass 3 with the emission of an electron that has about 17,000 ev maximum energy. Show that the sudden approximation can be applied to the extranuclear electron initially present in the hydrogen atom and is superior to other approximation methods that might be used. Calculate the numerical values of the probabilities that the resulting helium ion is found in its $1S$, $2S$, and $2P$ states if the hydrogen atom is initially in its $1S$ state. Give a qualitative discussion of the energy balance in this process.

9

Approximation Methods
in Collision Theory

As remarked at the beginning of Chap. 8, there are so few systems of physical interest for which exact solutions can be found that approximation methods play an important part in applications of the theory. Various methods that are useful in scattering problems are considered in this chapter. We start with the development of the scattering matrix; this provides a more general framework, in terms of which collision problems of all kinds may be discussed, than that of Chap. 5. Although not an approximation method in itself, it is a convenient starting point for perturbation and other approximations, some of which are considered later in this chapter.

36□THE SCATTERING MATRIX

The collision theory developed in Chap. 5 assumed that the scattering potential energy is independent of the time and hence was able to make use of energy eigenfunctions. Equation (18.10) describes a situation in which the incident flux is represented by a plane wave of infinite cross section. As pointed out in connection with Fig. 21, this is not realistic since the incident beam is always collimated. However, collimation can be taken into account by superposing infinite plane waves that travel in slightly different directions; their angular spread in direction, measured in radians, is of the order of the ratio of the particle wavelength to the diameter of the collimating aperture. This angle is so small in practical cases that it does not affect the calculation of the scattering amplitude. Another way of describing the situation represented by Fig. 21 is to say that the propagation vector $\mathbf{k}$ has a definite magnitude k given in terms of the energy by $E = \hbar^2 k^2 / 2\mu$ but that its transverse components k_x and k_y are very small in comparison with k; then k_z is practically equal to k, and the "wave packet" is well defined only in the two transverse directions. Since only a single energy E appears, the time-independent Schrödinger equation can be used.

It will also happen that the time-independent model of a constant incident flux and a steady outgoing scattered wave is not appropriate in some circumstances. It certainly cannot be correct when the scattering potential energy V depends on the time, either intrinsically or because it may be convenient to think of V as being "turned on" at one time and "turned off" at a later time. Even when V is constant in time, it may be desirable to replace the incident plane wave with a moving wave packet that is rather well defined in all three spatial directions and gives rise to an outgoing spherical pulse as it passes over the scattering potential. Such a wave packet can be constructed by superposing time-dependent plane waves, in a manner similar to that discussed in the one-dimensional case at the end of Secs. 12 and 17. It then follows from Eq. (12.18) that the spread in each of the three components of $\mathbf{k}$ is of order $1/R$, where R is the size of the wave packet. The corresponding spread in the energy is of order E/kR; although this is very small compared with E in practical cases, the time-dependent Schrödinger equation must still be used.[1]

We start by deriving integral equations for the wave function and for the closely related Green's functions, and we then define the scattering matrix. This matrix describes the asymptotic behavior of the system in the sense that the spatial separation of the interacting parts is so large that interaction can be neglected, or the times are such that interaction has not yet occurred or is no longer occurring. Thus the scattering matrix describes the observable aspects of the scattering process. Since it is obtained by integrating the wave function through the space-time domain of interaction, it contains whatever information resides in the interaction that is relevant to scattering. At the same time, it shows

[1] For a fuller account of the wave-packet approach, see M. L. Goldberger and K. M. Watson, "Collision Theory," chap. 3 (Wiley, New York, 1964); R. G. Newton, "Scattering Theory of Waves and Particles," chap. 6 (McGraw-Hill, New York, 1966).

what limitations are placed on possible scattering processes by the fact that the hamiltonian is physically meaningful or has certain symmetry properties.   When derived from the Schrödinger equation, the scattering matrix evidently contains no more information than the hamiltonian.   It can, however, also give useful results when the interactions that appear in the hamiltonian are not definitely known, as is the case in nuclear physics.

GREEN'S FUNCTIONS AND PROPAGATOR

Even though we shall not be working explicitly with moving wave packets, it is desirable to retain the generality inherent in the time-dependent situation for as long as possible.   We therefore start with the full Schrödinger equation

$$i\hbar \frac{\partial}{\partial t} \psi(\mathbf{r},t) = H\psi(\mathbf{r},t) = [H_0 + V(\mathbf{r},t)]\psi(\mathbf{r},t) \qquad H_0 = -\frac{\hbar^2}{2\mu} \nabla^2$$
$$(36.1)$$

which describes the relative motion of two particles with reduced mass μ. Since Eq. (36.1) gives the first time derivative of ψ in terms of ψ itself and since higher time derivatives do not appear in the equation, the values of ψ for all $\mathbf{r}$ and one particular time t suffice to determine ψ for all $\mathbf{r}$ and all t (both earlier and later).   Also, since the wave equation is linear in ψ, solutions can be superposed and the relation between ψ at different times must be linear.   This means that ψ must satisfy a homogeneous integral equation of the form

$$\psi(\mathbf{r}',t') = i\int G(\mathbf{r}',t';\mathbf{r},t)\psi(\mathbf{r},t)\, d^3r \qquad (36.2)$$

where the integration is over all space.   This equation also serves to define G, which is called the *Green's function* that corresponds to the hamiltonian H.

Equation (36.2) does not make a distinction between forward propagation of ψ in time ($t' > t$), and backward propagation ($t' < t$).   It is sometimes convenient to have a clear separation between these two cases.   For forward propagation we define the *retarded Green's function* or *propagator:*

$$G^+(\mathbf{r}',t';\mathbf{r},t) = G(\mathbf{r}',t';\mathbf{r},t) \qquad \text{for } t' > t$$
$$= 0 \qquad \text{for } t' < t$$
$$(36.3)$$

We also introduce the unit step function $\theta(\tau)$ defined by

$$\theta(\tau) = 1 \qquad \text{for } \tau > 0 \qquad \theta(\tau) = 0 \qquad \text{for } \tau < 0 \qquad (36.4)$$

Then the equation

$$\theta(t' - t)\psi(\mathbf{r}',t') = i\int G^+(\mathbf{r}',t';\mathbf{r},t)\psi(\mathbf{r},t)\,d^3r \qquad (36.5)$$

is the trivial identity $0 = 0$ for $t' < t$ and is the same as (36.2) for $t' > t$.

For backward propagation in time we can similarly define the *advanced Green's function:*

$$
\begin{aligned}
G^-(\mathbf{r}',t';\mathbf{r},t) &= -G(\mathbf{r}',t';\mathbf{r},t) &&\text{for } t' < t \\
&= 0 &&\text{for } t' > t
\end{aligned}
\qquad (36.6)
$$

The equation

$$\theta(t - t')\psi(\mathbf{r}',t') = -i\int G^-(\mathbf{r}',t';\mathbf{r},t)\psi(\mathbf{r},t)\,d^3r \qquad (36.7)$$

is again an identity for $t' > t$ and the same as (36.2) for $t' < t$. Thus Eqs. (36.5) and (36.7) together are equivalent to Eq. (36.2).

The following four integral relations involving $G^{\pm}$ can be obtained from Eqs. (36.5) and (36.7) by making use of the fact that ψ can be chosen arbitrarily at any instant of time (see Prob. 1):

$$
\begin{aligned}
G^+(\mathbf{r}',t';\mathbf{r},t) &= i\int G^+(\mathbf{r}',t';\mathbf{r}_1,t_1)G^+(\mathbf{r}_1,t_1;\mathbf{r},t)\,d^3r_1 &&\text{if } t' > t_1 > t \\
G^-(\mathbf{r}',t';\mathbf{r},t) &= -i\int G^-(\mathbf{r}',t';\mathbf{r}_1,t_1)G^-(\mathbf{r}_1,t_1;\mathbf{r},t)\,d^3r_1 &&\text{if } t' < t_1 < t \\
\delta^3(\mathbf{r} - \mathbf{r}') &= \int G^+(\mathbf{r}',t;\mathbf{r}_1,t_1)G^-(\mathbf{r}_1,t_1;\mathbf{r},t)\,d^3r_1 &&\text{if } t > t_1 \\
\delta^3(\mathbf{r} - \mathbf{r}') &= \int G^-(\mathbf{r}',t;\mathbf{r}_1,t_1)G^+(\mathbf{r}_1,t_1;\mathbf{r},t)\,d^3r_1 &&\text{if } t < t_1
\end{aligned}
\qquad (36.8)
$$

FREE–PARTICLE GREEN'S FUNCTIONS

An explicit expression for the Green's function defined by Eq. (36.2) is readily found for the case in which $V = 0$. We denote it by G_0; it is proportional to the bracket term in Eq. (10.19) in the free-particle case and may be evaluated in analogy with the solution of Prob. 8, Chap. 3. The result is

$$G_0(\mathbf{r}',t';\mathbf{r},t) = -i\left[\frac{\mu}{2\pi i\hbar(t' - t)}\right]^{\frac{3}{2}} \exp\frac{i\mu|\mathbf{r}' - \mathbf{r}|^2}{2\hbar(t' - t)} \qquad (36.9)$$

The corresponding retarded Green's function, or free-particle propagator, is obtained from Eq. (36.3):

$$G_0{}^+(\mathbf{r}',t';\mathbf{r},t) = \theta(t' - t)G_0(\mathbf{r}',t';\mathbf{r},t) \qquad (36.10)$$

The advanced Green's function is similarly obtained from Eq. (36.6):

$$G_0{}^-(\mathbf{r}',t';\mathbf{r},t) = -\theta(t - t')G_0(\mathbf{r}',t';\mathbf{r},t) \qquad (36.11)$$

The validity of Eqs. (36.8) in the free-particle case can then be verified by direct substitution.

It can also be seen from Eqs. (36.9) to (36.11) that there is a complex-conjugate relationship between G_0^+ and G_0^-:

$$G_0^+(\mathbf{r}',t';\mathbf{r},t) = G_0^{-*}(\mathbf{r},t;\mathbf{r}',t') \tag{36.12}$$

We shall see below that this relationship also holds for $G^\pm$ provided that V is real.

INTEGRAL EQUATION FOR ψ

We now obtain an iterated form of the integral equation (36.5) for ψ.[1] We imagine that V is turned off except for a number of very short intervals of time between t and t': from t_1 to $t_1 + \Delta t_1$, from t_2 to $t_2 + \Delta t_2$, etc., and finally from t_n to $t_n + \Delta t_n$, where $t' > t_n > \cdots > t_1 > t$. Then G_0^+ may be used as the propagator from each $t_i + \Delta t_i$ to t_{i+1}:

$$\theta(t_{i+1} - t_i - \Delta t_i)\psi(\mathbf{r}_{i+1}, t_{i+1})$$
$$= i\int G_0^+(\mathbf{r}_{i+1}, t_{i+1}; \mathbf{r}_i, t_i + \Delta t_i)\psi(\mathbf{r}_i, t_i + \Delta t_i)\, d^3r_i \tag{36.13}$$

Propagation from t_i to $t_i + \Delta t_i$ involves both H_0 and V. Since Δt_i will later be regarded as an infinitesimal, the two changes in ψ may be added. The H_0 part involves G_0^+ and may be taken in with (36.13). The V part of the change in ψ is easily obtained from (36.1) and is $-(i/\hbar)V(\mathbf{r}_i,t_i)\psi(\mathbf{r}_i,t_i)\,\Delta t_i$; this should be followed by free-particle propagation from $t_i + \Delta t_i$ to t_{i+1} in accordance with (36.13), but the Δt_i in the argument of G_0^+ can be omitted since we are interested only in quantities of first order in Δt_i. We thus obtain

$$\theta(t_{i+1} - t_i)\psi(\mathbf{r}_{i+1}, t_{i+1})$$
$$= i \int G_0^+(\mathbf{r}_{i+1},t_{i+1};\mathbf{r}_i,t_i) \left[1 - \frac{i}{\hbar} V(\mathbf{r}_i,t_i)\, \Delta t_i \right] \psi(\mathbf{r}_i,t_i)\, d^3r_i \tag{36.14}$$

The resultant propagation from t to t' then gives

$$\theta(t' - t)\psi(\mathbf{r}',t') = \int \cdots \int iG_0^+(\mathbf{r}',t';\mathbf{r}_n,t_n) \left[1 - \frac{i}{\hbar} V(\mathbf{r}_n,t_n)\, \Delta t_n \right]$$
$$iG_0^+(\mathbf{r}_n,t_n;\mathbf{r}_{n-1},t_{n-1}) \cdots iG_0^+(\mathbf{r}_2,t_2;\mathbf{r}_1,t_1) \left[1 - \frac{i}{\hbar} V(\mathbf{r}_1,t_1)\, \Delta t_1 \right]$$
$$iG_0^+(\mathbf{r}_1,t_1;\mathbf{r},t)\psi(\mathbf{r},t)\, d^3r_n \cdots d^3r_1\, d^3r$$

This may be multiplied out and simplified with the help of the first

---

[1] R. P. Feynman, *Phys. Rev.* **76**, 749 (1949); J. D. Bjorken and S. D. Drell, "Relativistic Quantum Mechanics," secs. 6.2, 6.3 (McGraw-Hill, New York, 1964).

of Eqs. (36.8):

$$\theta(t' - t)\psi(\mathbf{r}',t') = i \int G_0^+(\mathbf{r}',t';\mathbf{r},t)\psi(\mathbf{r},t) \, d^3r$$
$$+ \frac{i}{\hbar} \sum_i \iint G_0^+(\mathbf{r}',t';\mathbf{r}_i,t_i) V(\mathbf{r}_i,t_i)\Delta t_i G_0^+(\mathbf{r}_i,t_i;\mathbf{r},t)\psi(\mathbf{r},t) \, d^3r_i \, d^3r$$
$$+ \frac{i}{\hbar^2} \sum_{ij} \iiint G_0^+(\mathbf{r}',t';\mathbf{r}_i,t_i) V(\mathbf{r}_i,t_i)\Delta t_i G_0^+(\mathbf{r}_i,t_i;\mathbf{r}_j,t_j)$$
$$V(\mathbf{r}_j,t_j)\Delta t_j G_0^+(\mathbf{r}_j,t_j;\mathbf{r},t)\psi(\mathbf{r},t) \, d^3r_i \, d^3r_j \, d^3r + \cdots$$

where $t_i > t_j$ in the third term, etc. If now the time intervals Δt_i during which V is turned on become more frequent and of shorter duration until V is on continuously, the summations may be replaced by integrations:

$$\theta(t' - t)\psi(\mathbf{r}',t') = i \int G_0^+(\mathbf{r}',t';\mathbf{r},t)\psi(\mathbf{r},t) \, d^3r$$
$$+ \frac{i}{\hbar} \int dt_i \iint G_0^+(\mathbf{r}',t';\mathbf{r}_i,t_i) V(\mathbf{r}_i,t_i)G_0^+(\mathbf{r}_i,t_i;\mathbf{r},t)\psi(\mathbf{r},t) \, d^3r_i \, d^3r$$
$$+ \frac{i}{\hbar^2} \int dt_i \int dt_j \iiint G_0^+(\mathbf{r}',t';\mathbf{r}_i,t_i) V(\mathbf{r}_i,t_i)G_0^+(\mathbf{r}_i,t_i;\mathbf{r}_j,t_j)$$
$$V(\mathbf{r}_j,t_j)G_0^+(\mathbf{r}_j,t_j;\mathbf{r},t)\psi(\mathbf{r},t) \, d^3r_i \, d^3r_j \, d^3r + \cdots \quad (36.15)$$

Note that all integrations over times may be taken from t to t'; it is not necessary to require that $t_i > t_j$ in the third term, for example, since $G_0^+(\mathbf{r}_i,t_i;\mathbf{r}_j,t_j)$ vanishes unless this is so.

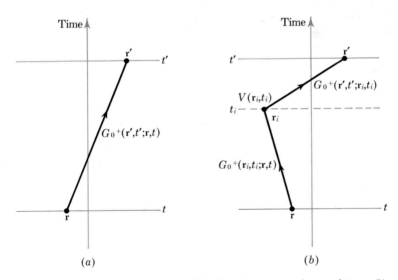

Fig. 33 Schematic representation of the first term (a) and second term (b) on the right side of Eq. (36.15).

It is natural to interpret Eq. (36.15) as a perturbation series, the first two terms of which are indicated schematically in Fig. 33. The first term on the right side represents the amplitude corresponding to free propagation from t to t' (Fig. 33a), the second the sum of all single interactions at t_i with free propagation from t to t_i and from t_i to t' (Fig. 33b), etc. We rewrite Eq. (36.15) for convenience as

$$\theta(t' - t)\psi(\mathbf{r}',t') = i \int G_0^+(\mathbf{r}',t';\mathbf{r},t)\psi(\mathbf{r},t)\ d^3r$$

$$+ \frac{1}{\hbar} \int dt_i \int G_0^+(\mathbf{r}',t';\mathbf{r}_i,t_i) V(\mathbf{r}_i,t_i) \left[i \int G_0^+(\mathbf{r}_i,t_i;\mathbf{r},t)\psi(\mathbf{r},t)\ d^3r \right.$$

$$+ \frac{i}{\hbar} \int dt_j \iint G_0^+(\mathbf{r}_i,t_i;\mathbf{r}_j,t_j) V(\mathbf{r}_j,t_j) G_0^+(\mathbf{r}_j,t_j;\mathbf{r},t)\psi(\mathbf{r},t)\ d^3r_j\ d^3r$$

$$\left. + \cdots \right] d^3r_i$$

If the series in brackets is assumed to converge, then in accordance with Eq. (36.15) it is equal to $\theta(t_i - t)\psi(\mathbf{r}_i,t_i)$ or simply to $\psi(\mathbf{r}_i,t_i)$ since $t_i > t$. We thus obtain an integral equation for ψ that, unlike (36.5), involves only G_0^+ and not G^+:

$$\theta(t' - t)\psi(\mathbf{r}',t') = i \int G_0^+(\mathbf{r}',t';\mathbf{r},t)\psi(\mathbf{r},t)\ d^3r$$

$$+ \frac{1}{\hbar} \int dt_i \int G_0^+(\mathbf{r}',t';\mathbf{r}_i,t_i) V(\mathbf{r}_i,t_i)\psi(\mathbf{r}_i,t_i)\ d^3r_i \quad (36.16)$$

The integration over t_i is from t to t'.

INTEGRAL EQUATION FOR THE PROPAGATOR

Comparison of Eqs. (36.5) and (36.15) shows that

$$G^+(\mathbf{r}',t';\mathbf{r},t) = G_0^+(\mathbf{r}',t';\mathbf{r},t)$$

$$+ \frac{1}{\hbar} \iint G_0^+(\mathbf{r}',t';\mathbf{r}_i,t_i) V(\mathbf{r}_i,t_i) G_0^+(\mathbf{r}_i,t_i;\mathbf{r},t)\ dt_i\ d^3r_i$$

$$+ \frac{1}{\hbar^2} \iiiint G_0^+(\mathbf{r}',t';\mathbf{r}_i,t_i) V(\mathbf{r}_i,t_i) G_0^+(\mathbf{r}_i,t_i;\mathbf{r}_j,t_j)$$

$$V(\mathbf{r}_j,t_j) G_0^+(\mathbf{r}_j,t_j;\mathbf{r},t)\ dt_i\ d^3r_i\ dt_j\ d^3r_j + \cdots \quad (36.17)$$

Again, if this series is assumed to converge, it may be summed to give the equation

$$G^+(\mathbf{r}',t';\mathbf{r},t) = G_0^+(\mathbf{r}',t';\mathbf{r},t)$$

$$+ \frac{1}{\hbar} \iint G_0^+(\mathbf{r}',t';\mathbf{r}_i,t_i) V(\mathbf{r}_i,t_i) G^+(\mathbf{r}_i,t_i;\mathbf{r},t)\ dt_i\ d^3r_i \quad (36.18)$$

USE OF THE ADVANCED GREEN'S FUNCTION

The results of the two preceding subsections can be cast in terms of advanced rather than retarded Green's functions and are given here for completeness even though they are not as useful as the propagator equations obtained above.

We now have that $t' < t$ and therefore we start by imagining that V is turned off except for the intervals from $t_n - \Delta t_n$ to t_n, from $t_{n-1} - \Delta t_{n-1}$ to t_{n-1}, etc., and finally from $t_1 - \Delta t_1$ to t_1, where $t' < t_n < \cdots < t_1 < t$. Then the basic equation (36.14) for forward propagation is replaced by the following equation for backward propagation in time:

$$\theta(t_i - t_{i+1})\psi(\mathbf{r}_{i+1}, t_{i+1})$$

$$= -i \int G_0{}^-(\mathbf{r}_{i+1}, t_{i+1}; \mathbf{r}_i, t_i) \left[1 + \frac{i}{\hbar} V(\mathbf{r}_i, t_i)\, \Delta t_i \right] \psi(\mathbf{r}_i, t_i)\, d^3 r_i \quad (36.19)$$

As compared with (36.14), the minus sign in front of the right side of (36.19) arises from the minus sign in (36.6) or (36.7), and the plus sign in the brackets appears because the change in ψ is calculated from t_i to $t_i - \Delta t_i$ rather than from t_i to $t_i + \Delta t_i$.

It is now apparent that Eqs. (36.15) and (36.16) can be rewritten correctly by making the following substitutions:

$$\theta(t' - t) \to \theta(t - t') \qquad G_0{}^+(\mathbf{r}', t'; \mathbf{r}, t) \to G_0{}^-(\mathbf{r}', t'; \mathbf{r}, t) \qquad i \to -i$$

$$(36.20)$$

In similar fashion, Eqs. (36.17) and (36.18) may be rewritten correctly by making the substitutions:

$$G_0{}^+(\mathbf{r}', t'; \mathbf{r}, t) \to G_0{}^-(\mathbf{r}', t'; \mathbf{r}, t) \qquad G^+(\mathbf{r}', t'; \mathbf{r}, t) \to G^-(\mathbf{r}', t'; \mathbf{r}, t) \quad (36.21)$$

In all the rewritten equations, all time integrations are from t' to t.

Equation (36.17), which expresses G^+ in terms of $G_0{}^+$, and the corresponding rewritten equation, which expresses G^- in terms of $G_0{}^-$, can now be used, with the help of (36.12), to show that

$$G^+(\mathbf{r}', t'; \mathbf{r}, t) = G^{-*}(\mathbf{r}, t; \mathbf{r}', t') \tag{36.22}$$

provided that V is real.

DIFFERENTIAL EQUATION FOR THE GREEN'S FUNCTIONS

Thus far we have used the differential equation (36.1) for ψ to construct the integral equations (36.2), (36.15), and (36.16) for ψ, and the corresponding integral equations (36.17) and (36.18) for $G^{\pm}$. The Green's functions also satisfy a differential equation analogous to (36.1); this equation is expected to be inhomogeneous since $G^{\pm}(\mathbf{r}', t'; \mathbf{r}, t)$ is, in effect, the wave function at $\mathbf{r}', t'$ that is generated by a momentary point source at $\mathbf{r}, t$.

We can find this equation for G^+ by operating on Eq. (36.5) with

$i(\partial/\partial t') - (1/\hbar)H'$, where H' is H expressed in terms of the primed variables $\mathbf{r}'$, t'. It is necessary to make use of the relation

$$\frac{d}{d\tau}\,\theta(\tau) = \delta(\tau) \tag{36.23}$$

which follows from (36.4).   The result is

$$i\delta(t' - t)\psi(\mathbf{r}',t') = i \int \left(i\frac{\partial}{\partial t'} - \frac{1}{\hbar}H'\right)G^+(\mathbf{r}',t';\mathbf{r},t)\psi(\mathbf{r},t)\,d^3r$$

where use has been made of Eq. (36.1).   This equation shows that the
right side must be proportional to $\delta(t' - t)$, so that only $\psi(\mathbf{r},t')$ can appear
in the integrand of the right side.   But since $\psi(\mathbf{r},t')$ can be an arbitrary
function of $\mathbf{r}$ at any particular time t', the rest of the integrand of the
right side must be proportional to $\delta^3(\mathbf{r}' - \mathbf{r})$.   We thus conclude that

$$\left(i\frac{\partial}{\partial t'} - \frac{1}{\hbar}H'\right)G^+(\mathbf{r}',t';\mathbf{r},t) = \delta^3(\mathbf{r}' - \mathbf{r})\,\delta(t' - t) \tag{36.24}$$

It is easily seen that, if in the preceding paragraph we had started
with Eq. (36.7), we would have found that G^- also satisfies (36.24).   Thus
G^+ and G^- satisfy the same inhomogeneous differential equation but of
course differ in their boundary conditions. $G^+(\mathbf{r}',t';\mathbf{r},t)$ is the solution of
Eq. (36.24) that is zero for $t' < t$, and $G^-(\mathbf{r}',t';\mathbf{r},t)$ is the solution that is
zero for $t' > t$.

SYMBOLIC RELATIONS

The integral and differential equations for the Green's functions, obtained
in the three preceding subsections, can be written in a symbolic form that
is instructive.   Equation (36.17) and the corresponding equation for G^-
may be written

$$G^\pm = G_0^\pm + \hbar^{-1}G_0^\pm VG_0^\pm + \hbar^{-2}G_0^\pm VG_0^\pm VG_0^\pm + \cdots \tag{36.25}$$

In similar fashion, we may write Eq. (36.18) in the form

$$G^\pm = G_0^\pm + \hbar^{-1}G_0^\pm VG^\pm \tag{36.26}$$

Again, the differential equation (36.24) and the corresponding equation
for G^- may be written

$$\left(i\frac{\partial}{\partial t} - \frac{1}{\hbar}H\right)G^\pm = 1 \tag{36.27}$$

where the primes have been dropped.   On omitting the V term in H, we
obtain in place of Eq. (36.27)

$$\left(i\frac{\partial}{\partial t} - \frac{1}{\hbar}H_0\right)G_0^\pm = 1 \tag{36.28}$$

Various checks can be made on the consistency of the last four equations. If we symbolically multiply both sides of Eq. (36.26) from the left with $i(\partial/\partial t) - (1/\hbar)H_0$, we obtain

$$\left(i\frac{\partial}{\partial t} - \frac{1}{\hbar}H_0 \right)G^\pm = \left(i\frac{\partial}{\partial t} - \frac{1}{\hbar}H_0 \right)G_0^\pm \left(1 + \frac{1}{\hbar}VG^\pm \right) = 1 + \frac{1}{\hbar}VG^\pm$$

where use has been made of (36.28); the result agrees with (36.27). As another consistency check, Eq. (36.26) may be written as

$$(1 - \hbar^{-1}G_0^\pm V)G^\pm = G_0^\pm$$

or as

$$G^\pm = (1 - \hbar^{-1}G_0^\pm V)^{-1}G_0^\pm \tag{36.29}$$

A formal expansion of the inverse operator into a power series gives

$$G^\pm = (1 + \hbar^{-1}G_0^\pm V + \hbar^{-2}G_0^\pm VG_0^\pm V + \cdots)G_0^\pm$$

which is the same as (36.25). This successful use of an inverse operator suggests that Eqs. (36.27) and (36.28) may be written symbolically as

$$G^\pm = \left(i\frac{\partial}{\partial t} - \frac{1}{\hbar}H \right)^{-1} \qquad \text{and} \qquad G_0^\pm = \left(i\frac{\partial}{\partial t} - \frac{1}{\hbar}H_0 \right)^{-1} \tag{36.30}$$

respectively.

Although such symbolic manipulations are often of heuristic value in suggesting new relationships, they cannot always be regarded as derivations or proofs of such relations. In particular, inverse operators of the type that appear in Eqs. (36.29) and (36.30) are often singular, and special care must be taken in the interpretation of the singularity. As an example of this, we note that both the retarded and advanced Green's functions are given by the same symbolic expressions in (36.30). We shall see in Sec. 37 that a suitable treatment of the singularity in the inverse operator serves to provide the boundary condition that distinguishes between forward and backward propagation in time.

APPLICATION TO SCATTERING

The formalism developed thus far can now be applied to a scattering situation. We imagine that V is not effective in the remote past or the far future, so that H can be replaced by H_0 for $t < -T_1$ and $t > T_2$, where T_1 and T_2 are large but finite times. This may be because V was turned on at one time and turned off at a later time or because the initial and final states consist of wave packets that lie outside of the scattering potential. We call the free-particle wave functions $\phi_\alpha(\mathbf{r},t)$; they satisfy Eq. (36.1) with V set equal to zero. The ϕ_α constitute a complete set of functions at each instant of time and are, for convenience, chosen to be orthonormal; it is shown in Prob. 3 that orthogonality is preserved in time.   Associated with each ϕ_α is a wave function $\psi_\alpha^+(\mathbf{r},t)$ that grows out of ϕ_α starting from a time in the remote past $(t < -T_1)$ before V was effective.   Since ψ_α^+ satisfies Eq. (36.1), it can be written, in accordance with Eq. (36.5), in the form

$$\psi_\alpha^+(\mathbf{r}',t') = i\int G^+(\mathbf{r}',t';\mathbf{r},t)\phi_\alpha(\mathbf{r},t)\, d^3r \qquad t < -T_1 \qquad (36.31)$$

where $\theta(t' - t)$ may now be omitted.   This ψ_α^+ is independent of the precise value chosen for t so long as it is less than $-T_1$.

At some time in the far future $(t > T_2)$, when V is again ineffective, ψ_α^+ is a solution of the free-particle Schrödinger equation and hence must be expressible as a generalized summation over the ϕ_β with constant coefficients.   Then the quantity

$$\langle\beta|S|\alpha\rangle \equiv (\phi_\beta,\psi_\alpha^+) \qquad t' > T_2 \qquad (36.32)$$

is the amplitude of the free-particle state β that is contained, after the scattering has taken place, in the state that grew out of what was the free-particle state α before the scattering took place.   Again, it is independent of the precise value chosen for t' so long as it is greater than T_2.   Equation (36.32) is the amplitude for the transition from α to β and defines an element of the *scattering matrix* or *S matrix*.[1]

Substitution of (36.31) into (36.32) gives a more symmetrical form for the S matrix element:

$$\langle\beta|S|\alpha\rangle = i\int\int\phi_\beta^*(\mathbf{r}',t')G^+(\mathbf{r}',t';\mathbf{r},t)\phi_\alpha(\mathbf{r},t)\, d^3r'\, d^3r$$
$$t < -T_1 \qquad t' > T_2 \quad (36.33)$$

Other forms can be obtained by making use of the following equation, which can be obtained from the complex conjugate of the free-particle version of Eq. (36.7) together with (36.12):

$$\theta(t - t')\phi_\beta^*(\mathbf{r}',t') = i\int G_0^{-*}(\mathbf{r}',t';\mathbf{r},t)\phi_\beta^*(\mathbf{r},t)\, d^3r$$
$$= i\int\phi_\beta^*(\mathbf{r},t)G_0^+(\mathbf{r},t;\mathbf{r}',t')\, d^3r \qquad (36.34)$$

Thus substitution of G^+ from (36.17) into (36.33), and use of (36.5) and (36.34), lead to

$$\langle\beta|S|\alpha\rangle = \langle\beta|\alpha\rangle - \frac{i}{\hbar}\iint \phi_\beta^*(\mathbf{r},t)V(\mathbf{r},t)\phi_\alpha(\mathbf{r},t)\, dt\, d^3r$$
$$- \frac{i}{\hbar^2}\iiiint \phi_\beta^*(\mathbf{r}',t')V(\mathbf{r}',t')G_0^+(\mathbf{r}',t';\mathbf{r},t)V(\mathbf{r},t)\phi_\alpha(\mathbf{r},t)\, dt'\, d^3r'\, dt\, d^3r$$
$$- \cdots \quad (36.35)$$

[1] J. A. Wheeler, *Phys. Rev.* **52**, 1107 (1937); W. Heisenberg, *Z. Naturforsch.* **1**, 608 (1946); C. Møller, *Kgl. Danske Videnskab. Selskab, Mat.-Fys. Medd.* **23**, 1 (1948).

where $\langle\beta|\alpha\rangle \equiv \int\phi_\beta^*(\mathbf{r},t)\phi_\alpha(\mathbf{r},t)\,d^3r$ and is independent of t. Similar substitution of G^+ from Eq. (36.18) gives

$$\langle\beta|S|\alpha\rangle = \langle\beta|\alpha\rangle - \frac{i}{\hbar}\iint \phi_\beta^*(\mathbf{r},t)V(\mathbf{r},t)\psi_\alpha^+(\mathbf{r},t)\,dt\,d^3r \qquad (36.36)$$

Each of the time integrations in Eqs. (36.35) and (36.36) extends at least from $-T_1$ to T_2 and thus includes the entire interval during which V is effective.

Expressions for the S matrix element similar to the above can be obtained by using the advanced Green's functions G_0^- and G^-. For example, associated with each ϕ_β there is a wave function $\psi_\beta^-(\mathbf{r},t)$ that grows into ϕ_β at some time in the far future $(t > T_2)$ after V has ceased to be effective. It may be written, by using Eq. (36.7) with primed and unprimed variables interchanged, in the form

$$\psi_\beta^-(\mathbf{r},t) = -i\int G^-(\mathbf{r},t;\mathbf{r}',t')\phi_\beta(\mathbf{r}',t')\,d^3r' \qquad t' > T_2 \qquad (36.37)$$

We might then expect that the S matrix element for the transition from α to β is given by the inner product of ψ_β^- and ϕ_α evaluated at a time in the remote past $(t < -T_1)$:

$$(\psi_\beta^-,\phi_\alpha) = i\iint G^{-*}(\mathbf{r},t;\mathbf{r}',t')\phi_\beta^*(\mathbf{r}',t')\phi_\alpha(\mathbf{r},t)\,d^3r'\,d^3r$$
$$t < -T_1 \qquad t' > T_2 \qquad (36.38)$$

Equation (36.22) shows that (36.38) is indeed the same as $\langle\beta|S|\alpha\rangle$ given by (36.33), provided that H is hermitian or V is real. The discrepancy when V is complex is physically plausible, since we saw in Eq. (20.2) that an absorptive potential (imaginary part of V negative) causes the total probability associated with a state to decrease as time increases. This means that $\psi_\alpha^+(\mathbf{r}',t')$ is generally smaller for $t' > T_2$ than the ϕ_α out of which it grows, whereas $\psi_\beta^-(\mathbf{r},t)$ is generally larger for $t < -T_1$ than the ϕ_β into which it grows. Thus (36.38) is expected to be larger than (36.32) if V is absorptive.

UNITARITY OF THE S MATRIX

An important property of the S matrix is that it is unitary if the hamiltonian is hermitian. In order to prove this, we must show that $SS^\dagger = 1$ and that $S^\dagger S = 1$. Any of the forms for $\langle\beta|S|\alpha\rangle$ obtained above, or the corresponding expressions containing advanced Green's functions or wave functions, can be used for this purpose. With the form (36.33), a typical matrix element of $SS^\dagger$ is

$$\langle\beta|SS^\dagger|\alpha\rangle = S_\gamma\langle\beta|S|\gamma\rangle\langle\gamma|S^\dagger|\alpha\rangle = S_\gamma\langle\beta|S|\gamma\rangle\langle\alpha|S|\gamma\rangle^*$$
$$= S_\gamma\iint\phi_\beta^*(\mathbf{r}',t')G^+(\mathbf{r}',t';\mathbf{r},t)\phi_\gamma(\mathbf{r},t)\,d^3r'\,d^3r$$
$$\iint\phi_\alpha(\mathbf{r}'',t')G^{+*}(\mathbf{r}'',t';\mathbf{r}''',t)\phi_\gamma^*(\mathbf{r}''',t)\,d^3r''\,d^3r'''$$
$$t < -T_1 \qquad t' > T_2$$

It is convenient to use the same times t and t' in the matrix elements of both S and $S^\dagger$, and it is permissible since (36.33) is independent of these times so long as V is not effective. Then since the ϕ's are complete and orthonormal, the summation over γ introduces $\delta^3(\mathbf{r} - \mathbf{r}''')$ in place of $\phi_\gamma \phi_\gamma^*$, and we have

$$\langle\beta|SS^\dagger|\alpha\rangle = \iiint \phi_\beta^*(\mathbf{r}',t') G^+(\mathbf{r}',t';\mathbf{r},t) G^-(\mathbf{r},t;\mathbf{r}'',t') \phi_\alpha(\mathbf{r}'',t')\, d^3r'\, d^3r\, d^3r''$$

where use has been made of Eq. (36.22). The third of Eqs. (36.8) then shows that the integral of the product of the two Green's functions over d^3r gives $\delta^3(\mathbf{r}' - \mathbf{r}'')$, so that the right side is simply $\langle\beta|\alpha\rangle$. That $S^\dagger S = 1$ is proved in similar fashion.[1]

SYMMETRY PROPERTIES OF THE S MATRIX

It is expected that the S matrix will possess symmetries that reflect the symmetries of the underlying hamiltonian. In order to see that this is the case, we consider first one of the symmetry operations discussed in Chap. 7 that can be represented by a unitary operator (space or time displacement, rotation, or space inversion). Any such operator U will transform a free-particle state ϕ_β into another state $\phi_{\beta'} = U\phi_\beta$ that represents a possible free motion of the system, since U commutes with H_0. If in addition U commutes with H, it will transform ψ_α^+ into a state $\psi_{\alpha'}^+ = U\psi_\alpha^+$ that also represents a possible motion of the system in the presence of the interaction V. Thus the S matrix element between transformed states, given by Eq. (36.32), is

$$\begin{aligned}
\langle\beta'|S|\alpha'\rangle &= (\phi_{\beta'}, \psi_{\alpha'}^+) = (U\phi_\beta, U\psi_\alpha^+) \\
&= (\phi_\beta, U^\dagger U\psi_\alpha^+) = (\phi_\beta, \psi_\alpha^+) = \langle\beta|S|\alpha\rangle
\end{aligned} \tag{36.39}$$

all evaluated for $t' > T_2$. For example, the amplitude for scattering between any pair of states caused by a spherically symmetric potential is numerically equal to the amplitude for scattering between those states

---

[1] The proof given here for the unitarity of S is satisfactory since V is turned on and off at finite times in the past and future. The situation is more complicated if V is strictly constant in time, and it becomes ineffective in the remote past and far future because the initial and final states consist of wave packets that lie outside the range of V. One complicating factor is that H may possess bound states, and it can then be shown that the wave-packet states are orthogonal to these bound states and hence do not form a complete set. Nevertheless, S is still unitary if V is real, since energy conservation prevents the bound states from becoming occupied. For further discussion, see C. Møller, *loc. cit.*; F. E. Low, in "Lecture Notes of Brandeis University 1959 Summer Institute in Theoretical Physics"; W. Brenig and R. Haag, *Fortschr. Physik* **7**, 183 (1959), Sec. 1, English translation published in M. Ross (ed.), "Quantum Scattering Theory," (Indiana University Press, Bloomington, Ind., 1963); Goldberger and Watson, *loc. cit.*; Newton, *loc. cit.*

that are obtained by rotating the two members of the original pair in the same way.

The left side of Eq. (36.39) may also be written $\langle\beta|U^\dagger SU|\alpha\rangle$. Then since the kets $|\alpha\rangle$ and $|\beta\rangle$ are arbitrary, we conclude that

$$U^\dagger SU = S \qquad \text{or} \qquad [U,S] = 0 \tag{36.40}$$

Thus if U commutes with H, it also commutes with the operator S.

For the antiunitary operation of time reversal, discussed in Sec. 29, the situation is somewhat more complicated. The time-reversal operator T transforms a free-particle state ϕ_β into another state that corresponds to reversed linear and angular momenta; we therefore denote it schematically by $\phi_{-\beta}$. However, in accordance with the discussion of Eq. (29.12), operation with T also reverses the sense of progression of time, so that

$$T\phi_\beta(t) = \phi_{-\beta}(-t) \tag{36.41}$$

For example, if $\phi_\beta(t) = C \exp i(\mathbf{k}_\beta \cdot \mathbf{r} - \omega_\beta t)$ for a spinless particle, then Eqs. (36.41) and (29.13) tell us that $\phi_{-\beta}(t) = C^* \exp i(-\mathbf{k}_\beta \cdot \mathbf{r} - \omega_\beta t)$, as expected.

Suppose now that T commutes with H, so that the interacting system is time-reversal invariant. The simplest situation is that in which V is constant in time except for being turned on and off in a symmetrical manner at $t = \pm T_0$. Then T will transform ψ_α^+ into a state that also represents a possible motion of the system. This state will not only have reversed linear and angular momenta but will also grow into $\phi_{-\alpha}$ in the far future rather than growing out of $\phi_{-\alpha}$ from the remote past; we therefore denote it by $\psi_{-\alpha}^-$. Again, operation with T reverses the sense of progression of time, so that the analog of (36.41) is

$$T\psi_\alpha^+(t) = \psi_{-\alpha}^-(-t) \tag{36.42}$$

For a system that is time-reversal invariant, so that H is hermitian or V is real, the discussion of Eq. (36.38) shows that an S matrix element can be written in the form

$$\langle-\alpha|S|-\beta\rangle = (\psi_{-\alpha}^-(t),\phi_{-\beta}(t))_{t<-T_0} = (\psi_{-\alpha}^-(-t),\phi_{-\beta}(-t))_{t>T_0}$$

We now substitute into this from (36.41) and (36.42) and make use of Eq. (29.13):

$$\begin{aligned}
\langle-\alpha|S|-\beta\rangle &= (T\psi_\alpha^+(t),T\phi_\beta(t)) = (UK\psi_\alpha^+(t),UK\phi_\beta(t)) \\
&= (K\psi_\alpha^+(t),K\phi_\beta(t)) = (\phi_\beta(t),\psi_\alpha^+(t)) \\
&= \langle\beta|S|\alpha\rangle
\end{aligned} \tag{36.43}$$

all evaluated for $t > T_0$. Equation (36.43) shows that the amplitude for scattering from an initial state α to a final state β is numerically equal to the amplitude for scattering from the momentum-reversed final state $-\beta$ to the momentum-reversed initial state $-\alpha$, if the system is time-reversal invariant. This is the reciprocity theorem [Eq. (20.16)] which was shown in Sec. 20 to be valid even when V is complex.

37□STATIONARY COLLISION THEORY

The S matrix theory developed in the preceding section includes the possibility of an arbitrary variation of H with time, subject only to the restriction that free-particle states can be defined for finite times in the remote past and the far future. Although it is interesting to have such a comprehensive formalism available in order to show that any scattering problem can be formulated in principle, useful results are generally obtainable only in special cases. The situation of greatest physical interest is that in which V is independent of the time, except for being turned on at one time and off at a later time.

We first consider this stationary situation by imagining that V is effective for a very long but finite time t_0. A particular S matrix element can then be related to a transition probability per unit time, in much the same way as in the time-dependent perturbation theory developed in Sec. 35, although without the restriction to the case in which V is a small perturbation. We then go a step further and relate this transition probability to a scattering cross section. Following this we develop an alternative procedure for the limit in which t_0 is infinite, so that the situation is strictly stationary. In this case it is not meaningful to think in terms of a transition probability; rather, we shall obtain the scattering amplitude and cross section directly.

TRANSITION MATRIX

The initial and final free-particle states ϕ_α and ϕ_β, in terms of which the S matrix element $\langle \beta | S | \alpha \rangle$ is specified, can be chosen to have well-defined energies. We shall suppose that the times during which V is being turned on and being turned off are of order Δt and that, in between, V is constant for a time t_0 that is much longer than Δt. This means that $V(\mathbf{r},t)$ is replaced by $V(\mathbf{r})g(t)$, where $g(t)$ has the general form shown in Fig. 34. Then the time Fourier transform of Vg contains frequencies that lie in a range of order $1/\Delta t$ about zero. It follows from (36.36) that $\langle \beta | (S - 1) | \alpha \rangle$ is very small unless the energy associated with $\psi_\alpha{}^+$ is in a range of order $\hbar/\Delta t$ about the energy associated with ϕ_β. We shall assume that Δt can be made large enough so that this energy range is experimentally unobservable. We shall also assume that t_0 can be made so large in comparison with Δt that the uncertainty in the effective on time of V is

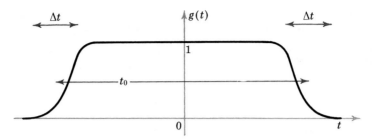

Fig. 34 Schematic plot of the function $g(t)$ that determines the time dependence of V.

unimportant. This means that V can be on for a well-defined time while energy is substantially conserved during the scattering process.

With this physical situation in mind, we put

$$\phi_\alpha(\mathbf{r},t) = u_\alpha(\mathbf{r})e^{-i\omega_\alpha t} \qquad (H_0 - E_\alpha)u_\alpha(\mathbf{r}) = 0$$
$$\psi_\alpha^+(\mathbf{r},t) = \chi_\alpha^+(\mathbf{r})e^{-i\omega_\alpha t} \qquad (H - E_\alpha)\chi_\alpha^+(\mathbf{r}) = 0 \tag{37.1}$$

where $E_\alpha = \hbar\omega_\alpha$ and $V(\mathbf{r},t)$ can be replaced by $V(\mathbf{r})g(t)$. We then make use of Eq. (36.36) to define an element of the *transition matrix* or T *matrix* through

$$\langle\beta|(S-1)|\alpha\rangle = -\frac{i}{\hbar}\langle\beta|T|\alpha\rangle\int_{-\infty}^{\infty}g(t)e^{i\omega_{\beta\alpha}t}\,dt \tag{37.2}$$
$$\langle\beta|T|\alpha\rangle \equiv \int u_\beta^*(\mathbf{r})V(\mathbf{r})\chi_\alpha^+(\mathbf{r})\,d^3r \qquad \omega_{\beta\alpha} \equiv \omega_\beta - \omega_\alpha$$

TRANSITION PROBABILITY

The definition of the scattering matrix [Eq. (36.32)] shows that $|\langle\beta|S|\alpha\rangle|^2$ is the probability that a system originally in the state α is finally found to be in the state β. So long as α and β are different states, this is equal to $|\langle\beta|(S-1)|\alpha\rangle|^2$, and we can use Eq. (37.2) to calculate the transition probability. If now we were to assume that $\Delta t = 0$ in Fig. 34, the situation would be similar to that described in connection with Eq. (35.12) and Fig. 31. In order to avoid this, we shall not assume such a square form for $g(t)$.

The initial and final states in a scattering problem are continuously distributed, or nearly so if box normalization is used. Thus there is always a group of final states β that have nearly the same energy and for which $\langle\beta|T|\alpha\rangle$ is roughly independent of β. Such a group of states will also have nearly the same values for all the other parameters, besides the energy, that specify the states. For example, if the final states are momentum eigenfunctions, the states β will be characterized by a small range of direction of the momentum vector as well as of its magnitude. We write the number of these states as $\rho(\beta)\,dE_\beta$, where dE_β is the energy range and $\rho(\beta)$ is evidently a differential in the other parameters. Then the total probability of finding the system in one or another of this group of final states is a summation of $|\langle\beta|(S-1)|\alpha\rangle|^2$:

$$\int |\langle\beta|(S-1)|\alpha\rangle|^2\rho(\beta)\,dE_\beta$$
$$= \hbar^{-2}\int |\langle\beta|T|\alpha\rangle|^2 \left| \int_{-\infty}^{\infty} g(t)e^{i\omega_{\beta\alpha}t}\,dt \right|^2 \rho(\beta)\hbar\,d\omega_{\beta\alpha}$$

where we have replaced dE_β by $\hbar\,d\omega_{\beta\alpha}$ since ω_α is constant. Now the Fourier transform of $g(t)$ is strongly peaked at $\omega_{\beta\alpha} = 0$, so that we can remove $\rho(\beta)|\langle\beta|T|\alpha\rangle|^2$ from inside the integral over $\omega_{\beta\alpha}$ and extend the limits to $\pm\infty$. Then

$$\int_{-\infty}^{\infty} \left| \int_{-\infty}^{\infty} g(t)e^{i\omega_{\beta\alpha}t}\,dt \right|^2 d\omega_{\beta\alpha} = 2\pi \int_{-\infty}^{\infty} |g(t)|^2\,dt$$

and this is essentially equal to $2\pi t_0$ if $g(t)$ has the form shown in Fig. 34. The transition probability per unit time is then given by

$$w \equiv \frac{1}{t_0}\int |\langle\beta|(S-1)|\alpha\rangle|^2\rho(\beta)\,dE_\beta = \frac{2\pi}{\hbar}\rho(\beta)|\langle\beta|T|\alpha\rangle|^2 \qquad (37.3)$$

Equation (37.3) is exact. Comparison of the second term on the right side of Eq. (36.35) with the corresponding term of (36.36) shows that a perturbation approximation to (37.3) is obtained by replacing χ_α^+ by u_α in (37.2). This replacement gives Fermi's "Golden Rule No. 2."[1]

SCATTERING CROSS SECTION

An expression for the differential scattering cross section is most conveniently obtained from Eq. (37.3) by using box normalization. We choose the u_β to be the momentum eigenfunctions

$$u_\beta(\mathbf{r}) = L^{-\frac{3}{2}}\exp{(i\mathbf{k}_\beta\cdot\mathbf{r})}$$

in which case $\rho(\beta)$ is given by Eq. (35.18):

$$\rho(\beta) = \frac{\mu L^3}{8\pi^3\hbar^2}k_\beta\,d\Omega_\beta \qquad (37.4)$$

where $d\Omega_\beta$ is the infinitesimal element of solid angle associated with the direction of $\mathbf{k}_\beta$.

The value of w obtained by substitution of (37.4) into (37.3) is the number of scatterings into $d\Omega_\beta$ per unit time when there is initially one system in the volume L^3. This is an incident flux of v_α/L^3 per unit area

---

[1] E. Fermi, "Nuclear Physics," p. 142 (University of Chicago Press, Chicago, 1950); see also Eq. (35.14).

and time, where v_α is the relative initial speed. Since the differential scattering cross section is defined as the scattering per unit incident flux, we have

$$\sigma(\mathbf{k}_\beta,\mathbf{k}_\alpha)\ d\Omega_\beta = \frac{w}{v_\alpha/L^3}$$

so that

$$\sigma(\mathbf{k}_\beta,\mathbf{k}_\alpha) = \frac{v_\beta}{v_\alpha}\left(\frac{\mu L^3}{2\pi\hbar^2}\right)^2 |\langle\beta|T|\alpha\rangle|^2 \tag{37.5}$$

where we have replaced k_β by $\mu v_\beta/\hbar$. In the case of elastic scattering now under consideration, energy is conserved and $v_\beta = v_\alpha$.

The wave functions u_β and χ_α^+ that appear in the T matrix element (37.2) are each normalized to one system in the volume L^3, so that $\langle\beta|T|\alpha\rangle$ is proportional to $1/L^3$. Thus the differential cross section is independent of L, as of course it must be. It is also worth noting that the total transition probability wt_0, where w is given by (37.3), is proportional to t_0/L^3. Since the use of box normalization implies that the limit $L \to \infty$ will ultimately be taken, the apparent difficulty associated with the fact that the probability wt_0 can be greater than unity if t_0 is made sufficiently large does not in fact arise. This probability actually becomes vanishingly small for any finite value of t_0 as $L \to \infty$.

GREEN'S FUNCTIONS FOR STATIONARY CASE

We now develop an alternative procedure that is applicable in the limit in which t_0 is infinite, so that the situation is strictly stationary and energy is strictly conserved. It is necessary to assume that the S-matrix formalism developed in Sec. 36 remains valid in this limit; this can be shown along the lines of the wave-packet approach referred to in the footnote near the end of that section. We cannot now think in terms of a transition probability per unit time but instead obtain the scattering amplitude and cross section directly. This strictly stationary situation is most easily and most directly approached by starting with the time-independent Schrödinger equation. Although we shall follow this procedure a little later, we first devote this and the next subsection to a treatment that starts from the time-dependent Green's functions already discussed in Sec. 36.

An explicit expression for the Green's function $G(\mathbf{r}',t';\mathbf{r},t)$, defined in Eq. (36.2), is easily obtained from Eq. (10.19) in the stationary case. In our present notation it is

$$G(\mathbf{r}',t';\mathbf{r},t) = -i\mathcal{S}_\alpha\chi_\alpha(\mathbf{r}')\chi_\alpha^*(\mathbf{r})e^{-i\omega_\alpha(t'-t)} \tag{37.6}$$

where the χ_α constitute a complete orthonormal set of solutions of the time-independent Schrödinger equation $(H - E_\alpha)\chi_\alpha = 0$. The fact that

G is a function only of $t' - t$, and not of t' and t separately, is a consequence of the invariance of H with respect to time displacement in the stationary case. In accordance with (36.3), the propagator is obtained by multiplying this G by $\theta(t' - t)$. Since the form (37.6) for G resembles a Fourier expansion in the time difference $t' - t$, the possibility of separating out the time dependence by expressing $\theta(t' - t)$ as a Fourier expansion suggests itself. We now show that this has the form

$$\theta(\tau) = \lim_{\epsilon \to 0^+} -\frac{1}{2\pi i} \int_{-\infty}^{\infty} e^{-i\omega\tau} \frac{d\omega}{\omega + i\epsilon} \tag{37.7}$$

We note first that the derivative of this with respect to τ is

$$\frac{1}{2\pi} \int_{-\infty}^{\infty} e^{-i\omega\tau} \, d\omega$$

which in accordance with Eq. (11.10) is equal to $\delta(\tau)$, as expected from Eq. (36.23). This result is independent of whether the denominator of the integrand in (37.7) is chosen to be $\omega + i\epsilon$ or $\omega - i\epsilon$, that is, whether the pole in the integrand is below or above the contour of integration, which is along the real axis. However, the two choices give different values for the integral. The first choice corresponds to a pole at $-i\epsilon$ as shown in Fig. 35a. For $\tau < 0$, this contour may be completed with an infinite semicircle in the positive imaginary half plane, as in Fig. 35b, since the exponential becomes vanishingly small there and contributes nothing to the integral; then $\theta(\tau) = 0$. For $\tau > 0$, the contour may be completed as in Fig. 35c, and the integral is equal to $-2\pi i$ times the residue of the integrand at the only pole ($\omega = -i\epsilon$) that lies within the contour. Then, in the limit $\epsilon \to 0^+$, $\theta(\tau) = 1$. It is easily verified that the second choice for the denominator, $\omega - i\epsilon$, leads to $\theta(\tau) - 1$ instead of to Eq. (36.4).

We now combine Eqs. (37.6) and (37.7) to obtain an expression for $G^+(\mathbf{r}',t';\mathbf{r},t)$. It is convenient to change the variable of integration from ω to $\omega + \omega_\alpha$ and to write G^+ in the form of a Fourier analysis:

$$G^+(\mathbf{r}',t';\mathbf{r},t) = \frac{1}{2\pi} \int_{-\infty}^{\infty} G_\omega^+(\mathbf{r}',\mathbf{r}) e^{-i\omega(t'-t)} \, d\omega$$

$$G_\omega^+(\mathbf{r}',\mathbf{r}) \equiv S_\alpha(\omega - \omega_\alpha + i\epsilon)^{-1} \chi_\alpha(\mathbf{r}') \chi_\alpha^*(\mathbf{r}) \tag{37.8}$$

where the limit $\epsilon \to 0^+$ is always implied. It is easily established that the advanced Green's functions $G^-(\mathbf{r}',t';\mathbf{r},t)$ and $G_\omega^-(\mathbf{r}',\mathbf{r})$ are related to each other by the first of Eqs. (37.8) and that G_ω^- is given by the second equation with $+i\epsilon$ replaced by $-i\epsilon$ in the denominator of the summand. In analogy with Eq. (36.24), it can also be shown from the completeness and

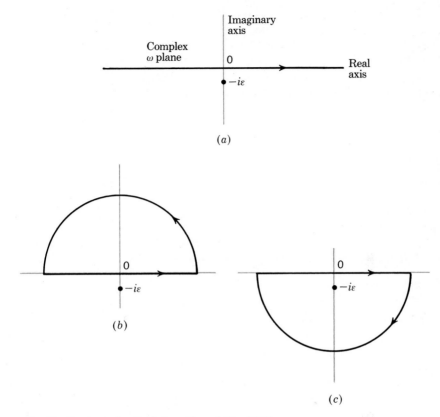

Fig. 35   Contours for the integration of Eq. (37.7).

orthonormality of the χ_α that $G_\omega{}^\pm$ satisfies the equation

$$\left(\omega - \frac{1}{\hbar}H'\right)G_\omega{}^\pm(\mathbf{r}',\mathbf{r}) = \delta^3(\mathbf{r}' - \mathbf{r}) \tag{37.9}$$

where H' is H expressed in terms of $\mathbf{r}'$.

GREEN'S FUNCTIONS AS INVERSE OPERATORS

We are now in a position to see how the inverse operators (36.30) can be written explicitly.   On restoring the primes dropped just before (36.24), the first of Eqs. (36.30) becomes

$$G^\pm(\mathbf{r}',t';\mathbf{r},t) = \left(i\frac{\partial}{\partial t'} - \frac{1}{\hbar}H'\right)^{-1}\delta^3(\mathbf{r}' - \mathbf{r})\delta(t' - t)$$

$$= \left(i\frac{\partial}{\partial t'} - \frac{1}{\hbar}H'\right)^{-1}S_\alpha\chi_\alpha(\mathbf{r}')\chi_\alpha^*(\mathbf{r})\frac{1}{2\pi}\int_{-\infty}^{\infty}e^{-i\omega(t'-t)}\,d\omega$$

Here, the completeness relation of the χ_α has been used to substitute for $\delta^3(\mathbf{r}' - \mathbf{r})$, and Eq. (11.10) has been used to substitute for $\delta(t' - t)$. A typical term of the summand-integrand, $\chi_\alpha(\mathbf{r}')e^{-i\omega t'}$, is an eigenfunction of the operator $i(\partial/\partial t') - (1/\hbar)H'$ with eigenvalue $\omega - \omega_\alpha$. We therefore try to replace any function of this operator, when operating on this typical term, by the same function of the eigenvalue. If this is done, we obtain

$$G^\pm(\mathbf{r}',t';\mathbf{r},t) = \frac{1}{2\pi} \int_{-\infty}^{\infty} S_\alpha(\omega - \omega_\alpha)^{-1}\chi_\alpha(\mathbf{r}')\chi_\alpha^*(\mathbf{r})e^{-i\omega(t'-t)}\, d\omega$$

This provides an example of the singularity mentioned below Eq. (36.30). The integral over ω is not well defined unless the pole at ω_α is removed from the real axis. This may be accomplished by replacing $\omega - \omega_\alpha$ by $\omega - \omega_\alpha \pm i\epsilon$ in the denominator of the integrand, and this leads to the correct $G^\pm$ as obtained in Eqs. (37.8). The insertion of $\pm i\epsilon$ both removes the singularity and specifies whether the Green's function propagates forward or backward in time.

STATIONARY PROPAGATOR

The stationary Green's functions $G_\omega^\pm(\mathbf{r}',\mathbf{r})$ defined in (37.8), which are the Fourier transforms of the time-dependent Green's functions $G^\pm(\mathbf{r}',t';\mathbf{r},t)$, can also be obtained directly from the time-independent Schrödinger equation. For a stationary scattering problem, we are interested in a solution of this equation that has the asymptotic form of a plane plus outgoing scattered wave, as in Eq. (18.10). We expect this to be associated with the propagator G_ω^+ rather than with G_ω^-, since $\psi_\alpha^+(\mathbf{r},t)$ was defined in Eq. (36.31) to be the wave function that grows out of the free-particle wave function $\phi_\alpha(\mathbf{r},t)$ starting from a time in the remote past before V was effective. In accordance with (37.1), we call this stationary solution $\chi_\alpha^+(\mathbf{r})$ and write it as

$$\chi_\alpha^+(\mathbf{r}) = C[\exp(i\mathbf{k}_\alpha \cdot \mathbf{r}) + v(\mathbf{r})] = u_\alpha(\mathbf{r}) + Cv(\mathbf{r}) \tag{37.10}$$

where $u_\alpha(\mathbf{r})$ is the suitably normalized plane wave defined in (37.1). The coefficient C is equal to $L^{-\frac{3}{2}}$ for box normalization and to $(2\pi)^{-\frac{3}{2}}$ for continuum or δ-function normalization (see Sec. 11). Since the scattered wave associated with χ_α^+ is outgoing, the asymptotic form of $v(\mathbf{r})$ may be written, in analogy with (18.10), as

$$v(\mathbf{r}) \xrightarrow[r \to \infty]{} \frac{1}{r} f(\mathbf{k}_r, \mathbf{k}_\alpha)e^{ik_\alpha r} \tag{37.11}$$

where the vector $\mathbf{k}_r$ that appears in the scattering amplitude f has magnitude k_α and the direction of $\mathbf{r}$. It is important to note that the coefficient C is the same for χ_α^+ and for u_α, since $v(\mathbf{r})$ contributes a negligible amount to the normalization integral. Further, this procedure is valid as well for complex V, since stationary scattering solutions (E_α real) can always be found.

Substitution of (37.10) into the wave equation

$$[H_0 + V(\mathbf{r}) - E_\alpha]\chi_\alpha^+(\mathbf{r}) = 0$$

shows that $v(\mathbf{r})$ satisfies the inhomogeneous differential equation

$$(H_0 - E_\alpha)v(\mathbf{r}) = -\frac{1}{C} V(\mathbf{r})\chi_\alpha^+(\mathbf{r})$$

This equation is easily solved with the help of the free-particle version of Eq. (37.9), to give

$$v(\mathbf{r}') = (\hbar C)^{-1}\int G_{0\omega\alpha}^+(\mathbf{r}',\mathbf{r}) V(\mathbf{r})\chi_\alpha^+(\mathbf{r}) \, d^3r \qquad (37.12)$$

Combination of (37.10) and (37.12) shows that χ_α^+ satisfies an inhomogeneous equation, called the *Lippmann-Schwinger equation*[1]:

$$\chi_\alpha^+(\mathbf{r}') = u_\alpha(\mathbf{r}') + \hbar^{-1}\int G_{0\omega\alpha}^+(\mathbf{r}',\mathbf{r}) V(\mathbf{r})\chi_\alpha^+(\mathbf{r}) \, d^3r \qquad (37.13)$$

By making use of the free-particle version of Eq. (37.9), we may write this symbolically as

$$\chi_\alpha^+ = u_\alpha + (E_\alpha - H_0 + i\epsilon)^{-1}V\chi_\alpha^+ \qquad (37.14)$$

Since H_0 is hermitian, its eigenvalues are real, and the inverse operator is nonsingular so long as ϵ is finite.

Equation (37.13) can be iterated to give an infinite series for χ_α^+:

$$\chi_\alpha^+(\mathbf{r}') = u_\alpha(\mathbf{r}') + \hbar^{-1}\int G_{0\omega\alpha}^+(\mathbf{r}',\mathbf{r}) V(\mathbf{r})u_\alpha(\mathbf{r}) \, d^3r$$
$$+ \hbar^{-2}\int\int G_{0\omega\alpha}^+(\mathbf{r}',\mathbf{r}_i) V(\mathbf{r}_i)G_{0\omega\alpha}^+(\mathbf{r}_i,\mathbf{r}) V(\mathbf{r})u_\alpha(\mathbf{r}) \, d^3r_i \, d^3r + \cdots \qquad (37.15)$$

Also, Eq. (37.14) can be manipulated symbolically to give

$$\chi_\alpha^+ = u_\alpha + (E_\alpha - H + i\epsilon)^{-1}Vu_\alpha \qquad (37.16)$$

which can be written out in the form

$$\chi_\alpha^+(\mathbf{r}') = u_\alpha(\mathbf{r}') + \hbar^{-1}\int G_{\omega\alpha}^+(\mathbf{r}',\mathbf{r}) V(\mathbf{r})u_\alpha(\mathbf{r}) \, d^3r \qquad (37.17)$$

Equation (37.17) can also be derived without using symbolic relations.

FREE-PARTICLE PROPAGATOR

In order to make use of equations like (37.13), we need an explicit expression for the free-particle propagator $G_{0\omega}^+(\mathbf{r}',\mathbf{r})$. For positive ω, the second

[1] B. A. Lippmann and J. Schwinger, *Phys. Rev.* **79**, 469 (1950).

of Eqs. (37.8) becomes

$$G_{0\omega}{}^+(\mathbf{r}',\mathbf{r}) = S_\alpha(\omega - \omega_\alpha + i\epsilon)^{-1} u_\alpha(\mathbf{r}') u_\alpha^*(\mathbf{r})$$

$$= \frac{\mu}{4\pi^3\hbar} \int (k^2 - k_\alpha{}^2 + i\epsilon)^{-1} \exp\left[i\mathbf{k}_\alpha \cdot (\mathbf{r}' - \mathbf{r})\right] d^3 k_\alpha \quad (37.18)$$

where $k^2 \equiv 2\mu\omega/\hbar$. Because of the space-displacement invariance of H_0, $G_{0\omega}{}^+$ is a function only of $\mathbf{r}' - \mathbf{r}$ and not of $\mathbf{r}'$ and $\mathbf{r}$ separately. Integration over the angles of $\mathbf{k}_\alpha$ with $\mathbf{r}' - \mathbf{r}$ as polar axis gives

$$G_{0\omega}{}^+(\mathbf{r}',\mathbf{r}) = \frac{\mu}{\pi^2\hbar\rho} \int_0^\infty (k^2 - k_\alpha{}^2 + i\epsilon)^{-1} k_\alpha \sin k_\alpha\rho \, dk_\alpha$$

where $\rho \equiv |\mathbf{r}' - \mathbf{r}|$. The k_α integral is most readily evaluated by extending the lower limit to $-\infty$, writing $\sin k_\alpha\rho$ in exponential form, and using residues as in the evaluation of (37.7). The result is

$$G_{0\omega}{}^+(\mathbf{r}',\mathbf{r}) = -\frac{\mu}{2\pi\hbar} |\mathbf{r}' - \mathbf{r}|^{-1} \exp(ik|\mathbf{r}' - \mathbf{r}|) \qquad \omega > 0$$

$$k = +\left(\frac{2\mu\omega}{\hbar}\right)^{\frac{1}{2}} \quad (37.19)$$

For negative ω, the only change is the replacement of ik in the exponent by $-k$, where now $k = +(2\mu|\omega|/\hbar)^{\frac{1}{2}}$. It can then be shown that substitution of this expression for negative ω, together with Eq. (37.19) for positive ω, into Eq. (37.8), leads to the expression for $G_0{}^+(\mathbf{r}',t';\mathbf{r},t)$ obtained from Eqs. (36.9) and (36.10).

SCATTERING AMPLITUDE

The scattering amplitude $f(\mathbf{k}_r, \mathbf{k}_\alpha)$ can now be found by comparing the asymptotic form of (37.12) with (37.11). We note that r is essentially restricted to finite values since $V(\mathbf{r})$ appears in the integrand of (37.12). Thus in the exponent of $G_{0\omega\alpha}^+$ we have

$$|\mathbf{r}' - \mathbf{r}| = r' - r \cos\theta' + O\left(\frac{r^2}{r'}\right)$$

and in the denominator

$$|\mathbf{r}' - \mathbf{r}|^{-1} = r'^{-1} + O\left(\frac{r}{r'^2}\right)$$

where θ' is the angle between $\mathbf{r}'$ and $\mathbf{r}$. Equation (37.19) then gives

$$G_{0\omega\alpha}^+(\mathbf{r}',\mathbf{r}) \xrightarrow[r'\to\infty]{} -\frac{\mu}{2\pi\hbar r'} e^{ik_\alpha(r' - r\cos\theta')}$$

and substitution into (37.12) gives the asymptotic behavior

$$v(\mathbf{r}') \xrightarrow[r'\to\infty]{} -\frac{\mu}{2\pi\hbar^2 C r'} e^{ik_\alpha r'} \int e^{-ik_\alpha r \cos\theta'} V(\mathbf{r}) \chi_\alpha^+(\mathbf{r}) \, d^3r \quad (37.20)$$

We now define a vector $\mathbf{k}_\beta$ which, like the vector $\mathbf{k}_r$ in Eq. (37.11), has magnitude k_α and the direction of $\mathbf{r}'$, so that $k_\alpha r \cos \theta' = \mathbf{k}_\beta \cdot \mathbf{r}$. Comparison of (37.11) and (37.20) then gives

$$f(\mathbf{k}_\beta,\mathbf{k}_\alpha) = -\frac{\mu}{2\pi\hbar^2 C} \int \exp(-i\mathbf{k}_\beta \cdot \mathbf{r}) V(\mathbf{r}) \chi_\alpha{}^+(\mathbf{r}) \, d^3r$$

$$= -\frac{\mu}{2\pi\hbar^2 |C|^2} \int u_\beta^*(\mathbf{r}) V(\mathbf{r}) \chi_\alpha{}^+(\mathbf{r}) \, d^3r$$

$$= -\frac{\mu}{2\pi\hbar^2 |C|^2} \langle \beta|T|\alpha \rangle \tag{37.21}$$

where the T matrix element is defined in Eq. (37.2). Since, in accordance with (37.10), u_β and $\chi_\alpha{}^+$ both have asymptotic magnitude $|C|$, the scattering amplitude is independent of the choice of C, as of course it must be.

As shown in Eq. (18.11), the differential scattering cross section from the initial propagation vector $\mathbf{k}_\alpha$ to the final propagation vector $\mathbf{k}_\beta$ is equal to $|f(\mathbf{k}_\beta,\mathbf{k}_\alpha)|^2$. Thus (37.21) is in agreement with (37.5) when box normalization is used.

INGOING WAVES

It is easily seen that Eqs. (37.13) to (37.19) can be rewritten correctly by making the following substitutions:

$$\chi_\alpha{}^+ \to \chi_\alpha{}^- \qquad G_{0\omega\alpha}^+(\mathbf{r}',\mathbf{r}) \to G_{0\omega\alpha}^-(\mathbf{r}',\mathbf{r}) \qquad i \to -i \tag{37.22}$$

In analogy with (37.11), $\chi_\alpha{}^-$ has the asymptotic form of a plane plus ingoing wave:

$$\chi_\alpha{}^-(\mathbf{r}) \xrightarrow[r \to \infty]{} C\left[\exp(i\mathbf{k}_\alpha \cdot \mathbf{r}) + \frac{1}{r} f^-(\mathbf{k}_r,\mathbf{k}_\alpha) e^{-ik_\alpha r} \right] \tag{37.23}$$

Comparison of the original and rewritten equations then shows that if V is real

$$\chi_\alpha{}^+(\mathbf{r}) = \chi_{-\alpha}^{-*}(\mathbf{r}) \qquad f(\mathbf{k}_r,\mathbf{k}_\alpha) = f^{-*}(\mathbf{k}_r,-\mathbf{k}_\alpha) \tag{37.24}$$

where $\chi_{-\alpha}^-$ is the time-reversed state to $\chi_\alpha{}^+$ and has the opposite momentum $-\mathbf{k}_\alpha$.

Still considering the case in which V is real, we can rewrite the T matrix element in terms of $\chi_\beta{}^-$. From Eqs. (37.2) and (37.16) we have

$$\langle \beta|T|\alpha \rangle = (u_\beta, V\chi_\alpha{}^+) = (u_\beta, Vu_\alpha) + [u_\beta, V(E - H + i\epsilon)^{-1} Vu_\alpha]$$

$$= (u_\beta, Vu_\alpha) + [(E - H - i\epsilon)^{-1} Vu_\beta, Vu_\alpha] \tag{37.25}$$

where $E = E_\alpha = E_\beta$. The rewritten version of (37.16) is

$$\chi_\beta{}^- = u_\beta + (E - H - i\epsilon)^{-1} Vu_\beta$$

so that (37.25) becomes

$$\langle \beta | T | \alpha \rangle = (\chi_\beta^-, V u_\alpha) \qquad V \text{ real} \qquad (37.26)$$

It is sometimes useful to have available an expression similar to (37.26) when V is complex. We accordingly define wave functions $\chi_\alpha^{T\pm}$, which are stationary solutions of the Schrödinger equation with V replaced by V^*:

$$\begin{aligned}
\chi_\alpha^{T\pm} &= u_\alpha + (E - H_0 \pm i\epsilon)^{-1} V^* \chi_\alpha^{T\pm} \\
&= u_\alpha + (E - H^\dagger \pm i\epsilon)^{-1} V^* u_\alpha
\end{aligned} \qquad (37.27)$$

$\chi_{-\alpha}^{T-}$ is the time-reversed state to χ_α^+ but does not represent a physically possible behavior of the system since H is not time-reversal invariant. Equation (37.26) then becomes

$$\langle \beta | T | \alpha \rangle = (\chi_\beta^{T-}, V u_\alpha) \qquad V \text{ complex} \qquad (37.28)$$

S MATRIX FOR STATIONARY CASE

An explicit expression for the S matrix element can be obtained by allowing the cutoffs on $g(t)$ in Eq. (37.2) to extend to $\pm \infty$:

$$\begin{aligned}
\langle \beta | (S - 1) | \alpha \rangle &= -\frac{2\pi i}{\hbar} \delta(\omega_\beta - \omega_\alpha) \langle \beta | T | \alpha \rangle \\
&= -\frac{2\pi \mu i}{\hbar^2 k_\alpha} \delta(k_\beta - k_\alpha) \langle \beta | T | \alpha \rangle
\end{aligned} \qquad (37.29)$$

where use has been made of the fifth of Eqs. (11.13). We also require an expression for $\langle \beta | \alpha \rangle$, which with continuum normalization is

$$\langle \beta | \alpha \rangle = \delta^3(\mathbf{k}_\beta - \mathbf{k}_\alpha) = \frac{\delta(k_\beta - k_\alpha)}{k_\alpha^2} \frac{\delta(\theta_\beta - \theta_\alpha)}{\sin \theta_\alpha} \delta(\phi_\beta - \phi_\alpha) \qquad (37.30)$$

where the weight functions appropriate for spherical coordinates have been included. We can now combine Eqs. (37.21), (37.29), and (37.30) with $C = (2\pi)^{-\frac{3}{2}}$, to obtain the S matrix element:

$$\langle \beta | S | \alpha \rangle = \frac{\delta(k_\beta - k_\alpha)}{k_\alpha^2} \left[\frac{\delta(\theta_\beta - \theta_\alpha)}{\sin \theta_\alpha} \delta(\phi_\beta - \phi_\alpha) + \frac{ik_\alpha}{2\pi} f(\mathbf{k}_\beta, \mathbf{k}_\alpha) \right] \qquad (37.31)$$

Equation (37.31), together with the assumption that S is unitary, can be used to derive the optical theorem and the generalized optical theorem, discussed in Sec. 20.

ANGULAR MOMENTUM REPRESENTATION

The S matrix element (37.31) is expressed in terms of the polar coordinates of the initial and final propagation vectors:

$$\langle \beta | S | \alpha \rangle = \langle k_\beta \theta_\beta \phi_\beta | S | k_\alpha \theta_\alpha \phi_\alpha \rangle$$

It can be transformed to the representation specified by the energy (or the magnitude of the propagation vector) and the angular momentum by making use of the unitary transformation matrix (27.29):

$$\langle \theta\phi | lm \rangle = Y_{lm}(\theta,\phi) \tag{37.32}$$

We then have

$$\langle k_\beta l_\beta m_\beta | S | k_\alpha l_\alpha m_\alpha \rangle$$
$$= S_{\theta_\beta\phi_\beta} S_{\theta_\alpha\phi_\alpha} \langle l_\beta m_\beta | \theta_\beta\phi_\beta \rangle \langle k_\beta \theta_\beta\phi_\beta | S | k_\alpha \theta_\alpha\phi_\alpha \rangle \langle \theta_\alpha\phi_\alpha | l_\alpha m_\alpha \rangle \tag{37.33}$$

The generalized summation symbols are angle integrations in this case and include the weight functions $\sin \theta_\beta$, $\sin \theta_\alpha$, as remarked after (27.29).

Equation (37.33) takes a particularly simple form if V is spherically symmetric, since then, in accordance with Eq. (36.40), S commutes with the angular momentum operator. The scattering amplitude depends only on the angle θ between $\mathbf{k}_\alpha$ and $\mathbf{k}_\beta$ and may be written as in Eq. (19.11):

$$f(\mathbf{k}_\beta,\mathbf{k}_\alpha) = \frac{1}{2ik_\alpha} \sum_l (2l + 1)(e^{2i\delta_l} - 1)P_l(\cos \theta) \tag{37.34}$$

Here $\cos \theta = \cos \theta_\beta \cos \theta_\alpha + \sin \theta_\beta \sin \theta_\alpha \cos (\phi_\beta - \phi_\alpha)$, and, in accordance with Eqs. (32.10) and (14.16),

$$P_l(\cos \theta) = \frac{4\pi}{2l + 1} \sum_{m=-l}^{l} Y_{lm}(\theta_\beta,\phi_\beta) Y_{lm}^*(\theta_\alpha,\phi_\alpha) \tag{37.35}$$

Substitution of Eqs. (37.31), (37.32), (37.34), and (37.35) into (37.33) gives

$$\langle k_\beta l_\beta m_\beta | S | k_\alpha l_\alpha m_\alpha \rangle$$
$$= \frac{\delta(k_\beta - k_\alpha)}{k_\alpha^2} \iiiint \sin \theta_\beta \, d\theta_\beta \, d\phi_\beta \sin \theta_\alpha \, d\theta_\alpha \, d\phi_\alpha \, Y_{l_\beta m_\beta}^*(\theta_\beta,\phi_\beta)$$

$$\left[\frac{\delta_\beta(\theta_\beta - \theta_\alpha)}{\sin \theta_\alpha} \delta(\phi_\beta - \phi_\alpha) + \sum_l \sum_{m=-l}^{l} (e^{2i\delta_l} - 1) Y_{lm}(\theta_\beta,\phi_\beta) Y_{lm}^*(\theta_\alpha,\phi_\alpha) \right]$$

$$Y_{l_\alpha m_\alpha}(\theta_\alpha,\phi_\alpha) = e^{2i\delta_{l_\alpha}} \frac{\delta(k_\beta - k_\alpha)}{k_\alpha^2} \delta_{l_\beta l_\alpha} \delta_{m_\beta m_\alpha} \tag{37.36}$$

where use has been made of the orthonormality of the spherical harmonics.

Thus S is diagonal in the representation specified by the wave number k (or the energy) and the angular momentum quantum numbers l and m. This is to be expected since a static spherically symmetric potential does not change either the energy or the angular momentum during the scattering process. This representation of the S matrix is easily verified to be unitary provided that the phase shifts are real, as is the case when H is hermitian or V is real. It should also be noted, from the discussion of Sec. 19, that the radially incoming wave $r^{-1}e^{-ikr}$ is not modified in the partial wave analysis, whereas the outgoing wave for a particular l is multiplied by $e^{2i\delta_l}$. Thus each diagonal element of the scattering matrix has a natural interpretation as the modification of a particular outgoing or scattered partial wave as compared with the corresponding incoming or incident partial wave.

38□APPROXIMATE CALCULATIONS

In the preceding section, an exact relation between the scattering amplitude and the T matrix element [Eq. (37.21)] was derived. The T matrix element in turn is expressed in terms of the stationary outgoing solution $\chi_\alpha^+(\mathbf{r})$ through Eq. (37.2), and an infinite perturbation series (37.15) is available for the calculation of χ_α^+. The first order of this perturbation series leads to the *Born approximation*,[1] which consists in replacing χ_α^+ by u_α. We show first how this method can be applied in some interesting cases of potential scattering and then how it can be generalized to treat scattering by a system with internal degrees of freedom (electron-atom scattering). Finally, we discuss the eikonal approximation, which is closely related to the WKB approximation.

BORN APPROXIMATION

The procedure outlined in the preceding paragraph leads at once to the Born expression for the scattering amplitude:

$$f_B(\mathbf{k}_\beta, \mathbf{k}_\alpha) = -\frac{\mu}{2\pi\hbar^2|C|^2} \int u_\beta^*(\mathbf{r}) V(\mathbf{r}) u_\alpha(\mathbf{r}) \, d^3r$$

$$= -\frac{\mu}{2\pi\hbar^2} \int V(\mathbf{r}) \exp(i\mathbf{q}\cdot\mathbf{r}) \, d^3r \qquad \mathbf{q} = \mathbf{k}_\alpha - \mathbf{k}_\beta$$

$$(38.1)$$

Thus the Born scattering amplitude is proportional to the spatial Fourier transform of the scattering potential with respect to $\mathbf{q}$, where $\hbar\mathbf{q}$ is the momentum transfer from the incident particle to the scattering potential during the collision. It is reminiscent of the time Fourier transform that appears in the perturbation expression for the transition amplitude [Eq. (35.9)]. If the potential V is spherically symmetric, Eq. (38.1) may be simplified by integrating over the angles of $\mathbf{r}$ with respect to $\mathbf{q}$ as polar

[1] M. Born, *Z. Physik* **38**, 803 (1926). This method appears to have been first used by Lord Rayleigh, *Phil. Mag.* **12**, 81 (1881); see also R. Gans, *Ann. Physik* **76**, 29 (1925).

axis. In this case, f_B depends only on the angle θ between $\mathbf{k}_\alpha$ and $\mathbf{k}_\beta$:

$$f_B(\theta) = -\frac{2\mu}{\hbar^2 q} \int_0^\infty r \sin qr \ V(r) \ dr \qquad q = 2k \sin \tfrac{1}{2}\theta \qquad (38.2)$$

where k is the magnitude of $\mathbf{k}_\alpha$ and $\mathbf{k}_\beta$.

An interesting example of the application of Eq. (38.2) is to the elastic scattering of an electron by a neutral atom that is represented by a simple form of screened coulomb potential: $V(r) = -(Ze^2/r)e^{-r/a}$. This behaves like the nuclear coulomb potential for atomic number Z when r is small and falls off rapidly when r is large in comparison with the "radius" a of the atomic electron cloud that screens the nucleus. The Thomas-Fermi statistical theory of the atom (see Sec. 47) shows that, for moderately heavy atoms, a is roughly equal to $\hbar^2/me^2Z^{\frac{1}{3}}$, where m is the electron mass. Substitution of this potential into (38.2) gives

$$f_B(\theta) = \frac{2\mu Ze^2}{\hbar^2 q} \int_0^\infty \sin qr \ e^{-r/a} \ dr = \frac{2\mu Ze^2}{\hbar^2(q^2 + a^{-2})} \qquad (38.3)$$

The cross section $|f_B(\theta)|^2$ is in agreement with the Rutherford result (21.11) when the momentum transfer is large enough so that $1/a^2$ can be neglected in comparison with q^2 in the denominator. In the analogous classical situation, the incident electron passes close enough to the nucleus so that the atomic electrons are relatively ineffective in screening the nuclear potential.

The total cross section is most easily evaluated by changing the variable of integration from θ to $q = 2k \sin \tfrac{1}{2}\theta$, in which case $\sin \theta \ d\theta$ is replaced by $q \ dq/k^2$:

$$\sigma = 2\pi \int_0^\pi |f_B(\theta)|^2 \sin \theta \ d\theta = \frac{2\pi}{k^2} \int_0^{2k} |f_B(q)|^2 q \ dq$$

$$= \frac{16\pi\mu^2 Z^2 e^4 a^4}{\hbar^4(4k^2a^2 + 1)}$$

With the above Thomas-Fermi expression for a, and neglecting the difference between m and μ, the total cross section becomes $4\pi Z^{\frac{2}{3}}/k^2$ at high energies $(ka \gg 1)$. This agrees in order of magnitude with the result of a numerical integration[1] of the scattering produced by the Thomas-Fermi potential.

VALIDITY OF THE BORN APPROXIMATION

Since the only approximation involved in the preceding subsection is the replacement of χ_α^+ by u_α in the T matrix element, a convenient criterion for the validity of the Born approximation can be obtained by requiring that $|v(\mathbf{r})|$ in Eq. (37.10) be small in comparison with $|\exp(i\mathbf{k}_\alpha \cdot \mathbf{r})| = 1$.

[1] E. C. Bullard and H. S. W. Massey, *Proc. Cambridge Phil. Soc.* **26**, 556 (1930).

We must use perturbation theory to estimate $v(\mathbf{r})$, by making use of (37.12) and replacing $\chi_\alpha{}^+$ by u_α in the integrand. It is then most convenient to make this estimate at $\mathbf{r} = 0$, and this should be satisfactory since it is likely that $v(\mathbf{r})$ is largest at the center of the scattering potential. The resulting validity criterion is probably sufficient but may be more stringent than is actually required; for example, the small-angle scattering (small momentum transfer) may be given correctly by the Born approximation when the large-angle scattering is not.

We obtain in this way

$$v(0) \approx (\hbar C)^{-1} \int G_{0\omega_\alpha}{}^+(0,\mathbf{r}) V(\mathbf{r}) u_\alpha(\mathbf{r}) \, d^3r$$

$$= -\frac{\mu}{\hbar^2} \int_0^\infty \int_{-1}^1 e^{ikr} V(r) e^{ikrw} \, r \, dr \, dw$$

$$= \frac{i\mu}{\hbar^2 k} \int_0^\infty (e^{2ikr} - 1) V(r) \, dr \tag{38.4}$$

where w is the cosine of the angle between $\mathbf{k}_\alpha$ and $\mathbf{r}$. With the screened coulomb potential substituted into (38.4), the condition $|v(0)| \ll 1$ becomes

$$\frac{2\mu Z e^2}{\hbar^2 k} \left| \int_0^\infty \sin x \, e^{ix - x/ka} \frac{dx}{x} \right| \ll 1$$

where $x = kr$ replaces r as the variable of integration. For $ka \ll 1$, this becomes $2\mu Z e^2 a/\hbar^2 \ll 1$ which, with the earlier approximate expression for a, is equivalent to $Z^{\frac{1}{3}} \ll 1$; thus the Born approximation cannot be used for the scattering of slow electrons by atoms. For $ka \gg 1$, the criterion becomes $(Z e^2/\hbar v) \ln ka \ll 1$, and the approximation is useful for fast electrons so long as Z is not too large. It turns out that this last result is substantially unaffected by relativity theory; thus the Born approximation becomes poor for the heavier elements since v cannot exceed c, and $e^2/\hbar c = \frac{1}{137}$.

SCATTERING FROM TWO POTENTIALS

It is sometimes convenient to write the potential as the sum of two parts, $V = V_1 + V_2$, and then to express the T matrix element as the sum of a part that would arise from V_1 alone and a correction term.[1] Such a procedure is useful if the wave equation for V_1 by itself is exactly soluble and if V_2 is small enough so that it can be regarded as a perturbation. For example, V_1 may be the coulomb interaction between an electron and a point nucleus of large Z, and V_2 the additional electrostatic interaction

[1] K. M. Watson, *Phys. Rev.* **88**, 1163 (1952); M. Gell-Mann and M. L. Goldberger, *Phys. Rev.* **91**, 398 (1953).

that arises because the nucleus is of finite size. As another example, V_1 may be the strong, short-range nuclear interaction between two protons, for which only a small number of partial waves need be calculated, and V_2 the much weaker coulomb interaction.

We note first that Eqs. (37.2), (37.28), (37.14), and (37.27) are, respectively,

$$\langle\beta|T|\alpha\rangle = (u_\beta, V\chi_\alpha^+) = (\chi_\beta{}^{T-}, Vu_\alpha)$$
$$\chi_\alpha^+ = u_\alpha + (E - H_0 + i\epsilon)^{-1}V\chi_\alpha^+ \tag{38.5}$$
$$\chi_\beta{}^{T-} = u_\beta + (E - H_0 - i\epsilon)^{-1}V^*\chi_\beta{}^{T-}$$

where $E = E_\alpha = E_\beta$. We may then substitute for u_β in the first of the expressions (38.5) for $\langle\beta|T|\alpha\rangle$ by using the equation

$$\chi_{1\beta}{}^{T-} = u_\beta + (E - H_0 - i\epsilon)^{-1}V_1^*\chi_{1\beta}{}^{T-}$$

which describes the scattering from V_1 alone. The result is

$$\begin{aligned}
\langle\beta|T|\alpha\rangle &= [u_\beta, (V_1 + V_2)\chi_\alpha^+] \\
&= [\chi_{1\beta}{}^{T-}, (V_1 + V_2)\chi_\alpha^+] \\
&\qquad - [(E - H_0 - i\epsilon)^{-1}V_1^*\chi_{1\beta}{}^{T-}, (V_1 + V_2)\chi_\alpha^+] \\
&= [\chi_{1\beta}{}^{T-}, (V_1 + V_2)\chi_\alpha^+] \\
&\qquad - [\chi_{1\beta}{}^{T-}, V_1(E - H_0 + i\epsilon)^{-1}(V_1 + V_2)\chi_\alpha^+]
\end{aligned}$$

We now note that $(E - H_0 + i\epsilon)^{-1}(V_1 + V_2)\chi_\alpha^+$ is equal to $\chi_\alpha^+ - u_\alpha$, and that $(\chi_{1\beta}{}^{T-}, V_1u_\alpha)$ is equal to $\langle\beta|T_1|\alpha\rangle$, the T matrix element that describes scattering by V_1 alone. We thus obtain

$$\langle\beta|T|\alpha\rangle = \langle\beta|T_1|\alpha\rangle + (\chi_{1\beta}{}^{T-}, V_2\chi_\alpha^+) \tag{38.6}$$

which is exact.

DISTORTED WAVE BORN APPROXIMATION

Equation (38.6) is most useful when V_2 is small, in which case the second term is given to first order in V_2 by replacing χ_α^+ by $\chi_{1\alpha}^+$. This gives the T matrix element in the *distorted wave Born approximation* (DWBA):[1]

$$\langle\beta|T|\alpha\rangle \approx \langle\beta|T_1|\alpha\rangle + (\chi_{1\beta}{}^{T-}, V_2\chi_{1\alpha}^+) \tag{38.7}$$

The form of Eq. (38.7) is reasonable insofar as it gives the correction term, $\langle\beta|(T - T_1)|\alpha\rangle$, as a matrix element of the second potential between states that are distorted by the first potential. However, it may at first seem strange that this matrix element is to be calculated between an initial state that is asymptotically a plane plus an outgoing spherical

[1] N. F. Mott and H. S. W. Massey, "The Theory of Atomic Collisions," p. 100 (Oxford. New York, 1933).

wave and a final state that is asymptotically a plane plus an ingoing spherical wave, rather than between two states of the outgoing type. This result can be made physically plausible in the following way.[1]

The calculation is intended to yield the probability amplitude for a transition in which V_2 causes scattering into the direction $\mathbf{k}_\beta$. However, if the final-state wave function were to be of the outgoing type, one would expect that a portion of this amplitude would be associated with scattering into directions other than $\mathbf{k}_\beta$, since all directions are included in the outgoing spherical wave. In the same way, a portion of the probability amplitude for scattering in the direction $\mathbf{k}_\beta$ would then be included in the calculations for other final-state directions, since their outgoing waves would include contributions to scattering in the direction $\mathbf{k}_\beta$. The only way to avoid this situation is to choose the final-state wave function in such a way that it contains no outgoing spherical wave; this is possible only if the wave function is asymptotically a plane plus an ingoing spherical wave.

PARTIAL WAVE ANALYSIS OF THE DWBA

If V_1 and V_2 are spherically symmetric, the distorted wave Born approximation can be expressed in terms of the scattering phase shifts δ_l that are associated with V_1 alone. A simple extension of the work of Secs. 19 and 37 shows that we can express $\chi_{1\alpha}{}^+(\mathbf{r})$ and $\chi_{1\beta}{}^{T-}(\mathbf{r})$ as follows:

$$\chi_{1\alpha}{}^+(\mathbf{r}) = C \sum_{l=0}^{\infty} (2l + 1)i^l R_l(r) P_l(\cos \theta_\alpha)$$

$$\xrightarrow[r \to \infty]{} C \left[\exp (i\mathbf{k}_\alpha \cdot \mathbf{r}) + \frac{1}{r} f(\mathbf{k}_r,\mathbf{k}_\alpha)e^{ikr} \right]$$

$$\chi_{1\beta}{}^{T-}(\mathbf{r}) = C \sum_{l=0}^{\infty} (2l + 1)i^l R_l^*(r) P_l(\cos \theta_\beta)$$

$$\xrightarrow[r \to \infty]{} C \left[\exp (i\mathbf{k}_\beta \cdot \mathbf{r}) + \frac{1}{r} f^{T-}(\mathbf{k}_r,\mathbf{k}_\beta) \, e^{-ikr} \right] \qquad (38.8)$$

$$f(\mathbf{k}_r,\mathbf{k}_\alpha) = (2ik)^{-1} \sum_{l=0}^{\infty} (2l + 1)(e^{2i\delta_l} - 1)P_l(\cos \theta_\alpha)$$

$$f^{T-}(\mathbf{k}_r,\mathbf{k}_\beta) = (2ik)^{-1} \sum_{l=0}^{\infty} (2l + 1)(-1)^l(1 - e^{-2i\delta_l{}^*})P_l(\cos \theta_\beta)$$

$$R_l(r) \xrightarrow[r \to \infty]{} \frac{e^{i\delta_l}}{kr} \sin (kr - \tfrac{1}{2}l\pi + \delta_l)$$

[1] A. Sommerfeld, "Wellenmechanik" (Ungar, New York) or "Atombau und Spektrallinien," vol. 2, footnote p. 457 (F. Vieweg & Sohn, Brunswick, Germany, 1939); G. Breit and H. A. Bethe, *Phys. Rev.* **93,** 888 (1954).

Here, $k = k_\alpha = k_\beta$, θ_α is the angle between $\mathbf{r}$ and $\mathbf{k}_\alpha$, and θ_β is the angle between $\mathbf{r}$ and $\mathbf{k}_\beta$. Note that, for any angle θ, $f(\theta) = f^{T-*}(\pi - \theta)$, a relation that agrees with the second of Eqs. (37.24) when V is real.

Substitution from Eqs. (38.8) into the second term of (38.7) gives

$$(\chi_{1\beta}{}^{T-}, V_2\chi_{1\alpha}{}^+) = 4\pi|C|^2 \sum_{l=0}^{\infty} (2l + 1)P_l(\cos \theta) \int_0^\infty V_2(r)R_l{}^2(r)r^2 \, dr$$

$$(38.9)$$

where θ is the angle between $\mathbf{k}_\beta$ and $\mathbf{k}_\alpha$, and use has been made of the addition theorem for the Legendre polynomials, Eq. (32.10). Equation (38.9) is not very convenient for computational purposes, since it is an infinite series over l even when V_1 is of short range so that only a few of the δ_l are different from zero. This suggests that we subtract $V_2(r)j_l{}^2(kr)$ from each integrand and add in a compensating series. Since $R_l(r)$ is equal to $j_l(kr)$ if $\delta_l = 0$, this means that $\int V_2(r)[R_l{}^2(r) - j_l{}^2(kr)]r^2 \, dr$ is zero unless δ_l is different from zero. Further, the compensating series that has been added in can be summed by making use of the formula[1]

$$\sum_{l=0}^{\infty} (2l + 1)j_l{}^2(kr)P_l(\cos \theta) = \frac{\sin qr}{qr} \qquad q = 2k \sin \tfrac{1}{2}\theta \qquad (38.10)$$

and this leads to the Born approximation amplitude for V_2 alone.

Combination of Eqs. (37.21), (38.2), (38.7), (38.9), and (38.10) leads to the distorted wave Born approximation amplitude for spherically symmetric scattering:[2]

$$f_{\text{DWBA}}(\theta) = f_1(\theta) + f_{2B}(\theta)$$

$$- \frac{2\mu}{\hbar^2} \sum_{l=0}^{\infty} (2l + 1)P_l(\cos \theta) \int_0^\infty V_2(r)[R_l{}^2(r) - j_l{}^2(kr)]r^2 \, dr \quad (38.11)$$

Here, f_1 is the exact scattering amplitude for V_1 alone and f_{2B} is the Born approximation amplitude for V_2 alone. The series represents the effect of the plane-wave distortion produced by V_1 on the first-order scattering caused by V_2; the only l values that appear in this series are those for which $\delta_l \neq 0$. It should be noted that the integrals in (38.9) and (38.11) converge only if V_2 falls off more rapidly than $1/r$ for large r, so that special care must be taken if V_2 is an unscreened coulomb potential.

---

[1] G. N. Watson, "Theory of Bessel Functions," 2d ed., p. 366 (Macmillan, New York, 1945).

[2] L. I. Schiff, *Progr. Theoret. Phys., Suppl. Extra Number* (1965) 400.

APPROXIMATE EXPRESSION FOR THE PHASE SHIFTS

We now return to the case in which the potential is not divided into two parts. If V is spherically symmetric, we may substitute the expansions

$$\chi_\alpha^+(\mathbf{r}) = C \sum_{l=0}^{\infty} (2l + 1)i^l R_l(r) P_l(\cos \theta_\alpha)$$

$$u_\beta(\mathbf{r}) = C \sum_{l=0}^{\infty} (2l + 1)i^l j_l(kr) P_l(\cos \theta_\beta)$$

into (37.21), where θ_α is the angle between $\mathbf{r}$ and $\mathbf{k}_\alpha$, and θ_β is the angle between $\mathbf{r}$ and $\mathbf{k}_\beta$. We thus obtain the following as an exact expression for the scattering amplitude:

$$f(\theta) = -\frac{2\mu}{\hbar^2} \sum_{l=0}^{\infty} (2l + 1) P_l(\cos \theta) \int_0^\infty V(r) R_l(r) j_l(kr) r^2 \, dr \qquad (38.12)$$

Comparison of Eqs. (19.11) and (38.12) shows that the phase shifts are given by

$$e^{i\delta_l} \sin \delta_l = -\frac{2\mu k}{\hbar^2} \int_0^\infty V(r) R_l(r) j_l(kr) r^2 \, dr \qquad (38.13)$$

An approximate expression for δ_l, valid to first order in V, can be obtained by replacing the whole left side of (38.13) by δ_l, and $R_l(r)$ by $j_l(kr)$ in the integrand on the right side. This is the Born approximation for the phase shift:

$$\delta_{Bl} = -\frac{2\mu k}{\hbar^2} \int_0^\infty V(r) j_l^2(kr) r^2 \, dr \qquad (38.14)$$

It may happen that the first few phase shifts are large enough so that (38.14) is not a good approximation and the remaining δ_l are small but not negligible. In this case Eq. (19.11) can be written

$$f(\theta) \approx f_B(\theta) + \frac{1}{2ik} \sum_{l=0}^{\infty} (2l + 1)(e^{2i\delta_l} - 1 - 2i\delta_{Bl}) P_l(\cos \theta) \qquad (38.15)$$

where use has been made of Eqs. (38.2), (38.10), and (38.14). Each term in the summation on the right side of (38.15) is zero through first order in V or δ_l, so that only the first few terms fail to vanish in the present case.

SCATTERER WITH INTERNAL DEGREES OF FREEDOM

We shall now extend the T matrix formalism to the case in which the scatterer has internal degrees of freedom, so that it can be excited during the scattering process. For example, an electron may be scattered by an atom that is initially in its ground state; after the collision, the atom may be left in its ground state (elastic scattering) or in an excited state (inelastic scattering). However, in either case, the total energy of the electron and atom is conserved so that we are dealing with a stationary situation. We leave out of consideration the possibility that the incident electron changes places with the atomic electron; such exchange collisions will be discussed in Chap. 10.

We divide the total hamiltonian into a part H_0 that describes the internal motion of the scatterer together with the kinetic energy of the relative motion of incident particle and scatterer, and a part H' that represents the interaction between the two. For example, in the scattering of an electron (coordinate $\mathbf{r}_1$) by a hydrogen atom (atomic-electron coordinate $\mathbf{r}_2$), we have

$$H = H_0 + H'$$

$$H_0 = -\frac{\hbar^2}{2\mu}\nabla_1{}^2 - \frac{\hbar^2}{2m}\nabla_2{}^2 - \frac{e^2}{r_2} \qquad H' = \frac{e^2}{r_{12}} - \frac{e^2}{r_1} \qquad (38.16)$$

The distinction between the reduced mass μ of the electron-atom system and the electron mass m is unimportant here but could be significant in a nuclear collision.

The eigenfunctions of H_0 are specified by two parameters:

$$H_0 u_{\alpha a} = E_{\alpha a} u_{\alpha a}$$

$$u_{\alpha a}(\mathbf{r}_1,\mathbf{r}_2) = C\exp{(i\mathbf{k}_\alpha \cdot \mathbf{r}_1)}\,w_a(\mathbf{r}_2) \qquad E_{\alpha a} \equiv \hbar\omega_{\alpha a} = \frac{\hbar^2 k_\alpha{}^2}{2\mu} + \epsilon_a$$

$$(38.17)$$

where w_a and ϵ_a are a typical eigenfunction and eigenvalue of the hamiltonian of the scatterer. The corresponding eigenfunction of H that corresponds to outgoing waves has the asymptotic form

$$\chi_{\alpha a}{}^+(\mathbf{r}_1,\mathbf{r}_2) \xrightarrow[r_1 \to \infty]{} C\left[\exp{(i\mathbf{k}_\alpha \cdot \mathbf{r}_1)}w_a(\mathbf{r}_2)\right.$$
$$\left. + \sum_b r_1{}^{-1}e^{ik_r r_1}f(\mathbf{k}_r,b;\mathbf{k}_\alpha,a)w_b(\mathbf{r}_2)\right] \quad (38.18)$$

Here $\mathbf{k}_r$ is a vector whose direction is that of $\mathbf{r}_1$ and whose magnitude is given by the energy conservation relation $(\hbar^2 k_r{}^2/2\mu) + \epsilon_b = E_{\alpha a}$. The amplitude f with $b = a$ describes elastic scattering, and those with $b \neq a$ describe inelastic scattering.

ELASTIC AND INELASTIC CROSS SECTIONS

The wave function $\chi_{\alpha a}{}^+$ satisfies a Lippmann-Schwinger equation which is an obvious generalization of (37.13):

$$\chi_{\alpha a}{}^+(\mathbf{r}_1',\mathbf{r}_2') = u_{\alpha a}(\mathbf{r}_1',\mathbf{r}_2')$$
$$+ \hbar^{-1}\!\int\!\!\int G_{0\omega_{\alpha a}}^+(\mathbf{r}_1',\mathbf{r}_2';\mathbf{r}_1,\mathbf{r}_2)H'(\mathbf{r}_1,\mathbf{r}_2)\chi_{\alpha a}{}^+(\mathbf{r}_1,\mathbf{r}_2)\,d^3r_1\,d^3r_2 \quad (38.19)$$

The propagator associated with H_0 may be obtained by generalizing the second of Eqs. (37.8) and making use of the analysis that leads to (37.19):

$$G_{0\omega_{\alpha a}}^+(\mathbf{r}_1',\mathbf{r}_2';\mathbf{r}_1,\mathbf{r}_2) = S_\beta S_b(\omega_{\alpha a} - \omega_{\beta b} + i\epsilon)^{-1} u_{\beta b}(\mathbf{r}_1',\mathbf{r}_2') u_{\beta b}^*(\mathbf{r}_1,\mathbf{r}_2)$$

$$= S_b w_b(\mathbf{r}_2') w_b^*(\mathbf{r}_2) \frac{\mu}{4\pi^3\hbar} \int (k_b{}^2 - k_\beta{}^2 + i\epsilon)^{-1} \exp\left[i\mathbf{k}_\beta \cdot (\mathbf{r}_1' - \mathbf{r}_1)\right] d^3k_\beta$$

$$= -\frac{\mu}{2\pi\hbar} S_b w_b(\mathbf{r}_2') w_b^*(\mathbf{r}_2) |\mathbf{r}_1' - \mathbf{r}_1|^{-1} \exp\left(i k_b |\mathbf{r}_1' - \mathbf{r}_1|\right) \quad (38.20)$$

$$k_b = +\left[k_\alpha{}^2 + \frac{2\mu}{\hbar^2}(\epsilon_a - \epsilon_b)\right]^{\frac{1}{2}}$$

where k_b has been obtained from energy conservation.

It is now a simple matter to extend the derivation of Eq. (37.21) to the present situation. Substitution of (38.20) into (38.19) and comparison of its asymptotic form with (38.18) lead to

$$f(\mathbf{k}_r,b;\mathbf{k}_\alpha,a) = -\frac{\mu}{2\pi\hbar^2 C} \iint e^{-ik_b r_1 \cos\theta'} w_b^*(\mathbf{r}_2) H'(\mathbf{r}_1,\mathbf{r}_2) \chi_{\alpha a}^+(\mathbf{r}_1,\mathbf{r}_2) d^3r_1 d^3r_2$$

where θ' is the angle between $\mathbf{k}_r$ or $\mathbf{r}_1'$ and $\mathbf{r}_1$. We now define a vector $\mathbf{k}_\beta$, which has magnitude k_b and the direction of $\mathbf{r}_1'$, to give

$$f(\mathbf{k}_\beta,b;\mathbf{k}_\alpha,a) = -\frac{\mu}{2\pi\hbar^2 |C|^2} \langle \beta b | T | \alpha a \rangle$$

$$\langle \beta b | T | \alpha a \rangle = \iint u_{\beta b}^*(\mathbf{r}_1,\mathbf{r}_2) H'(\mathbf{r}_1,\mathbf{r}_2) \chi_{\alpha a}^+(\mathbf{r}_1,\mathbf{r}_2) d^3r_1 d^3r_2 \quad (38.21)$$

Equations (38.21) are an obvious generalization of (37.21); further generalization to scatterers with several internal coordinates can easily be made.

The elastic differential cross section is obtained from the asymptotic form of $\chi_{\alpha a}^+$ as in Sec. 18 and is equal to the square of the magnitude of the amplitude f for which $b = a$:

$$\sigma(\mathbf{k}_\beta,a;\mathbf{k}_\alpha,a) = |f(\mathbf{k}_\beta,a;\mathbf{k}_\alpha,a)|^2 \quad (38.22)$$

In calculating the inelastic cross section, however, account must be taken of the fact that the incident flux is proportional to the relative initial speed $v_\alpha = \hbar k_\alpha/\mu$ while the scattered flux is proportional to v_β. We thus obtain the same multiplying factor v_β/v_α that appeared in the derivation of Eq. (37.5). Thus the inelastic differential cross section is

$$\sigma(\mathbf{k}_\beta,b;\mathbf{k}_\alpha,a) = \frac{v_\beta}{v_\alpha} |f(\mathbf{k}_\beta,b;\mathbf{k}_\alpha,a)|^2 \quad (38.23)$$

ELECTRON SCATTERING FROM HYDROGEN

Equations (38.22) and (38.23) provide an exact description of electron-atom scattering, except for the neglect of exchange between the incident and atomic electrons, which is discussed in Sec. 43. As before, the Born approximation is obtained by replacing $\chi_{\alpha a}{}^+$ in the T matrix element (38.21) by $u_{\alpha a}$. The resulting integrals are not difficult to evaluate in the case of hydrogen.

Equations (38.16) and (38.17) give for the Born matrix element

$$\iint u_{\beta b}^*(\mathbf{r}_1,\mathbf{r}_2)H'(\mathbf{r}_1,\mathbf{r}_2)u_{\alpha a}(\mathbf{r}_1,\mathbf{r}_2)\,d^3r_1\,d^3r_2$$

$$= |C|^2 e^2 \iint \exp\,(i\mathbf{q}\cdot\mathbf{r}_1)\left(\frac{1}{r_{12}}-\frac{1}{r_1}\right)w_b^*(\mathbf{r}_2)w_a(\mathbf{r}_2)\,d^3r_1\,d^3r_2 \quad (38.24)$$

It is convenient to evaluate the r_1 integration first and, moreover, to integrate the $1/r_{12}$ and $1/r_1$ parts separately. However, it must be recognized that these separate parts are not strictly convergent, since for large r_1 (that is, for $r_1 \gg r_2$), the behavior of the first integrand is like that of the second, which gives

$$\int \frac{\exp\,(i\mathbf{q}\cdot\mathbf{r}_1)}{r_1}\,d^3r_1 = \frac{4\pi}{q}\int_0^\infty \sin qr_1\,dr_1 \quad (38.25)$$

Because of the similar behavior for large r_1, the difference between the two parts falls off like $1/r_1^2$ rather than like $1/r_1$, so that, when both are taken together, there is in effect an extra power of r_1 in the denominator of the integrand of (38.25), and the integral converges. The convenience of integrating the two parts separately can be retained by introducing an integrating factor $e^{-\alpha r_1}$ into the integrand of (38.24) and subsequently taking the limit $\alpha \to 0$:

$$\int \frac{\exp\,(i\mathbf{q}\cdot\mathbf{r}_1)}{r_1}\,d^3r_1 = \lim_{\alpha\to 0}\frac{4\pi}{q}\int_0^\infty \sin qr_1 e^{-\alpha r_1}\,dr_1 = \frac{4\pi}{q^2} \quad (38.26)$$

With this preamble, we now write the $1/r_{12}$ part of the r_1 integration in (38.24) as

$$\int \frac{\exp\,(i\mathbf{q}\cdot\mathbf{r}_1)}{r_{12}}\,d^3r_1 = \exp\,(i\mathbf{q}\cdot\mathbf{r}_2)\int \frac{\exp\,(i\mathbf{q}\cdot\boldsymbol{\varrho})}{\rho}\,d^3\rho$$

$$= \frac{4\pi}{q^2}\exp\,(i\mathbf{q}\cdot\mathbf{r}_2)$$

where we have put $\boldsymbol{\varrho} = \mathbf{r}_1 - \mathbf{r}_2$ and made use of (38.26). The Born matrix element (38.24) then becomes

$$\frac{4\pi|C|^2 e^2}{q^2}\int [\exp\,(i\mathbf{q}\cdot\mathbf{r}_2) - 1]w_b^*(\mathbf{r}_2)w_a(\mathbf{r}_2)\,d^3r_2 \quad (38.27)$$

The w's are the hydrogen-atom wave functions given in Eqs. (16.24) and have a simple enough structure so that the r_2 integration is elementary.

For elastic scattering from the ground state the Born amplitude is

$$f_B(\theta) = -\frac{2\mu e^2}{\hbar^2 q^2}\left[(1 + \tfrac{1}{4}q^2 a_0^2)^{-2} - 1\right]$$

$$q = 2k_\alpha \sin \tfrac{1}{2}\theta \qquad k_\beta = k_\alpha$$

(38.28)

Comparison of Eqs. (38.3) and (38.28) shows that the screened coulomb potential used at the beginning of this section does not provide a very good model for hydrogen, although it is better for heavier atoms.

Similar results may be obtained for inelastic scattering. For the transition from the $1S$ ground state ($n = 1$, $l = m = 0$) to the $2S$ first excited state ($n = 2$, $l = m = 0$), the second term in the integrand of (38.27) is zero because of the orthogonality of the initial and final atomic wave functions, and the amplitude is

$$f_B(\theta) = -\frac{8\sqrt{2}\mu a_0^2 e^2}{\hbar^2}(q^2 a_0^2 + \tfrac{9}{4})^{-3}$$

$$q^2 = k_a^2 + k_\beta^2 - 2k_\alpha k_\beta \cos\theta \qquad k_\beta^2 = k_\alpha^2 - \frac{3}{4a_0^2}$$

(38.29)

In the high-energy case, for which the Born approximation is best, $k_\alpha a_0$ is large compared with unity, k_β is nearly equal to k_α, and q is approximately equal to $2k_\alpha \sin\tfrac{1}{2}\theta$. Then (38.29) shows that most of the scattering occurs for $qa_0 \lesssim 1$, which is equivalent to $\theta \lesssim 1/k_\alpha a_0$. Beyond this, the differential cross section falls off with increasing angle approximately as $\operatorname{cosec}^{12}\tfrac{1}{2}\theta$. This is a much more rapid decrease with angle than the $\operatorname{cosec}^4\tfrac{1}{2}\theta$ dependence obtained for elastic scattering from (38.28). The difference occurs because the nucleus contributes to the elastic scattering, and the orthogonality of initial and final wave functions means that only the much more diffuse electron cloud is effective in the inelastic case.

Total cross sections are more easily obtained by integrating over q than over θ. This is accomplished by making use of the second of Eqs. (38.29) to replace $\sin\theta \, d\theta$ by $q \, dq/k_\alpha k_\beta$. The result for elastic scattering in the high-energy case is $7\pi/3k_\alpha^2$, which is about five times as large as the $1S \to 2S$ total cross section, $(\tfrac{2}{3})^{10}(128\pi/5k_\alpha^2)$. Excitation to the states that have $n = 2$, $l = 1$ ($1S \to 2P$ transitions) is most easily calculated by choosing the three final states ($m = 0, \pm 1$) with their polar axis along the momentum transfer vector $\mathbf{q}$. Then the factors $e^{\pm i\phi}$ that appear in the wave functions for $m = \pm 1$ make these matrix elements vanish, and only the state with $m = 0$ is excited. This corresponds physically to the inability of the incident electron, whose momentum loss is along $\mathbf{q}$, to exert a torque on the atomic electron about this axis.

The high-energy total cross section for this process turns out to be $(\frac{2}{3})^{12}(576\pi/k_\alpha^2)[\ln 4k_\alpha a_0 - \frac{137}{120}]$. The appearance of the logarithm derives from an extra factor $1/q^2$ in the differential cross section. Thus, in comparison with the $1S \rightarrow 2S$ scattering, the $1S \rightarrow 2P$ differential scattering is more pronounced at small angles and the total scattering decreases less rapidly with increasing energy at high energies.

PRODUCTION OF A CLOUD CHAMBER TRACK

It seems surprising at first that a fast electron, which we can assume possesses a definite momentum (magnitude and direction) and hence cannot be localized in space, can produce a sharp track in a cloud chamber. This phenomenon may be considered from various points of view. In accordance with Ehrenfest's theorem (Sec. 7), we can represent the electron by a wave packet whose center of gravity moves like a classical particle. If the wavelength is short enough, the packet can be fairly small without spreading rapidly and will then interact only with atoms that lie close to the path of its center. This implies that the electron is represented by a superposition of plane waves and hence has an uncertainty in its momentum that enables its position to be sufficiently well defined.

Another approach consists in describing the electron by a single plane wave and regarding its interaction with the first atom that it excites or ionizes as a position measurement that carries with it an uncertainty of the order of the atomic size. Thereafter, the electron is represented by a packet, like that described in the preceding paragraph, which is well localized if the first atom is large in comparison with the wavelength ($ka \gg 1$).

We consider here in detail still a third description in which the electron and the atoms of the cloud chamber gas are treated as parts of a single system, so that we do not have to regard an atomic interaction as a position determination that changes the structure of the electron's wave function. To simplify matters, we assume that there are just two atoms present in their ground states and that their nuclei are far apart from each other and are fixed in space. We then calculate the cross section for a process in which both atoms are excited and the electron is scattered inelastically. For a fast incident electron, perturbation theory can be used; however, since the interactions of the electron with the two atoms are distinct, the process does not take place in first order, and it is necessary to go to second order. The calculation is interesting both because of the answer obtained and because it provides an instructive example of second-order perturbation theory.[1]

[1] W. Heisenberg, "The Physical Principles of the Quantum Theory," pp. 66–76 (University of Chicago Press, Chicago, 1930).

The result of the calculation is that the cross section is very small unless the momentum vector of the incident electron is nearly parallel to the line that joins the two nuclei, and also unless the initial and final electron momenta are nearly parallel. These three directions can have an angular spread in radians that is of the order of the ratio of the wavelength of the electron to the size of the atom. This is analogous to the result obtained in the preceding subsection for the inelastic collision of a fast electron with a hydrogen atom: The angular spread of the scattered electron was found to be roughly $1/k_a a_0$. It is also in agreement with the wave-packet description of the process, since a localization of the electron by an atomic size a in a direction transverse to its motion produces an uncertainty in the transverse-momentum component of amount $\hbar/a$ and an angular spread of order $\hbar/ap \approx 1/ka$.

SECOND-ORDER PERTURBATION THEORY

The first-order perturbation or Born approximation for the T matrix element (38.21) was obtained by replacing $\chi_{\alpha a}^+$ by $u_{\alpha a}$. In similar fashion, the second-order approximation is obtained by replacing $\chi_{\alpha a}^+$ by the second term of the perturbation series that is analogous to Eq. (37.15), to obtain

$$\frac{1}{\hbar} \iiiint u_{\beta b}^*(\mathbf{r}_1',\mathbf{r}_2')H'(\mathbf{r}_1',\mathbf{r}_2')G_{0\omega\alpha a}^+(\mathbf{r}_1',\mathbf{r}_2';\mathbf{r}_1,\mathbf{r}_2)H'(\mathbf{r}_1,\mathbf{r}_2)$$

$$u_{\alpha a}(\mathbf{r}_1,\mathbf{r}_2)\, d^3r_1'\, d^3r_2'\, d^3r_1\, d^3r_2$$

Substitution for the propagator can be made as in the first line of Eq. (38.20), where now the summations are over γ and c rather than over β and b. We thus obtain for the second-order contribution to the T matrix element[1]

$$S_\gamma S_c (E_{\alpha a} - E_{\gamma c} + i\epsilon)^{-1}\langle\beta b|H'|\gamma c\rangle\langle\gamma c|H'|\alpha a\rangle \tag{38.30}$$

This expression may be thought of as describing a two-step process in which the system makes a transition from the initial state αa to all possible intermediate states γc under the influence of the perturbation H', and then a similar transition from γc to the final state βb. Energy is conserved between initial and final states but need not be for the intermediate states. These have only a transient existence, and according to the uncertainty relation (3.3) it is impossible to determine the energy of such short-lived states with any precision. Thus it is not surprising that their contributions to the second-order T matrix element are inversely proportional to this energy discrepancy. Similar second-

[1] This was called "Golden Rule No. 1" by E. Fermi, "Nuclear Physics," p. 148 (University of Chicago Press, Chicago, 1950).

order matrix elements appeared in Eqs. (31.20) in connection with the perturbation of discrete energy levels.

The notation underlying (38.30) must be generalized before it can be applied to the present situation. The hamiltonian for the electron and the two well-separated atoms is

$$H = H_0 + H'$$

$$H_0 = -\frac{\hbar^2}{2m}\nabla^2 + H_1(1) + H_2(2)$$

$$H'(\mathbf{r},1,2) = H_1'(\mathbf{r},1) + H_2'(\mathbf{r},2)$$

Here $\mathbf{r}$ is the electron coordinate, H_1 is the hamiltonian for the first atom by itself, 1 denotes all the internal coordinates of that atom, and H_1' is the interaction between the electron and the first atom; the second atom is described in similar fashion. The expression (38.30) may then be written

$$S_\gamma S_{c_1} S_{c_2}(E_{\alpha a_1 a_2} - E_{\gamma c_1 c_2} + i\epsilon)^{-1}\langle \beta b_1 b_2|H'|\gamma c_1 c_2\rangle\langle\gamma c_1 c_2|H'|\alpha a_1 a_2\rangle$$

It is apparent that there are two possible groups of intermediate states $\gamma c_1 c_2$: that in which the first atom has made a transition from state a_1 to state b_1 under the influence of H_1' ($c_1 = b_1$) while the second atom has not changed its state ($c_2 = a_2$), and that in which $c_1 = a_1$ while the second atom has changed its state from a_2 to b_2 under the influence of H_2' ($c_2 = b_2$). Thus the second-order matrix element may be written

$$S_\gamma(E_{\alpha a_1} - E_{\gamma b_1} + i\epsilon)^{-1}\langle\beta b_2|H_2'|\gamma a_2\rangle\langle\gamma b_1|H_1'|\alpha a_1\rangle$$
$$+ S_\gamma(E_{\alpha a_2} - E_{\gamma b_2} + i\epsilon)^{-1}\langle\beta b_1|H_1'|\gamma a_1\rangle\langle\gamma b_2|H_2'|\alpha a_2\rangle \quad (38.31)$$

EVALUATION OF THE SECOND-ORDER MATRIX ELEMENT

We now evaluate the first summation in (38.31) explicitly and later indicate the changes that are to be made in the result to obtain the second summation. The factors that appear there may be written in analogy with (38.24) and (38.20):

$$\langle\gamma b_1|H_1'|\alpha a_1\rangle = |C|^2\iint \exp\left(-i\mathbf{k}_\gamma\cdot\mathbf{r} + i\mathbf{k}_\alpha\cdot\mathbf{r}\right)$$
$$\times H_1'(\mathbf{r},1)w_{b_1}^*(1)w_{a_1}(1)\,d^3r\,d\tau_1$$
$$\langle\beta b_2|H_2'|\gamma a_2\rangle = |C|^2\iint \exp\left(-i\mathbf{k}_\beta\cdot\mathbf{r}' + i\mathbf{k}_\gamma\cdot\mathbf{r}'\right)$$
$$\times H_2'(\mathbf{r}',2)w_{b_2}^*(2)w_{a_2}(2)\,d^3r'\,d\tau_2$$

$$(38.32)$$

$$E_{\alpha a_1} - E_{\gamma b_1} + i\epsilon = \frac{\hbar^2}{2m}\left(\kappa^2 - k_\gamma{}^2 + i\epsilon\right)$$

$$\kappa^2 \equiv k_\alpha{}^2 - \frac{2m}{\hbar^2}\left(\epsilon_{b_1} - \epsilon_{a_1}\right)$$

Then, in analogy with the derivation of Eq. (37.18), the summation over γ can be carried out to give

$$- \frac{m|C|^2}{2\pi\hbar^2} \iint |\mathbf{r}' - \mathbf{r}|^{-1} \exp{(i\kappa|\mathbf{r}' - \mathbf{r}| - i\mathbf{k}_\beta \cdot \mathbf{r}' + i\mathbf{k}_\alpha \cdot \mathbf{r})}\, d^3r'\, d^3r$$
$$\times \int w_{b_2}^*(2)H_2'(\mathbf{r}',2)w_{a_2}(2)\, d\tau_2 \int w_{b_1}^*(1)H_1'(\mathbf{r},1)w_{a_1}(1)\, d\tau_1 \quad (38.33)$$

The nucleus of the first atom can, without loss of generality, be placed at the origin, and that of the second atom at the point $\mathbf{R}$. Then the integral over the internal coordinates of the first atom will be very small unless $\mathbf{r}$ is close to zero, and the corresponding integral for the second atom will be very small unless $\mathbf{r}'$ is close to $\mathbf{R}$. We therefore write

$$F_1(\mathbf{r}) \equiv \int w_{b_1}^*(1)H_1'(\mathbf{r},1)w_{a_1}(1)\, d\tau_1$$
$$F_2(\mathbf{r}' - R) \equiv \int w_{b_2}^*(2)H_2'(\mathbf{r}',2)w_{a_2}(2)\, d\tau_2$$

These F's are very small except when their arguments differ from zero by distances of the order of the size of the atom. We put $\mathbf{r}'' \equiv \mathbf{r}' - \mathbf{R}$, so that practically all the contribution to (38.33) comes from small values of $\mathbf{r}$ and $\mathbf{r}''$. We can then obtain the leading term of (38.33) for large R by approximating

$$|\mathbf{r}' - \mathbf{r}| = |\mathbf{R} + \mathbf{r}'' - \mathbf{r}| \approx R + \frac{\mathbf{R} \cdot \mathbf{r}''}{R} - \frac{\mathbf{R} \cdot \mathbf{r}}{R} \qquad |\mathbf{r}' - \mathbf{r}|^{-1} \approx R^{-1}$$

It is convenient to define a vector $\mathbf{\kappa}$ that has the magnitude κ and the direction of $\mathbf{R}$. Then substitution into (38.33) gives

$$- \frac{m|C|^2}{2\pi\hbar^2} \frac{1}{R} \exp{[i(\mathbf{\kappa} - \mathbf{k}_\beta) \cdot \mathbf{R}]} \int F_2(\mathbf{r}'') \exp{[i(\mathbf{\kappa} - \mathbf{k}_\beta) \cdot \mathbf{r}'']}\, d^3r''$$
$$\times \int F_1(\mathbf{r}) \exp{[i(\mathbf{k}_\alpha - \mathbf{\kappa}) \cdot \mathbf{r}]}\, d^3r \quad (38.34)$$

In similar fashion, the second summation in (38.31) becomes

$$- \frac{m|C|^2}{2\pi\hbar^2} \frac{1}{R} \exp{[i(\mathbf{\kappa}' + \mathbf{k}_\alpha) \cdot \mathbf{R}]} \int F_2(\mathbf{r}'') \exp{[-i(\mathbf{\kappa}' + \mathbf{k}_\beta) \cdot \mathbf{r}'']}\, d^3r''$$
$$\times \int F_1(\mathbf{r}) \exp{[i(\mathbf{k}_\alpha + \mathbf{\kappa}') \cdot \mathbf{r}]}\, d^3r \quad (38.35)$$

where $\mathbf{\kappa}'$ is a vector in the direction of $\mathbf{R}$ whose magnitude is given by the last of Eqs. (38.32) with $\epsilon_{b_1} - \epsilon_{a_1}$ replaced by $\epsilon_{b_2} - \epsilon_{a_2}$.

The differential cross section is obtained by substituting the sum of (38.34) and (38.35) in place of the T matrix element in the scattering amplitude (38.21) and then into Eq. (38.23). Conservation of energy requires that $k_\beta^2 = k_\alpha^2 - (2m/\hbar^2)(\epsilon_{b_1} + \epsilon_{b_2} - \epsilon_{a_1} - \epsilon_{a_2})$.

DISCUSSION OF THE CROSS SECTION

The integrals that appear in (38.34) and (38.35) have the characteristic structure associated with the perturbation treatment of collision problems. They are very small unless the propagation vector that appears in the exponent of the integrand has a magnitude that is of order $1/a$ or less, where a is a typical linear dimension of the atom (F significantly different from zero). It follows that (38.34) is appreciable only when the vectors $\mathbf{k}_\alpha$, $\mathbf{\kappa}$, and $\mathbf{k}_\beta$ are nearly equal in magnitude and direction. Because of the assumption that the incident electron is fast, the magnitudes are very nearly equal in any event; also, the direction of $\mathbf{\kappa}$ is the same as that of $\mathbf{R}$. Thus the cross section that arises from (38.34) is appreciable only when the vectors $\mathbf{R}$ and $\mathbf{k}_\beta$ are nearly parallel to $\mathbf{\kappa}_\alpha$. The permitted angular deviation from parallelism is easily seen to be of order $1/k_\alpha a$.

Similarly, it follows that (38.35) is appreciable only when $\mathbf{\kappa}'$, and hence $\mathbf{R}$, is nearly antiparallel to both $\mathbf{k}_\alpha$ and $\mathbf{k}_\beta$, in which case the latter two vectors are nearly parallel to each other.

The two terms together show that excitation of both atoms occurs with appreciable probability only when the line joining the two atoms is nearly parallel to the direction of the incident electron. There is, however, no further restriction on the location of the atoms, since the choice of origin of the coordinate system is arbitrary. Thus, although the cloud chamber track has a well-defined orientation in space, it may appear anywhere if the incident electron is described by a plane wave. It is apparent also that the cross section falls off inversely as the square of the distance R between the two atoms, as would be expected.

EIKONAL APPROXIMATION

The perturbation methods developed earlier in this section replace χ_α^+ in the T matrix element (37.2) by the first one or two terms on the right side of Eq. (37.15). A quite different approximation for χ_α^+ can also be found along the lines of the WKB approximation, which was discussed in Sec. 34; substitution into (37.2) then yields the *eikonal approximation*.[1]

The WKB approximation starts from the exact equations (34.2) and expands $S(\mathbf{r})$, the logarithm of the wave function, in powers of $\hbar$ in the one-dimensional case. The leading term, S_0, approximates the phase of the wave function, and the next term, S_1, approximates the magnitude. A rough validity criterion was obtained in (34.9); in three dimensions it corresponds to the requirement that

$$\left| \frac{\boldsymbol{\nabla} k}{k^2} \right| \ll 1 \qquad k(\mathbf{r}) \equiv +\frac{1}{\hbar} \{2\mu[E_\alpha - V(\mathbf{r})]\}^{\frac{1}{2}}$$

[1] G. Molière, *Z. Naturforsch.* **2,** 133 (1947). The earlier history of this approach, in connection with optics and classical mechanics, is reviewed by M. Born and E. Wolf, "Principles of Optics," pp. 111, 132 (Pergamon Press, New York, 1959).

Physically, this means that the potential energy changes so slowly that the local momentum $\hbar k(\mathbf{r})$ is sensibly constant over many wavelengths.

For the present application, we shall assume in addition that S_1 can be neglected in comparison with S_0 and that $V(\mathbf{r})$ is everywhere small in comparison with E_α. We thus have a high-energy approximation in which $V(\mathbf{r})$ does not vary rapidly. It might therefore be thought at first that the end result is equivalent to the Born approximation. However, Eq. (38.4) shows that, at high energies, $\left| (\hbar v_\alpha)^{-1} \int_0^\infty V(r)\, dr \right|$ must be small in comparison with unity in order for the Born approximation to be valid. This parameter can be larger than unity for a weak potential of long range even though $V \ll E_\alpha$; the eikonal approximation does not limit its value and so is superior to the Born approximation.

We therefore put

$$\chi_\alpha{}^+(\mathbf{r}) \approx C \exp \frac{iS_0(\mathbf{r})}{\hbar} \qquad (\boldsymbol{\nabla} S_0)^2 = 2\mu[E_\alpha - V(\mathbf{r})] = \hbar^2 k^2(\mathbf{r})$$

$$(38.36)$$

The solution of this differential equation for S_0 when V can be neglected is $S_0(\mathbf{r}) = \hbar \mathbf{k}_\alpha \cdot \mathbf{r}$, where $\mathbf{k}_\alpha$ is any vector with magnitude $k_\alpha = (2\mu E_\alpha/\hbar^2)^{\frac{1}{2}}$. In this case $\chi_\alpha{}^+$ is simply u_α, as would be expected, and the Born approximation is obtained. It is convenient to choose the positive z axis to lie along the direction of $\mathbf{k}_\alpha$, so that $S_0(\mathbf{r}) = \hbar k_\alpha z$ when V can be neglected.

When V is finite but small in comparison with E_α, we try the following approximate solution of (38.36):

$$S_0(\mathbf{r}) \approx \hbar k_\alpha z - \frac{1}{v_\alpha} \int_{z_0}^z V(x,y,z')\, dz' \tag{38.37}$$

where the relative velocity is $v_\alpha = \hbar k_\alpha/\mu$ and z_0 is a constant to be determined shortly; the integral is assumed to converge for all $\mathbf{r}$ and z_0. Substitution of (38.37) into the second of Eqs. (38.36) shows that the latter is satisfied apart from terms of order $\mu V^2/E_\alpha$; these may be neglected in comparison with $2\mu V$ since $V \ll E_\alpha$. We thus obtain

$$\chi_\alpha{}^+(\mathbf{r}) \approx C \exp \left\{ i \left[k_\alpha z - \frac{1}{\hbar v_\alpha} \int_{z_0}^z V(x,y,z')\, dz' \right] \right\} \tag{38.38}$$

Within the limitations of the approximations introduced above, (38.38) is a solution of the wave equation but is not necessarily of the outgoing type. We now show that $\chi_\alpha{}^\pm$ is obtained according as z_0 is chosen to be $\mp \infty$. To see this, we first write (38.38) in the form of a plane plus a scattered wave:

$$u_\alpha(\mathbf{r}) + C e^{ik_\alpha z} \left\{ \exp \left[-\frac{i}{\hbar v_\alpha} \int_{z_0}^z V(x,y,z')\, dz' \right] - 1 \right\}$$

This scattered wave vanishes outside of a tube whose diameter is that of the potential and which is centered on the z axis. If we choose $z_0 = -\infty$, the asymptotic scattered wave also vanishes in the negative-z half of the tube and is a constant multiple of $e^{ik_\alpha z}$ in the positive-z half so that it represents an outgoing wave. Similarly, if we choose $z_0 = +\infty$, the asymptotic scattered wave vanishes in the positive-z half of the tube and is an ingoing wave in the negative-z half.

As remarked above, the eikonal approximation goes beyond the Born approximation in that the phase difference between χ_α^+ and u_α is taken into account in lowest order at high energies. This shows that the Born approximation is valid at high energies so long as this phase difference is small in comparison with unity:

$$\left[(\hbar v_\alpha)^{-1} \int_{-\infty}^{z} V(x,y,z')\, dz' \right] \ll 1 \qquad \text{for all } \mathbf{r} \qquad (38.39)$$

This validity criterion is more general than that inferred from (38.4) since it is applicable when $V(\mathbf{r})$ is not spherically symmetric. The use of χ_α^+ in place of u_α corresponds to neglect of the change in direction of the velocity of the particle as it moves through the potential and to inclusion of the effect of change in velocity magnitude insofar as it affects the phase but not the amplitude of the wave function.

SCATTERING AMPLITUDE AND CROSS SECTION

Substitution of (38.38) into (37.20) gives for the scattering amplitude

$$f(\mathbf{k}_\beta, \mathbf{k}_\alpha) \approx -\frac{\mu}{2\pi\hbar^2} \int V(\mathbf{r}) \exp\left\{ i\left[\mathbf{q} \cdot \mathbf{r} - \frac{1}{\hbar v_\alpha} \int_{-\infty}^{z} V(x,y,z')\, dz' \right] \right\} d^3r$$

It can be shown that this expression is valid only so long as the scattering angle θ is small in comparison with $(k_\alpha a)^{-\frac{1}{2}}$, where a is the range of the potential.[1] For this range of θ, $\mathbf{q} \cdot \mathbf{r}$ can be replaced by $q_x x + q_y y$; this is because $q_x x$ and $q_y y$ are $\lesssim k_\alpha a\theta$, which may be much larger than unity, whereas $q_z z \lesssim k_\alpha a\theta^2$, which is much smaller than unity. The integration over z can then be performed and leads to

$$f(\mathbf{k}_\beta, \mathbf{k}_\alpha) \approx \frac{ik_\alpha}{2\pi} \int_{-\infty}^{\infty} \int_{-\infty}^{\infty} e^{i(q_x x + q_y y)}$$
$$\left\{ 1 - \exp\left[-\frac{i}{\hbar v_\alpha} \int_{-\infty}^{\infty} V(x,y,z)\, dz \right] \right\} dx\, dy \qquad (38.40)$$

[1] L. I. Schiff, *Phys. Rev.* **103**, 443 (1956). Similar expressions that are valid for larger angles are derived in this paper and more comprehensively by D. S. Saxon and L. I. Schiff, *Nuovo Cimento* **6**, 614 (1957). For a detailed review of the small-angle case and derivation of additional results, see R. J. Glauber, in W. E. Brittin and L. G. Dunham (eds.), "Lectures in Theoretical Physics," vol. I, p. 315 (Interscience, New York, 1959).

The total cross section can be obtained from (38.40) with the help of the optical theorem (20.23):

$$\sigma_{\text{tot}} = \frac{4\pi}{k_\alpha} \text{Im} \left[f(\mathbf{k}_\alpha, \mathbf{k}_\alpha) \right] \approx 2 \int_{-\infty}^{\infty} \int_{-\infty}^{\infty} \left\{ 1 - \right.$$
$$\left. \exp\left[-\frac{1}{\hbar v_\alpha} \int_{-\infty}^{\infty} V_I(x,y,z)\, dz \right] \cos\left[\frac{1}{\hbar v_\alpha} \int_{-\infty}^{\infty} V_R(x,y,z)\, dz \right] \right\} dx\, dy$$

$$(38.41)$$

As in Sec. 20, we have put $V = V_R - iV_I$, where V_R is real and V_I is real and positive.

It is interesting to see if this expression for the total cross section is consistent with plausible estimates for the total elastic cross section σ_{el} and for the sum of the total absorption and inelastic cross sections σ_{abs}. It is reasonable to suppose that, even though (38.40) is not valid at large angles, the amplitude gets very small there, and most of the contribution to σ_{el} comes from small angles. We can then put $q_x \approx k_\alpha\theta \cos\phi$, $q_y \approx k_\alpha \sin\phi$, and replace the solid angle element as follows: $\sin\theta\, d\theta\, d\phi \approx \theta\, d\theta\, d\phi \approx dq_x\, dq_y/k_\alpha^2$. In the interest of simplicity, we approximate further by extending the limits on q_x and q_y to $\pm\infty$. We thus obtain

$$\sigma_{\text{el}} \approx \frac{1}{k_\alpha^2} \int_{-\infty}^{\infty} \int_{-\infty}^{\infty} |f(\mathbf{k}_\beta, \mathbf{k}_\alpha)|^2 \, dq_x\, dq_y$$
$$\approx \int_{-\infty}^{\infty} \int_{-\infty}^{\infty} \left\{ 1 - 2\exp\left[-\frac{1}{\hbar v_\alpha} \int_{-\infty}^{\infty} V_I(x,y,z)\, dz \right] \right.$$
$$\left. \times \cos\left[\frac{1}{\hbar v_\alpha} \int_{-\infty}^{\infty} V_R(x,y,z)\, dz \right] + \exp\left[-\frac{2}{\hbar v_\alpha} \int_{-\infty}^{\infty} V_I(x,y,z)\, dz \right] \right\} dx\, dy$$

$$(38.42)$$

where use has been made of Eq. (11.10). In similar fashion, Eq. (20.3) can be used to calculate σ_{abs} if we substitute for ψ from Eq. (38.38) with $C = 1$ and $z_0 = -\infty$:

$$\sigma_{\text{abs}} \approx \frac{2}{\hbar v_\alpha} \int_{-\infty}^{\infty} \int_{-\infty}^{\infty} \int_{-\infty}^{\infty} V_I(x,y,z)$$
$$\exp\left[-\frac{2}{\hbar v_\alpha} \int_{-\infty}^{z} V_I(x,y,z')\, dz' \right] dx\, dy\, dz$$
$$= \int_{-\infty}^{\infty} \int_{-\infty}^{\infty} \left\{ 1 - \exp\left[-\frac{2}{\hbar v_\alpha} \int_{-\infty}^{\infty} V_I(x,y,z)\, dz \right] \right\} dx\, dy$$

$$(38.43)$$

It is evident that Eqs. (38.41) to (38.43) are indeed consistent with each other.

All equations (38.40) to (38.43) have the form of integrals over the transverse coordinates x and y. Each x, y pair may be thought of as defining a classical trajectory; to our approximation it is a straight line parallel to the z axis, with *impact parameter* $b = (x^2 + y^2)^{\frac{1}{2}}$, since, as remarked at the end of the preceding subsection, the change in direction of the particle velocity as it moves through the potential has been neglected. The scattering amplitude and cross sections are then sums of contributions from all possible impact parameters. In the case in which V is symmetric about the z axis, $\int_{-\infty}^{\infty} \int_{-\infty}^{\infty} dx\,dy$ can be replaced by $2\pi \int_{0}^{\infty} b\,db$; for example, (38.40) then becomes

$$f(\theta) \approx ik_\alpha \int_0^\infty J_0\,(qb) \left\{ 1 - \exp\left[-\frac{i}{\hbar v_\alpha} \int_{-\infty}^{\infty} V(b,z)\,dz \right] \right\} b\,db$$
$$q \approx k_\alpha \theta \quad (38.44)$$

where J_0 is the ordinary Bessel function of order zero.

PERFECT ABSORBER

A simple example of the foregoing results is provided by a perfect absorber: an object for which, even though $V_I \ll E_\alpha$, $(\hbar v_\alpha)^{-1} \int_{-\infty}^{\infty} V_I(x,y,z)\,dz$ is so large that the exponential is negligibly small compared with unity for all trajectories x, y that pass through the object. In this case it follows from Eqs. (38.41) to (38.43) that

$$\sigma_{\text{el}} \approx \sigma_{\text{abs}} \approx A \qquad \sigma_{\text{tot}} \approx 2A \tag{38.45}$$

where A is the cross-sectional area of the object. This result is closely related to that noted in connection with Eq. (19.24). In that case there was no absorption, but the elastic scattering could be divided into equal contributions πa^2 arising from spherically symmetric scattering by the rigid sphere of radius a and from a diffraction peak in the forward direction. In the present case there is no large-angle scattering, but the elastic diffraction scattering is equal to the absorption.

The angular dependence of the diffraction scattering is easily obtained if the absorber is a sphere of radius a. Equation (38.44) then becomes

$$f(\theta) \approx ik_\alpha \int_0^a J_0(k_\alpha b\theta)b\,db = \frac{ia}{\theta} J_1(k_\alpha a\theta)$$

The differential elastic scattering cross section $|f(\theta)|^2$ has a peak at $\theta = 0$ with height $\frac{1}{4}k_\alpha{}^2 a^4$ and angular breadth of order $1/k_\alpha a$. The total elastic cross section may again be estimated by extending the upper limit on θ to ∞, to obtain

$$\sigma_{\text{el}} \approx 2\pi \int_0^\infty |f(\theta)|^2\theta\,d\theta = 2\pi a^2 \int_0^\infty J_1{}^2(z)\,\frac{dz}{z} = \pi a^2$$

in agreement with (38.45).

39□ANALYTIC PROPERTIES AND DISPERSION RELATIONS

Stationary collision theory, developed and applied in the two preceding sections, deals with elements of the scattering and transition matrices for particular values of the energy. Although most of the discussion was concerned with special situations, it was pointed out that useful general results could be obtained from the assumed symmetry and unitarity of the S matrix. General results of a different kind can be obtained from the assumptions that the S and T matrix elements are analytic functions of the energy and of other physical parameters, such as scattering angle and angular momentum, when these parameters are regarded as complex variables. These results are expressed in the form of *dispersion relations*. A typical disperison relation connects T matrix elements at different physical values of the energy, that is, at real rather than complex energies. The assumed analytic dependence of the T matrix element on the energy even when the energy is complex (and hence unphysical) provides a bridge between physical values by way of the complex-energy plane.

Thus a dispersion relation can be derived only after the analytic behavior of the T matrix element has been established or conjectured, so that the locations of poles and branch cuts and the asymptotic dependence are believed to be known. As originally derived in optics by Kronig and Kramers,[1] the analytic behavior underlying the dispersion relation was inferred from *causality*: the statement that a light signal has a limiting speed c, so that the scattered electromagnetic radiation cannot outrun the incident wave. Causality connects events that occur at different times and hence relates Fourier components of the electromagnetic field that correspond to different frequencies. But in nonrelativistic quantum mechanics there is no limiting speed and hence no causality of this kind, so that it might at first be thought that there are no dispersion relations. However, solutions of the Schrödinger equation that correspond to different values of the energy or the angular momentum are in fact connected by the assumption that the potential energy is independent of these parameters (or in more complicated situations has a specified dependence on them).

In this section we first consider the analytic properties of a diagonal element of the S matrix in the angular momentum representation when the potential energy is spherically symmetric. From Eq. (37.36), this is equal to $e^{2i\delta_l(k)}$, where the lth phase shift depends on the energy or on k. Some useful results, including dispersion relations, can be derived once the analytic behavior is established. We then obtain a dispersion relation for the forward scattering amplitude, which is also valid when the potential is spherically symmetric. Through the optical theorem [Eq. (20.23)],

---

[1] See, for example, R. G. Newton, "Scattering Theory of Waves and Particles," sec. 4.2 (McGraw-Hill, New York, 1966).

this relates the forward scattering differential cross section (which requires knowledge of both the real and imaginary parts of the forward amplitude) to an integral over the energy of the total cross section.

No attempt is made at mathematical rigor, and some needed results are stated without proof. More detailed derivations are given in the references cited below and in the original papers to which they in turn refer.

RADIAL SOLUTIONS[1]

The regular solution of the radical wave equation (19.2) can be specified in terms of its boundary condition near the origin:

$$\phi_l(k,r) \xrightarrow[r \to 0]{} \frac{r^{l+1}}{(2l + 1)!!} \tag{39.1}$$

$\phi_l(k,r)$ is an even function of k since it depends on k only through k^2, and it is real when k is real since $V(r)$ is assumed to be real. We work with $\phi_l(k,r)$, rather than with the proportional solution $rR_l(r)$ that was introduced in Sec. 19, because the boundary condition (39.1) is independent of k. This means that use can be made of a theorem of Poincaré, which applies to the solution of an ordinary differential equation like (19.2) with the property that the dependence of the equation on some parameter k is only through an entire function[2] of k, in this case k^2. According to this theorem, a solution specified by a boundary condition that is independent of k is itself an entire function of k. Thus, for fixed r, $\phi_l(k,r)$ is an entire function of k whereas $rR_l(r)$ need not be.

$\phi_l(k,r)$ is a standing wave and has the asymptotic form of a sinusoidal function of kr. Since it is convenient to have traveling wave solutions of (19.2) available as well, we define another solution $f_l(k,r)$ through an asymptotic boundary condition:

$$f_l(k,r) \xrightarrow[r \to \infty]{} i^l e^{-ikr} \tag{39.2}$$

This is evidently irregular at the origin, where it is proportional to $rn_l(kr)$ and hence behaves like r^{-l}. [For $l = 0$, we follow the procedure of Sec. 15

---

[1] For a fuller account of the analytic properties of partial wave amplitudes, see R. G. Newton, *J. Math. Phys.* **1,** 319 (1960) and "Scattering Theory of Waves and Particles," chap. 12 (McGraw-Hill, New York, 1966); M. L. Goldberger and K. M. Watson, "Collision Theory," sec. 6.5 (Wiley, New York, 1964); V. De Alfaro and T. Regge, "Potential Scattering," chaps. 4, 5 (Wiley, New York, 1965). The notation used in Newton's book is slightly different from that followed here or in the other references cited.

[2] An entire function or an integral function of k is an analytic function of k that is regular for all finite values of k.

and regard the solution that behaves like $r j_0(kr) \propto r$ at the origin as regular, and the solution that behaves like $r n_0(kr) \xrightarrow[r \to 0]{}$ constant as irregular.]

As remarked in Sec. 19, the asymptotic form (39.2) requires that $V(r)$ fall off faster than $1/r$ for large r. It is also easy to see that the power dependence of (39.1) requires that $V(r)$ become infinite less rapidly than $1/r^2$ as $r \to 0$. We shall actually assume the more restrictive conditions

$$\int_0^\infty r |V(r)|\, dr < \infty \qquad \text{and} \qquad \int_0^\infty r^2 |V(r)|\, dr < \infty \qquad (39.3)$$

throughout this section and occasionally limit the asymptotic behavior of $V(r)$ even more severely.

Except at $k = 0$, a third solution $f_l(-k,r)$ is linearly independent of $f_l(k,r)$ and has the asymptotic form

$$f_l(-k,r) \xrightarrow[r \to \infty]{} i^l e^{ikr} \qquad (39.4)$$

Thus $\phi_l(k,r)$ can be expressed as a linear combination of $f_l(\pm k,r)$. This corresponds to the procedure, followed in Sec. 19, of writing $r R_l(r)$ in the asymptotic region as a linear combination of $e^{\pm ikr}$. The ratio between the coefficients of these two terms is essentially the S matrix element (37.36):

$$S_l(k) \equiv e^{2i\delta_l(k)} \qquad (39.5)$$

Thus we can study the analytic properties of $S_l(k)$ by studying those of $f_l(k,r)$ and making use of the fact that $\phi_l(k,r)$ is an entire function of k.

The analytic properties of $f_l(k,r)$ can be established by working with an integral equation that it satisfies, as is done in the references cited above. The conclusion is that, for fixed $r > 0$, $f_l(k,r)$ is an analytic function of k that is regular in the open lower half of the complex k plane; it is also continuous onto the real axis except at $k = 0$. If the potential satisfies not only (39.3) but also the condition

$$\int_0^\infty r |V(r)| e^{\mu r}\, dr < \infty \qquad \mu > 0 \qquad (39.6)$$

the region of regularity also includes the strip in the upper half of the k plane for which $\text{Im } k < \frac{1}{2}\mu$, except for a pole of order l at $k = 0$. Further, if $V(r)$ vanishes asymptotically faster than any exponential, so that (39.6) is satisfied for arbitrarily large μ, then $k^l f_l(k,r)$ is an entire function of k for all fixed $r > 0$. This will occur, for example, if $V(r)$ falls off like a gaussian function for large r or vanishes identically for r greater than some finite value.

It follows from (39.2), (39.4), and the reality of the differential equation (19.2) that

$$[f_l(-k,r)]^* = (-1)^l f_l(k,r) \qquad (39.7)$$

for real k.   If now we move away from the real axis but stay in a region in which $f_l(k,r)$ is analytic, we note that f_l^* satisfies the same equation with k^* that f_l satisfies with k.   The boundary conditions (39.2) and (39.4) are then consistent with each other for complex k if we replace (39.7) with

$$[f_l(-k^*,r)]^* = (-1)^l f_l(k,r) \tag{39.8}$$

In similar fashion, the fact that $\phi_l(k,r)$ is an entire function of k that is real for real k implies, by Schwarz's reflection principle, that

$$[\phi_l(k^*,r)]^* = \phi_l(k,r) \tag{39.9}$$

for all finite complex k.

JOST FUNCTION

As remarked just after (39.4), $\phi_l(k,r)$ can be expressed as a linear combination of $f_l(\pm k,r)$.   We write this combination in the form

$$\phi_l(k,r) = \tfrac{1}{2}ik^{-l-1}[f_l(-k)f_l(k,r) - (-1)^l f_l(k)f_l(-k,r)] \tag{39.10}$$

which is consistent with the requirement that $\phi_l(k,r)$ be an even function of k.   The coefficient $f_l(k)$ is called the *Jost function*[1] and is closely related to $S_l(k)$.   This relation is obtained by comparing the asymptotic form of (39.10),

$$\phi_l(k,r) \xrightarrow[r \to \infty]{} \frac{1}{2}\left(\frac{i}{k}\right)^{l+1} [f_l(-k)e^{-ikr} - (-1)^l f_l(k)e^{ikr}] \tag{39.11}$$

with the asymptotic form of $rR_l(r)$ given by (19.8):

$$rR_l(r) \xrightarrow[r \to \infty]{} \frac{1}{2k}\, i^{l+1}e^{i\delta_l}[e^{-ikr-i\delta_l} - (-1)^l e^{ikr+i\delta_l}] \tag{39.12}$$

It follows from this comparison and the definition (39.5) that

$$S_l(k) = e^{2i\delta_l(k)} = \frac{f_l(k)}{f_l(-k)} \tag{39.13}$$

As might be expected from the form of Eq. (39.13), the analytic properties of the S matrix element are somewhat more complicated than those of the Jost function; for example, $S_l(k)$ generally has poles both at the poles of $f_l(k)$ and at the zeros of $f_l(-k)$.

The complex conjugate of Eq. (39.10) is

$$[\phi_l(k,r)]^* = -\tfrac{1}{2}i(k^*)^{-l-1}[f_l(-k)f_l(k,r) - (-1)^l f_l(k)f_l(-k,r)]^*$$

On substituting k^* for k throughout this equation and making use of

[1] R. Jost, *Helv. Phys. Acta* **20**, 256 (1947).

Eqs. (39.8) and (39.9), we find that

$$[f_l(-k^*)]^* = f_l(k) \tag{39.14}$$

For real k, Eqs. (39.13) and (39.14) show that $|S_l(k)| = 1$, so that the S matrix is unitary and $\delta_l(k)$ is real, as is expected for a real potential. It also follows that

$$f_l(k) = |f_l(k)| e^{i\delta_l(k)} \tag{39.15}$$

for real k.

We now wish to make use of our knowledge of the analytic properties of $\phi_l(k,r)$ and $f_l(k,r)$ to determine the analytic properties of $f_l(k)$. To accomplish this, we use Eq. (39.10), which defines $f_l(k)$, to obtain an explicit expression for $f_l(k)$ in terms of $\phi_l(k,r)$ and $f_l(k,r)$. We note that, for a differential equation of the form (19.2), the wronskian

$$W[f_l(k,r),\phi_l(k,r)] \equiv f_l(k,r) \frac{\partial}{\partial r} \phi_l(k,r) - \phi_l(k,r) \frac{\partial}{\partial r} f_l(k,r)$$

of any two solutions of the equation with the same k is independent of r. Substitution from (39.10) gives

$$W[f_l(k,r),\phi_l(k,r)] = \tfrac{1}{2} i(-k)^{-l-1} f_l(k) W[f_l(k,r),f_l(-k,r)]$$

The wronskian on the right side can be evaluated for large r by using the asymptotic forms (39.2) and (39.4); it leads to

$$f_l(k) = k^l W[f_l(k,r),\phi_l(k,r)] \tag{39.16}$$

The radial derivatives of $f_l(k,r)$ and $\phi_l(k,r)$ have the same analytic properties with respect to k as the function themselves. Then, since $\phi_l(k,r)$ is an entire function of k, Eq. (39.16) shows that $f_l(k)$ has the same analytic properties as $k^l f_l(k,r)$. For example, if $V(r)$ has a finite range, $f_l(k)$ is an entire function of k.

ENHANCEMENT FACTOR

Equation (39.15) shows that the argument of the complex Jost function is the scattering phase shift. It is of interest to note that the magnitude $|f_l(k)|$ also has a simple physical interpretation. Comparison of (39.11) and (39.12) shows that

$$rR_l(r) = \frac{k_l}{f_l(-k)} \phi_l(k,r) \tag{39.17}$$

Thus, as r approaches zero, (39.1) shows that $rR_l(r)$ approaches $r(kr)^l / f_l(-k)(2l + 1)!!$ whereas (15.7) shows that the free solution $rj_l(kr)$ approaches $r(kr)^l / (2l + 1)!!$. Thus the magnitude of the wave function in the neighborhood of the origin is multiplied by the factor $1/|f_l(k)|$ on account of the scattering potential. This *enhancement factor* is of importance in computing the effect of interaction among particles in the final state of scattering or production processes.[1]

JOST FUNCTION FOR LARGE $|k|$

The asymptotic properties of $f_l(k)$ are established in the references cited earlier and will not be derived here. On the real axis and in the lower half of the complex k plane,

$$f_l(k) \xrightarrow[|k| \to \infty]{} 1 + \frac{\mu}{k\hbar^2} \int_0^\infty V(r)\, dr \qquad \text{Im } k \leq 0 \qquad (39.18)$$

where it is assumed that the integral is finite.

Since $V(r)$ is real, Eqs. (39.15) and (39.18) show that for real k

$$\delta_l(k) \xrightarrow[k \to \infty]{} -\frac{\mu}{k\hbar^2} \int_0^\infty V(r)\, dr \qquad (39.19)$$

This may be compared with the Born approximation for the phase shift, given in Eq. (38.14). For fixed l in the limit of very large k, Eq. (15.8) shows that $j_l^2(kr)$ may be approximated by $1/2k^2r^2$ for all except the smallest values of r. It then follows that (38.14) and (39.19) are in agreement.

BOUND STATES

A bound state, if it exists, is described by a regular solution $\phi_l(k,r)$ for which k^2 is real and negative and the r dependence for large r is a decreasing exponential. This means that one of the two terms in the asymptotic expression (39.11) must be zero; it is easily seen that the same result is obtained in both cases. With $k = \pm i\kappa$, we find that a bound state is given by

$$\phi_l(\pm i\kappa,r) \xrightarrow[r \to \infty]{} \tfrac{1}{2}(-\kappa)^{-l-1} f_l(i\kappa) e^{-\kappa r} \qquad f_l(-i\kappa) = 0 \qquad \kappa > 0 \qquad (39.20)$$

provided that $k = i\kappa$ is in a region of analyticity of $f_l(k)$ that is connected with the real axis. The energy of such a state is $-\hbar^2\kappa^2/2\mu$.

We conclude in this case that a zero of the Jost function on the negative imaginary k axis corresponds to a bound state. Further, $f_l(i\kappa)$ cannot vanish, since in accordance with (39.20) this would cause $\phi_l(i\kappa,r)$ to be identically zero; thus the S matrix element (39.13) has a zero at $k = -i\kappa$ and a pole at $k = i\kappa$. It can be shown that each such zero and pole are simple. Although all negative imaginary zeros of the Jost function give bound states, this is not true of all negative imaginary zeros or

[1] See, for example, J. Gillespie, "Final-State Interactions," p. 17 (Holden-Day, San Francisco, 1964).

positive imaginary poles of $S_l(k)$; an example of this will be given below in connection with the theory of the effective range.

DISPERSION RELATIONS FOR THE JOST FUNCTION

The function $f_l(k) - 1$ is analytic for Im $k \le 0$ if the potential satisfies the conditions (39.3); also, in accordance with (39.18), it is of order $1/k$ as $|k| \to \infty$. We can therefore make use of Cauchy's theorem to write

$$f_l(k) - 1 = -\frac{1}{2\pi i} \int_C \frac{f_l(k') - 1}{k' - k} \, dk' \qquad \text{Im } k < 0 \qquad (39.21)$$

where the contour C is shown in Fig. 36a. Since the integral over the semicircle vanishes in the limit in which its radius approaches infinity, the contour integral can be replaced by an integral over the entire real axis. A limit may then be taken in which k approaches the real axis from below, in accordance with Fig. 36b. For a vanishingly small radius of the semi-circle, the integral along the real axis is the principal value, and the integral over the semicircle is $-\pi i[f_l(k) - 1]$. Thus (39.21) becomes

$$f_l(k) - 1 = \frac{i}{\pi} P \int_{-\infty}^{\infty} \frac{f_l(k') - 1}{k' - k} \, dk' \qquad k \text{ real} \qquad (39.22)$$

Equations that relate the real and imaginary parts of $f_l(k) - 1$ can be found by taking the real and imaginary parts of Eq. (39.22):

$$\text{Re}\,[f_l(k) - 1] = -\frac{1}{\pi} P \int_{-\infty}^{\infty} \frac{\text{Im}\,[f_l(k') - 1]}{k' - k} \, dk'$$

$$\text{Im}\,[f_l(k) - 1] = \frac{1}{\pi} P \int_{-\infty}^{\infty} \frac{\text{Re}\,[f_l(k') - 1]}{k' - k} \, dk' \qquad (39.23)$$

Since they obey the relations (39.23), the real and imaginary parts of $f_l(k) - 1$ are said to be *Hilbert transforms* of each other. The dispersion relations (39.23) can be used as the basis of an approximate calculation,

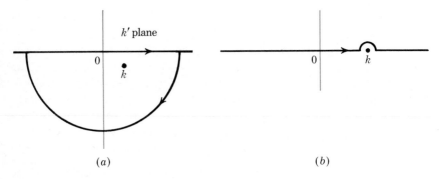

(a)   (b)

Fig. 36 Contours for the evaluation of Eq. (39.21).

by starting with the Born expression (38.14) for the phase shift. In accordance with the discussion below Eq. (39.17), $f_l(k) = 1$ in the absence of a scattering potential, so that $\mathrm{Im}\,[f_l(k) - 1] = \delta_{Bl}(k) + 0(V^2)$. This can be substituted into the first of Eqs. (39.23) to obtain an approximate expression for $\mathrm{Re}\,[f_l(k) - 1]$. Then, from (39.15), the ratio of the imaginary to the real part of $f_l(k)$ gives an improved expression for $\tan \delta_l(k)$.[1]

DISPERSION RELATION FOR $\ln f_l(k)$

Another dispersion relation can be obtained by starting with $\ln f_l(k)$ instead of $f_l(k) - 1$ in Eq. (39.21). If we assume for the moment that there are no bound states, then $\ln f_l(k)$ is also analytic in the lower half plane and is of order $1/k$ as $|k| \to \infty$. From (39.15), we have that $\ln f_l(k) = \ln |f_l(k)| + i\delta_l(k)$, where $\delta_l(k)$ is assumed to be defined so that it vanishes at $k = \pm \infty$, in agreement with (38.14) and (39.19). Then the first of Eqs. (39.23) becomes

$$\ln |f_l(k)| = -\frac{1}{\pi} P \int_{-\infty}^{\infty} \frac{\delta_l(k')}{k' - k}\, dk \qquad (39.24)$$

We add $i\delta_l(k)$ to both sides of this equation; then the left side is $\ln f_l(k)$, and $i\delta_l(k)$ can be replaced on the right side by

$$-\frac{1}{\pi} \int_{C'} \frac{\delta_l(k')}{k' - k}\, dk'$$

where the contour C' is the small semicircle in Fig. 36b. We thus obtain

$$\ln f_l(k) = -\frac{1}{\pi} \int_{C''} \frac{\delta_l(k')}{k' - k}\, dk'$$

where C'' is the full contour shown in Fig. 36b. This can also be written as an integral along the entire real axis:

$$\ln f_l(k) = -\frac{1}{\pi} \int_{-\infty}^{\infty} \frac{\delta_l(k')}{k' - k + i\epsilon}\, dk' \qquad (39.25)$$

where the limit $\epsilon \to 0^+$ is understood.

EFFECT OF BOUND STATES

Thus far we have assumed that there are no bound states. If there are bound states with energies $E_n < 0$, they produce zeros of $f_l(k)$ at $k = -i\kappa_n$, where $\kappa_n = +(-2\mu E_n/\hbar^2)^{\frac{1}{2}}$. These zeros of $f_l(k)$ give rise to branch points of $\ln f_l(k)$, and the foregoing analysis fails. We can, however, define a reduced Jost function

$$\bar{f}_l(k) \equiv f_l(k) \prod_n \frac{k - i\kappa_n}{k + i\kappa_n} \qquad (39.26)$$

[1] J. J. Giambiagi and T. W. B. Kibble, *Ann. Phys.* (*N.Y.*) **7**, 39 (1959).

such that $\ln \bar{f}_l(k)$ has the same analytic and asymptotic behavior that $\ln f_l(k)$ has in the absence of bound states. In places of (39.15), we now have that $\bar{f}_l(k) = |\bar{f}_l(k)| e^{i\bar{\delta}_l(k)}$, where $|\bar{f}_l(k)| = |f_l(k)|$ and

$$\bar{\delta}_l(k) = \delta_l(k) + i \sum_n \left[\ln\left(1 + \frac{i\kappa_n}{k}\right) - \ln\left(1 - \frac{i\kappa_n}{k}\right) \right] \tag{39.27}$$

Thus the dispersion relation (39.25) is valid when bars are placed over f_l and δ_l.

We therefore substitute (39.27) into the integrand of (39.25). Each of the first group of logarithms introduces a branch point at $k' = -i\kappa_n$ and at $k' = 0$, which can be connected by a cut. Thus the integral along the real axis can be closed by an infinite semicircle in the upper half plane, which contributes nothing. The branch point at $k' = 0$ causes no difficulty with the integration along the real axis, since this integration can be regarded as a principal value at $k' = 0$ right from the beginning, and the logarithm gives no contribution from the infinitesimal neighborhood of the origin. It follows that each of the first group of logarithms integrates to zero since the pole at $k' = k - i\epsilon$ lies outside the contour. The branch points for the second group of logarithms are at $i\kappa_n$ and 0, so that the contour is closed by an infinite semicircle in the lower half plane and contains the pole at $k - i\epsilon$.

We conclude, then, that Eq. (39.25), with bars placed over f_l and δ_l, reads as follows:

$$\ln \bar{f}_l(k) = -\frac{1}{\pi} \int_{-\infty}^{\infty} \frac{\delta_l(k')}{k' - k + i\epsilon} \, dk' + 2 \sum_n \ln\left(1 - \frac{i\kappa_n}{k}\right)$$

Substitution for $\bar{f}_l$ in terms of f_l from (39.26) gives[1]

$$\ln f_l(k) = -\frac{1}{\pi} \int_{-\infty}^{\infty} \frac{\delta_l(k')}{k' - k + i\epsilon} \, dk' + \sum_n \ln\left(1 + \frac{\kappa_n{}^2}{k^2}\right) \tag{39.28}$$

The corresponding equation that is analogous to (39.24) is

$$\ln |f_l(k)| = -\frac{1}{\pi} P \int_{-\infty}^{\infty} \frac{\delta_l(k')}{k' - k} \, dk' + \sum_n \ln\left(1 + \frac{\kappa_n{}^2}{k^2}\right) \tag{39.29}$$

Equation (39.28) makes it possible to calculate $f_l(k)$, and hence also $S_l(k)$, in terms of the scattering phase shift and bound-state energies $-\hbar^2\kappa_n{}^2/2\mu$; similarly, the enhancement factor $1/|f_l(k)|$ can be calculated from (39.29).

---

[1] R. Jost and W. Kohn, *Phys. Rev.* **87**, 977 (1952); R. G. Newton, *J. Math. Phys.* **1**, 319 (1960), Sec. 5.

In using these equations, we note from (39.14) and (39.15) that, for real k,

$$e^{i\delta_l(-k)} = e^{-i\delta_l(k)} \qquad \text{if} \qquad \mathcal{f}_l(k) \neq 0 \qquad (39.30)$$

Now it is convenient to continue our earlier convention that $\delta_l(k)$ vanishes at $k = \pm \infty$; this is in agreement with Eqs. (38.14) and (39.19). It then follows from (39.30) that $\delta_l(-k) = -\delta_l(k)$ for real k. However, this does not necessarily imply that $\delta_l(0) = 0$, since the limiting values of $\delta_l(k)$ as k approaches zero from the two sides need not be the same. We therefore extend our convention as follows:

$$\delta_l(-k) = -\delta_l(k) \qquad \text{for real } k \neq 0 \qquad \delta_l(k) \xrightarrow[k \to \infty]{} 0 \qquad (39.31)$$

LEVINSON'S THEOREM

There is an interesting relation between the number n_l of bound states of given l and the corresponding phase shift $\delta_l(0)$ at zero energy, defined as the limit from positive k. We assume for the moment that $f_l(0) \neq 0$ and form the contour integral

$$-\frac{1}{2\pi i} \int_C \frac{f_l'(k)}{f_l(k)} \, dk = -\frac{1}{2\pi i} \int_C d[\ln f_l(k)] \qquad (39.32)$$

where the contour C is that shown in Fig. 36a. The integrand has simple poles of unit strength at the zeros of $f_l(k)$, each of which corresponds to a bound state. Thus the integral on the left side of (39.32) is equal to n_l. As before, we can put $\ln f_l(k) = \ln |f_l(k)| + i\delta_l(k)$; $f_l(k)$ changes continuously around the contour and is never zero on it, so that $\ln |f_l(k)|$ is continuous and the contour integral of this term on the right side is zero. In accordance with (39.31), $\delta_l(k)$ changes continuously from $\delta_l(0)$ at one end of the contour just to the right of the origin to $-\delta_l(0)$ at the other end of the contour just to the left of the origin, so that the integral is equal to $-2i\delta_l(0)$. We thus obtain a portion of *Levinson's theorem*:[1]

$$\delta_l(0) = \pi n_l \qquad f_l(0) \neq 0 \qquad (39.33)$$

For the exceptional situation in which $f_l(0) = 0$, the contour must be indented with a semicircle of infinitesimal radius ϵ in the lower half plane. It is still true that the real part of the integrand, $\ln |f_l(k)|$, contributes nothing to the integral. There is, however, an additional contribution from the integral of the imaginary part around the infinitesimal semicircle. In order to calculate this, we must know how $f_l(k)$ approaches zero as $k \to 0$. It can be shown that, if $f_l(0) = 0$, then $f_l(k) \approx ak^q$, where $q = 1$ for $l = 0$ and $q = 2$ for $l > 0$. If we put $k = \epsilon e^{i\phi}$ on the semicircle, where ϕ goes from π to 2π, the imaginary part of $\ln f_l(k)$ is $q\phi$, and the

[1] N. Levinson, *Kgl. Danske Videnskab. Selskab, Mat.-Fys. Medd.* **25**, (9) (1949).

integral over the semicircle is $i\pi q$. Thus the complete integral (39.32) with the indented contour is equal to

$$\frac{1}{\pi}\,\delta_l(0) - \tfrac{1}{2}q \qquad (39.34)$$

With $l = 0$, the zero of $f_0(k)$ at $k = 0$ does not correspond to a bound state. The situation here is similar to the resonance scattering case discussed in Secs. 19 and 34: In the absence of a centrifugal barrier ($l = 0$), and with a potential that obeys (39.3) (so that V falls off faster than $1/r^3$), the wave function "leaks" out. Then n_0 is equal to (39.34) with $q = 1$, so that

$$\delta_0(0) = \pi(n_0 + \tfrac{1}{2}) \qquad f_0(0) = 0 \qquad (39.35)$$

With $l > 0$, the zero of $f_l(k)$ at $k = 0$ *does* correspond to a bound state since, as shown in Sec. 34, the centrifugal barrier prevents a zero-energy wave function from leaking out. Then, since this state has been excluded by the indented contour, n_l is greater by one unit than (39.34) with $q = 2$, or n_l is equal to $\delta_l(0)/\pi$. This is the same as (39.33), and so we can write both cases, together with (39.35), as

$$\begin{aligned}\delta_l(0) &= \pi(n_l + \tfrac{1}{2}) \qquad \text{if } l = 0 \qquad \text{and} \qquad f_l(0) = 0\\[4pt] \delta_l(0) &= \pi n_l \qquad \text{otherwise}\end{aligned} \qquad (39.36)$$

Equations (39.36) are the full statement of Levinson's theorem.

EFFECTIVE RANGE

As a simple explicit example of a Jost function, we now consider

$$f_0(k) = \frac{k + i\kappa}{k - i\alpha} \qquad (39.37)$$

where κ and α are real and positive. [We neglect any deviation of $f_l(k)$ from unity for $l > 0$.] Note that this $f_0(k)$ has the correct asymptotic behavior (39.18), that it has a simple zero at $k = -i\kappa$ which corresponds to a bound state of energy $-\hbar^2\kappa^2/2\mu$, and that it is analytic except for a simple pole at $k = i\alpha$. Equation (39.37) can also be written

$$f_0(k) = \left(\frac{k^2 + \kappa^2}{k^2 + \alpha^2}\right)^{\tfrac{1}{2}} e^{i\delta_0(k)}$$

$$\delta_0(k) = \tan^{-1}\frac{\kappa}{k} + \tan^{-1}\frac{\alpha}{k} = \tan^{-1}\frac{k(\kappa + \alpha)}{k^2 - \kappa\alpha} \qquad (39.38)$$

Low-energy scattering information, especially in nuclear physics, is often presented as a series expansion for $k \cot \delta_0(k)$ in powers of k^2:

$$k \cot \delta_0(k) = -\frac{1}{a} + \tfrac{1}{2}r_0 k^2 + \cdots \qquad (39.39)$$

where a is called the *scattering length* and r_0 the *effective range*. It follows from the second of Eqs. (39.38) that

$$k \cot \delta_0(k) = -\frac{\kappa\alpha}{\kappa + \alpha} + \frac{k^2}{\kappa + \alpha} \qquad (39.40)$$

so that the effective-range formula describes the scattering exactly in this case.[1] Comparison of (39.39) and (39.40) gives

$$r_0 = \frac{2}{\kappa + \alpha} \qquad a = \frac{1}{\kappa} + \frac{1}{\alpha} \qquad (39.41)$$

In order for (39.37) to describe the experimental situation, it is necessary that the three experimentally determinable parameters, a, r_0, and κ, satisfy the equation obtained from (39.41) by elimination of α:

$$\frac{1}{a} = \kappa - \tfrac{1}{2}r_0\kappa^2 \qquad (39.42)$$

Equation (39.42) is in fact well satisfied for neutron-proton scattering in the triplet spin state, in which case κ corresponds to the bound state of the deuteron (see Sec. 50).

The S matrix element that corresponds to (39.37) is, from (39.13),

$$S_0(k) = \frac{(k + i\kappa)(k + i\alpha)}{(k - i\kappa)(k - i\alpha)} \qquad (39.43)$$

It evidently contains less information than the Jost function, since there is no way of telling from $S_0(k)$ alone whether the bound state corresponds to κ or to α. This provides an explicit example of the remarks in the paragraph below Eq. (39.20).

Effective-range theory can be used as well when there is no bound state. Consider the situation when α remains fixed while κ decreases to zero and then becomes negative. When $\kappa = 0$, (39.37) shows that $f_0(0) = 0$, so that there is a zero-energy resonance; also, (39.41) shows that the scattering length becomes infinite. For κ small and negative, the scattering length is negative, and the parameters can be chosen to describe low-energy neutron-proton scattering in the singlet spin state.

For all three of these cases, the phase shift $\delta_0(k)$ at first increases from zero as k decreases from infinity. With a bound state, it increases monotonically to π at $k = 0$, and with a zero-energy resonance it increases to $\tfrac{1}{2}\pi$. When κ is negative, the phase shift passes through a maximum and then decreases to zero at $k = 0$. All this behavior is in agreement with Levinson's theorem (39.36).

[1] V. Bargmann, *Rev. Mod. Phys.* **21,** 488 (1949); R. G. Newton, *J. Math. Phys.* **1,** 319 (1960), Sec. 10(f).

FORWARD SCATTERING AMPLITUDE

We now derive a dispersion relation for the forward scattering amplitude, still assuming that the potential is spherically symmetric.[1] It is convenient to work with the T matrix element (37.2), which is related to the amplitude by (37.21). We define

$$T(E_\alpha) \equiv |C|^{-2}\langle\alpha|T|\alpha\rangle = |C|^{-2} \int u_\alpha^*(\mathbf{r})V(r)\chi_\alpha^+(\mathbf{r})\, d^3r$$

$$= -\frac{2\pi\hbar^2}{\mu} f(\mathbf{k}_\alpha, \mathbf{k}_\alpha) \quad (39.44)$$

Substitution from (37.17) gives

$$T(E_\alpha) = |C|^{-2}[\int u_\alpha^*(\mathbf{r})V(r)u_\alpha(\mathbf{r})\, d^3r$$
$$+ \hbar^{-1}\int\int u_\alpha^*(\mathbf{r}')V(r')G_{\omega\alpha}^+(\mathbf{r}',\mathbf{r})V(r)u_\alpha(\mathbf{r})\, d^3r'\, d^3r]$$

We thus obtain

$$T(E) = T_B + \hbar^{-1}\int\int \exp(-i\mathbf{k}\cdot\mathbf{r}')$$
$$V(r')G_\omega^+(\mathbf{r}',\mathbf{r})V(r) \exp(i\mathbf{k}\cdot\mathbf{r})\, d^3r'\, d^3r \quad (39.45)$$
$$T_B = \int V(r)\, d^3r$$

where the Born matrix element T_B is independent of the energy and the subscript α has been dropped.

The Green's function that appears in (39.45) is defined in Eq. (37.8). We adopt δ-function normalization for the continuum and break up the generalized summation S_α in (37.8) into a sum over bound states n and an integral over continuum states α:

$$\hbar^{-1}G_\omega^+(\mathbf{r}',\mathbf{r}) = \sum_n \frac{\chi_n(\mathbf{r}')\chi_n^*(\mathbf{r})}{E - E_n} + \int d\alpha \frac{\chi_\alpha(\mathbf{r}')\chi_\alpha^*(\mathbf{r})}{E - E_\alpha + i\epsilon} \quad (39.46)$$

The χ_n are normalized to unity, and $i\epsilon$ can be dropped in this sum since the E_n are negative. The normalization of the continuum states is such that if $\chi_\alpha(\mathbf{r})$ has the asympototic form $\exp(i\mathbf{k}\cdot\mathbf{r})$, the differential $d\alpha$ becomes $d^3k/(2\pi)^3$.

Equation (39.46) shows that G_ω^+, regarded as a function of E as a complex variable, is analytic everywhere except for discrete poles at the negative real bound-state energies E_n and a cut parallel to and just below the positive real axis. We define

$$T(\mathbf{r}',\mathbf{r},E) \equiv \hbar^{-1}G_\omega^+(\mathbf{r}',\mathbf{r})V(r')V(r) \exp[i\mathbf{k}\cdot(\mathbf{r} - \mathbf{r}')] \quad (39.47)$$

[1] N. N. Khuri, *Phys. Rev.* **107**, 1148 (1957); A. Klein and C. Zemach, *Ann. Phys.* (*N.Y.*) **7**, 440 (1959). The present treatment follows most closely that of M. L. Goldberger and K. M. Watson, "Collision Theory," sec. 10.4 (Wiley, New York, 1964).

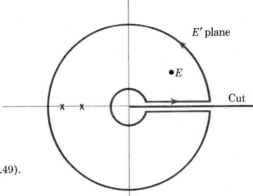

Fig. 37 Contour C in Eq. (39.49).

such that

$$T(E) = T_B + \iint T(\mathbf{r'},\mathbf{r},E)\, d^3r'\, d^3r \tag{39.48}$$

The analytic properties of $T(\mathbf{r'},\mathbf{r},E)$ are the same as those of G_ω^+, so that a dispersion relation can be obtained for it by starting with Cauchy's theorem, as in (39.21). We thus consider the integral

$$\frac{1}{2\pi i}\int_C \frac{T(\mathbf{r'},\mathbf{r},E')}{E' - E}\, dE'$$

where the contour C, shown in Fig. 37, does not cross the cut. This integral is equal to a sum of residues at the bound-state poles, which are denoted schematically by crosses in the figure, together with a residue from the pole at E:

$$\frac{1}{2\pi i}\int_C \frac{T(\mathbf{r'},\mathbf{r},E')}{E' - E}\, dE' = \sum_n \frac{\Gamma_n(\mathbf{r'},\mathbf{r})}{E_n - E} + T(\mathbf{r'},\mathbf{r},E) \tag{39.49}$$

Here $\Gamma_n(\mathbf{r'},\mathbf{r})$ is the residue of $T(\mathbf{r'},\mathbf{r},E)$ at the pole $E = E_n$; that is, $T(\mathbf{r'},\mathbf{r},E)$ behaves like $\Gamma_n(\mathbf{r'},\mathbf{r})/(E - E_n)$ in the neighborhood of $E = E_n$.

DISPERSION RELATION FOR $T(E)$

The contour consists of three parts: the infinitesimal circle about the origin, the straight lines just above and just below the positive real axis on the two sides of the cut, and the large circle to which we assign the radius E_0. With regard to the infinitesimal circle, we note from (39.46) that the bound-state contributions to G_ω^+ are finite as $E \to 0$ since these states are assumed to have finite negative energies. Also, the continuum contribution to G_ω^+ is finite since the k^2 in E_α in the denominator is canceled by the k^2 in the differential d^3k. Thus, with the help of (39.47), we see that $T(\mathbf{r'},\mathbf{r},E)$ remains finite as $E' \to 0$ in the cut plane, and there is no contribution from the infinitesimal circle.

The contribution to the left side of (39.49) from the two sides of the positive real axis is

$$\frac{1}{2\pi i} \int_0^{E_0} \frac{T(\mathbf{r}',\mathbf{r},E'^+) - T(\mathbf{r}',\mathbf{r},E'^-)}{E' - E} dE$$

where $E'^\pm$ are just above and below the cut. It is convenient to replace this integral with

$$\frac{1}{2\pi i} \int_0^{E_0} \frac{T(\mathbf{r}',\mathbf{r},E'^+) - T(\mathbf{r},\mathbf{r}',E'^-)}{E' - E} dE'$$

which yields the same result when integrated over $\mathbf{r}$ and $\mathbf{r}'$, as is done in (39.48). We now wish to show that $T^*(\mathbf{r}',\mathbf{r},E^+) = T(\mathbf{r},\mathbf{r}',E^-)$. We are interested in situations that possess time reversal invariance, so that V is real; further, $\{\exp[i\mathbf{k}^+ \cdot (\mathbf{r} - \mathbf{r}')]\}^* = \exp[i\mathbf{k}^- \cdot (\mathbf{r}' - \mathbf{r})]$, so that in accordance with (39.47) we need only show that $G_{\omega^+}{}^{+*}(\mathbf{r}',\mathbf{r}) = G_{\omega^-}{}^+(\mathbf{r},\mathbf{r}')$. Equations (36.22) and (37.8) show that $G_{\omega^+}{}^{+*}(\mathbf{r}',\mathbf{r}) = G_{\omega^-}{}^-(\mathbf{r},\mathbf{r}')$ when time reversal obtains; however, since we are off the real axis, the limit $\epsilon \to 0$ can be taken and the distinction between G^+ and G^- disappears. Thus we have established that the second term in the numerator of the integrand is the complex conjugate of the first, so that the contribution to the left side of (39.49) from the real-axis integrations is

$$\frac{1}{\pi} \int_0^{E_0} \frac{\operatorname{Im} T(\mathbf{r}',\mathbf{r},E'^+)}{E' - E} dE' \tag{39.50}$$

Finally, we wish to show that the contribution from the large circle vanishes in the limit $E_0 \to \infty$. The careful analysis required is given in the references cited above, and only an indication is mentioned here. The main assumption we need is the plausible one that G_ω^+ approaches the free Green's function $G_{0\omega}^+$ as $E \to \infty$, where from (37.19)

$$G_{0\omega}^+(\mathbf{r}',\mathbf{r}) = -\frac{\mu}{2\pi\hbar} |\mathbf{r}' - \mathbf{r}|^{-1} \exp(ik|\mathbf{r}' - \mathbf{r}|)$$

It is evidently important that k approach infinity with a positive imaginary part. That this is actually what happens follows from the earlier identification of bound states with poles of the S matrix element or scattering amplitude on the positive imaginary k axis and from the present identification of bound states with poles on the negative real E axis. Thus the full Riemann sheet of the cut E plane with which we are working is to be mapped onto the upper half of the k plane, in accordance with $E = \hbar^2 k^2/2\mu$.[1] It can then be shown that the exponential in the Green's function dominates the plane waves in (39.47), so that $\int\int T(\mathbf{r}',\mathbf{r},E)\,d^3r'\,d^3r$

---

[1] This is called the *physical sheet* of E; the *unphysical sheet* maps onto the lower half of the k plane.

vanishes as $E \to \infty$. A similar argument shows that the integral (39.50) converges as the upper limit approaches infinity.

We now substitute (39.50) with $E_0 = \infty$ on the left side of (39.49) and integrate over $\mathbf{r}'$ and $\mathbf{r}$. With the help of (39.48), we obtain

$$T(E) = T_B + \sum_n \frac{\Gamma_n}{E - E_n} + \frac{1}{\pi} \int_0^\infty \frac{\text{Im } T(E')}{E' - E - i\epsilon} \, dE' \qquad (39.51)$$

where we have replaced the integration variable $E'^+ = E' + i\epsilon$ by E' in the last integral and put $\Gamma_n \equiv \iint \Gamma_n(\mathbf{r}',\mathbf{r}) \, d^3r' \, d^3r$. Equation (39.51) is the dispersion relation for the forward scattering amplitude. We recall that $T(E) = -(2\pi\hbar^2/\mu)f(\mathbf{k},\mathbf{k})$ from (39.44), that $T_B = \int V(r) \, d^3r$ from (39.45), and that $\text{Im } T(E) = -(\hbar^2k/2\mu)\sigma_{\text{tot}}(E)$ from (20.13). The only quantity that remains to be evaluated is Γ_n, which is the residue of $T(E)$ at the bound-state pole $E = E_n$.

As a simple example, we note that, if there is a bound state that is described by effective range theory, the S matrix element (39.43) is given approximately by[1]

$$\frac{2i\kappa(\kappa + \alpha)}{(\kappa - \alpha)(k - i\kappa)}$$

near the pole at $k = i\kappa$. Then, near the corresponding pole at $k^2 = -\kappa^2$, $T(E)$ is dominated by $(-2\pi\hbar^2/2\mu)(1/2ik)$ times this S matrix element, so that

$$T(E) \approx -\frac{4\pi\hbar^2}{\mu} \frac{\kappa(\kappa + \alpha)}{(\kappa - \alpha)(k^2 + \kappa^2)}$$

We thus obtain

$$\Gamma = -\frac{2\pi\hbar^4}{\mu^2} \frac{\kappa(\kappa + \alpha)}{\kappa - \alpha} = \frac{2\pi\hbar^4}{\mu^2} \frac{\kappa}{1 - \kappa r_0} \qquad (39.52)$$

where the effective range r_0 can be determined experimentally from (39.39).

SUBTRACTED DISPERSION RELATION

The dispersion relation (39.51) relates a number of measurable quantities and hence can, at least in principle, be put to experimental test. Thus $|T(E)|^2$ is proportional to the differential cross section in the forward direction at energy E, $|T_B|^2$ is the same quantity at infinite energy, $\text{Im } T(E)$ is proportional to the total cross section, and in the effective-range approximation Γ can be found from (39.52).

[1] It can be shown that the pole of (39.43) at $k = i\alpha$, which appears in the $l = 0$ partial wave but does not correspond to a bound state, is not present in the full amplitude $T(E)$.

It may happen, however, that the high-energy region is not very accessible or that the integral in (39.51) does not converge rapidly enough to be evaluated with available experimental data. In this case a *subtracted dispersion relation* can be obtained from (39.51), by subtracting from $T(E)$ the similar expression for $T(E_0)$, where E_0 is an arbitrarily chosen energy. The result is

$$
T(E) = T(E_0) + (E_0 - E) \left[\sum_n \frac{\Gamma_n}{(E - E_n)(E_0 - E_n)} \right.
$$
$$
\left. - \frac{1}{\pi} \int_0^\infty \frac{\mathrm{Im}\, T(E')}{(E' - E - i\epsilon)(E' - E_0 - i\epsilon)}\, dE' \right] \quad (39.53)
$$

It is apparent that this becomes (39.51) when $E_0 = \infty$. An advantage of Eq. (39.53) is that the integral converges more rapidly than that in (39.51), since its integrand has a higher power of E' in the denominator; on the other hand, it cannot be used unless $T(E_0)$ is known.

PROBLEMS

1. Derive the four equations (36.8) by making use of the arbitrariness of ψ at any instant of time.

2. Make use of the expression (36.9) for G_0 to show explicitly that the first of Eqs. (36.8) is valid for G_0^+.

3. Show that the inner product of any two solutions of the time-dependent Schrödinger equation is constant in time if the hamiltonian is hermitian. Use this result first to show that the orthogonality of any two solutions is preserved in time and, second, to obtain an expression for $\langle \beta | S | \alpha \rangle$ in the form of an inner product that can be evaluated at any time [not just at $t' > T_2$ as in (36.32) or at $t < -T_1$ as in (36.38)].

4. Show what the connection is between Eq. (35.9) and the second term on the right side of Eq. (36.35).

5. Evaluate the right side of Eq. (37.7) with $+i\epsilon$ replaced by $-i\epsilon$, and show that it is equal to $\theta(\tau) - 1$.

6. Derive Eq. (37.16) by symbolic manipulation of (37.14). Then derive Eq. (37.17) without using symbolic relations.

7. Evaluate $G_{0\omega}^-(\mathbf{r}',\mathbf{r})$, defined by Eq. (37.8) with $+i\epsilon$ replaced by $-i\epsilon$, and obtain it in a form similar to (37.19). Also show that the substitutions (37.22) are justified.

8. Make use of the unitarity of the S matrix, as given in Eq. (37.31), to derive the generalized optical theorem and then the optical theorem as a special case.

9. Show that the total scattering cross section by a real potential that falls off at great distances like r^{-n} is finite if and only if $n > 2$, first by means of the Born approximation amplitude (38.2) and, second, by means of the Born approximation phase shifts (38.14).

10. Find the differential scattering cross section for a real potential $V(r) = -V_0 e^{-r/a}$, using the Born approximation. What is the validity criterion in this case, and under what circumstances is it satisfied?

11. Use the Born approximation to discuss qualitatively the scattering by a crystal lattice of identical atoms.

12. Use the optical theorem and the Born approximation amplitude (38.1) to calculate the total cross section for a real potential. Discuss your result. Repeat for a complex potential.

13. A proton is scattered from an atom that can be represented by a screened coulomb potential $(Ze^2/r)e^{-r/a}$, together with a real attractive short-range square well potential of depth $-V_0$ and radius R that arises from the nucleus. Use the distorted wave Born approximation to calculate the scattering amplitude. Assume that only the $l = 0$ partial wave is affected by the nuclear potential; threat this exactly, and treat the coulomb field to first order.

14. Use the perturbation theory to calculate the differential collision cross section for the $1S \to 2P$ excitation of a hydrogen atom by an electron. Show that the total cross section becomes the expression given below Eq. (38.29) at high bombarding energy.

15. Use the eikonal approximation to calculate the total cross section for scattering by the potential $V(r) = -V_0(1 + i\xi)$ for $r < a$, $V(r) = 0$ for $r > a$, where V_0 and ξ are positive. Find a situation in which you believe that your result should agree with that obtained in Prob. 11, Chap. 5, and then check to see if there is indeed agreement.

16. Calculate the Jost function for $l = 0$, $f_0(k)$, for a real attractive square well potential of depth $-V_0$ and radius a. Use it to give as full a discussion as you can of any bound states in this potential and of the scattering phase shift.

10
Identical Particles and Spin

The quantum-mechanical theory of particles presented thus far is deficient in three respects. First, whenever two or more particles are described at once, like the electron and proton of the hydrogen atom (Sec. 16) or the incident and atomic electrons in an inelastic collision (Sec. 38), it is assumed that the particles can be distinguished from each other. This is a valid assumption in the first example, since electrons and protons possess quite different masses and electrical charges. In the second example, however, there is no observable difference between the incident and atomic electrons, and the consequences of this *identity* should appear in the formalism. The second defect of the theory is that spin has not yet been incorporated into the description of the motion.[1] Third, no mention has been made of the special theory of relativity, which is expected to affect the theoretical description of particles that move with speeds close to that of light.

[1] See Sec. 27. Spin was first discovered in connection with electrons by G. E. Uhlenbeck and S. Goudsmit, *Naturwiss.* **13**, 953 (1925); *Nature* **117**, 264 (1926).

The ways in which the first two of these defects can be remedied are described in this chapter, and illustrative examples are discussed. Relativistic effects are taken up in Chap. 13.

40□IDENTICAL PARTICLES

Identical particles cannot be distinguished by means of any inherent property, since otherwise they would not be identical in all respects. In classical mechanics, the existence of sharply definable trajectories for individual particles makes it possible in principle to distinguish between particles that are identical except for their paths, since each particle can be followed during the course of an experiment. In quantum mechanics, the finite size and the spreading of the wave packets that can describe individual particles often make it impossible to distinguish between identical particles because of their positions, especially if they interact with each other to an appreciable extent. This is true of the electrons in a single atom, where we have seen that the description in terms of moving wave packets breaks down completely. However, the electrons of different atoms that are well separated from each other may, to good approximation, be regarded as distinguishable. This section considers some of the effects of identity on the quantum-mechanical treatment of systems of two or more particles. Other effects that involve the spin explicitly will be taken up in the remainder of this chapter.

PHYSICAL MEANING OF IDENTITY

The impossibility, in principle, of distinguishing between identical particles in most quantum-mechanical problems can lead to effects that have no classical analog. As an example, we compare the elastic collision of two identical particles that have a particular interaction between them with the collision of two different particles that have the same interaction between them.

In a classical treatment, there is no difference of principle between the results of these two experiments, since it is possible to distinguish between the incident and struck particles in the first case as well as in the second. In practice, however, this distinction would usually be made only in the second experiment. Thus, according to classical mechanics, the measured differential cross section in the first experiment is equal to the sum of the corresponding cross sections measured for the incident and struck particles in the second experiment. In the corresponding quantum-mechanical situation, the identical particles in the first experiment cannot be distinguished by means of their trajectories, since they cannot be well localized without interfering with the scattering process. Thus the distinction between incident and struck particles has no physical significance, and the simple connection between the results of the two experiments that is found in the classical case need not exist.

We use the word *identical* to describe particles that can be substituted for each other under the most general possible circumstances with no change in the physical situation. Identical particles can in some cases be distinguished from each other, as when their wave packets do not overlap. Another case, discussed more fully in Sec. 41, arises when each of the particles possesses an intrinsic spin angular momentum, which is a constant of the motion in a particular collision. Then, since the component of the spin along some axis is assumed not to change during this collision, the particles can be distinguished if they have different spin components. Results of this kind must, of course, be a consequence of the formalism that we now set up.

SYMMETRIC AND ANTISYMMETRIC WAVE FUNCTIONS

The Schrödinger wave equation for n identical particles is

$$i\hbar \frac{\partial}{\partial t} \psi (1,2, \ldots ,n;t) = H(1,2, \ldots ,n)\psi(1,2, \ldots ,n;t) \qquad (40.1)$$

where each of the numbers represents all the coordinates (positional and spin) of one of the particles. The hamiltonian H is symmetrical in its arguments, since the identity of the particles means that they can be substituted for each other without changing H or, indeed, any other observable.

There are two kinds of solutions ψ of Eq. (40.1) that possess symmetry properties of particular interest. A wave function is *symmetric* if the interchange of any pair of particles among its arguments leaves the wave function unchanged. A wave function is *antisymmetric* if the interchange of any pair of particles changes the sign of ψ. We now show that the symmetry character of a wave function does not change in time. If ψ_S is symmetric at a particular time t, then $H\psi_S$ is also symmetric, and (40.1) states that $\partial\psi_S/\partial t$ is symmetric. Since ψ_S and its time derivative are symmetric at time t, ψ_S at an infinitesimally later time $t + dt$ is given by $\psi_S + (\partial\psi_S/\partial t) \, dt$ and is also symmetric. Such a step-by-step integration of the wave equation can, in principle, be continued for arbitrarily large time intervals, and ψ_S is seen to remain symmetric always. In similar fashion, if ψ_A is antisymmetric at any time, $H\psi_A$ and hence $\partial\psi_A/\partial t$ are antisymmetric, and integration of the wave equation shows that ψ_A is always antisymmetric.

The foregoing proof is not altered if H and ψ have as their arguments the coordinates of two or more different groups of identical particles; thus a wave function that is initially set up to be symmetric or antisymmetric in the coordinates of each identical particle group always retains this character. This makes it possible for the different groups of identical particles found in nature to have definite symmetry characters, and this is actually found to be the case. Although symmetry characters other than these two would also be preserved in time by a symmetric hamiltonian, they do not appear to correspond to particles found in nature.[1]

CONSTRUCTION FROM UNSYMMETRIZED FUNCTIONS

We now show how ψ_S or ψ_A can be constructed from a general unsymmetrized solution ψ of Eq. (40.1). If the arguments of ψ are permuted in any way, the resulting function is a solution of (40.1). That this is true follows from the observation that the same permutation applied throughout Eq. (40.1) does not impair its validity, since it corresponds simply to a relabeling of the particles; then, since H is symmetric, the permuted H is the same as the original H, and the resulting equation is the same as (40.1) for the permuted ψ. In this way $n!$ solutions can be obtained from any one solution, each of which corresponds to one of the $n!$ permutations of the n arguments of ψ. It is evident that any linear combination of these functions is also a solution of the wave equation (40.1).

The sum of all these functions is a symmetric (unnormalized) wave function ψ_S, since the interchange of any pair of particles changes any one of the component functions into another of them and the latter into the former, leaving the entire wave function unchanged. An antisymmetric unnormalized wave function can be constructed by adding together all the permuted functions that arise from the original solution by means of an even number of interchanges of pairs of particles, and subtracting the sum of all the permuted functions that arise by means of an odd number of interchanges of pairs of particles in the original solution. It is apparent that a nonvanishing antisymmetric wave function cannot be formed from a solution that is unaltered by the interchange of any pair of particles.

In the event that the hamiltonian does not involve the time, stationary solutions $\psi(1,2, \ldots ,n;t) = u(1,2, \ldots ,n)e^{-iEt/\hbar}$ can be found, where

$$[H(1,2 \ldots ,n) - E]u(1,2, \ldots ,n) = 0$$

The earlier discussion shows that the solutions derived from any u by means of permutations of its arguments are degenerate with the original u; this is called *exchange degeneracy*.

---

[1] For fuller discussion of this point, see O. W. Greenberg and A. M. L. Messiah, *Phys. Rev.* **138**, B1155 (1965); M. D. Girardeau, *Phys. Rev.* **139**, B500 (1965).

THE SYMMETRIC GROUP[1]

The symmetry of the hamiltonian with respect to permutations of its arguments implies the existence of a group of transformations on the state functions, in accordance with the general discussion of Chap. 7. We again adopt the Schrödinger picture and write in analogy with Eq. (26.1)

$$\psi_{\alpha'}[P(1,2, \ldots ,n);t] = \psi_\alpha(1,2 \ldots ,n;t) \tag{40.2}$$

where P is some permutation of the n arguments. Then the analog of Eqs. (26.2) are

$$U_p(P)|\alpha\rangle = |\alpha'\rangle \qquad \text{or} \qquad U_p(P)\psi_\alpha(1,2, \ldots ,n;t)$$
$$= \psi_{\alpha'}(1,2, \ldots ,n;t) \tag{40.3}$$

where $U_p(P)$ is the unitary permutation operator. Combination of Eqs. (40.2) and (40.3) leads to the analog of (26.3):

$$U_p(P)\psi_\alpha(1,2, \ldots ,n;t) = \psi_\alpha[P^{-1}(1,2, \ldots ,n);t] \tag{40.4}$$

where P^{-1} is the inverse permutation to P, such that $PP^{-1} = P^{-1}P = 1$, the identity permutation. It also follows, in analogy with Eq. (26.5), that the symmetry of the hamiltonian implies that $[U_p(P),H] = 0$ and hence that a permuted solution represents a possible motion of the system.

The $n!$ permutations P of n objects evidently form a discrete group with $n!$ elements, which is called the *symmetric group*. The $n!$ operators $U_p(P)$ are isomorphic to the permutations.

When $n = 2$, there are only two permutations, the identity and the interchange, which we call 1 and P, respectively. If P is applied twice in succession to two objects, we obtain the identity. Thus the symmetric group of two objects is isomorphic to the space-inversion group discussed in Sec. 29. When use is made of Eq. (40.4), it is apparent that the analog of Eqs. (29.3) are (on omitting the time dependence)

$$U_p(P)u(1,2) = \omega u(2,1) \qquad U_p{}^2(P)u(1,2) = \omega^2 u(1,2)$$

Again, $U_p{}^2(P)$ is expected to bring a state into itself, so that ω^2 is a number of unit magnitude. Unlike the situation with inversion, there is now no reason to assume that ω^2 is anything other than unity. Thus $\omega = \pm 1$, and these characterize the symmetric and antisymmetric states, respectively. We thus obtain two (unit rank) matrix representations of the

[1] E. P. Wigner, "Group Theory," chap. 13 (Academic, New York, 1959); A. Messiah, "Quantum Mechanics," App. D IV (North Holland Publishing Company, Amsterdam, 1962).

symmetric group when $n = 2$:

$$U_p(1) = 1 \quad U_p(P) = 1 \quad \text{and} \quad U_p(1) = 1 \quad U_p(P) = -1 \quad (40.5)$$

The corresponding eigenfunctions of these operators are

$$u(1,2) \pm u(2,1) \qquad\qquad (40.6)$$

It can be shown for any value of n that the only two matrix representations $U_p(P)$ that are of unit rank are the analogs of (40.5): the symmetric representation $U_p(P) = 1$ for all P and the antisymmetric representation $U_p(P) = \pm 1$ according as the number of interchanges that make up the permutation P is even or odd. For example, with $n = 3$, the symmetric and antisymmetric eigenfunctions are

$$[u(1,2,3) + u(2,3,1) + u(3,1,2)] \pm [u(2,1,3) + u(1,3,2) + u(3,2,1)]$$
$$(40.7)$$

It can also be shown that there is only one other independent representation of the $U_p(P)$ when $n = 3$; this consists of six 2×2 matrices and hence operates on pairs of eigenfunctions (see Prob. 1).

DISTINGUISHABILITY OF IDENTICAL PARTICLES

It is to be expected that the result of an experiment is independent of the symmetry character of the wave function if the coordinates of the particles do not overlap. This corresponds to a situation in which the particles can be distinguished by means of their positions (or their spin components) even though they are identical. Such a situation implies, in the case of two particles, that the wave function $u(1,2)$ is different from zero only when the coordinate 1 is in some region A, the coordinate 2 is in a region B, and A and B have no common domain.

The coordinate probability density associated with the wave function $u(1,2)$ is $|u(1,2)|^2$, and the densities associated with the symmetrized wave functions (40.6) are

$$|u(1,2) \pm u(2,1)|^2 = |u(1,2)|^2 + |u(2,1)|^2 \pm 2 \, \text{Re} \, [u(1,2)u^*(2,1)]$$
$$(40.8)$$

where Re denotes the real part of the expression in brackets. If now $u(1,2)$ vanishes whenever 1 is not in A and 2 is not in B, and A and B do not overlap, the bracket term is zero everywhere, and (40.8) becomes $|u(1,2)|^2 + |u(2,1)|^2$.

Thus the density associated with either of the symmetrized wave functions (40.6) is the sum of the densities associated with $u(1,2)$ and $u(2,1)$ separately. This is precisely the result that will be obtained if the particles are not identical but no attempt is made to distinguish between them in performing the experiment. Thus the interference effects between exchange-degenerate wave functions, represented by the bracket term in (40.8), disappear when the coordinates of the particles do not overlap.

THE EXCLUSION PRINCIPLE

In many problems, a useful zero-order approximation can be obtained by neglecting the interactions between the particles that make up the system under consideration. The approximate (unperturbed) hamiltonian is the sum of equal hamiltonian functions for the separate particles

$$H_0(1,2, \ldots ,n) = H_0'(1) + H_0'(2) + \ldots + H_0'(n) \tag{40.9}$$

and the approximate energy eigenfunction is a product of one-particle eigenfunctions of H_0':

$$u(1,2, \ldots ,n) = v_\alpha(1)v_\beta(2) \cdots v_\nu(n)$$
$$E = E_\alpha + E_\beta + \cdots + E_\nu \tag{40.10}$$
$$H_0'(1)v_\alpha(1) = E_\alpha v_\alpha(1) \qquad \text{etc.}$$

If the particles are electrons, an antisymmetric wave function must be constructed from the u given by (40.10). This is most easily expressed as a determinant of the v's:

$$u_A(1,2, \ldots n) = \begin{vmatrix} v_\alpha(1) & v_\alpha(2) & \cdots & v_\alpha(n) \\ v_\beta(1) & v_\beta(2) & \cdots & v_\beta(n) \\ \cdots & \cdots & \cdots & \cdots \\ \cdots & \cdots & \cdots & \cdots \\ v_\nu(1) & v_\nu(2) & \cdots & v_\nu(n) \end{vmatrix} \tag{40.11}$$

The (unnormalized) u_A given in (40.11) is clearly an antisymmetric solution of the approximate wave equation $(H_0 - E)u_A = 0$.

Equation (40.11) has the interesting property that it vanishes if two or more of the v's are the same. This is a special case of the general result stated earlier that an antisymmetric wave function cannot be constructed from a solution that is unaltered by the interchange of any pair of particles. Thus the approximate hamiltonian H_0 has no solutions for which there is more than one electron in any one of the states $\alpha, \beta, \ldots , \nu$. This result is known as the *exclusion principle* and was first postulated by Pauli[1] as an explanation of the periodic system of the chemical elements.

[1] W. Pauli, *Z. Physik* **31**, 765 (1925).

CONNECTION WITH STATISTICAL MECHANICS

The unsymmetrized zero-order solution given in Eq. (40.10) can be used to construct a symmetric as well as an antisymmetric wave function. Such a symmetric (unnormalized) function is easily seen to be the sum of all different permutations of the numbers 1, 2, . . . , n among the one-particle eigenfunctions v_α, v_β, . . . , v_ν. This wave function is unique and can be specified simply by stating how many particles are in each of the states α, β, ... In the same way, an antisymmetric wave function can be specified by stating how many particles are in each state. The fundamental statistical difference between particles that are described by antisymmetric and by symmetric wave functions is that the number of the former type that can occupy any state is limited to 0 or 1, whereas any number (0,1,2, . . .) of the latter type of particles can occupy any state.

The treatment of aggregates of large numbers of noninteracting (or weakly interacting) particles for which the states can be enumerated in these two ways forms the subject matter of quantum *statistical mechanics*. Particles that are described by antisymmetric wave functions are said to obey *Fermi-Dirac statistics* and are called *fermions*, and particles that are described by symmetric wave functions obey *Einstein-Bose statistics* and are called *bosons*.[1]

Of the material particles whose statistics are definitely known, electrons, protons, and neutrons are fermions, and π mesons are bosons.[2] Also, light quanta, or photons, insofar as they can be treated as particles, obey Einstein-Bose statistics. Further, aggregates of particles that are sufficiently tightly bound so that they can be regarded as "particles" are described either by symmetric or by antisymmetric wave functions.

For example, the nucleus of a helium atom is made up of two protons, two neutrons, and an indeterminate number of π mesons, which are strongly bound together. If we consider a number of helium nuclei that interact with each other weakly enough so that the changes in the internal motions of the nuclei can be neglected, we can see that the motions of the centers of gravity of the nuclei can be described approximately by a symmetric wave function. The interchange of a pair of helium nuclei can be thought of as the resultant of the interchanges of two pairs of protons, two pairs of neutrons, and a number of pairs of π mesons. Since the actual wave function is antisymmetric in all the protons and in all the neutrons, the resultant of the first four interchanges leaves the approximate wave function unchanged; the symmetry of the wave function in the π mesons is such that the latter interchanges also have no effect. By an

---

[1] See, for example, K. Huang, "Statistical Mechanics," chap. 9 (Wiley, New York, 1963).

[2] See, for example, the references cited on page 205.

extension of this argument, we see that strongly bound "particles" that interact weakly with each other (nuclei, atoms, or molecules) obey Einstein-Bose statistics when each of them consists of an even total number of electrons, protons, and neutrons, and they obey Fermi-Dirac statistics when each consists of an odd total number of these particles.[1]

COLLISIONS OF IDENTICAL PARTICLES

When the only forces acting on two particles result from their mutual interaction, the overall motion can be separated into motion of the center of mass of the two particles and motion of the particles relative to each other, as discussed in Secs. 16 and 18. It is apparent that an interchange of two identical particles does not affect the position vector of the center of mass [which is $\frac{1}{2}(\mathbf{r}_1 + \mathbf{r}_2)$ since the particles have equal masses] but changes the sign of the relative position vector $\mathbf{r}$ ($= \mathbf{r}_1 - \mathbf{r}_2$). We postpone consideration of the spins of the particles until the next section and see now what effect symmetry or antisymmetry of the space part of the wave function has on the elastic scattering of a particle by another that is identical with it.

The asymptotic form of the unsymmetrized scattering wave function in the center-of-mass coordinate system is given by Eq. (18.10).

$$u(\mathbf{r}) \xrightarrow[r \to \infty]{} e^{ikz} + r^{-1}f(\theta,\phi)e^{ikr} \tag{40.12}$$

where r, θ, ϕ are the polar coordinates of the relative position vector $\mathbf{r}$. Since the polar coordinates of the vector $-\mathbf{r}$ are r, $\pi - \theta$, $\phi + \pi$, the asymptotic forms of the symmetric and antisymmetric wave functions formed from (40.12) are given by

$$(e^{ikz} \pm e^{-ikz}) + [f(\theta,\phi) \pm f(\pi - \theta, \phi + \pi)]r^{-1}e^{ikr} \tag{40.13}$$

with upper and lower signs, respectively.

From the discussion of Sec. 18, it follows that the differential scattering cross section in the center-of-mass coordinate system is the square of the magnitude of the bracket term in (40.13):

$$\sigma(\theta,\phi) = |f(\theta,\phi)|^2 + |f(\pi - \theta, \phi + \pi)|^2$$
$$\pm 2 \operatorname{Re} [f(\theta,\phi)f^*(\pi - \theta, \phi + \pi)] \tag{40.14}$$

The normalization adopted here can be justified by noticing that in the classical limit, where the identical particles are distinguishable and the last (interference) term in Eq. (40.14) drops out, $\sigma(\theta,\phi)$ becomes just the sum of the differential cross sections for observation of the incident

---

[1] A more rigorous treatment that leads to the same conclusion has been given by P. Ehrenfest and J. R. Oppenheimer, *Phys. Rev.* **37**, 333 (1931).

particle ($|f(\theta,\phi)|^2$) and of the struck particle ($|f(\pi - \theta, \phi + \pi)|^2$), as it should.

In the usual case, for which f is independent of ϕ, it is apparent that the scattering per unit solid angle is symmetrical about $\theta = 90°$ in the center-of-mass coordinate system. It is easily seen from Eq. (18.7) with $\gamma = 1$ that the scattering per unit angle (not per unit solid angle) in the laboratory coordinate system,

$$\sigma_0(\theta_0) \sin \theta_0 = 4 \cos \theta_0 \sin \theta_0 \{|f(2\theta_0)|^2$$
$$+ |f(\pi - 2\theta_0)|^2 \pm 2 \operatorname{Re} [f(2\theta_0)f^*(\pi - 2\theta_0)]\}$$

is symmetrical about $\theta_0 = 45°$.

41☐SPIN ANGULAR MOMENTUM

The treatment of identical particles presented in the preceding section must now be supplemented by inclusion of the spin angular momenta of the particles. It was shown in Sec. 27 that the spin angular momentum **S** of a particle can be defined so that **S**^{2} commutes with all dynamical variables. Then **S**^{2} is strictly a constant of the motion and can be replaced by $s(s + 1)\hbar^2$, where s is an integer or half an odd integer.

CONNECTION BETWEEN SPIN AND STATISTICS

As remarked in Sec. 27, electrons, protons, neutrons, neutrinos, and muons have $s = \frac{1}{2}$, and pions have $s = 0$. Aggregates of particles that are sufficiently tightly bound can be regarded as "particles" and can be characterized by definite magnitudes of their total internal angular momenta, so long as their internal motions and the relative spin orientations of their component particles are not significantly affected by the interactions between aggregates. This is exactly analogous to the situation with regard to the statistics obeyed by the aggregates, discussed in the preceding section.

The treatment of the addition of angular momenta presented in Sec. 28 shows how to calculate the possible magnitudes of the total internal angular momentum of any aggregate of fundamental particles; we call this the *spin* of the aggregate. If it consists of n particles, each of which has $s = \frac{1}{2}$, and any number of particles with $s = 0$, and if the internal orbital angular momentum of these particles is ignored, the total s can be any integer from 0 to $\frac{1}{2}n$ if n is even or can vary by integer steps from $\frac{1}{2}$ to $\frac{1}{2}n$ if n is odd. The total orbital angular momentum quantum number can 'be shown to be an integer or zero in general;[1] its inclusion

[1] The work of Secs. 27 and 28 shows that this is true for noninteracting particles that move in central force fields, and the result turns out not to be affected by particle interactions.

extends the maximum value of s for the aggregate but does not alter the conclusion that s is zero or an integer if n is even and is half an odd integer if n is odd.

We see then that, for the known fundamental particles and for aggregates of them that have a definite spin, there is a unique connection between the spin and the statistics. Particles or aggregates that have zero or integer spin are described by symmetric wave functions and obey Einstein-Bose statistics, and particles or aggregates that have half-odd-integer spin are described by antisymmetric wave functions and obey Fermi-Dirac statistics. There is good theoretical reason, based on relativistic quantum mechanics,[1] to believe that this connection also holds for other fundamental particles whose spin and statistics have not as yet both been determined (other mesons and neutrinos).

SPIN MATRICES AND EIGENFUNCTIONS

The spin can be included in the formalism developed in Sec. 40 by having each of the numbers $1, 2, \ldots, n$ that appear as the arguments of ψ and u represent a spin coordinate as well as the three space coordinates of that particle. The spin coordinate differs from the space coordinates in that it takes on only $2s + 1$ values for a particle (or aggregate) of spin s, instead of the infinite number of values that are taken on by each space coordinate. The spin wave function of a single particle is completely determined by the specification of $2s + 1$ numbers, whereas the space wave function involves the specification of a continuously infinite set of numbers (which is equivalent to a continuous function of the space coordinates).[2]

A convenient set of orthonormal one-particle spin functions is provided by the normalized eigenfunctions of the J^2 and J_z matrices given in Eqs. (27.26). These eigenfunctions are $(2s + 1)$-row, one-column matrices that have zeros in all positions except one. For example, if $s = \frac{3}{2}$, the four spin eigenfunctions are easily seen to be

$$v(\tfrac{3}{2}) = \begin{bmatrix} 1 \\ 0 \\ 0 \\ 0 \end{bmatrix} \qquad v(\tfrac{1}{2}) = \begin{bmatrix} 0 \\ 1 \\ 0 \\ 0 \end{bmatrix} \qquad v(-\tfrac{1}{2}) = \begin{bmatrix} 0 \\ 0 \\ 1 \\ 0 \end{bmatrix} \qquad v(-\tfrac{3}{2}) = \begin{bmatrix} 0 \\ 0 \\ 0 \\ 1 \end{bmatrix}$$

$$(41.1)$$

---

[1] R. F. Streater and A. S. Wightman, "PCT, Spin and Statistics, and All That," sec. 4-4 (Benjamin, New York, 1964).

[2] If the space and spin motions are closely enough coupled together, the space wave function may depend on the spin coordinate, so that $2s + 1$ space functions are required.

and correspond to S_z eigenvalues of $\frac{3}{2}\hbar$, $\frac{1}{2}\hbar$, $-\frac{1}{2}\hbar$, and $-\frac{3}{2}\hbar$, respectively. The orthonormality is demonstrated by multiplying the hermitian adjoint of one spin function into itself or another function

$$[0 \ 1 \ 0 \ 0]\begin{bmatrix} 0 \\ 1 \\ 0 \\ 0 \end{bmatrix} = 1 \qquad\qquad [0 \ 1 \ 0 \ 0]\begin{bmatrix} 0 \\ 0 \\ 1 \\ 0 \end{bmatrix} = 0 \qquad \text{etc.}$$

with the help of the usual rule for matrix multiplication.

Symmetric or antisymmetric many-particle wave functions can be constructed from unsymmetrized solutions that include the spin by following the procedure outlined in the preceding section. It is sometimes convenient to choose the unsymmetrized solutions to be eigenfunctions of the square of the magnitude of the total spin of the identical particles $(\mathbf{S}_1 + \mathbf{S}_2 + \cdots + \mathbf{S}_n)^2$ and of the z component of this total spin $S_{1z} + S_{2z} + \cdots + S_{nz}$. These quantities are constants of the motion if the hamiltonian does not contain interaction terms between the spins and other angular momenta. In addition, such functions are often useful as zero-order wave functions when the spin interactions are weak enough to be regarded as a perturbation. There is no loss of generality in choosing the unsymmetrized solutions in this way, since any solution can be expressed as a linear combination of total-spin eigenfunctions.

COLLISIONS OF IDENTICAL PARTICLES

The effect of spin on the collision of two identical particles (or aggregates) can now be taken into account if the interaction between the particles does not involve the spin. Since each particle has $2s + 1$ spin eigenfunctions, there are altogether $(2s + 1)^2$ independent spin functions for the pair, each of which is a product of one-particle spin functions.

Any $(2s + 1)^2$ linearly independent combinations of these products can be used in place of them. These are conveniently divided into three classes. The first class consists of products of one-particle functions in which both particles are in the same spin state with S_z value $m\hbar$:

$$v_1(m)v_2(m) \qquad -s \leq m \leq s$$

where the subscript specifies which of the particles is in each state; there are evidently $2s + 1$ such states. The second class consists of sums of products

$$v_1(m')v_2(m'') + v_1(m'')v_2(m') \qquad m' \neq m''$$

There are $s(2s + 1)$ of these states. The third class consists of differences of products

$$v_1(m')v_2(m'') - v_1(m'')v_2(m') \qquad m' \neq m''$$

Again there are $s(2s + 1)$ of these.

The first two classes are clearly symmetric in an interchange of the spin coordinates of the two particles, and the third class is antisymmetric in such an interchange. Thus the total of $(2s + 1)^2$ states can be divided into $(s + 1)(2s + 1)$ symmetric and $s(2s + 1)$ antisymmetric states. Associated with the symmetric spin states must be a symmetric space state if s is an integer (symmetric total wave function), and an anti-symmetric space state if s is half an odd integer (antisymmetric total wave function). Similarly, the antisymmetric spin states multiply antisymmetric space states if $2s$ is even and multiply symmetric states if $2s$ is odd. We can see then that, if all the spin states are equally likely to appear in a collision,[1] a fraction $(s + 1)/(2s + 1)$ of the collisions will be described by the wave function (40.13) with the upper sign, and a fraction $s/(2s + 1)$ will be described by (40.13) with the lower sign, if $2s$ is even.

This and the similar result for $2s$ odd can be summarized by rewriting Eq. (40.14):

$$\sigma(\theta) = |f(\theta)|^2 + |f(\pi - \theta)|^2 + \frac{(-1)^{2s}}{2s + 1} 2 \, \text{Re} \, [f(\theta)f^*(\pi - \theta)] \qquad (41.2)$$

where f is assumed to be independent of ϕ.

Equation (41.2) can also be derived by making use of the earlier observation that particles that have different spin components are distinguishable, in which case the interference term in (40.14) disappears. This occurs in a fraction $2s/(2s + 1)$ of the collisions. In the remaining fraction $1/(2s + 1)$ of the collisions, the particles have the same spin component, and the symmetric or antisymmetric space state (upper or lower sign in the interference term) must be used according as $2s$ is even or odd.

ELECTRON SPIN FUNCTIONS

In the remainder of this section we consider only electron spin functions ($s = \frac{1}{2}$). The spin matrices are given by the first line of Eq. (27.26) and may be written as $\mathbf{S} = \frac{1}{2}\hbar\boldsymbol{\sigma}$, where

$$\sigma_x = \begin{bmatrix} 0 & 1 \\ 1 & 0 \end{bmatrix} \qquad \sigma_y = \begin{bmatrix} 0 & -i \\ i & 0 \end{bmatrix} \qquad \sigma_z = \begin{bmatrix} 1 & 0 \\ 0 & -1 \end{bmatrix} \qquad (41.3)$$

are the Pauli spin matrices (27.30). The normalized eigenfunctions of S_z

---

[1] This is the fundamental postulate of quantum statistical mechanics; see, for example, Huang, *loc. cit.*

may be written in analogy with Eqs. (41.1) as

$$v(\tfrac{1}{2}) = \begin{bmatrix} 1 \\ 0 \end{bmatrix} \qquad v(-\tfrac{1}{2}) = \begin{bmatrix} 0 \\ 1 \end{bmatrix} \tag{41.4}$$

and have eigenvalues $\tfrac{1}{2}\hbar$ and $-\tfrac{1}{2}\hbar$, respectively; they are both eigenfunctions of $\mathbf{S}^2$ with the same eigenvalue $\tfrac{3}{4}\hbar^2$.

Since we shall have occasion to write the products of spin functions for different electrons, it is convenient to abbreviate the notation as follows:

$$v_1(\tfrac{1}{2})v_2(-\tfrac{1}{2})v_3(\tfrac{1}{2})v_4(\tfrac{1}{2}) = (+-++) \qquad \text{etc.}$$

where the first particle has the eigenvalue $\tfrac{1}{2}\hbar$ for S_{1z}, the second has the eigenvalue $-\tfrac{1}{2}\hbar$ for S_{2z}, etc. $\mathbf{S}_1$ has no effect on the spin functions of any but the first particle.

The following formulas are easily obtained from (41.3) and (41.4):

$$\sigma_x\sigma_y = -\sigma_y\sigma_x = i\sigma_z \qquad \text{etc.}$$

$$\sigma_x(+) = (-) \qquad \sigma_y(+) = \ i(-) \qquad \sigma_z(+) = \ (+)$$

$$\sigma_x(-) = (+) \qquad \sigma_y(-) = -i(+) \qquad \sigma_z(-) = -(-) \tag{41.5}$$

There are four linearly independent spin functions for a pair of electrons: $(++)$, $(+-)$, $(-+)$, $(--)$. These are orthonormal, since the one-particle spin functions (41.4) are orthonormal. As remarked earlier, it is often convenient to regroup these functions into combinations that are eigenfunctions of $(\mathbf{S}_1 + \mathbf{S}_2)^2$ and $S_{1z} + S_{2z}$. These combinations are easily found by using Eq. (28.1) with the Clebsch-Gordan coefficients (28.12); the orthonormality and the indicated eigenvalues can also be verified with the help of (41.5):

	$(\mathbf{S}_1 + \mathbf{S}_2)^2$	$S_{1z} + S_{2z}$
$(++)$	$2\hbar^2$	$\hbar$
$2^{-\frac{1}{2}}[(+-) + (-+)]$	$2\hbar^2$	0
$(--)$	$2\hbar^2$	$-\hbar$
$2^{-\frac{1}{2}}[(+-) - (-+)]$	0	0

$$\tag{41.6}$$

As expected from Sec. 28, the first three of the two-particle spin functions (41.6) together behave in all respects like a single "particle" of spin $s = 1$, and the last of the spin functions (41.6) behaves like a single "particle" of spin $s = 0$.[1] Not only do they have the proper eigenvalues of the square of the magnitude of the total spin and the z component of the total spin, but the result of operating on the triplet spin function with the x or y components of the total spin is in agreement with the corresponding matrices in the second set of Eq. (27.26).

[1] The first three states are called a *triplet* and the last a *singlet*. In the old quantum theory, the triplet corresponds to parallel electron spins and the singlet to antiparallel spins.

THE HELIUM ATOM

The ground state of the helium atom was considered from the point of view of the variation method in Sec. 32. We now consider the ground and first excited states of helium with the help of the somewhat simpler first-order perturbation theory of Sec. 31; the symmetry effects of the spins of the two electrons are taken into account, although spin-dependent forces are neglected. We use products of hydrogenic wave functions u_{nlm} (with $Z = 2$) as the unperturbed eigenfunctions of the problem and are interested in classifying the states according to symmetry and spin properties rather than in obtaining accurate energy levels.

In spectroscopic notation, the ground state of helium is the $1s^2$ state: Both electrons are in the hydrogenic state u_{100}. Since this space state is symmetric, the spin state that multiplies it must be the antisymmetric singlet given as the last of the functions (41.6), for which the total spin is zero.

The space part of the first excited state of helium is eightfold degenerate in the zero-order approximation. The spectroscopic configurations are $1s2s$ and $1s2p$. Apart from electron exchange, the first state is nondegenerate and the second is triply degenerate (because of the three $2p$ states); the exchange degeneracy doubles the number of states, since either electron can occupy the $1s$ state and the other the $2s$ or $2p$ state. In order to simplify matters, we consider here only the doubly (exchange) degenerate $1s2s$ state; it is not difficult to show that the $1s2p$ states can be treated separately (see Prob. 7).

The perturbation energy is the electrostatic repulsion between the electrons e^2/r_{12}, and the unperturbed states are $u_{100}(\mathbf{r}_1)u_{200}(\mathbf{r}_2)$ and $u_{100}(\mathbf{r}_2)u_{200}(\mathbf{r}_1)$. The spin need not be considered explicitly at this point since the spin-dependent forces are neglected; appropriate spin functions will be multiplied in later to make the entire wave function antisymmetric. The matrix of the perturbation for these two states has the structure obtained from Eqs. (31.15) and can be written

$$\begin{bmatrix} J & K \\ K & J \end{bmatrix} \tag{41.7}$$

where

$$J = \iint u_{100}^*(\mathbf{r}_1)u_{200}^*(\mathbf{r}_2) \frac{e^2}{r_{12}} u_{100}(\mathbf{r}_1)u_{200}(\mathbf{r}_2) \, d^3r_1 \, d^3r_2$$

$$K = \iint u_{100}^*(\mathbf{r}_1)u_{200}^*(\mathbf{r}_2) \frac{e^2}{r_{12}} u_{100}(\mathbf{r}_2)u_{200}(\mathbf{r}_1) \, d^3r_1 \, d^3r_2 \tag{41.8}$$

J is often called the *direct* or *coulomb energy*, and K the *exchange energy*.

Application of the diagonalization technique of Sec. 31 (see the treatment of the first-order Stark effect in hydrogen) shows that the eigenvalues of the perturbation (41.7) are $J + K$ and $J - K$; they correspond to the normalized eigenfunctions $2^{-\frac{1}{2}}[u_{100}(\mathbf{r}_1)u_{200}(\mathbf{r}_2) + u_{100}(\mathbf{r}_2)u_{200}(\mathbf{r}_1)]$ and $2^{-\frac{1}{2}}[u_{100}(\mathbf{r}_1)u_{200}(\mathbf{r}_2) - u_{100}(\mathbf{r}_2)u_{200}(\mathbf{r}_1)]$, respectively. Since the first of these is a symmetric space function, it must be multiplied by the anti-symmetric singlet spin function. Similarly the second, which is an anti-symmetric space function, must be multiplied by one of the symmetric spin functions that make up the triplet in (41.6). Since K turns out to be positive, the singlet spin state has a substantially higher energy than the triplet spin state. This is due not to a spin-dependent interaction but to a coupling between the spins and the electrostatic interaction that is introduced by the exclusion principle (use of antisymmetric wave functions). From a physical point of view, the exclusion principle causes the electrons to be in different space states if they have parallel spins. They then tend to keep away from each other, and this reduces the electro-static repulsion between them and hence lowers the energy.

SPIN FUNCTIONS FOR THREE ELECTRONS

In the treatment of exchange scattering from helium given in Sec. 43, we shall require eigenfunctions of the total spin of three electrons that are analogous to those given in Eqs. (41.6) for two electrons. We can regard three electrons as $1 + 2$ electrons, in the sense that we can combine an electron ($s = \frac{1}{2}$) with the triplet two-electron function ($s = 1$) and with the singlet function ($s = 0$). In the first case, the results on addition of angular momenta, given in Sec. 28, show that we should get two groups of three-electron spin functions that correspond to $s = \frac{1}{2}$ and $s = \frac{3}{2}$; in the second case we should get a single group that corresponds to $s = \frac{1}{2}$. We thus expect one *quartet* group of spin states ($s = \frac{3}{2}$) and two distinct *doublet* groups of spin states ($s = \frac{1}{2}$), or a total of $4 + 2 + 2 = 8$ individual three-electron spin states. These must be expressible as linear combinations of the $2^3 = 8$ products of one-electron spin functions.

Again, these combinations are obtained from Eq. (28.1), with the Clebsch-Gordan coefficients now being given by (28.13); the two-electron functions required (for electrons 2 and 3) are those of (41.6). We thus obtain

	$(\mathbf{S}_1 + \mathbf{S}_2 + \mathbf{S}_3)^2$	$S_{1z} + S_{2z} + S_{3z}$
$(+++)$	$\frac{15}{4}\hbar^2$	$\frac{3}{2}\hbar$
$3^{-\frac{1}{2}}[(++-) + (+-+) + (-++)]$	$\frac{15}{4}\hbar^2$	$\frac{1}{2}\hbar$
$3^{-\frac{1}{2}}[(-+-) + (--+) + (+--)]$	$\frac{15}{4}\hbar^2$	$-\frac{1}{2}\hbar$
$(---)$	$\frac{15}{4}\hbar^2$	$-\frac{3}{2}\hbar$
$6^{-\frac{1}{2}}[2(-++) - (++-) - (+-+)]$	$\frac{3}{4}\hbar^2$	$\frac{1}{2}\hbar$
$6^{-\frac{1}{2}}[(-+-) + (--+) - 2(+--)]$	$\frac{3}{4}\hbar^2$	$-\frac{1}{2}\hbar$
$2^{-\frac{1}{2}}[(++-) - (+-+)]$	$\frac{3}{4}\hbar^2$	$\frac{1}{2}\hbar$
$2^{-\frac{1}{2}}[(-+-) - (--+)]$	$\frac{3}{4}\hbar^2$	$-\frac{1}{2}\hbar$

$$(41.9)$$

The orthonormality and the indicated eigenvalues can be verified directly. The first four (quartet) states are symmetric in the interchange of any pair of particles. The division of the four doublet states into two pairs is such that the first pair is symmetric in the interchange of particles 2 and 3, and the second pair is antisymmetric in 2 and 3. The symmetry with respect to interchanges of the other two pairs is characterized by the 2×2 matrices mentioned below Eq. (40.7); these matrices operate on either pair of doublet spin states that have the same m value (see Prob. 8).

42☐DENSITY OPERATOR AND DENSITY MATRIX

The theoretical development thus far has dealt entirely with systems in a *pure quantum state* which is represented by a single ket $|\alpha\rangle$. It often happens, however, that our knowledge of the state of a system is incomplete; for example, we may be able to say no more than that the system has nonnegative probabilities p_α, p_β, . . . for being in the states $|\alpha\rangle$, $|\beta\rangle$, ... This incompleteness may be unimportant, in which case the theory of pure states is adequate; otherwise, a statistical approach is necessary.[1] This can be developed in close analogy with the classical situation. A pure classical state is one that is represented by a single moving point in phase space, that has definite values of the coordinates $q_1 \cdots q_f$ and their canonical momenta $p_1 \cdots p_f$ at each instant of time. A statistical state, on the other hand, can be described by a nonnegative density function $\rho(q_1 \cdots q_f, p_1 \cdots p_f, t)$ such that the probability that a system is found in the interval $dq_1 \cdots dp_f$ at time t is $\rho \, dq_1 \cdots dp_f$. The quantum analog of the classical density function is the *density operator* or its representation as a *density matrix*. Before introducing it, we discuss an alternative description of pure quantum states.

EXPECTATION VALUE AND PROJECTION OPERATOR

The expectation value of an operator Ω for a discrete normalized pure state $|\alpha\rangle$ is $\langle\alpha|\Omega|\alpha\rangle$. It may be written in terms of any complete orthonormal set of kets $|i\rangle$ as

$$\langle\alpha|\Omega|\alpha\rangle = \langle\alpha|i\rangle\langle i|\Omega|j\rangle\langle j|\alpha\rangle = \langle i|\Omega|j\rangle\langle j|P_\alpha|i\rangle \tag{42.1}$$

Here $P_\alpha \equiv |\alpha\rangle\langle\alpha|$ is the projection operator for the single state α, defined as in Eq. (23.36); the generalized summations over i and j are omitted in accordance with the convention (23.33). The right side of (42.1) can be written $\langle i|\Omega P_\alpha|i\rangle$ or $\langle j|P_\alpha\Omega|j\rangle$; we thus have the relations

$$\langle\alpha|\Omega|\alpha\rangle = \text{tr } (\Omega P_\alpha) = \text{tr } (P_\alpha\Omega) \tag{42.2}$$

[1] For a general review, see U. Fano, *Rev. Mod. Phys.* **29**, 74 (1957).

As remarked in connection with Eqs. (23.40), P_α is hermitian, and

$$P_\alpha{}^2 = P_\alpha \qquad \text{tr}\,(P_\alpha) = 1 \tag{42.3}$$

It is apparent that P_α contains the same information as $|\alpha\rangle$, except for an overall multiplicative phase factor which does not enter into the calculation of expectation values.

We shall adopt the Schrödinger picture throughout this section and omit the subscript S. Then the equation of motion for P_α can be obtained from Eqs. (24.1) and (24.2)

$$\begin{aligned}
i\hbar \frac{d}{dt} P_\alpha &= i\hbar \left(\frac{d}{dt}|\alpha\rangle\right)\langle\alpha| + i\hbar|\alpha\rangle\left(\frac{d}{dt}\langle\alpha|\right) \\
&= H|\alpha\rangle\langle\alpha| - |\alpha\rangle\langle\alpha|H = [H,P_\alpha]
\end{aligned} \tag{42.4}$$

Equation (42.4) resembles the Heisenberg equation of motion (24.10), except for a sign; however, the resemblance is misleading, and it must be remembered that P_α is being viewed in the Schrödinger picture. Indeed, in the Heisenberg picture $|\alpha\rangle$ and hence also P_α are constants.

DENSITY OPERATOR

As remarked above, we shall assume that a system that is not necessarily in a pure quantum state can be described by a set of probabilities p_α, p_β, . . . for being in the states $|\alpha\rangle$, $|\beta\rangle$, . . . , with random phase differences between their amplitudes.[1] This is called a *statistical state*. A pure state is then a special case of a statistical state, in which one of the p_α's is equal to unity and all the others are zero.

It is convenient to assume that the states α are orthonormal, although not necessarily complete, so that

$$P_\alpha P_\beta = \delta_{\alpha\beta}P_\alpha \qquad \sum_\alpha p_\alpha = 1 \qquad p_\alpha \geq 0 \tag{42.5}$$

We now define a hermitian operator ρ that corresponds to this set of probabilities

$$\rho \equiv \sum_\alpha p_\alpha P_\alpha = \sum_\alpha |\alpha\rangle p_\alpha \langle\alpha| \tag{42.6}$$

It then follows from (42.2) and (42.5) that the average expectation value of Ω that corresponds to these probabilities is

$$\langle\Omega\rangle_{\text{av}} \equiv \sum_\alpha p_\alpha\langle\alpha|\Omega|\alpha\rangle = \text{tr}\,(\Omega\rho) = \text{tr}\,(\rho\Omega) \tag{42.7}$$

---

[1] For a discussion of statistical ensembles and of the relation of the density operator and matrix to statistical thermodynamics, see Huang, *loc. cit.*

It is also apparent that, in analogy with Eqs. (42.3),

$$\mathrm{tr}\,(\rho) = 1 \qquad \mathrm{tr}\,(\rho^2) = \sum_\alpha p_\alpha{}^2 \leq 1 \tag{42.8}$$

where the last equal sign can hold only if the state is pure.

EQUATIONS OF MOTION

The equation of motion of ρ in the Schrödinger picture, which is being used here, is easily obtained from Eqs. (42.4) and (42.6):

$$i\hbar \frac{d\rho}{dt} = [H,\rho] \tag{42.9}$$

Use has been made here of the fact that the p_α are constant in time. This is evidently true for an isolated system and is also true in general if H is designed to include external influences. Again, the resemblance to the Heisenberg equation of motion (24.10) is misleading since ρ, like P_α above, is being viewed in the Schrödinger picture. As with P_α, ρ is constant in the Heisenberg picture; this can also be verified by transforming (42.9) from the Schrödinger to the Heisenberg picture.

The equation of motion of $\langle \Omega \rangle_{\mathrm{av}}$ is also of interest since it is sometimes what is observed in an experiment. It follows from Eqs. (42.7) and (42.9), when it is remembered that the Schrödinger picture is being used for Ω as well as for ρ, that

$$i\hbar \frac{d}{dt} \langle \Omega \rangle_{\mathrm{av}} = i\hbar\,\mathrm{tr}\left(\frac{\partial \Omega}{\partial t}\,\rho\right) + \mathrm{tr}\,(\Omega[H,\rho])$$

$$= \mathrm{tr}\left[\left(i\hbar \frac{\partial \Omega}{\partial t} + [\Omega,H]\right)\rho\right] \tag{42.10}$$

The classical equation that corresponds to (42.9) is known as *Liouville's theorem;*[1] it may be written in either of the forms

$$\frac{d\rho}{dt} = 0 \qquad \frac{\partial \rho}{\partial t} = \{H,\rho\} \tag{42.11}$$

which are equivalent to each other on account of Eq. (24.22). Once again, Eqs. (42.11), taken together with (24.23), agree with the quantum results that ρ is constant in the Heisenberg picture.

The classical analog of $\langle \Omega \rangle_{\mathrm{av}}$ defined by (42.7) is

$$\Omega_{\mathrm{av}} \equiv \int \cdots \int \Omega(q_1 \cdots p_f, t)\rho(q_1 \cdots p_f, t)\,dq_1 \cdots dp_f \tag{42.12}$$

so that the integral over phase space is the classical analog of the quantum

[1] Huang, *op. cit.*, p. 76.

trace. Its time derivative is

$$
\frac{d}{dt}\,\Omega_{\mathrm{av}} = \int \cdots \int \left(\frac{\partial\Omega}{\partial t}\,\rho + \Omega\,\frac{\partial\rho}{\partial t}\right) dq_1 \cdots dp_f
$$
$$
= \int \cdots \int \left(\frac{\partial\Omega}{\partial t}\,\rho + \Omega\{H,\rho\}\right) dq_1 \cdots dp_f \qquad (42.13)
$$
$$
= \int \cdots \int \left(\frac{\partial\Omega}{\partial t} + \{\Omega,H\}\right) \rho\,dq_1 \cdots dp_f
$$

Equation (42.11) has been used in going from the first to the second line of (42.13), and partial integration with respect to $q_1 \cdots p_f$ has been used in going from the second to the third line. The agreement between Eqs. (42.10) and (42.13), when (24.23) is used, seems surprising when the earlier remarks concerning our use of the Schrödinger picture are recalled. However, this agreement is to be expected, since the numerical values of matrix elements such as $\langle\alpha|\Omega|\alpha\rangle$, from which $\langle\Omega\rangle_{\mathrm{av}}$ is computed, are independent of the picture.

PROJECTION OPERATOR FOR A SPIN $\frac{1}{2}$ PARTICLE

The foregoing formalism is conveniently illustrated with a spin $\frac{1}{2}$ particle, since in this case a pure state can be specified by only two parameters. Such a particle in the state $|\alpha\rangle$ can be represented by a normalized spin wave function, or *spinor*, that is a generalization of the $v(\frac{1}{2})$ given in (41.4):

$$
|\alpha\rangle = \begin{bmatrix} \alpha_1 \\ \alpha_2 \end{bmatrix} \qquad \langle\alpha| = [\alpha_1^*,\alpha_2^*]
$$
$$
\langle\alpha|\alpha\rangle = |\alpha_1|^2 + |\alpha_2|^2 = 1 \qquad (42.14)
$$

The four parameters associated with the two complex numbers α_1, α_2 are reduced to two by the normalization condition and the irrelevance of the overall phase. The generalization from $v(\frac{1}{2})$ to $|\alpha\rangle$ consists merely in a rotation acting on the ket, which can be chosen so as to bring one into the other (see Prob. 12). For this state, the projection operator P_α is the 2×2 matrix

$$
P_\alpha = |\alpha\rangle\langle\alpha| = \begin{bmatrix} \alpha_1 \\ \alpha_2 \end{bmatrix} [\alpha_1^*,\alpha_2^*] = \begin{bmatrix} |\alpha_1|^2 & \alpha_1\alpha_2^* \\ \alpha_2\alpha_1^* & |\alpha_2|^2 \end{bmatrix} \qquad (42.15)
$$

It is easily verified that tr $(P_\alpha) = 1$ and that $P_\alpha{}^2 = P_\alpha$, as expected.

Any hermitian 2×2 matrix can be written as a linear combination of the four linearly independent hermitian matrices 1, σ_x, σ_y, σ_z [see the discussion of Eq. (27.32)]. We write this combination in the form

$$
P_\alpha = a_0 + \mathbf{a} \cdot \boldsymbol{\sigma} \qquad (42.16)
$$

where the four numbers a_0, a_x, a_y, a_z are real. Since each component of $\boldsymbol{\sigma}$ has zero trace, the condition that tr $(P_\alpha) = 1$ means that $a_0 = \frac{1}{2}$. We also have $P_\alpha{}^2 = a_0{}^2 + 2a_0\mathbf{a} \cdot \boldsymbol{\sigma} + (\mathbf{a} \cdot \boldsymbol{\sigma})^2$. This may be simplified by noting, with the help of the first of Eqs. (41.5), that $(\mathbf{a} \cdot \boldsymbol{\sigma})^2 = \mathbf{a}^2$. Then the requirement that $P_\alpha{}^2 = P_\alpha$ means that $\mathbf{a}^2 = \frac{1}{4}$. We can thus write P_α in the form

$$P_\alpha = \tfrac{1}{2}(1 + \boldsymbol{\pi}_\alpha \cdot \boldsymbol{\sigma}) = \frac{1}{2}\begin{bmatrix} 1 + \pi_{\alpha z} & \pi_{\alpha x} - i\pi_{\alpha y} \\ \pi_{\alpha x} + i\pi_{\alpha y} & 1 - \pi_{\alpha z} \end{bmatrix} \tag{42.17}$$

where $\boldsymbol{\pi}_\alpha$ is a real vector of unit length. It also follows from (42.2) and (42.17) that

$$\langle \alpha | \boldsymbol{\sigma} | \alpha \rangle = \text{tr } (\boldsymbol{\sigma} P_\alpha) = \tfrac{1}{2} \text{ tr } (\boldsymbol{\sigma}) + \tfrac{1}{2} \text{ tr } [(\boldsymbol{\pi}_\alpha \cdot \boldsymbol{\sigma})\boldsymbol{\sigma}] = \boldsymbol{\pi}_\alpha \tag{42.18}$$

Comparison of Eqs. (42.15) and (42.17) shows that a pure state of a spin $\frac{1}{2}$ particle can be completely specified in terms of a single unit vector. The two parameters referred to above are now the polar angles of this vector. We also see from (42.18) that $\boldsymbol{\pi}_\alpha$ has the physical significance of being the expectation value of the spin operator, and so we call it the *polarization vector* that corresponds to the state α.

DENSITY MATRIX FOR A SPIN $\frac{1}{2}$ PARTICLE

It is not difficult to see that the pure state $|\beta\rangle$ that is orthogonal to $|\alpha\rangle$ has the polarization vector $\boldsymbol{\pi}_\beta = -\boldsymbol{\pi}_\alpha$ (Prob. 13). The density matrix that corresponds to the probabilities p_α, p_β may then be obtained from Eqs. (42.6) and (42.17):

$$\rho = p_\alpha P_\alpha + p_\beta P_\beta = \tfrac{1}{2}[1 + (p_\alpha - p_\beta)\boldsymbol{\pi}_\alpha \cdot \boldsymbol{\sigma}] \tag{42.19}$$

The average expectation value of $\boldsymbol{\sigma}$ that corresponds to this ρ is

$$\langle \boldsymbol{\sigma} \rangle_{\text{av}} = \text{tr } (\boldsymbol{\sigma}\rho) = (p_\alpha - p_\beta)\boldsymbol{\pi}_\alpha \tag{42.20}$$

We see then that a statistical state for a spin $\frac{1}{2}$ particle has a polarization vector whose length is less than the unit value that corresponds to a pure state.

POLARIZATION VECTOR FOR A SPIN s PARTICLE

The spin angular momentum of a particle with spin s can be represented by matrices of the form (27.26) with $2s + 1$ rows and columns. A pure state $|\alpha\rangle$ is then a one-column matrix with $2s + 1$ rows, which can be specified (apart from normalization and overall phase) by $2(2s + 1) - 2 =$

$4s$ real parameters. The projection operator analogous to (42.15) is

$$
P_\alpha = |\alpha\rangle\langle\alpha| =
\begin{bmatrix}
\alpha_1 \\
\cdot \\
\cdot \\
\cdot \\
\alpha_{2s+1}
\end{bmatrix}
[\alpha_1^* \ \cdots \ \alpha_{2s+1}^*]
\tag{42.21}
$$

Such a hermitian matrix can be written as a linear combination of $(2s + 1)^2$ linearly independent hermitian matrices. It is convenient for one of these to be the unit matrix and for the remaining $(2s + 1)^2 - 1$ matrices to have zero trace [see the discussion of Eq. (27.33)]. The latter can be chosen to represent the multipole moment operators that are permitted for a particle of spin s (see the remark at the end of Sec. 28). For example, with $s = \frac{1}{2}$, the remaining $2^2 - 1 = 3$ matrices represent the spin or dipole moment operator, and with $s = 1$, the remaining $3^2 - 1 = 8$ matrices represent dipole and quadrupole moment operators.

In the general case, we can put, in analogy with (42.16),

$$
P_\alpha = a_0 + \mathbf{a} \cdot \mathbf{d} + P_\alpha'
\tag{42.22}
$$

where as before a_0, a_x, a_y, a_z are real. $\mathbf{d}$ is now the generalization of the Pauli matrices to higher spin and is the appropriate set of matrices (27.26) divided by $s\hbar$. The remainder P_α' includes all the higher multipole moment matrices and is defined to be orthogonal to $1, \mathbf{d}$ in the sense that

$$
\text{tr}\,(1P_\alpha') = \text{tr}\,(\mathbf{d}P_\alpha') = 0
\tag{42.23}
$$

Equation (42.23) is a natural generalization of the situation with spin $\frac{1}{2}$, in which the trace of the product of any two of the four matrices $1, \sigma_x$, σ_y, σ_z is zero (see also Prob. 14). It follows from (42.22), (42.23), and Prob. 15 that

$$
\text{tr}\,(P_\alpha) = (2s + 1)a_0 = 1 \qquad \pi_\alpha \equiv \text{tr}\,(\mathbf{d}P_\alpha) = \frac{(s + 1)(2s + 1)}{3s}\,\mathbf{a}
\tag{42.24}
$$

where π_α is the polarization vector.

The transition from a pure state to a statistical state is effected as before and leads to the polarization vector

$$
\langle\mathbf{d}\rangle_{\text{av}} = \text{tr}\,(\mathbf{d}\rho) = \sum_\alpha p_\alpha \pi_\alpha
\tag{42.25}
$$

where the summation is over $2s + 1$ orthonormal states.

PRECESSION OF THE POLARIZATION VECTOR

As a simple example of the equation of motion (42.10), we now consider the precession of a spin s particle in a magnetic field. We assume that the particle has the magnetic moment operator

$$\boldsymbol{\mu} = \gamma \mathbf{S} = \gamma s \hbar \boldsymbol{\sigma} \tag{42.26}$$

where γ is called the *gyromagnetic ratio*. The hamiltonian that describes the interaction of the spin with a magnetic field $\mathbf{H}$ is then

$$H = -\boldsymbol{\mu} \cdot \mathbf{H} = -\gamma s \hbar \boldsymbol{\sigma} \cdot \mathbf{H} \tag{42.27}$$

The rate of change of the polarization vector is given by Eq. (42.10):

$$\frac{d}{dt} \langle \boldsymbol{\sigma} \rangle_{\mathrm{av}} = \frac{1}{i\hbar} \operatorname{tr} ([\boldsymbol{\sigma},H]\rho) \tag{42.28}$$

since $\boldsymbol{\sigma}$ has no explicit dependence on the time. The angular momentum commutation relations (27.15), together with (42.26), give

$$\boldsymbol{\sigma} \times \boldsymbol{\sigma} = \frac{i}{s} \boldsymbol{\sigma} \tag{42.29}$$

Thus, from (42.27) and (42.29), we obtain for a typical component of $\boldsymbol{\sigma}$:

$$[\sigma_x,H] = -\gamma s \hbar([\sigma_x,\sigma_y]\mathsf{H}_y + [\sigma_x,\sigma_z]\mathsf{H}_z)$$
$$= -\gamma i\hbar(\sigma_z \mathsf{H}_y - \sigma_y \mathsf{H}_z) = \gamma i\hbar(\boldsymbol{\sigma} \times \mathbf{H})_x$$

Substitution into (42.28) then gives

$$\frac{d}{dt} \langle \boldsymbol{\sigma} \rangle_{\mathrm{av}} = \gamma \operatorname{tr} [(\boldsymbol{\sigma} \times \mathbf{H})\rho] = \gamma \langle \boldsymbol{\sigma} \rangle_{\mathrm{av}} \times \mathbf{H} \tag{42.30}$$

Equation (42.30) is just the classical equation for the precession. This agreement between quantum and classical equations of motion can also be justified by an argument based on Ehrenfest's theorem.[1]

43☐REARRANGEMENT COLLISIONS

The calculation of the elastic and inelastic scattering of an electron from a hydrogen atom was discussed in Sec. 38, with neglect of exchange between the incident and atomic electrons. Electron exchange is a special case of a *rearrangement collision*, in which the component parts of the colliding systems are redistributed during the scattering process. We first set up the formalism for the general case and then apply it to electron-atom scattering. The identity and spin of the incident and atomic electrons introduce additional effects that must be taken into account. As examples, we shall discuss exchange collisions of electrons with hydrogen and helium atoms by means of the Born approximation.

[1] F. Bloch, *Phys. Rev.* **70**, 460 (1946).

NOTATION FOR REARRANGEMENT COLLISIONS

The collision of two systems a and b may result in the same final systems in their original states (elastic scattering) or in different states (inelastic scattering). Or it may result in different final systems that are formed by rearrangement of the component parts of a and b. We shall consider the reaction $a + b \rightarrow c + d$ and not take identity and spin of the parts into account until later. The full hamiltonian can be written in either of two ways:

$$H = H_{ab} + H'_{ab} = H_{cd} + H'_{cd} \tag{43.1}$$

Here H_{ab} describes the internal and kinetic energies of a and b, and H'_{ab} their interaction; H_{cd} and H'_{cd} are defined similarly. We shall assume that all the H's that appear in Eq. (43.1) are hermitian; otherwise it is likely that H_{ab} or H_{cd} will have absorptive parts, and there will be no stationary states for some of the systems a, b, c, d.

We shall be especially interested in exact solutions $\chi_{ab}{}^+$ and $\chi_{cd}{}^-$ of the full hamiltonian that correspond to total energy E and satisfy Lippmann-Schwinger equations that are obvious generalizations of (37.14):

$$
\begin{aligned}
\chi_{ab}{}^+ &= u_{ab} + (E - H_{ab} + i\epsilon)^{-1} H'_{ab} \chi_{ab}{}^+ \\
\chi_{cd}{}^- &= u_{cd} + (E - H_{cd} - i\epsilon)^{-1} H'_{cd} \chi_{cd}{}^-
\end{aligned}
\tag{43.2}
$$

where

$$(H_{ab} - E)u_{ab} = 0 \qquad (H_{cd} - E)u_{cd} = 0 \tag{43.3}$$

ALTERNATIVE EXPRESSION FOR THE T MATRIX ELEMENT

The T matrix element that describes this collision cannot be written in analogy with the earlier work, since in the present case there is not a unique interaction V. We therefore go back to the original definition (36.32) for the S matrix element and rewrite it in the stationary case with the help of (37.1):

$$
\begin{aligned}
\langle \beta | (S - 1) | \alpha \rangle &= (\phi_\beta, (\psi_\alpha{}^+ - \phi_\alpha))_{t'=T_2} \\
&= (u_\beta, (\chi_\alpha{}^+ - u_\alpha)) e^{(i/\hbar)(E_\beta - E_\alpha)T_2}
\end{aligned}
\tag{43.4}
$$

Also the first of Eqs. (37.2) is

$$\langle \beta | (S - 1) | \alpha \rangle = -\frac{i}{\hbar} \langle \beta | T | \alpha \rangle \int_{-\infty}^{T_2} g(t) e^{(i/\hbar)(E_\beta - E_\alpha)t} \, dt \tag{43.5}$$

since the interaction in the initial state is turned off at T_2. We now follow the general procedure illustrated by the propagator in (37.14) and replace E_α by $E_\alpha + i\epsilon$ on the right sides of (43.4) and (43.5), where the limit $\epsilon \rightarrow 0^+$ is understood. This causes the integral in (43.5) to converge at its lower limit, so that $g(t)$ can be replaced by unity. Then, with

$E_\beta = E_\alpha$, we obtain

$$\langle \beta|T|\alpha \rangle = i\epsilon(u_\beta, (\chi_\alpha{}^+ - u_\alpha)) \qquad (43.6)$$

Although this derivation is somewhat heuristic, it is easily verified that (43.6) agrees with the second of Eqs. (37.2) in the simpler case considered earlier (see Prob. 17). For our present purpose, Eq. (43.6) has the advantage of not involving the interaction explicitly and hence being applicable when the interaction is different in the initial and final states.

T MATRIX ELEMENT FOR REARRANGEMENTS[1]

We can now start from the expression (43.6) that is appropriate for a rearrangement collision and derive from it a form that is similar to (37.2). We first introduce $E - H_{cd} + i\epsilon$ operating on the right member of the inner product, and its reciprocal adjoint on the left member:

$$\langle cd|T|ab \rangle = i\epsilon(u_{cd}, (\chi_{ab}{}^+ - u_{ab}))$$
$$= i\epsilon((E - H_{cd} - i\epsilon)^{-1}u_{cd}, (E - H_{cd} + i\epsilon)(\chi_{ab}{}^+ - u_{ab}))$$

The second of Eqs. (43.3) shows that the left member of the inner product is now $(-i\epsilon)^{-1}u_{cd}$; since the complex conjugate of the left member is to be taken, the factor $(-i\epsilon)^{-1}$ cancels the factor $i\epsilon$ preceding the term in brackets. Equation (43.1) can then be used to replace H_{cd} by $H_{ab} + H'_{ab} - H'_{cd}$ in the right member of the inner product:

$$\langle cd|T|ab \rangle = (u_{cd}, (E - H_{ab} + i\epsilon + H'_{cd} - H'_{ab})(\chi_{ab}{}^+ - u_{ab}))$$
$$= (u_{cd}, (E - H_{ab} + i\epsilon)(\chi_{ab}{}^+ - u_{ab}))$$
$$+ (u_{cd}, (H'_{cd} - H'_{ab})\chi_{ab}{}^+) - (u_{cd}, (H'_{cd} - H'_{ab})u_{ab}) \qquad (43.7)$$

Substitution for $\chi_{ab}{}^+ - u_{ab}$ from the first of Eqs. (43.2) shows that the first term on the right side of (43.7) is equal to $(u_{cd}, H'_{ab}\chi_{ab}{}^+)$, so that it cancels part of the second term. Further, the last term on the right side vanishes since

$$(u_{cd}, (H'_{cd} - H'_{ab})u_{ab}) = (u_{cd}, (H_{ab} - H_{cd})u_{ab})$$
$$= (u_{cd}, H_{ab}u_{ab}) - (H_{cd}u_{cd}, u_{ab}) = 0 \qquad (43.8)$$

with the help of (43.3).

We thus obtain

$$\langle cd|T|ab \rangle = (u_{cd}, H'_{cd}\chi_{ab}{}^+) \qquad (43.9)$$

which is similar in structure to (37.2). An equivalent expression in which the roles of initial and final states are interchanged can be obtained either by starting over with a form analogous to (43.6) or by manipulating

[1] B. A. Lippmann, *Phys. Rev.* **102**, 264 (1956); E. Gerjuoy, *Ann. Phys.* (*N.Y.*) **5**, 58 (1958).

(43.9):

$$\langle cd|T|ab\rangle = (\chi_{cd}^-, H'_{ab} u_{ab}) \tag{43.10}$$

Equations (43.9) and (43.10) are usually referred to as the *post* and *prior* forms of the T matrix element, respectively, since the first involves the interaction in the final state and the second that in the initial state. These two equations show incidentally that the reaction does not occur if there is no interaction in either the initial or the final state, as would be expected.

As in Sec. 38, the Born approximation consists in using (43.2) to replace χ_{ab}^+ by u_{ab} in (43.9) or χ_{cd}^- by u_{cd} in (43.10). The two expressions obtained in this way are equal on account of (43.8):

$$\langle cd|T|ab\rangle_B = (u_{cd}, H'_{cd} u_{ab}) = (u_{cd}, H'_{ab} u_{ab}) \tag{43.11}$$

PRESENCE OF A CORE INTERACTION

A situation of particular interest occurs when part of H'_{ab} and H'_{cd} arises from the interaction of one of the colliding systems with an infinitely massive core in the other. An example is provided by the exchange scattering of an electron by an atom, in which the atomic nucleus is so massive that it can be regarded as such a core of infinite mass. We have already seen in Sec. 38 that, in nonexchange scattering, the interaction between the incident electron and the nucleus cannot lead to excitation of the atom (inelastic scattering), because of the orthogonality of the initial and final wave functions of the atomic electron. In somewhat similar fashion, we might expect that exchange scattering can be caused only by interaction between the incident and atomic electrons that exchange places and not by interaction of either electron with the nucleus. Yet Eqs. (43.9) to (43.11) do not suggest in any obvious way that the contribution of this core interaction to the T matrix element is zero. We now show rather generally how the core interaction can be eliminated.[1]

The reaction we consider may be represented schematically as

$$1 + (2, \text{core})_a \rightarrow 2 + (1, \text{core})_b$$

where, for example, the first parenthesis indicates that 2 is bound to the core in state a. The full hamiltonian is

$$H = K_1 + K_2 + U_1 + U_2 + V_{12} \tag{43.12}$$

where K_1 and K_2 are the kinetic energy operators for 1 and 2, U_1 and U_2 are the interactions of 1 and 2 with the core, and V_{12} is the interaction of

---

[1] We follow the derivation given by T. B. Day, L. S. Rodberg, G. A. Snow, and J. Sucher, *Phys. Rev.* **123**, 1051 (1961). The extension to the case in which the core is not infinitely massive is discussed in footnote 6 of this paper.

1 and 2 with each other.   The quantities defined in connection with Eq. (43.1) are then

$$H_{ab} = K_1 + K_2 + U_2 \qquad H'_{ab} = U_1 + V_{12}$$
$$H_{cd} = K_1 + K_2 + U_1 \qquad H'_{cd} = U_2 + V_{12} \tag{43.13}$$

We now call the exact initial and final solutions $\chi_{ab}{}^+ = \chi_i{}^+$ and $\chi_{cd}{}^- = \chi_f{}^-$, and the unperturbed initial and final solutions $u_{ab} = u_\alpha(1)w_a(2)$ and $u_{cd} = w_b(1)u_\beta(2)$.   Here w_a and w_b are the core-bound initial and final wave functions that satisfy the equations

$$(K_2 + U_2 - \epsilon_a)w_a(2) = 0 \qquad (K_1 + U_1 - \epsilon_b)w_b(1) = 0$$
$$\epsilon_a,\ \epsilon_b < 0 \tag{43.14}$$

and u_α and u_β are the corresponding free wave functions that satisfy

$$(K_1 - E + \epsilon_a)u_\alpha(1) = 0 \qquad (K_2 - E + \epsilon_b)u_\beta(2) = 0 \tag{43.15}$$

The "post" form of the exact T matrix element (43.9) is then

$$\langle cd|T|ab\rangle = [w_b u_\beta, (U_2 + V_{12})\chi_i{}^+] \tag{43.16}$$

ELIMINATION OF THE CORE TERM

Our objective is the elimination of the U_2 term in Eq. (43.16).   The only general way in which to accomplish this is to rewrite the matrix element so that U_2 appears only between exact states of 1 that correspond to different energies; then the orthogonality of these states, together with the fact that U_2 does not depend on the coordinates of 1, will cause this term to vanish.   Thus we shall require, in addition to the exact core-bound state $w_b(1)$ that corresponds to energy ϵ_b, the exact core-scattering state $\chi_\alpha{}^+(1)$ that is analogous to $u_\alpha(1)$ and corresponds to the energy $E - \epsilon_a$.   We therefore introduce the equations

$$(K_1 + U_1 - E + \epsilon_a)\chi_\alpha{}^+(1) = 0$$
$$(K_2 + U_2 - E + \epsilon_b)\chi_\beta{}^-(2) = 0 \tag{43.17}$$

Lippmann-Schwinger equations of the form (37.14) for $\chi_i{}^+$ and of the form (37.16) for $\chi_\beta{}^-$ are the only ones needed if we start from the "post" expression (43.16):

$$\chi_i{}^+ = \chi_\alpha{}^+(1)w_a(2) + (E - K_1 - K_2 - U_1 - U_2 + i\epsilon)^{-1}V_{12}\chi_i{}^+ \tag{43.18}$$

$$\chi_\beta{}^-(2) = u_\beta(2) + (E - \epsilon_b - K_2 - U_2 - i\epsilon)^{-1}U_2 u_\beta(2) \tag{43.19}$$

Equation (43.19) can be multiplied through by $w_b(1)$, which commutes with $(E - \epsilon_b - K_2 - U_2 - i\epsilon)^{-1}U_2$ since this operator does not involve the coordinates of 1:

$$w_b(1)\chi_\beta^-(2) = w_b(1)u_\beta(2)$$
$$+ (E - \epsilon_b - K_2 - U_2 - i\epsilon)^{-1}U_2w_b(1)u_\beta(2) \quad (43.20)$$

At this point we must make the assumption that the core is infinitely massive, since we shall soon have to make use of the fact that the inverse operator in (43.20) can be the adjoint of that in (43.18). The two are adjoints if we can use the second of Eqs. (43.14) to replace $\epsilon_b w_b(1)$ by $(K_1 + U_1)w_b(1)$ in (43.20), and this replacement is valid only if $K_1 + U_1$ commutes with U_2. Suppose now that the core has finite mass. Then we must work in the center-of-mass coordinate system, and the total kinetic energy operator cannot be separated into parts K_1 and K_2 that commute with U_2 and U_1, respectively. This corresponds physically to the fact that the recoil of the finite-mass core under the impact of 1 can shake off 2, so that the interaction with the core does, in fact, contribute to exchange scattering.

With a core of infinite mass, we can replace (43.20) by

$$w_b(1)\chi_\beta^-(2) = w_b(1)u_\beta(2)$$
$$+ (E - K_1 - K_2 - U_1 - U_2 - i\epsilon)^{-1}U_2w_b(1)u_\beta(2) \quad (43.21)$$

Equation (43.16) can then be rewritten in a series of steps that make use of some of the foregoing relations:

$$\langle cd|T|ab\rangle = (w_bu_\beta, U_2\chi_i^+) + (w_b\chi_\beta^-, V_{12}\chi_i^+)$$
$$- [(E - K_1 - K_2 - U_1 - U_2 - i\epsilon)^{-1}U_2w_bu_\beta, V_{12}\chi_i^+]$$
$$= (w_bu_\beta, U_2\chi_i^+) + (w_b\chi_\beta^-, V_{12}\chi_i^+)$$
$$- [w_bu_\beta, U_2(E - K_1 - K_2 - U_1 - U_2 + i\epsilon)^{-1}V_{12}\chi_i^+]$$
$$= (w_bu_\beta, U_2\chi_i^+) + (w_b\chi_\beta^-, V_{12}\chi_i^+)$$
$$- [w_bu_\beta, U_2(\chi_i^+ - \chi_\alpha^+w_a)]$$
$$= (w_b\chi_b^-, V_{12}\chi_i^+) + (w_bu_\beta, U_2\chi_\alpha^+w_a) \quad (43.22)$$

The second term on the right side of (43.22) vanishes because of the orthogonality of $w_b(1)$ and $\chi_\alpha^+(1)$, as was remarked at the beginning of this subsection. We thus obtain for the "post" form of the exact T matrix element

$$\langle cd|T|ab\rangle = [w_b(1)\chi_\beta^-(2), V_{12}\chi_i^+] \quad (43.23)$$

In similar fashion, the "prior" form can be written

$$\langle cd|T|ab\rangle = [\chi_f^-, V_{12}\chi_\alpha^+(1)w_a(2)] \quad (43.24)$$

These expressions show at once that the process does not occur if there is no interaction between 1 and 2.

Equations (43.23) and (43.24) can be used to obtain a distorted wave Born approximation expression for the T matrix element, which is of first order in V_{12} but exact in U_1 and U_2. This is accomplished by replacing χ_i^+ by $\chi_\alpha^+(1)w_a(2)$ from (43.18) or χ_f^- by $w_b(1)\chi_\beta^-(2)$:

$$\langle cd|T|ab\rangle_{\mathrm{DWBA}} = [w_b(1)\chi_\beta^-(2), V_{12}\chi_\alpha^+(1)w_a(2)] \tag{43.25}$$

The Born approximation is obtained by replacing $\chi_\beta^-(2)$ by $u_\beta(2)$ from (43.19) and $\chi_\alpha^+(1)$ by $u_\alpha(1)$:

$$\langle cd|T|ab\rangle_B = [w_b(1)u_\beta(2), V_{12}u_\alpha(1)w_a(2)] \tag{43.26}$$

EXCHANGE COLLISIONS OF ELECTRONS WITH HYDROGEN

As a first example of a rearrangement collision in which effects of identity and spin appear, we consider the elastic scattering of an electron from a hydrogen atom. In a problem of this type, we must know the asymptotic forms of the unsymmetrized wave function for all permutations of identical particles.[1] A wave function that has the proper symmetry can then be constructed by the methods outlined in Secs. 40 and 41.

Since there are two electrons, we require asymptotic forms for the exact unsymmetrized wave function $\chi_i^+(\mathbf{r}_1,\mathbf{r}_2)$ when r_1 is large and also when r_2 is large. In the first case, the asymptotic behavior is of the general form (38.18):

$$\chi_i^+(\mathbf{r}_1,\mathbf{r}_2) \xrightarrow[r_1\to\infty]{} C[\exp{(i\mathbf{k}_\alpha \cdot \mathbf{r}_1)} + r_1^{-1}e^{ik\alpha r_1}f_D(\mathbf{k}_r,\mathbf{k}_\alpha)]w_a(\mathbf{r}_2) + \cdots \tag{43.27}$$

Here f_D is the direct or nonexchange elastic scattering amplitude, for which the incident electron is scattered and the atomic electron is left in its original state; the dots represent other terms in the series of (38.18) and correspond to excitation of the atomic electron. As in (38.18), $\mathbf{k}_r$ is in the direction of $\mathbf{r}_1$. The asymptotic behavior when r_2 is large has the form

$$\chi_i^+(\mathbf{r}_1,\mathbf{r}_2) \xrightarrow[r_2\to\infty]{} Cr_2^{-1}e^{ik\alpha r_2}f_E(\mathbf{k}_r,\mathbf{k}_\alpha)w_a(\mathbf{r}_1) + \cdots \tag{43.28}$$

Here f_E is the exchange elastic scattering amplitude, the dots again represent atomic excitation, and $\mathbf{k}_r$ is now in the direction of $\mathbf{r}_2$. There is no plane wave state in (43.28), since $w_a(\mathbf{r}_2)$ vanishes when r_2 is large.

As in Secs. 40 and 41, we want to work with the symmetric and antisymmetric combinations $\chi_i^+(\mathbf{r}_1,\mathbf{r}_2) \pm \chi_i^+(\mathbf{r}_2,\mathbf{r}_1)$ and find their asymptotic forms as r_1 or r_2 becomes infinite (because of the symmetrization, either one will do). Our immediate problem, then, is to express the direct and exchange amplitudes f_D and f_E in terms of the corresponding T matrix elements, which we know. The exact direct T matrix element

[1] J. R. Oppenheimer, *Phys. Rev.* **32**, 361 (1928).

is, from (38.21),

$$T_D = C^*e^2 \iint \exp\left(-i\mathbf{k}_\beta \cdot \mathbf{r}_1\right) w_a^*(\mathbf{r}_2) \left(\frac{1}{r_{12}} - \frac{1}{r_1}\right) \chi_i^+(\mathbf{r}_1, \mathbf{r}_2) \, d^3r_1 \, d^3r_2$$

$$(43.29)$$

Similarly, the "post" form of the exact exchange T matrix element is obtained from (43.23):

$$T_E = e^2 \iint w_a^*(\mathbf{r}_1) \chi_\beta^{-*}(\mathbf{r}_2) \frac{1}{r_{12}} \chi_i^+(\mathbf{r}_1, \mathbf{r}_2) \, d^3r_1 \, d^3r_2 \qquad (43.30)$$

We already know the relation between f_D and T_D from (37.21) or (38.21):

$$f_D = -\frac{m}{2\pi\hbar^2|C|^2} T_D \qquad (43.31)$$

Although it seems likely that the relation (43.31) also holds between f_E and T_E, it is not obvious that this is the case, and we shall give a proof in the next subsection. Before embarking on this, however, it is interesting to compare the structures of Eqs. (43.29) and (43.30), both of which are exact. The expression for T_D is a matrix element of the full interaction, including the core term $-e^2/r_1$ and with the free final state $\exp(i\mathbf{k}_\beta \cdot \mathbf{r}_1)$ for the outgoing electron. We might have written T_E in an analogous form, by making use of (43.16). However it is preferable for subsequent perturbation approximations to express T_E as a matrix element of only the interelectron interaction e^2/r_{12}; the electron-nucleus interaction is then taken into account through the use of the exact core-scattering wave function $\chi_\beta^-(\mathbf{r}_2)$ for the outgoing electron.

RELATION BETWEEN AMPLITUDE AND MATRIX ELEMENT

We now show that the exchange scattering amplitude and T matrix element, f_E and T_E, are related by (43.31). The interaction is different in the initial and final states of a rearrangement collision; thus it is advantageous to start with the expression (43.6) for the T matrix element since it does not involve the interaction explicitly. As a check on the calculation, we first rederive Eq. (43.31) and then show how the derivation can be extended to the exchange case.

We wish then to evaluate the integral

$$T_D = i\epsilon \iint C^* \exp\left(-i\mathbf{k}_\beta \cdot \mathbf{r}_1\right) w_a^*(\mathbf{r}_2)[\chi_i^+(\mathbf{r}_1, \mathbf{r}_2)$$
$$- C \exp\left(i\mathbf{k}_\alpha \cdot \mathbf{r}_1\right) w_a(\mathbf{r}_2)] \, d^3r_1 \, d^3r_2 \quad (43.32)$$

where the limit $\epsilon \to 0^+$ is understood. Since ϵ multiplies the integral, only terms that are proportional to ϵ^{-1} are of interest. The contribution to the integral from finite values of r_1 is finite; hence this part of T_D vanishes in the limit $\epsilon \to 0$. Thus we can use the asymptotic form (43.27) for $\chi_i{}^+(\mathbf{r}_1,\mathbf{r}_2)$. The excitation terms that are represented by dots can be omitted since w's that correspond to different states are orthogonal and vanish on integration over $\mathbf{r}_2$.

The bracket in (43.32) is then proportional to $w_a(\mathbf{r}_2)$, so that the integration over $\mathbf{r}_2$ gives unity. We drop the subscript from $\mathbf{r}_1$ and write

$$T_D = i\epsilon|C|^2 \!\int r^{-1} \exp\left(-i\mathbf{k}_\beta \cdot \mathbf{r} + ik_\alpha r\right) f_D(\mathbf{k}_r,\mathbf{k}_\alpha)\, d^3r \tag{43.33}$$

As in the derivation of (43.6), we replace E_α by $E_\alpha + i\epsilon$ or, equivalently, k_α by $k_\alpha + i\epsilon m/\hbar^2 k_\alpha$. It is convenient to choose the direction of $\mathbf{k}_\beta$ as the polar axis for the integration and to denote the polar angles of $\mathbf{r}$ or $\mathbf{k}_r$ with respect to this axis by θ, ϕ. With $w = \cos\theta$, f_D is some function of w and ϕ, and we may write

$$T_D = i\epsilon|C|^2 \int r^{-1} \exp\left[-\frac{\epsilon m}{\hbar^2 k_\alpha} r + ik_\alpha r(1 - w)\right] f_D(w,\phi)\, d^3r \tag{43.34}$$

since $k_\beta = k_\alpha$.

It is most convenient to perform the w integration first by using the partial-integration or stationary-phase method discussed in connection with Eq. (20.14):

$$\int_{-1}^{1} f_D(w,\phi) e^{ik_\alpha r(1-w)}\, dw = \frac{i}{k_\alpha r}\left[f_D(1,\phi) - f_D(-1,\phi) e^{2ik_\alpha r}\right]$$
$$- \frac{i}{k_\alpha r}\int_{-1}^{1} \frac{\partial f_D}{\partial w}\, e^{ik_\alpha r(1-w)}\, dw \tag{43.35}$$

On substitution into (43.34), the first two terms on the right side of Eq. (43.35) make contributions to the r integration that are proportional to ϵ^{-1} and $[\epsilon - (2i\hbar^2 k_\alpha^2/m]^{-1}$, respectively. The integral on the right side of (43.35) acquires higher powers of r in the denominator on further partial integrations, so that its leading contribution to the r integration is of order $\ln\epsilon$. Further, $f_D(1,\phi)$ is evidently independent of ϕ and is equal to $f_D(\mathbf{k}_\beta,\mathbf{k}_\alpha)$. We thus obtain, on taking the limit $\epsilon \to 0^+$,

$$T_D = -\frac{2\pi\hbar^2|C|^2}{m} f_D(\mathbf{k}_\beta,\mathbf{k}_\alpha) \tag{43.36}$$

This is the same as (43.31).

The exchange T matrix element can be calculated in similar fashion, starting from (43.6). Instead of (43.32), we now wish to evaluate the integral

$$T_E = i\epsilon\!\int\!\!\int w_a^*(\mathbf{r}_1) C^* \exp\left(-i\mathbf{k}_\beta \cdot \mathbf{r}_2\right)[\chi_i{}^+(\mathbf{r}_1,\mathbf{r}_2)$$
$$- C \exp\left(i\mathbf{k}_\alpha \cdot \mathbf{r}_1\right) w_a(\mathbf{r}_2)]\, d^3r_1\, d^3r_2 \tag{43.37}$$

where again the limit $\epsilon \to 0^+$ is understood. The contribution to the integral from finite values of r_2 is finite; hence this part of T_E vanishes in the limit $\epsilon \to 0$.   We can therefore neglect the second term in the bracket and use the asymptotic form (43.28) for $\chi_i{}^+(\mathbf{r}_1,\mathbf{r}_2)$; the excitation terms represented by dots can again be omitted.   The $\mathbf{r}_1$ integration gives unity, and we drop the subscript from $\mathbf{r}_2$ to write

$$T_E = i\epsilon |C|^2 \textstyle\int r^{-1} \exp\left(-i\mathbf{k}_\beta \cdot \mathbf{r} + ik_\alpha r\right) f_E(\mathbf{k}_r,\mathbf{k}_\alpha)\, d^3r$$

This is evaluated in exactly the same way as (43.33) and leads to

$$T_E = -\frac{2\pi\hbar^2 |C|^2}{m} f_E(\mathbf{k}_\beta,\mathbf{k}_\alpha) \tag{43.38}$$

EFFECTS OF IDENTITY AND SPIN

We shall assume, as in the discussion of identical particle collisions in Sec. 41, that the interaction does not depend on the spin.   Then all we need do in order to take into account the identity and spin of the two electrons is to form an antisymmetric wave function from products of $\chi_i{}^+(\mathbf{r}_1,\mathbf{r}_2)$ and appropriate spin functions.   The spin functions can be taken to be the set of four given after Eq. (41.5); however, it is simpler to make use of the four symmetrized combinations (41.6).   The spin of the incident electron is not assumed to have any definite relation to the spin of the atomic electron.   In this case we can use either of these sets of spin functions, calculate the scattering with each of the four spin states of a set, and then average the results with equal weights for each state.[1]   The first three of the spin functions (41.6) are symmetric and must be multiplied by the antisymmetric space function $\chi_i{}^+(\mathbf{r}_1,\mathbf{r}_2) - \chi_i{}^+(\mathbf{r}_2,\mathbf{r}_1)$; the fourth spin function is antisymmetric and must be multiplied by $\chi_i{}^+(\mathbf{r}_1,\mathbf{r}_2) + \chi_i{}^+(\mathbf{r}_2,\mathbf{r}_1)$.

The asymptotic forms of the symmetrized space functions for large values of one of the electron coordinates, say r_1, are obtained from (43.27) and (43.28):

$$\chi_i{}^+(\mathbf{r}_1,\mathbf{r}_2) \pm \chi_i{}^+(\mathbf{r}_2,\mathbf{r}_1) \xrightarrow[r_1 \to \infty]{} C\{\exp\left(i\mathbf{k}_\alpha \cdot \mathbf{r}_1\right)$$
$$+ r_1{}^{-1} e^{ik_\alpha r_1}[f_D(\theta) \pm f_E(\theta)]\}w_a(\mathbf{r}_2) + \cdots \tag{43.39}$$

The dots represent atomic excitation, and θ is the angle between $\mathbf{r}_1$ and $\mathbf{k}_\alpha$.   The differential cross section must be computed with the upper sign in one quarter of the collisions and with the lower sign in three quarters of the cases.   We thus obtain

$$\sigma(\theta) = \tfrac{1}{4}|f_D(\theta) + f_E(\theta)|^2 + \tfrac{3}{4}|f_D(\theta) - f_E(\theta)|^2 \tag{43.40}$$

Equation (43.40) can also be derived without explicit reference to the spin wave functions, as was Eq. (41.2), by making use of the earlier

---

[1] This is the fundamental postulate of quantum statistical mechanics referred to in the derivation of Eq. (41.2).

observation that particles that have different spin components are distinguishable. If half the collisions, the electrons have different spin components, and the cross section is just the sum $|f_D(\theta)|^2 + |f_E(\theta)|^2$ of the direct and exchange cross sections; in the other half, the electrons are indistinguishable, and the antisymmetric space function must be used. We thus obtain

$$\sigma(\theta) = \tfrac{1}{2}(|f_D(\theta)|^2 + |f_E(\theta)|^2) + \tfrac{1}{2}|f_D(\theta) - f_E(\theta)|^2$$

which is easily seen to be the same as (43.40).

EXCHANGE COLLISIONS WITH HELIUM

We now consider the elastic scattering of an electron from a helium atom in its ground state and again assume that the interaction does not depend on the spin. According to the discussion of Sec. 41, the two electrons in the helium atom are in a symmetric space state and an antisymmetric (singlet) spin state. We therefore write the partially symmetrized wave function that corresponds to incident electron 1 and atomic electrons 2 and 3 as the product of a space function $\chi_i{}^+(\mathbf{r}_1,\mathbf{r}_2,\mathbf{r}_3)$ that is symmetric in $\mathbf{r}_2$ and $\mathbf{r}_3$, and a spin function $v(1,2,3)$ that is antisymmetric in 2 and 3. The eight spin functions for three electrons are grouped in (41.9) according to their symmetry in 2 and 3; it is apparent that $v(1,2,3)$ must be one of the last doublet pair given there.

A straightforward extension of the earlier work leads to the asymptotic forms

$$\chi_i{}^+(\mathbf{r}_1,\mathbf{r}_2,\mathbf{r}_3) \xrightarrow[r_1 \to \infty]{} C[\exp{(i\mathbf{k}_\alpha \cdot \mathbf{r}_1)} + r_1{}^{-1}e^{ik_\alpha r_1}f_D(\theta)]w_a(\mathbf{r}_1,\mathbf{r}_2)$$

$$\xrightarrow[r_2 \to \infty]{} Cr_2{}^{-1}e^{ik_\alpha r_2}f_E(\theta)w_a(\mathbf{r}_3,\mathbf{r}_1) \qquad (43.41)$$

$$\xrightarrow[r_3 \to \infty]{} Cr_3{}^{-1}e^{ik_\alpha r_3}f_E(\theta)w_a(\mathbf{r}_1,\mathbf{r}_2)$$

where w_a is the helium ground-state space function and excited states are ignored; θ is the angle between the asymptotic coordinate and $\mathbf{k}_\alpha$. The direct amplitude f_D is related to T_D by (43.31), where now

$$T_D = |C|^2 e^2 \iiint \exp{(-i\mathbf{k}_\beta \cdot \mathbf{r}_1)}\ w_a{}^*(\mathbf{r}_2,\mathbf{r}_3)$$

$$\left(\frac{1}{r_{12}} + \frac{1}{r_{13}} - \frac{2}{r_1}\right) \chi_i{}^+(\mathbf{r}_1,\mathbf{r}_2,\mathbf{r}_3)\ d^3r_1\,d^3r_2\,d^3r_3 \quad (43.42)$$

The exchange amplitude f_E is evidently the same for the last two of the asymptotic forms (43.41). It is related to T_E by (43.38), where now

$$T_E = |C|^2 e^2 \iiint w_a{}^*(\mathbf{r}_1,\mathbf{r}_2)\chi_\beta{}^{-*}(\mathbf{r}_3) \left(\frac{1}{r_{13}} + \frac{1}{r_{23}}\right)$$

$$\chi_i{}^+(\mathbf{r}_1,\mathbf{r}_2,\mathbf{r}_3)\ d^3r_1\,d^3r_2\,d^3r_3 \quad (43.43)$$

The completely antisymmetric wave function for the three electrons is easily seen to be

$$\chi_i^+(\mathbf{r}_1,\mathbf{r}_2,\mathbf{r}_3)v(1,2,3) + \chi_i^+(\mathbf{r}_2,\mathbf{r}_3,\mathbf{r}_1)v(2,3,1) + \chi_i^+(\mathbf{r}_3,\mathbf{r}_1,\mathbf{r}_2)v(3,1,2)$$

$$(43.44)$$

We wish now to calculate (43.44) when one of the electron coordinates, say r_1, is large and the other two electrons are in the ground state of a helium atom. This means that we take the asymptotic form in r_1 and also project the spin functions onto $v(1,2,3)$; with the help of (43.41), this is

$$C\{\exp(i\mathbf{k}_\alpha \cdot \mathbf{r}_1) + r_1^{-1}e^{ik_\alpha r_1}[f_D(\theta) + f_E(\theta)v^\dagger(1,2,3)v(2,3,1)$$
$$+ f_E(\theta)v^\dagger(1,2,3)v(3,1,2)]\}w_a(\mathbf{r}_2,\mathbf{r}_3)v(1,2,3) \quad (43.45)$$

We take for $v(1,2,3)$ the next to the last spin function of (41.9); then

$$v^\dagger(1,2,3)v(2,3,1)$$
$$= \tfrac{1}{2}[(++-)^\dagger - (+-+)^\dagger][(-++) - (++-)] = -\tfrac{1}{2}$$

and also $v^\dagger(1,2,3)v(3,1,2) = -\tfrac{1}{2}$. The differential cross section obtained from (43.45) is then

$$\sigma(\theta) = |f_D(\theta) - f_E(\theta)|^2 \qquad (43.46)$$

Like Eqs. (41.2) and (43.40), Eq. (43.46) can be derived without explicit reference to the spin functions. Since the two atomic electrons must have antiparallel spins (singlet state) in order for the helium atom to be in its ground state, the spin component of the incident electron is the same as that of one of the atomic electrons and is different from that of the other. It cannot exchange with the latter in an elastic collision, since then both the resulting atomic electrons would be in the same spin state and the exclusion principle would force the atom into an excited state. Thus it can exchange only with the electron with which it is indistinguishable, so that the antisymmetric combination of direct and exchange amplitudes must be used; this gives Eq. (43.46).

In the absence of spin-dependent interactions, the excitation of a triplet state of helium by electron impact can be accomplished only by exchange between the incident electron and one of the atomic electrons. In this case, there is no direct amplitude and hence no interference between direct and exchange amplitudes.

PROBLEMS

1. Find a set of six 2×2 unitary matrices that represent the $3! = 6$ permutations of three objects.

2. Show that the antisymmetric wave function given in Eq. (40.11) vanishes if there is an identical linear relation between the functions v_α, v_β, . . . , v_ν.

3. Show that, if a wave function $u(1,2, . . . ,n)$ is an energy eigenfunction of a symmetric hamiltonian that corresponds to a nondegenerate eigenvalue, it is either symmetric or antisymmetric.

4. Make use of Eqs. (41.5) to verify that the spin wave functions given in (41.6) are eigenfunctions of $(S_1 + S_2)^2$ and $S_{1z} + S_{2z}$ with the indicated eigenvalues. Show also that the result of operating on these functions with the x and y components of the total spin is in agreement with the appropriate matrices given in Eqs. (27.26).

5. Carry through the calculations of Prob. 4 for the spin functions given in (41.9).

6. Use Eq. (41.2) to derive an expression for the scattering of protons on protons in the center-of-mass coordinate system, assuming that the coulomb interaction extends in to $r = 0$. Discuss the classical limit of the cross section ($\hbar \to 0$), particularly in the neighborhood of $\theta = 90°$, and show that the interference term drops out if the average scattering over an arbitrarily small but finite range of angle is computed.

7. Show that the $1s2p$ configurations in helium can be treated separately from the $1s2s$ configurations so far as the first-order energy-level calculation of Sec. 41 is concerned.

8. Show how the matrices found in Prob. 1 can operate on either pair of the doublet spin states (41.9) that have the same m value, to give the correct symmetry properties.

9. What would be the unperturbed ground-state wave functions of helium if each electron had spin angular momentum $\hbar$ and obeyed Einstein-Bose statistics?

10. Write down the unperturbed ground-state wave function for a neutral lithium atom.

11. Use the coordinate representation to verify that the second of Eqs. (42.3) is valid, that is, that tr $(P_\alpha) = 1$.

12. Make use of the answer to Prob. 9, Chap. 7, to find the unitary matrix that rotates the state $v(\frac{1}{2})$ into the state $|\alpha\rangle$ that has polarization vector π_α with polar angles θ_α, ϕ_α. Then show that the P_α's calculated from Eqs. (42.15) and (42.17) agree with each other.

13. Show that, if two pure states of a spin $\frac{1}{2}$ particle are orthogonal, the polarization vectors for these states are equal and opposite.

14. Show that the trace of the product of any two perpendicular components of $\mathbf{d}$ for a spin s particle is zero.

15. Evaluate the trace of the square of any component of $\mathbf{d}$ for a spin s particle.

16. Calculate the polarization vector explicitly for an arbitrary pure state of a spin 1 particle. Show that the length of this vector is less than or equal to unity. Find the condition on the state such that the length is equal to unity.

17. Show explicitly that the expression (43.6) for $\langle\beta|T|\alpha\rangle$ is the same as that given in the second of Eqs. (37.2).

18. Derive Eq. (43.10) by manipulating Eq. (43.9).

19. Show by direct calculation that Eq. (43.40) is obtained if the incident and atomic electrons are assumed to be described by the four spin functions $(++)$, $(+-)$, $(-+)$, and $(--)$, rather than by the triplet and singlet combinations.

20. Make use of Eqs. (43.30) and (43.38) to obtain the Born approximation for the exchange scattering amplitude of an electron from a hydrogen atom. Evaluate this in the forward direction, and compare the result with the corresponding direct scattering amplitude obtained from Eq. (38.28).

11
Semiclassical Treatment of Radiation

No account has thus far been given in this book of the interaction between material particles and electromagnetic radiation. As would be expected, a treatment that is consistent with the foregoing theory of material particles requires that quantum equations of motion of the electromagnetic field be found that are analogous to Maxwell's equations. Indeed, it is only in this way that Planck's original quantum hypotheses can be fitted into a general theoretical framework. The development of the elements of a quantum theory of radiation will be postponed until Chap. 14. In the present chapter we treat the electromagnetic field classically and the particles with which the field interacts by quantum mechanics. Such a semiclassical treatment is bound to be incomplete and not wholly satisfactory, although it is simpler in principle than the quantum field theory presented in Chap. 14. We shall find that it is possible in this approximate way to give a plausible and correct account of the influence of an external radiation field on a system of particles (absorption and induced emission) but not of the influence of the particles on the field (spontaneous emission). Nevertheless, the results of the classical treatment of the latter phenomenon can be converted to quantum theory in a correct, if not very convincing, manner. Some simple applications of the theory are given in Sec. 46.

44☐ABSORPTION AND INDUCED EMISSION

The Schrödinger wave equation for the motion of a particle of mass m and charge e in an electromagnetic field described by the potentials $\mathbf{A}$, ϕ, with an additional potential energy V, is obtained by adding a term $V\psi$ to the right side of Eq. (24.39):

$$i\hbar\, \frac{\partial \psi}{\partial t} = \left[-\frac{\hbar^2}{2m}\, \nabla^2 + \frac{ie\hbar}{mc}\, \mathbf{A} \cdot \nabla + \frac{ie\hbar}{2mc}\, (\nabla \cdot \mathbf{A}) \right.$$
$$\left. + \frac{e^2}{2mc^2}\, \mathbf{A}^2 + e\phi + V \right] \psi \quad (44.1)$$

We regard V as the potential energy that binds the particle (of electrostatic origin if the particle is an electron); $\mathbf{A}$, ϕ represent an electromagnetic field that is weak enough so that those terms can be regarded as a perturbation. Our object is to calculate the probabilities of transitions between stationary states of the particle in the potential energy V, that are produced by the field. We first discuss some properties of the field and its plane wave solutions.

MAXWELL'S EQUATIONS

Maxwell's equations of motion for the electromagnetic field are, in gaussian units,

$$\nabla \times \mathbf{E} + \frac{1}{c}\, \frac{\partial \mathbf{H}}{\partial t} = 0 \qquad \nabla \times \mathbf{H} - \frac{1}{c}\, \frac{\partial \mathbf{E}}{\partial t} = \frac{4\pi}{c}\, \mathbf{J}$$
$$\nabla \cdot \mathbf{E} = 4\pi\rho \qquad \nabla \cdot \mathbf{H} = 0 \quad (44.2)$$

If the divergence of the second of these equations is combined with the time derivative of the third, we obtain the equation of continuity for the electric charge and current densities ρ and $\mathbf{J}$:

$$\nabla \cdot \mathbf{J} + \frac{\partial \rho}{\partial t} = 0 \quad (44.3)$$

The electric and magnetic field strengths can be expressed in terms of the potentials by Eqs. (24.30):

$$\mathbf{E} = -\frac{1}{c}\, \frac{\partial \mathbf{A}}{\partial t} - \nabla \phi \qquad \mathbf{H} = \nabla \times \mathbf{A} \quad (44.4)$$

which cause the first and fourth of Eqs. (44.2) to be satisfied identically. The potentials are not defined uniquely by Eqs. (44.4), since any $\mathbf{A}$, ϕ that give the correct $\mathbf{E}$ and $\mathbf{H}$ can evidently be replaced by new potentials $\mathbf{A}'$,

ϕ' without altering the field strengths, where

$$\mathbf{A}' = \mathbf{A} + \nabla\chi \qquad \phi' = \phi - \frac{1}{c}\frac{\partial\chi}{\partial t} \tag{44.5}$$

and χ is an arbitrary function of $\mathbf{r}$ and t. This change in the potentials without changing the fields is called a *gauge transformation*. It is easily shown that ψ must also be replaced by

$$\psi' = \psi e^{iex/\hbar c} \tag{44.6}$$

if the form of the wave equation (44.1) is to be preserved (see Prob. 3). Equations (44.6) and (44.5) are often called gauge transformations of the first and second kinds, respectively.

Substitution of (44.4) into the second and third of Eqs. (44.2) gives

$$\nabla \times \nabla \times \mathbf{A} + \frac{1}{c^2}\frac{\partial^2\mathbf{A}}{\partial t^2} + \frac{1}{c}\nabla\frac{\partial\phi}{\partial t} = \frac{4\pi}{c}\mathbf{J}$$

$$\frac{1}{c}\frac{\partial}{\partial t}\nabla\cdot\mathbf{A} + \nabla^2\phi = -4\pi\rho \tag{44.7}$$

If the vector $\mathbf{A}$ is written in rectangular coordinates, we can put

$$\nabla \times \nabla \times \mathbf{A} = \nabla(\nabla\cdot\mathbf{A}) - \nabla^2\mathbf{A}$$

where the last term is the vector whose components are the laplacians of the components of $\mathbf{A}$. We can therefore simplify Eqs. (44.7) by making a gauge transformation (44.5) from $\mathbf{A}$, ϕ to $\mathbf{A}'$, ϕ' such that the new potentials satisfy the *Lorentz condition*:

$$\nabla\cdot\mathbf{A}' + \frac{1}{c}\frac{\partial\phi'}{\partial t} = 0 \tag{44.8}$$

The gauge function χ then satisfies the equation

$$\nabla^2\chi - \frac{1}{c^2}\frac{\partial^2\chi}{\partial t^2} = -\left(\nabla\cdot\mathbf{A} + \frac{1}{c}\frac{\partial\phi}{\partial t}\right)$$

Equations (44.7) then become

$$\nabla^2\mathbf{A}' - \frac{1}{c^2}\frac{\partial^2\mathbf{A}'}{\partial t^2} = -\frac{4\pi}{c}\mathbf{J}$$

$$\nabla^2\phi' - \frac{1}{c^2}\frac{\partial^2\phi'}{\partial t^2} = -4\pi\rho \tag{44.9}$$

PLANE ELECTROMAGNETIC WAVES

If $\mathbf{J} = 0$ and $\rho = 0$ (completely empty space), it can be shown that it is possible to choose the gauge function so that $\nabla\cdot\mathbf{A}' = 0$ and $\phi' = 0$ for all $\mathbf{r}$ and t, without loss of generality (see Prob. 1). Then transverse plane wave solutions can be found for $\mathbf{A}'$ and hence also for $\mathbf{E}$ and $\mathbf{H}$. We drop the primes and have in this case

$$\nabla^2 \mathbf{A} - \frac{1}{c^2} \frac{\partial^2 \mathbf{A}}{\partial t^2} = 0 \qquad \nabla \cdot \mathbf{A} = 0 \qquad (44.10)$$

A typical plane wave solution of (44.10) is one that represents a real potential with the propagation vector $\mathbf{k}$ and the real polarization vector $|\mathbf{A}_0|$:

$$\begin{aligned} \mathbf{A}(\mathbf{r},t) &= 2|\mathbf{A}_0| \cos (\mathbf{k} \cdot \mathbf{r} - \omega t + \alpha) \\ &= \mathbf{A}_0 \exp [i(\mathbf{k} \cdot \mathbf{r} - \omega t)] + \text{c.c.} \end{aligned} \qquad (44.11)$$

Here "c.c." denotes the complex conjugate of the term that precedes it, and the constant complex vector $\mathbf{A}_0$ is defined to be $|\mathbf{A}_0|e^{i\alpha}$. The first of Eqs. (44.10) is satisfied if $\omega = kc$, where k is the magnitude of $\mathbf{k}$, and the second is satisfied if $\mathbf{A}_0$ is perpendicular to $\mathbf{k}$.

The electric and magnetic fields associated with the vector potential (44.11) are

$$\mathbf{E} = -2k|\mathbf{A}_0| \sin (\mathbf{k} \cdot \mathbf{r} - \omega t + \alpha)$$

$$\mathbf{H} = -2\mathbf{k} \times |\mathbf{A}_0| \sin (\mathbf{k} \cdot \mathbf{r} - \omega t + \alpha)$$

The *Poynting vector* $(c/4\pi)\mathbf{E} \times \mathbf{H}$ is evidently in the direction of $\mathbf{k}$; its magnitude averaged over a period $2\pi/\omega$ of the oscillation is

$$\frac{\omega^2}{2\pi c} |\mathbf{A}_0|^2 \qquad (44.12)$$

where $|\mathbf{A}_0|^2$ is equal to the scalar product of $|\mathbf{A}_0|$ with itself ($|\mathbf{A}_0| \cdot |\mathbf{A}_0|$) or the scalar product of $\mathbf{A}_0$ and its complex conjugate ($\mathbf{A}_0 \cdot \mathbf{A}_0^*$). The quantity (44.12) is the intensity associated with the plane wave (44.11).

USE OF PERTURBATION THEORY

We now return to Eq. (44.1) and use it to calculate the probability of a transition between stationary states that is produced by the vector potential (44.11), which is regarded as a small perturbation. The third term ($\nabla \cdot \mathbf{A}$) and fifth term (ϕ) on the right side of (44.1) are now zero. The ratios of the second to the first term and the fourth to the second term on the right side of (44.1) are of order eA/cp, where p is the momentum of the particle. The magnitude of this quantity is estimated in a practical case in Prob. 2 and is so small that the perturbation approximation is justified. Thus, to the first order of perturbation theory, we can neglect the term $e^2\mathbf{A}^2/2mc^2$ and rewrite Eq. (44.1):

$$i\hbar \frac{\partial \psi}{\partial t} = (H_0 + H')\psi$$

$$H_0 = -\frac{\hbar^2}{2m} \nabla^2 + V(\mathbf{r}) \qquad H' = \frac{ie\hbar}{mc} \mathbf{A} \cdot \nabla$$

(44.13)

We proceed as in Sec. 35 and expand ψ in stationary eigenfunctions $u_k(\mathbf{r})$ of the unperturbed hamiltonian H_0 with time-dependent coefficients $a_k(t)$. If the system is initially in the state n and the perturbation is turned on at $t = 0$, the first-order amplitudes at time t are given by an expression similar to (35.11):

$$a_k{}^{(1)}(t) = -\frac{\langle k|H'^0|n\rangle}{\hbar} \frac{e^{i(\omega_{kn}-\omega)t}-1}{\omega_{kn}-\omega} - \frac{\langle k|H''^0|n\rangle}{\hbar} \frac{e^{i(\omega_{kn}+\omega)t}-1}{\omega_{kn}+\omega}$$

$$\langle k|H'^0|n\rangle = \frac{ie\hbar}{mc} \int u_k^* \exp{(i\mathbf{k}\cdot\mathbf{r})}\mathbf{A}_0 \cdot \boldsymbol{\nabla} \, u_n \, d^3r \qquad (44.14)$$

$$\langle k|H''^0|n\rangle = \frac{ie\hbar}{mc} \int u_k^* \exp{(-i\mathbf{k}\cdot\mathbf{r})}\mathbf{A}_0^* \cdot \boldsymbol{\nabla} \, u_n \, d^3r$$

As discussed in Sec. 35, the probability of finding the system in the state k is appreciable only when the denominator of one or the other of the two terms in (44.14) is practically zero. There is no interference between the two terms; the first is important when $E_k \approx E_n + \hbar\omega$, and the second is important when $E_k \approx E_n - \hbar\omega$. Thus the probability of finding the system in a state k that has an energy higher than the initial state by about $\hbar\omega$ is proportional to $|\langle k|H'^0|n\rangle|^2$, and the probability of finding the system in a state k' that has a correspondingly lower energy is proportional to $|\langle k'|H''^0|n\rangle|^2$.

TRANSITION PROBABILITY

The discussion of Sec. 35 shows that the transition probability per unit time is independent of the time only if the final state can be any of a very closely spaced or continuously distributed group. The need for a group of final states arises from the dependence of the probability $|a_k{}^{(1)}(t)|^2$ on the energy, which is shown in Fig. 31; it is the area under this curve, not the ordinate at a particular absicssa, that is proportional to t.

In the same way, a constant transition probability per unit time is obtained in the present problem if the incident radiation is monochromatic (definite value of ω) and transitions can occur to any of a group of closely spaced or continuously distributed final states. The result is Eq. (35.14) with either $\langle k|H'^0|n\rangle$ or $\langle k|H''^0|n\rangle$ substituted for $\langle k|H'|m\rangle$. However, the computation of a transition probability between two discrete states is often of interest. In this case, the transition probability per unit time is not constant in time, if the incident radiation is strictly monochromatic, and depends markedly on the difference between ω and

$$|\omega_{kn}| = \frac{|E_k - E_n|}{\hbar}$$

What we do in this case is to assume that the radiation covers a spread of frequencies with no phase relations between the different frequency components, so that the radiation can be characterized by an intensity per unit frequency range that is constant in the neighborhood of $|\omega_{kn}|$.[1]

The probability of finding the system in the final state is then proportional to $|\langle k|H'^0|n\rangle|^2$ or $|\langle k|H''^0|n\rangle|^2$, which in turn is proportional to $|\mathbf{A}_0|^2$ and hence to the intensity. If the intensity in the small angular frequency range $\Delta\omega$ is $I(\omega)\,\Delta\omega$, Eq. (44.12) tells us that we can put

$$|\mathbf{A}_0|^2 = \frac{2\pi c}{\omega^2} I(\omega)\,\Delta\omega \tag{44.15}$$

where $\mathbf{A}_0$ is the vector potential amplitude that characterizes the frequency range $\Delta\omega$. The probability that a transition in which the system is left in a higher energy state ($E_k \approx E_n + \hbar\omega$) has taken place at the time t is then

$$|a_k^{(1)}(t)|^2 = \sum_\omega \frac{4|\langle k|H'^0|n\rangle|^2 \sin^2 \frac{1}{2}(\omega_{kn} - \omega)t}{\hbar^2(\omega_{kn} - \omega)^2}$$

$$= \sum_\omega \frac{8\pi e^2}{m^2 c\omega^2} I(\omega)\,\Delta\omega \left| \int u_k^* \exp{(i\mathbf{k}\cdot\mathbf{r})} \nabla_A u_n \, d^3r \right|^2$$

$$\frac{\sin^2 \frac{1}{2}(\omega_{kn} - \omega)t}{(\omega_{kn} - \omega)^2} \tag{44.16}$$

where ∇_A is the component of the gradient operator along the polarization vector $\mathbf{A}_0$. The contributions to the probability from various frequency ranges are additive, since there are no phase relations between the radiation components of different frequencies.

Each frequency range $\Delta\omega$ in (44.16) can be made infinitesimally small, and the summation replaced by an integration. Since the time factor has a sharp maximum at $\omega = \omega_{kn}$, the other factors that involve ω can be taken outside the integral and the limits on ω extended to $\pm\infty$, as was done in going from Eq. (35.13) to (35.14). Thus the transition probability per unit time for an upward transition becomes

$$\frac{1}{t}|a_k^{(1)}(t)|^2 = \frac{8\pi e^2}{m^2 c\omega_{kn}^2} I(\omega_{kn}) \left| \int u_k^* \exp{(i\mathbf{k}\cdot\mathbf{r})} \nabla_A u_n \, d^3r \right|^2$$

$$\int_{-\infty}^{\infty} \frac{\sin^2 \frac{1}{2}(\omega_{kn} - \omega)t}{t(\omega_{kn} - \omega)^2} \, d\omega$$

$$= \frac{4\pi^2 e^2}{m^2 c\omega_{kn}^2} I(\omega_{kn}) \left| \int u_k^* \exp{(i\mathbf{k}\cdot\mathbf{r})} \nabla_A u_n \, d^3r \right|^2 \tag{44.17}$$

where the magnitude of $\mathbf{k}$ is now ω_{kn}/c. An expression very similar to (44.17) is obtained for the probability per unit time of a downward

[1] For a discussion of the situation in which the intensity is not constant near $|\omega_{kn}|$, see W. Heitler, "The Quantum Theory of Radiation," 3d ed., sec. 20 (Oxford, New York, 1954).

transition $(E_{k'} \approx E_n - \hbar\omega)$:

$$\frac{4\pi^2 e^2}{m^2 c \omega_{nk'}{}^2} I(\omega_{nk'}) \left| \int u_{k'}^* \exp(-i\mathbf{k} \cdot \mathbf{r}) \nabla_A u_n \, d^3r \right|^2 \qquad (44.18)$$

In this case the magnitude of $\mathbf{k}$ is $\omega_{nk'}/c$.

INTERPRETATION IN TERMS OF ABSORPTION AND EMISSION

Equations (44.17) and (44.18) give probabilities per unit time for transitions of the particle between stationary states under the influence of a classical radiation field. These expressions can now be interpreted in terms of absorption and emission of quanta of electromagnetic radiation. It is necessary to assume that such quanta exist and provide the energy units of the radiation field and that energy is conserved between field and particle. The particle gains the amount of energy $E_k - E_n$ in an upward transition under the influence of radiation of angular frequency ω_{kn}. The quantum energy of this radiation is $\hbar\omega_{kn} = E_k - E_n$, so that it is reasonable to associate with the upward transition of the particle the *absorption* of one quantum from the radiation field.

In similar fashion the downward transition is associated with the emission of one quantum whose energy corresponds to the frequency of the radiation field. In accordance with Eq. (44.18), the emission probability is proportional to the intensity of the radiation present. This process is therefore referred to as *induced emission*.

It is sometimes convenient to rewrite Eq. (44.18) in terms of the reverse transition to that which appears in (44.17). Equation (44.17) describes the transition from an initial lower state n to a final upper state k; (44.18) can be made to describe the transition from an initial upper state k to a final lower state n, if n is replaced by k and k' by n. Then (44.18) becomes

$$\frac{4\pi^2 e^2}{m^2 c \omega_{kn}{}^2} I(\omega_{kn}) \left| \int u_n^* \exp(-i\mathbf{k} \cdot \mathbf{r}) \nabla_A u_k \, d^3r \right|^2 \qquad (44.19)$$

We can now show that the integral in (44.19) is just minus the complex conjugate of the integral in (44.17). By means of a partial integration, or with the help of Eq. (23.21), the integral in (44.19) is seen to be equal to[1]

$$-\int u_k \, \Delta_A \, [u_n^* \exp(-i\mathbf{k} \cdot \mathbf{r})] \, d^3r$$

Since only the component of the gradient along the polarization vector $\mathbf{A}_0$ appears, and this direction is perpendicular to the propagation vector $\mathbf{k}$, the operator ∇_A does not affect $\exp(-i\mathbf{k} \cdot \mathbf{r})$. Thus the integral in

---

[1] In using Eq. (23.21), it must be remembered that the operator $i\nabla$, not the operator ∇, is hermitian.

(44.19) is equal to

$$-\int u_k \exp\left(-i\mathbf{k}\cdot\mathbf{r}\right) \nabla_A u_n^* \, d^3r$$

and the square of its magnitude is equal to the square of the magnitude of the integral that appears in (44.17).

Since (44.17) and (44.19) are the same, the probabilities of reverse transitions between any pair of states under the influence of the same radiation field are equal.

ELECTRIC DIPOLE TRANSITIONS

In most cases of practical interest, the wavelength of the radiation is many times greater than the linear dimensions of the wave functions that describe the motion of the particle. This means that the quantity $\mathbf{k}\cdot\mathbf{r}$ that appears in the exponential in the integral of (44.17) is small in comparison with unity wherever u_n and u_k are large enough to give an appreciable contribution to the integral. A good approximation is then obtained by replacing $\exp\left(i\mathbf{k}\cdot\mathbf{r}\right)$ by 1.

The resulting integral can be simplified by expressing it as a matrix element of the momentum of the particle

$$\int u_k^* \nabla_A u_n \, d^3r = \frac{i}{\hbar}\int u_k^* p_A u_n \, d^3r = \frac{i}{\hbar}\langle k|p_A|n\rangle$$

where p_A is the component of the particle momentum $\mathbf{p}$ along the direction of polarization of the incident radiation. The matrix theory of Sec. 24 shows that the momentum matrix of the unperturbed particle is given by $\mathbf{p} = m(d\mathbf{r}/dt)$. Thus from Eq. (24.16)

$$\frac{1}{m}\langle k|\mathbf{p}|n\rangle = \frac{d}{dt}\langle k|\mathbf{r}|n\rangle = i\omega_{kn}\langle k|\mathbf{r}|n\rangle$$

The integral in Eq. (44.17) becomes, in this approximation,

$$\int u_k^* \nabla_A u_n \, d^3r = -\frac{m}{\hbar}\omega_{kn}\int u_k^* r_A u_n \, d^3r \qquad (44.20)$$

where r_A is the component of $\mathbf{r}$ along the direction of polarization. Equation (44.20) can, of course, also be derived without recourse to matrix methods (see Prob. 5).

Transitions for which the probability can be computed by substitution of (44.20) into (44.17) are called *electric dipole transitions*, since only the matrix element of the electric dipole moment $e\mathbf{r}$ of the particle is involved.[1] The transition probabilities per unit time for absorption and

---

[1] The quantity $e\mathbf{r}$ is the electric dipole moment of the particle of charge e with respect to an arbitrarily placed origin; the addition of a constant vector (corresponding to a shift in the origin) to $\mathbf{r}$ does not affect the matrix element (44.20), since u_k and u_n are orthogonal.

induced emission then become, in the dipole approximation,

$$\frac{4\pi^2 e^2}{\hbar^2 c} I(\omega_{kn})|\langle k|r_A|n\rangle|^2 \tag{44.21}$$

It is convenient to denote by $\langle k|\mathbf{r}|n\rangle$ the vector whose cartesian components are the kn matrix elements of x, y, and z and to put

$$|\langle k|\mathbf{r}|n\rangle|^2 = \langle k|\mathbf{r}|n\rangle \cdot \langle k|\mathbf{r}|n\rangle^* \tag{44.22}$$

which is the scalar product of $\langle k|\mathbf{r}|n\rangle$ and its complex conjugate. The reason for doing this is that there are usually pairs of states k and n for which $|\langle k|\mathbf{r}|n\rangle|^2$ is the same but for which the vector $\langle k|\mathbf{r}|n\rangle$ has various orientations in space.[1] Then, if Θ is the angle between $\langle k|\mathbf{r}|n\rangle$ and the direction of polarization of the incident radiation, $|\langle k|\mathbf{r}|n\rangle|^2 \cos^2\Theta$ can be substituted for $|\langle k|r_A|n\rangle|^2$ in Eq. (44.21), and an average performed over Θ. The average of (44.21) for such pairs of states is then

$$\frac{4\pi^2 e^2}{3\hbar^2 c} I(\omega_{kn})|\langle k|\mathbf{r}|n\rangle|^2 \tag{44.23}$$

FORBIDDEN TRANSITIONS

It may happen that the dipole matrix element $\langle k|\mathbf{r}|n\rangle$ is zero for particular states k and n. In that case the approximate replacement of $\exp(i\mathbf{k}\cdot\mathbf{r})$ by 1 in the integral of (44.17) is not justified. The exponential can be expanded in a power series

$$\exp(i\mathbf{k}\cdot\mathbf{r}) = 1 + i\mathbf{k}\cdot\mathbf{r} + \frac{1}{2!}(i\mathbf{k}\cdot\mathbf{r})^2 + \cdots$$

or in a series of spherical harmonics like (19.9)

$$\exp(i\mathbf{k}\cdot\mathbf{r}) = j_0(kr) + 3ij_1(kr)P_1(\cos\theta) - 5j_2(kr)P_2(\cos\theta) + \cdots$$

where θ is the angle between $\mathbf{k}$ and $\mathbf{r}$. The second series is more convenient than the first if, as is usually the case, the wave functions u_k and u_n can be expressed in terms of spherical harmonics.

With either series, the dominant factor in the nth term is proportional to $(kr)^n$ if $kr \ll 1$ [see the first of Eqs. (15.7)]. Thus if the dipole matrix element vanishes but the next term of each series does not, the transition matrix element is reduced by a factor that has the order of magnitude ka, where the linear dimensions of the particle wave functions are of order a. A transition of this type is called a *forbidden transition*,

---

[1] For example, if the particle moves in a spherically symmetric potential $V(r)$, the state k can have $l = 0$, and the states n can have $l = 1$ and three values $(0, \pm 1)$ for the magnetic quantum number m.

since its probability is reduced by a factor $(ka)^2$ with respect to dipole or *allowed transitions*, and usually $ka \ll 1$. Successive terms in the series can be interpreted in terms of electric dipole, quadrupole, etc., transitions and involve successively higher powers of ka.

If both the states u_k and u_n are spherically symmetric, the integral $\int u_k^* \exp{(i\mathbf{k} \cdot \mathbf{r})} \nabla_A u_n \, d^3r$ is identically zero. This can be seen by choosing cartesian coordinates for performing the integration such that the x axis is along the direction of polarization. Then $\nabla_A u_n$ is an odd function of x, whereas u_k is an even function of x, and $\exp{(i\mathbf{k} \cdot \mathbf{r})} = e^{i(k_y y + k_z z)}$ is also even in x, since the vector $\mathbf{k}$ is perpendicular to the direction of polarization and hence is in the yz plane. Thus the integrand is an odd function of x, and the integral in (44.17) vanishes. The transition between these states is said to be *strictly forbidden*, since the first-order probability given by (44.17) is zero. It is still possible for transitions to be produced by higher orders of the perturbation H' given in Eq. (44.13); in such a calculation, the previously neglected term $e^2\mathbf{A}^2/2mc^2$ must be included in H'. However, it can be shown with the help of quantum electrodynamics that such higher-order transitions involve more than one quantum and hence are not simple emission or absorption processes in which the quantum energy is equal to the energy difference between the unperturbed states k and n of the particle.

45□SPONTANEOUS EMISSION

A classical charged oscillator can absorb energy from a radiation field or give up energy to it, depending on the phase relation between the field and the oscillator. These effects are analogous to the absorption and induced emission of the preceding section. A classical oscillator also emits radiation spontaneously, whether or not an external radiation field is present. In this section, we calculate the electromagnetic radiation from a classical oscillating charge-current distribution in the absence of external fields and somewhat arbitrarily rewrite the formulas in terms of quantum matrix elements to obtain a probability for *spontaneous emission*. The results are then verified by comparison with Planck's expression for the distribution of thermal radiation in a cavity.

CLASSICAL RADIATION FIELD

A charge-current distribution can be completely specified by the current density $\mathbf{J}$, since $\mathbf{J}$ determines the charge density ρ through the equation of continuity (44.3). In similar fashion, the electromagnetic fields in empty space, away from charges and currents, can be completely specified by either $\mathbf{E}$ or $\mathbf{H}$, because of the connections (44.2) between them. A wave equation for H is readily obtained by taking the curl of the first of Eqs. (44.9).

$$\nabla^2 H - \frac{1}{c^2} \frac{\partial^2}{\partial t^2} H = -\frac{4\pi}{c} \nabla \times J \tag{45.1}$$

Thus H can be obtained in terms of J alone, whereas the similar equation for E involves both J and ρ (although ρ can, of course, be eliminated). We proceed by solving Eq. (45.1) for H when the three cartesian components of J vary harmonically in time with the same angular frequency ω but not necessarily with the same phase:

$$\begin{aligned} J_x(\mathbf{r},t) &= 2|J_x(\mathbf{r})| \cos (\omega t - \eta_x) = J_x(\mathbf{r})e^{-i\omega t} + \text{c.c.} \\ J_x(\mathbf{r}) &= |J_x(\mathbf{r})|e^{i\eta_x} \end{aligned} \tag{45.2}$$

with similar expressions for the y and z components. We are interested only in the steady-state solutions for E and H that have the same frequency ω

$$\begin{aligned} E_x(\mathbf{r},t) &= 2|E_x(\mathbf{r})| \cos (\omega t - \xi_x) = E_x(\mathbf{r})e^{i\omega t} + \text{c.c.} \\ H_x(\mathbf{r},t) &= 2|H_x(\mathbf{r})| \cos (\omega t - \zeta_x) = H_x(\mathbf{r})e^{-i\omega t} + \text{c.c.} \\ E_x(\mathbf{r}) &= |E_x(\mathbf{r})|e^{i\xi_x} \qquad H_x(\mathbf{r}) = |H_x(\mathbf{r})|e^{i\zeta_x} \end{aligned} \tag{45.3}$$

again with similar expressions for the y and z components. From the second of Eqs. (44.2), E is given in terms of H in empty space by

$$E(\mathbf{r}) = \frac{ic}{\omega} \nabla \times H(\mathbf{r}) \tag{45.4}$$

With substitutions from (45.2) and (45.3), Eq. (45.1) becomes

$$(\nabla^2 + k^2)H(\mathbf{r}) = -\frac{4\pi}{c} \nabla \times J(\mathbf{r}) \qquad k = \frac{\omega}{c} \tag{45.5}$$

This is an inhomogeneous equation, the solution of which can be expressed in terms of a propagator like (37.19), and is

$$H(\mathbf{r}) = \frac{1}{c} \int \frac{\nabla \times J(\mathbf{r}')}{|\mathbf{r} - \mathbf{r}'|} \exp (ik|\mathbf{r} - \mathbf{r}'|) \, d^3r' \tag{45.6}$$

Equation (45.6) is the retarded solution of (45.5); for large r, this solution is an outgoing wave that varies with r and t like $r^{-1}e^{i(kr-\omega t)} + \text{c.c.}$, so that the field produced by a current element occurs at a later time and hence is retarded with respect to the current element.

ASYMPTOTIC FORM

We are interested in the energy and angular momentum carried away by the field. As shown below, the energy can be found from the leading terms in the asymptotic expression for the field at very large r, which vary as $1/r$; the angular momentum requires in addition some terms that vary as $1/r^2$. The r-dependent part of the integrand of (45.6) can be expanded in powers of $1/r$:

$$\frac{\exp{(ik|\mathbf{r} - \mathbf{r}'|)}}{|\mathbf{r} - \mathbf{r}'|} \xrightarrow[r \to \infty]{} \frac{1}{r} \left(1 + \frac{r' \cos \theta + \frac{1}{2}ikr'^2 \sin^2 \theta}{r}\right) e^{ik(r - r' \cos \theta)}$$

$$(45.7)$$

where θ is the angle between $\mathbf{r}'$ and $\mathbf{r}$. Substitution of (45.7) into (45.6) gives, together with (45.4), a complete specification of the asymptotic electromagnetic field through terms of order $1/r^2$.

RADIATED ENERGY

The Poynting vector, which is the energy-flux vector, is equal to

$$\frac{c}{4\pi} [\mathbf{E}(\mathbf{r},t) \times \mathbf{H}(\mathbf{r},t)]$$

From (45.3), we see that its time average $\mathbf{P}(\mathbf{r})$ over a period of the oscillation has a typical component

$$P_z(\mathbf{r}) = \frac{c}{\pi} \{|E_x(\mathbf{r})| \, |H_y(\mathbf{r})|[\cos{(\omega t - \xi_x)} \cos{(\omega t - \zeta_y)}]_{\text{time av}}$$

$$- |E_y(\mathbf{r})| \, |H_x(\mathbf{r})|[\cos{(\omega t - \xi_y)} \cos{(\omega t - \zeta_x)}]_{\text{time av}}\}$$

$$= \frac{c}{2\pi} [|E_x(\mathbf{r})| \, |H_y(\mathbf{r})| \cos{(\xi_x - \zeta_y)}$$

$$- |E_y(\mathbf{r})| \, |H_x(\mathbf{r})| \cos{(\xi_y - \zeta_x)}]$$

This and the other two components can be put in the form

$$\mathbf{P}(\mathbf{r}) = \frac{c}{2\pi} \text{Re} [\mathbf{E}(\mathbf{r}) \times \mathbf{H}^*(r)] \tag{45.8}$$

where Re denotes the real part of the expression that follows. Now we are interested only in those terms in the energy flux that fall off as $1/r^2$, since only these correspond to radiated energy; we therefore require only the terms of order $1/r$ in $\mathbf{E}$ and $\mathbf{H}$.

It is convenient in writing explicit expressions for the fields to choose cartesian axes such that the z axis is along the vector $\mathbf{r}$, which goes from the center of the charge-current distribution to the point at which the field is measured. Equations (45.4), (45.6), and (45.7) then give, to order $1/r$ (where now $r = z$),

$$H_x \rightarrow -\frac{ik}{rc} e^{ikr} \int J_y(\mathbf{r}')e^{-ikz'} d^3r'$$

$$H_y \rightarrow \frac{ik}{rc} e^{ikr} \int J_x(\mathbf{r}')e^{-ikz'} d^3r'$$

$$H_z \rightarrow 0 \qquad\qquad (45.9)$$

$$E_x \rightarrow \frac{ik}{rc} e^{ikr} \int J_y(\mathbf{r}')e^{-ikz'} d^3r'$$

$$E_y \rightarrow \frac{ik}{rc} e^{ikr} \int J_y(\mathbf{r}')e^{-ikz'} d^3r'$$

$$E_z \rightarrow 0$$

Partial integration has been used to get rid of the derivatives of $\mathbf{J}$ in the integrand of $\mathbf{H}$. Equations (45.9) show that the asymptotic fields are transverse to the direction of propagation. They also relate the polarization of the emitted radiation to the current distribution and show that only the component of the current perpendicular to the direction of propagation contributes to the radiated energy. Substitution into (45.8) gives

$$P_z = \frac{k^2}{2\pi r^2 c} \left(\left| \int J_x e^{-ikz'} d^3r' \right|^2 + \left| \int J_y e^{-ikz'} d^3r' \right|^2 \right) \qquad (45.10)$$

Equation (45.10) can be generalized to give the average energy flux in the direction of a vector $\mathbf{k}$:

$$\frac{k^2}{2\pi r^2 c} \left| \int J_{\perp \mathbf{k}}(\mathbf{r}') \exp(-i\mathbf{k} \cdot \mathbf{r}') d^3r' \right|^2 \qquad (45.11)$$

where $J_{\perp \mathbf{k}}$ is the component of $\mathbf{J}$ perpendicular to $\mathbf{k}$.

DIPOLE RADIATION

Equation (45.11) is an exact expression for the energy radiated by the classical current distribution (45.2). As in Sec. 44, the electric dipole approximation is obtained in the long-wavelength limit by assuming that $kr' \ll 1$ and replacing $\exp(-i\mathbf{k} \cdot \mathbf{r}')$ by 1 in the integrand. The energy flux is then

$$\frac{k^2}{2\pi r^2 c} \left| \int J_{\perp \mathbf{k}}(\mathbf{r}') d^3r' \right|^2 \qquad (45.12)$$

From Eqs. (45.9) with the same approximation, it is apparent that the polarization (direction of the electric field) of the radiation is determined by the total current vector $\mathbf{J}_0 \equiv \int \mathbf{J}(\mathbf{r}') d^3r'$. The radiation is linearly polarized if $\mathbf{J}_0$ has only one component in the plane perpendicular to the direction of propagation, circularly polarized if $\mathbf{J}_0$ has two equal components in this plane that are perpendicular to each other and 90° out of phase (so that one component is i times the other), etc.

If $\mathbf{J}_0$ has only one component, the angular distribution of the radiation can be found by replacing $|\int J_{\perp \mathbf{k}}(\mathbf{r}') \, d^3r'|^2$ in (45.12) by

$$(\mathbf{J}_0 \cdot \mathbf{J}_0^*) \sin^2 \theta = |\mathbf{J}_0|^2 \sin^2 \theta$$

where θ is the angle between $\mathbf{J}_0$ and $\mathbf{k}$, and $|\mathbf{J}_0|^2$ is an abbreviation for the scalar product of $\mathbf{J}_0$ and its complex conjugate. The total power radiated is then the integral of (45.12) over the surface of a sphere of radius r:

$$\frac{4k^2}{3c} |\mathbf{J}_0|^2 \tag{45.13}$$

Equation (45.13) is also valid if $\mathbf{J}_0$ has more than one component, and these do not necessarily have the same phase (see Prob. 11).

ANGULAR MOMENTUM

The angular momentum radiated per unit time is equal to the torque exerted on a large, perfectly absorbing sphere that is centered at the charge-current distribution that constitutes the source of radiation. The average energy flux is $\mathbf{P}$, so that the (directed) energy density is $(1/c)\mathbf{P}$ and the momentum density is $(1/c^2)\mathbf{P}$. Since the radiation travels outward with speed c, the torque exerted on a perfectly absorbing differential element of area, dA, that is perpendicular to $\mathbf{r}$ is $c \, dA$ times the vector product of $\mathbf{r}$ and the momentum density: $(dA/c)(\mathbf{r} \times \mathbf{P})$. Integration of this quantity over the sphere of radius r gives the angular momentum radiated by the source per unit time. Thus only the components of $\mathbf{P}$ tangential to the sphere are involved: In the notation of Eqs. (45.9), these are P_x and P_y, since the z axis is along $\mathbf{r}$.

If E_z and H_z were zero, the tangential components P_x and P_y would also be zero, and no angular momentum would be radiated. The third and sixth of Eqs. (45.9) imply only that the z (radial) components of the field are of smaller order than $1/r$; actually they are of order $1/r^2$. This means that P_x and P_y fall off as $1/r^3$ for large r. Then since $\mathbf{r} \times \mathbf{P}$ appears in the expression for the angular momentum, and the area of the absorbing sphere is proportional to r^2, the total angular momentum absorbed by a large sphere is independent of r.

We require the $1/r^2$ terms in E_z and H_z but not in the other field components.

$$\mathsf{H}_z \to \frac{ik}{r^2c} e^{ikr} \int [y'J_x(\mathbf{r}') - x'J_y(\mathbf{r}')]e^{-ikz'} \, d^3r'$$

$$\mathsf{E}_z \to \frac{1}{r^2c} e^{ikr} \int [2J_z(\mathbf{r}') + ikx'J_x(\mathbf{r}') + iky'J_y(\mathbf{r}')]e^{-ikz'} \, d^3r' \tag{45.14}$$

Equations (45.9) and (45.14) are sufficient for an exact calculation of the radiated angular momentum.[1]

DIPOLE CASE

The expressions for P_x and P_y are simplified by the dipole approximation since only the terms of lowest order in kr' need be retained in (45.9) and (45.14). It is easy to see that the leading term in P_x, for example, is $-(c/2\pi)\,\mathrm{Re}\,(\mathsf{E}_z\mathsf{H}_y^*)$ and not $(c/2\pi)\,\mathrm{Re}\,(\mathsf{E}_y\mathsf{H}_z^*)$. We obtain to lowest order in kr'

$$P_x = \frac{k}{\pi r^3 c}\,\mathrm{Re}\left(i\int J_z\,d^3r'\int J_x^*d^3r'\right)$$

$$P_y = \frac{k}{\pi r^3 c}\,\mathrm{Re}\left(i\int J_z\,d^3r'\int J_y^*d^3r'\right) \tag{45.15}$$

Equations (45.15) refer to axes fixed with respect to the element dA of absorbing area at $\mathbf{r}$. They must now be rewritten in terms of general cartesian coordinates, in order that the angular momentum component about a particular axis fixed in space can be found. This is analogous to the rewriting of the energy-flux expression (45.10) in the general form (45.11) but is somewhat more complicated. To accomplish this, we choose new cartesian coordinates x', y', z' that are fixed in space. With respect to these, the orientation of the old axes depends on $\mathbf{r}$ in the following way (see Fig. 38): the z axis is in the direction of $\mathbf{r}$ and has the polar angles θ, ϕ with respect to the new axes, the y axis is perpendicular to $\mathbf{r}$ and in the plane of $\mathbf{r}$ and z', and the x axis is perpendicular to the plane of $\mathbf{r}$ and z'. If now we wish to calculate the contribution to the z' component of angular momentum from absorption by the element of area

$$dA = r^2 \sin\theta\,d\theta\,d\phi$$

at $\mathbf{r}$, we need only P_x given in (45.15). This can be written in terms of the components of the total current vector $\mathbf{J}_0$ along the new axes as

$$P_x = \frac{k}{\pi r_3 c}\,\mathrm{Re}\,[i(J_{0x'}\sin\theta\cos\phi + J_{0y'}\sin\theta\sin\phi + J_{0z'}\cos\theta)$$

$$(J_{0y'}^*\cos\phi - J_{0x'}^*\sin\phi)] \tag{45.16}$$

The moment arm about the z' axis associated with P_x is $r\sin\theta$, so that the differential element of angular momentum component is

$$dL_{z'} = \frac{1}{c}\,r\sin\theta\,P_x r^2\sin\theta\,d\theta\,d\phi \tag{45.17}$$

[1] For a more general discussion see W. K. H. Panofsky and M. Phillips, "Classical Electricity and Magnetism," 2d ed., sec. 14-10 (Addison-Wesley, Reading, Mass., 1962); J. D. Jackson, "Classical Electrodynamics," sec. 16.3 (Wiley, New York, 1962).

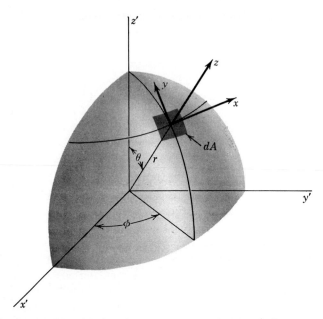

Fig. 38 The relation between the unprimed coordinate system of Eqs. (45.15) and the primed coordinate system of Eq. (45.16).

Substitution of (45.16) into (45.17) and integration over the polar angles give

$$L_{z'} = \frac{4ik}{3c^2} \left(J_{0x'} J_{0y'}^* - J_{0y'} J_{0x'}^* \right) \tag{45.18}$$

It is apparent from Eq. (45.18) that the radiation of a particular component of angular momentum depends only on the particular components of $\mathbf{J}_0$. Moreover, there must be two such perpendicular components that are out of phase with each other, for if $J_{0x'}$ and $J_{0y'}$ are both real or have the same phase, the parenthesis in (45.18) is zero. Thus a linear dipole ($\mathbf{J}_0$ entirely in one direction) radiates no angular momentum. The maximum angular momentum for a given value of $|\mathbf{J}_0|^2$ is radiated when $\mathbf{J}_0$ has two equal perpendicular components that are 90° out of phase with each other and the third perpendicular component is zero. If the nonvanishing components are along x' and y' we can put $J_{0y'} = iJ_{0x'}$; Eq. (45.18) then becomes

$$L_{z'} = \frac{8k}{3c^2} |J_{0x'}|^2 = \frac{4k}{3c^2} |\mathbf{J}_0|^2 \tag{45.19}$$

and the other two components of $\mathbf{L}$ are zero.

Comparison of Eqs. (45.13) and (45.19) shows that the maximum angular momentum radiated per unit time by an oscillating electric dipole is $1/kc = 1/\omega$ times the energy radiated per unit time. If this relation is taken over into quantum theory, it shows that a quantum of energy, $\hbar\omega$, radiated by an electric dipole carries with it an amount of angular momentum that does not exceed $\hbar$.

CONVERSION FROM CLASSICAL TO QUANTUM THEORY

We now convert to quantum theory the classical expression (45.13) for the power radiated by an electric dipole. This requires that we find a quantum analog for the total current vector $\mathbf{J}_0$ and associate the radiated power with a transition probability between states of the particle that is doing the radiating.

We want to replace $\mathbf{J}$ by a current density that is associated with an initial upper state u_k and a final lower state u_n, since energy is radiated during the transition from k to n. It is natural to represent the current density as the product of a charge density and a velocity and to take for the velocity the momentum operator divided by the mass: $-(i\hbar/m)\boldsymbol{\nabla}$. The charge density for a stationary state is expected to be the charge of the particle times its position probability density: $e|\psi|^2$. However, we are concerned here with a transition between states, and so we replace this by $eu_n^* u_k$.[1] The way in which the $\boldsymbol{\nabla}$ that appears in the velocity operates on the wave functions that appear in the change density is determined by arguments of the type presented in Sec. 7 [see Eq. (7.3)]. We thus arrive at a quantity to substitute for the classical current density:

$$\mathbf{J}(\mathbf{r}) \to -\frac{ie\hbar}{m}\, u_n^*(\mathbf{r})\,\boldsymbol{\nabla}u_k(\mathbf{r}) \tag{45.20}$$

We assume that (45.20) can be substituted into all the foregoing classical expressions to give quantum results.[2]

Integration of (45.20) over the coordinates gives the total current vector

$$\mathbf{J}_0 = -\frac{ie\hbar}{m}\int u_n^*\boldsymbol{\nabla}u_k\,d^3r = -ie\omega_{nk}\int u_n^*\mathbf{r}u_k\,d^3r = ie\omega_{kn}\langle k|\mathbf{r}|n\rangle^* \tag{45.21}$$

with the help of Eq. (44.20). Substitution of (45.21) into (45.13) then gives the radiated power. We interpret this power as the product of the

---

[1] The use of ψ rather than the u_k has been discussed by F. E. Low, *Am. J. Phys.* **29**, 298 (1961).

[2] The exponential that appears in (45.11), for example, can be placed either before or after the $\boldsymbol{\nabla}$ operator, since only the component of $\boldsymbol{\nabla}$ that is perpendicular to $\mathbf{k}$ enters in.

spontaneous rate of transition from k to n and the quantum energy $\hbar\omega_{kn} = E_k - E_n$ given off in each transition. The transition probability per unit time for spontaneous emission then becomes

$$\frac{4e^2k^2\omega_{kn}}{3\hbar c} \, |\langle k|\mathbf{r}|n\rangle|^2 = \frac{4e^2\omega_{kn}^3}{3\hbar c^3} \, |\langle k|\mathbf{r}|n\rangle|^2 \tag{45.22}$$

where use has been made of the relation $\omega_{kn} = kc$.

PLANCK DISTRIBUTION FORMULA

The transition from the classical expression (45.13) to the quantum expression (45.22) can claim only a moderate amount of plausibility. The correctness of the latter result can, however, be verified by showing that Planck's formula for the spectral distribution of thermal radiation in a cavity follows from (45.22) and (44.23). This is the way in which the relation between the probabilities for absorption, induced emission, and spontaneous emission was first obtained.[1]

We assume that the walls of the cavity contain particles of charge e and mass m, each of which is bound by a potential V of the type that appears in (44.1). When these particles are in equilibrium with thermal radiation at the absolute temperature T, there must be as many quanta of each frequency emitted as absorbed per unit time. The rate of emission of quanta of frequency ω_{kn} is the sum of (44.23) and (45.22), multiplied by the number of particles that are in the upper state k. The rate of absorption of these quanta is the product of (44.23) and the number of particles in the lower state n. From statistical mechanics,[2] the equilibrium ratio of the number of particles in the upper state to the number in the lower state is given by $e^{-(E_k-E_n)/\kappa T}$, where κ is Boltzmann's constant. We thus obtain, on dropping the subscripts from ω_{kn},

$$e^{-\hbar\omega/\kappa T}\left[\frac{4\pi^2e^2}{3\hbar^2c} I(\omega)|\langle k|\mathbf{r}|n\rangle|^2 + \frac{4e^2\omega^3}{3\hbar c^3} |\langle k|\mathbf{r}|n\rangle|^2\right] = \frac{4\pi^2e^2}{3\hbar^2c} I(\omega)|\langle k|\mathbf{r}|n\rangle|^2$$

This is readily solved to give $I(\omega)$, or equivalently

$$\text{Energy density} = \frac{I(\omega)\,\Delta\omega}{c} = \frac{\hbar\omega^3\,\Delta\omega}{\pi^2c^3(e^{\hbar\omega/\kappa T} - 1)} \tag{45.23}$$

It is interesting to note that the parameters e, m, and $\langle k|\mathbf{r}|n\rangle$ of the particle that emits and absorbs the radiation drop out of the expression for $I(\omega)$.

[1] A. Einstein, *Phys. Z.* **18**, 121 (1917). Einstein's A coefficient is just (45.22), and his B coefficient is (44.23) divided by the energy density of radiation $I(\omega_{kn})/c$ (this is expressed in terms of the angular frequency ω_{kn} rather than the circular frequency $\omega_{kn}/2\pi$).

[2] See, for example, K. Huang, "Statistical Mechanics," sec. 9.3 (Wiley, New York, 1963).

The agreement between Eq. (45.23) and the Planck distribution formula provides a verification of the ratio of (44.23) to (45.22) and hence shows that the latter expression is correct if the former is.

LINE BREADTH

A classical oscillator that radiates electromagnetic waves loses energy, so that the amplitude of its oscillation decreases in time.   Thus the electromagnetic fields given off by it have a damped sinusoidal time dependence: $e^{-\frac{1}{2}\gamma t} \cos(\omega_0 t + \alpha)$.   The Fourier analysis of these fields gives the frequency spectrum of the radiation from the oscillator.   The radiated intensity per unit frequency range at the angular frequency ω is proportional to

$$\frac{1}{(\omega - \omega_0)^2 + \frac{1}{4}\gamma^2} \tag{45.24}$$

According to (45.24), the intensity of the emitted spectral line has half its maximum value when $\omega = \omega_0 \pm \frac{1}{2}\gamma$.   The quantity γ is called the *natural line breadth* and in cases of practical interest is small in comparison with ω_0.

The line breadth is evidently twice the initial fractional rate of decrease of the amplitude of the classical oscillator or is equal to the initial fractional rate of decrease of the oscillator's energy.   It is plausible to associate the rate of decrease of the energy of the classical oscillator with the rate of decrease of the probability of finding the corresponding quantum system in its initial upper state.   If this is done, the quantum analog of the classical natural line breadth γ is the initial transition probability per unit time for spontaneous emission given in (45.22). Although this result is correct if the final state is the ground state, there will be an additional broadening of the line if the final state has a finite breadth.[1]

The foregoing relation between transition probability and line breadth can be arrived at in a qualitative but more general way by means of the uncertainty relation (3.3).   The reciprocal of the transition probability per unit time is of the order of magnitude of the time that the quantum system stays in its upper state.   Thus a determination of the energy of the upper state cannot occupy a time that is of larger order of magnitude than the lifetime $1/\gamma$ of this state.   According to (3.3), this means that the energy cannot be determined with an accuracy much greater than $\hbar$ divided by the lifetime, or $\hbar\gamma$.   If the energy of the upper state is uncertain by this amount, the frequency of the emitted line will be uncertain (broadened) by γ.   In general, a quantum energy level is

---

[1] For further discussion of line breadth, see Heitler, *op. cit.*, sec. 18.

broadened by any process that shortens its lifetime; the level is perfectly sharp only if the lifetime of the state is infinite (true stationary energy eigenfunction).

A qualitative idea of the natural breadth of electric dipole lines emitted by a quantum system can be obtained by rewriting the expression (45.22) for γ in the form

$$\frac{\gamma}{\omega_{kn}} = \frac{4}{3}\frac{e^2}{\hbar c}\,k^2|\langle k|\mathbf{r}|n\rangle|^2$$

The factor $e^2/\hbar c$ is a dimensionless constant that is very nearly equal to $\frac{1}{137}$ if e is the electronic charge,[1] and the factor $k^2|\langle k|\mathbf{r}|n\rangle|^2$ has already been assumed small in comparison with unity in arriving at the dipole approximation. Thus the ratio of line breadth to angular frequency is expected to be quite small (it is of the order of 10^{-6} for typical atomic dipole lines).

46□SOME APPLICATIONS OF RADIATION THEORY

The semiclassical radiation theory developed earlier in this chapter is applied in this section first to the determination of the conditions for allowed transitions and then to the theory of the photoelectric effect.

SELECTION RULES FOR A SINGLE PARTICLE

The discussion of forbidden transitions at the end of Sec. 44 shows that the probabilities for absorption and induced emission are reduced by a factor of at least $(ka)^2$ with respect to allowed transitions if the dipole matrix element $\langle k|\mathbf{r}|n\rangle$ vanishes. The same remarks apply to the probability for spontaneous emission, since the integral in (45.11) is the same as that in (44.19) when the substitution (45.20) is made for $\mathbf{J}$.

The conditions on u_k and u_n for which the dipole matrix element is different from zero constitute the *selection rules*. They are easily formulated if the potential V that appears in the unperturbed hamiltonian of (44.13) is spherically symmetric. It is shown in Sec. 14 that the energy eigenfunctions can then be written as products of functions of the radical distance r and spherical harmonics $Y_{lm}(\theta,\phi)$ defined in Eq. (14.16). The matrix element $\langle k|\mathbf{r}|n\rangle$ is the vector whose cartesian components are the corresponding matrix elements of x, y, and z. The matrix element of z is $\int u_k^* r \cos\theta u_n\, d^3r$, which can be written as a product of an integral over r and the angular integral

$$\int_0^\pi \int_0^{2\pi} Y_{lm}^*(\theta,\phi)\cos\theta\, Y_{l'm'}(\theta,\phi)\sin\theta\, d\theta\, d\phi \qquad (46.1)$$

---

[1] This is the *fine structure constant* that appears in the theory of the fine structure of atomic energy levels (see Chap. 13).

where the primed and unprimed subscripts are the angular momentum quantum numbers for the lower state u_n and the upper state u_k, respectively.

The ϕ integration in (46.1) is $\int_0^{2\pi} e^{i(m'-m)\phi}\,d\phi$, which is zero unless $m' = m$. The integration can then be written, apart from numerical factors,

$$\int_{-1}^{1} wP_l^m(w)P_{l'}^m(w)\,dw \qquad w = \cos\theta \qquad (46.2)$$

Now it can be shown with the help of the generating function (14.13) for the associated Legendre functions that

$$wP_l^m(w) = \frac{l+|m|}{2l+1}P_{l-1}^m(w) + \frac{l-|m|+1}{2l+1}P_{l+1}^m(w)$$

Substitution of this into (46.2) shows, with the help of the orthogonality integral (14.15), that the matrix element of z vanishes unless $m' = m$ and $l' = l \pm 1$. A similar treatment shows that the matrix element of $x + iy$ vanishes unless $m' = m - 1$ and $l' = l \pm 1$, and the matrix element of $x - iy$ vanishes unless $m' = m + 1$ and $l' = l \pm 1$. These selection rules also follow from the discussion at the end of Sec. 28 and determine the possible allowed (electric dipole) transitions of a single charged particle that moves in a central force field.

POLARIZATION OF EMITTED RADIATION

The discussion following Eq. (45.12) shows that the polarization of the emitted radiation is determined by the total current vector $\mathbf{J}_0$ and hence [because of (45.21)] by the dipole matrix element. When the initial and final states have l values that differ by unity and the same magnetic quantum number m with respect to the z axis, only the matrix element of z fails to vanish. The radiation is then linearly polarized along the z axis if viewed in the xy plane, and there is no radiation along the z axis. When the magnetic quantum numbers of the initial and final states differ by unity, the x and y components of the dipole matrix element are 90° out of phase, and the z component vanishes; the radiation is then circularly polarized if viewed along the z axis and is linearly polarized perpendicular to the z axis if viewed in the xy plane. These results are of interest in connection with the polarization of the radiation from atoms placed in a magnetic field (see the discussion of the Zeeman effect in Sec. 48).

CONSERVATION OF ANGULAR MOMENTUM

The discussion of Eqs. (45.18) and (45.19) shows that the angular momentum that is carried away by an emitted quantum has its maximum value $\hbar$ and is directed along the z axis, when $J_{0y} = iJ_{0x}$. From (45.21) we see that this is the case in which $\langle k|y|n\rangle^* = i\langle k|x|n\rangle^*$, or $\langle k|y|n\rangle = -i\langle k|x|n\rangle$. Now $x = r \sin\theta \cos\phi = \frac{1}{2}r \sin\theta \cdot (e^{i\phi} + e^{-i\phi})$, and $y = r \sin\theta \sin\phi = -\frac{1}{2}ir \sin\theta(e^{i\phi} - e^{-i\phi})$. Then it is apparent from the ϕ integration in (46.1) that, in order for the matrix element of y to equal $-i$ times the matrix element of x, the magnetic quantum number of the initial state u_k must be greater than the magnetic quantum number of the final state u_n by unity. Application of Eq. (14.23) shows that the z component of angular momentum of the particle has decreased by $\hbar$ during the transition. Thus angular momentum is conserved between the radiating particle and the emitted quantum.

The foregoing result is based on the connection between the classical and quantum current densities assumed in (45.20). The successful derivation of the Planck distribution law in Sec. 45 shows that (45.20) is correct so far as magnitude is concerned. The above demonstration of the conservation of angular momentum shows in addition that the phases of the initial and final states are inserted properly in (45.20); if, for example, $\mathbf{J}$ had been assumed proportional to $u_k^*\nabla u_n$, an inconsistent result would have been obtained in the preceding paragraph.

If the magnetic quantum number does not change in a transition, only the matrix element of z fails to vanish, and the discussion of (45.18) shows that the quantum carries off no angular momentum. This might seem at first to be in contradiction with the change by one unit of the orbital angular momentum quantum number l. The x and y components of the angular momentum of the particle do not commute with the z component (which in this case is known to be $m\hbar$ and does not change), so that they cannot be precisely specified. Their expectation or average values for states that are described by quantum numbers l and m are zero, since the diagonal elements of the matrices for the x and y components of the angular momentum are all zero [see Eqs. (27.26)]. Thus there is no observable change in any of the components of the particle's angular momentum, and so the expectation value of the angular momentum carried off by the quantum should be zero. The x and y angular-momentum components for a particle in a stationary state can be thought of as fluctuating about zero in such a way that their average values are zero, although their average squares are not. The change in l corresponds to changes in these average squares.

SELECTION RULES FOR MANY-PARTICLE SYSTEMS

When a quantum-mechanical system consists of several particles that do not interact with each other, the total hamiltonian is simply a sum of terms like $H_0 + H'$ that appear in (44.13). The unperturbed energy eigenfunctions are products of single-particle eigenfunctions such as are discussed in Sec. 40 (they can be unsymmetrized if the particles are not identical). It is clear that the matrix element that appears in the first-order perturbation theory of Sec. 44 (absorption and induced emission) involves a multiple integral of the form

$$\int \cdots \int u_{a'}^{*}(1)u_{b'}^{*}(2) \cdots [H'(1) + H'(2)$$
$$+ \cdots]u_a(1)u_b(2) \cdots d^3r_1\, d^3r_2 \cdots$$

Because of the orthogonality of different u's for the same particle, this integral vanishes unless all the single-particle functions $u_{a'}, \ldots$ are equal to the corresponding functions $u_a, \ldots$, except for one. Thus only one of the particles can change its state in a transition, and the selection rules for a central force field are precisely those given above. Since the spontaneous transition probability can be related to the same integral through the Planck distribution formula, these selection rules hold for spontaneous emission as well as for absorption and induced emission.

If the system consists of several charged particles whose mutual interactions cannot be neglected, we must base the selection rules on general conservation laws for total angular momentum and parity. It is not difficult to generalize the work of Secs. 44 and 45 to show that the dominant term, when the wavelength of the radiation is large in comparison with the dimensions of the system, is the matrix element of the total electric dipole moment $e_1\mathbf{r}_1 + e_2\mathbf{r}_2 + \cdots$. The angular momentum radiated by an oscillating dipole cannot, according to the discussion of (45.19), exceed $\hbar$ per quantum; this classical argument is based on an arbitrary current distribution, so that it is not invalidated if several particles contribute to the dipole. The interpretation of the conservation of angular momentum between the emitted quantum and the radiating system is complicated by the semiclassical nature of the entire treatment. A consistent treatment based on quantum electrodynamics shows that the correct selection rule based on this conservation law is that the total angular momentum quantum number of the system can remain unchanged or can increase or decrease by unity. An exceptional case is that in which this quantum number is zero for both initial and final states. The initial and final wave functions are then spherically symmetric, and an extension of the argument given at the end of Sec. 44 shows that a radiative transition between these states is not only forbidden (no allowed dipole transition) but strictly forbidden (no first-order transition whatever).

The discussion of parity in Sec. 29 is easily extended to show that the parity of each energy eigenfunction can be well defined (even or odd) if the total hamiltonian is unchanged by reflection of the coordinates of all particles through the origin. The electric dipole moment operator given above is evidently odd with respect to reflection of all coordinates; thus its matrix elements vanish in this case unless the initial and final states have opposite parities. This selection rule is known as the *Laporte rule*.

PHOTOELECTRIC EFFECT

When a bound system that contains charged particles is irradiated by sufficiently high-energy quanta, there is a finite probability that the system will be broken up. This process is usually called the *photoelectric effect* in the case of atoms and *photodisintegration* in the case of nuclei. As an example, we consider the ejection of an electron from an atom by a photon of energy $\hbar\omega > \epsilon$, where $-\epsilon$ is the ground-state energy of the electron. The initial wave function of the electron is $u_0(\mathbf{r})$, and in its final state it has the kinetic energy

$$\frac{\hbar^2 k^2}{2m} = \hbar\omega - \epsilon \tag{46.3}$$

We suppose the radiation to be incident along the positive z axis and to be polarized with its electric vector along the x axis. Then the matrix element for the transition is given by the second of Eqs. (44.14)

$$\langle k|H'^0|0\rangle = \frac{ie\hbar}{mc} \int u_k^* e^{i\omega z/c} A_0 \left(\frac{\partial u_0}{\partial x}\right) d^3r \tag{46.4}$$

We assume that the final state can be represented to sufficient accuracy by the plane wave $u_k(\mathbf{r}) = L^{-\frac{3}{2}} \exp(i\mathbf{k} \cdot \mathbf{r})$. This is equivalent to the assumption that the Born approximation is valid for the scattering of the electron by the remaining ion.

With the help of a partial integration, Eq. (46.4) becomes

$$\langle k|H'^0|0\rangle = -\frac{e\hbar A_0 k_x}{mcL^{\frac{3}{2}}} \int u_0 \exp\left[i\left(\frac{w_z}{c} - \mathbf{k} \cdot \mathbf{r}\right)\right] d^3r$$

From Eqs. (35.14) and (35.18), the transition probability per unit time from the bound to the ionized state is

$$w = \frac{mkL^3}{4\pi^2\hbar^3} |\langle k|H'^0|0\rangle|^2 \sin\theta \, d\theta \, d\phi$$

It is convenient for what follows to introduce the momentum $\hbar\mathbf{K}$ that is transferred to the atom:

$$\mathbf{K} = \frac{\omega}{c} \mathbf{1}_z - \mathbf{k} \tag{46.5}$$

where $\mathbf{1}_z$ is a unit vector in the z direction. The differential cross section for the photoelectric effect is equal to w divided by the incident flux of photons. This flux is obtained by dividing the incident intensity (44.12) by $\hbar\omega$, so that

$$\sigma(\theta,\phi) \sin\theta \, d\theta \, d\phi = \frac{e^2 k k_x{}^2}{2\pi m c \omega} \left| \int u_0 \exp(i\mathbf{K} \cdot \mathbf{r}) \, d^3 r \right|^2 \sin\theta \, d\theta \, d\phi$$

$$(46.6)$$

ANGULAR DISTRIBUTION

There are two factors in Eq. (46.6) that determine the angular distribution of the ejected photoelectrons. One of these is the factor $k_x{}^2$, which shows that the electrons tend to have a cosine-squared distribution with respect to the polarization vector of the incident radiation. If the radiation is unpolarized, $k_x{}^2$ must be replaced by $\frac{1}{2}(k_x{}^2 + k_y{}^2)$, so that there is a sine-squared distribution with respect to the direction of incidence. In either case, the electrons are ejected preferentially at right angles to the incident beam of photons.

The appearance of the momentum transfer vector $\mathbf{K}$ in the integrand of (46.6) also affects the angular distribution. The discussion of Eq. (38.29) shows that integrals of the kind that appear in Eq. (46.6) generally decrease as K increases. Now K is smallest when $\mathbf{k}$ is in the z direction, so that the K dependence of (46.6) tends to shift the maximum in the differential cross section toward the forward direction. However, this effect is appreciable only when k and ω/c are comparable in magnitude. If we assume for the moment that ϵ can be neglected in Eq. (46.3), the quantity $\omega/ck \approx \hbar k/2mc = v/2c$, where v is the speed of the ejected electron. Thus the forward shift of the cross-section maximum occurs for high-energy photons and ejected electrons, in which case ϵ can in fact be neglected as assumed above.[1]

CROSS SECTION FOR THE ATOMIC PHOTOELECTRIC EFFECT

We now specialize to the situation in which the photoelectron is ejected from the lowest state (K or $1s$ shell) of an atom. The initial wave function $u_0(\mathbf{r})$ is then the wave function $u_{100}(r,\theta,\phi)$ of Eq. (16.24) and is given by

$$u_0(r) = (\pi a^3)^{-\frac{1}{2}} e^{-r/a} \qquad a = \frac{a_0}{Z} \qquad a_0 = \frac{\hbar^2}{me^2} \qquad (46.7)$$

So long as u_0 is spherically symmetric, the angle integration in (46.6) is easily performed and gives

$$\sigma(\theta,\phi) = \frac{8\pi e^2 k k_x{}^2}{mc\omega K^2} \left| \int_0^\infty u_0(r) \sin Kr \, r \, dr \right|^2 \qquad (46.8)$$

---

[1] The quantities k and ω/c can also be comparable very close to the photoelectric threshold, when $\hbar\omega$ is only slightly greater than ϵ. However, the Born approximation is not valid in this case.

Substitution of (46.7) into (46.8) yields

$$\sigma(\theta,\phi) = \frac{32e^2a^3kk_x^2}{mc\omega(1 + K^2a^2)^4} \tag{46.9}$$

The discussion of Eq. (38.4) shows that the Born approximation is most nearly valid for high energy and for $Ze^2/\hbar v \ll 1$. Now $\epsilon = Z^2e^2/2a_0$, so that $\hbar^2k^2/2m\epsilon = (\hbar v/Ze^2)^2$. Thus ϵ can be neglected in Eq. (46.3). Since, as was shown above, $\omega/ck \approx v/2c$ in this case, the magnitude of K given by Eq. (46.5) is approximately $k(1 - v\cos\theta/2c)$. Further, $ka = \hbar v/Ze^2 \gg 1$. Thus the factor $1 + K^2a^2$ in the denominator of Eq. (46.9) can be replaced approximately by $k^2a^2(1 - v\cos\theta/c)$. We then obtain for the high-energy photoelectric differential cross section

$$\sigma(\theta,\phi) \approx \frac{32e^2}{mc\omega(ka)^5}\sin^2\theta\cos^2\phi\left(1 + \frac{4v}{c}\cos\theta\right) \tag{46.10}$$

Since the electron has been treated nonrelativistically, v/c must be fairly small in comparison with unity, and therefore terms of order v^2/c^2 have been neglected in Eq. (46.10). Integration over the angles yields the total cross section

$$\sigma \approx \frac{128\pi}{3}\frac{e^2}{mc\omega(ka)^5} \tag{46.11}$$

It follows from (46.3) and (46.7) that σ is proportional to $Z^5/(\hbar\omega)^{\frac{7}{2}}$. In using Eq. (46.11), it must be remembered that σ is the total cross section for each of the K electrons and hence must be doubled to obtain the total atomic cross section for the K-shell photoelectric effect.

It is interesting to note that the leading term of Eq. (46.10), in which v/c is neglected in comparison with unity, and all of Eq. (46.11) result from the electric dipole approximation discussed in Sec. 44. In this approximation, $e^{i\omega z/c}$ is replaced by unity in Eq. (46.4).

IMPROVEMENT ON THE BORN APPROXIMATION

There are two respects in which the foregoing calculation is based on first-order perturbation theory. First, the matrix element (46.4) is regarded as small, so that the interaction between the electron and the electromagnetic field is treated to first order. Second, the electron wave function is taken to be a plane wave in the final state, so that the effect of the ionic potential on this state is neglected. It is very difficult to improve on the calculation from the first point of view, and it is hardly worthwhile because of the smallness of the electron-radiation interaction. On the other hand, an improvement with regard to the second point is feasible, and some trouble in this regard is justified since the results would then be applicable to low energies and to large values of Z; that is, $Ze^2/\hbar v$ would not then have to be small in comparison with unity. This can be accomplished by making use of the distorted wave Born approximation that was discussed in Sec. 38.

PROBLEMS

1. Show that, if $\nabla \cdot \mathbf{J} = \rho = 0$, the most general solution of Maxwell's equations can be expressed in terms of potentials such that $\nabla \cdot \mathbf{A} = \phi = 0$.

2. Show that the probability density associated with Eq. (44.1) is given by (7.1) and that the probability current density must be changed from (7.3).

3. Show that, if the gauge transformation (44.5) is accompanied by the transformation $\psi' = \psi e^{iex/\hbar c}$, the form of the wave equation (44.1) is unaffected.

4. Estimate the order of magnitude of eA/cp, when e is the electronic charge, A is the magnitude of the vector potential for the visible part of the spectrum that corresponds to the radiation in a cavity at several thousand degrees centigrade, and p is the momentum of an electron in the first excited state of hydrogen.

5. Verify Eq. (44.20) by means of the wave equation, without recourse to matrix methods.

6. Show that the transition probability for spontaneous emission is equal to the transition probability for induced emission that would result from an isotropic field of such intensity that there is one quantum per state of the field in the neighborhood of the transition frequency.

7. A hydrogen atom in its first excited ($2P$) state is placed in a cavity. At what temperature of the cavity are the transition probabilities for spontaneous and induced emission equal?

8. What is the spontaneous transition probability per unit time, expressed in $\sec^{-1}$, of a hydrogen atom in its first excited state?

9. What is the selection rule for allowed transitions of a linear harmonic oscillator? What is the spontaneous transition probability per unit time, expressed in $\sec^{-1}$, of an oscillator in its first excited state, when e, m, and ω are the same as in Prob. 8?

10. Show that a logarithmic factor like that obtained in Prob. 14, Chap. 9, always appears in the cross section for excitation of a one-electron atom by electron impact, if the corresponding radiative transition is allowed. Derive the simplest relation that you can between the differential cross section for excitation by electron impact and the corresponding transition probability for spontaneous emission, assuming the transition is allowed.

11. Make use of the dipole expression (45.12) for the radiated intensity to find the angular distribution of the radiation when $J_{0y} = iJ_{0x}$, $J_{0z} = 0$. Show also that the total power radiated is still given by Eq. (45.13).

12. Show that $\mathbf{k} \cdot \mathbf{r}$ in Eq. (44.19) is of order $e^2/\hbar c \approx \frac{1}{137}$ for a hydrogen atom transition.

13. Assume that the interaction between the neutron and the proton that make up a deuteron can be represented by a square well potential for which $a = 0$ (zero-range or δ-function interaction), and that the only bound energy level of the system has $l = 0$ and $\epsilon = 2.23$ Mev (million electron volts). Show that no error is involved in the calculation of the photodisintegration cross section if the final-state wave function is taken to be a plane wave. Find the differential and total cross sections for unpolarized photons.

12

Atoms, Molecules, and Atomic Nuclei

This chapter is not intended to be a complete survey of the properties of atomic systems. It is primarily a presentation of a relatively few problems that arise in connection with the structure of matter, selected because they supply interesting and instructive applications of quantum mechanics. These problems are grouped according to subject; enough explanatory material is included so that the treatment is coherent, although severely limited in scope.

47□APPROXIMATIONS IN ATOMIC STRUCTURE[1]

The ground states of the two lightest atoms, hydrogen and helium, were considered in Secs. 16 and 32, respectively. Variation calculations similar to those described for helium have been carried through for others of

[1] For a more detailed discussion of the material of this section and the next, see E. U. Condon and G. H. Shortley, "The Theory of Atomic Spectra" (Cambridge, London, and Macmillan, New York, 1935); J. C. Slater, "Quantum Theory of Atomic Structure," vol. II (McGraw-Hill, New York, 1960).

the light atoms.   This section describes some of the approximations that have been used for the heavier atoms.   The alkali atoms are discussed separately in Sec. 48.

CENTRAL-FIELD APPROXIMATION

The starting point of calculations on all except the lightest atoms is the *central-field approximation*.   This assumes that each of the atomic electrons moves in a spherically symmetric potential energy $V(r)$ that is produced by the nucleus and all the other electrons.   The approximation is a good one if the deviation from the $V(r)$ for one electron produced by close passage of other electrons is relatively small.   This is actually the case, since the constant nuclear potential is of the order of Z times as large as the fluctuating potential due to each nearby electron, and the latter varies quite slowly (inversely) with the separation distance.   The two principal problems are then the calculation of the central field and the correction of the approximate results obtained from it.   Before considering these problems, we discuss some general properties of the central field.

The potential energy $V(r)$ for a neutral atom has the coulomb form $-e^2/r$ at a great distance r from the nucleus, since the removal of the electron whose potential is being measured leaves a singly charged positive ion.   The electron in the hydrogen atom, for which the potential energy is $-e^2/r$ at all r, was shown in Sec. 16 to have an infinite number of bound energy levels characterized by the quantum numbers n, l, and m. An infinite number of energy levels is also expected for $V(r)$, since for large n the electron wave function is small near the nucleus, and only the form of $V(r)$ for large r is significant.   An important difference between the two situations is that the degeneracy between states of the same n and different l that occurs in hydrogen is removed in a noncoulomb central field.   This is because the electrons that have smaller angular momentum penetrate closer to the nucleus, and $V(r)$ is stronger (more negative) than $-e^2/r$ there, since the nucleus is less completely screened by the other electrons.   Thus, for given n, the states of lowest l have the lowest energy.   The degeneracy with respect to m is not affected, since this occurs whenever the potential is spherically symmetric.

Because of the spin, four quantum numbers n, l, m_l, and m_s are required to specify the state of an electron in a central field.   The orbital quantum numbers l and m_l are the same as l and m in the hydrogen atom, $m_s = \pm\frac{1}{2}$ specifies the spin orientation, and n is a natural generalization of the total quantum number that appears in hydrogen.   Equation (16.14) shows that $n - l - 1$ is the number of nodes of the radial part of the hydrogen wave function; this definition of n is carried over to the general central field, so that l does not exceed $n - 1$.

PERIODIC SYSTEM OF THE ELEMENTS

According to the Pauli exclusion principle (see the discussion of anti-symmetric wave functions in Sec. 40), not more than one electron in an atom can have a particular set of values of the four quantum numbers given above. As Z increases, electrons fill the one-electron states of lowest energy in succession; the ground state of an atom in the central-field approximation is that in which there are no unfilled electron states that have lower energy than any that are occupied. Because of the degeneracy with respect to m_l and m_s, there can be as many as $2(2l + 1)$ electrons with the same energy in a *shell* that is specified by n and l. It is apparent, then, that the ground-state *configuration* of the electrons in an atom can be described by specifying the number of electrons in each shell. In the central-field approximation, all shells that contain any electrons are full except perhaps that which has the highest energy.

The chemical properties of atoms are determined for the most part by the least tightly bound, or *valence*, electrons, which are in the shell of highest energy. The most important factors are the number of occupied and unoccupied electron states in this shell, and the energy interval between this and the next higher (empty) shell. For example, an atom tends to be chemically inert if its highest shell is full and there is an appreciable energy gap to the next higher shell, since then electrons are not readily shared with other atoms to form a molecule. The quasi-periodic recurrence of similar highest shell structures as Z increases is responsible for the *periodic system* of the chemical elements.

In the usual spectroscopic notation, the n value of a shell is given as a number, the l value as a letter, and the number of electrons in the shell as a numerical superscript. The letter code for l and the maximum number $2(2l + 1)$ of electrons in a shell are as follows:

$$l = 0, \quad 1, \quad 2, \quad 3, \quad 4, \quad 5, \ldots$$
$$s, \quad p, \quad d, \quad f, \quad g, \quad h, \ldots$$
$$2(2l + 1) = 2, \quad 6, \quad 10, \quad 14, \quad 18, \quad 22, \ldots$$

For example, the ground-state configurations of sodium ($Z = 11$) and of mercury ($Z = 80$) are

Na: $1s^2 2s^2 2p^6 3s$

Hg: $1s^2 2s^2 2p^6 3s^2 3p^6 4s^2 3d^{10} 4p^6 5s^2 4d^{10} 5p^6 6s^2 4f^{14} 5d^{10}$

The ground-state configurations of many of the elements can be written down simply from a knowledge of the order in which the energies of the shells increase. This order can be inferred from spectroscopic evidence and is as follows:

$1s, 2s, 2p, 3s, 3p, [4s, 3d], 4p, [5s, 4d], 5p, [6s, 4f, 5d], 6p, [7s, 5f, 6d]$

The brackets enclose shells that have so nearly the same energy that they are not always filled in sequence. These shell energies are close together because the increase in n and the decrease in l tend to compensate each other; thus the $4s$ state, which has a higher energy than the $3d$ state in hydrogen, is depressed by the penetration caused by its low angular momentum. The s shell in each bracket is always filled first, although it can lose one or both of its electrons as the other shells in the bracket fill up. Apart from the brackets, there are no deviations from the indicated order of filling.

Table 2 gives the ground-state configurations of each of the elements. An atom contains all the full shells that occur above and to the left of its position in the table. Since the number of s electrons varies as each d shell fills, the d columns are subdivided to show the number of s electrons. The two groups of atoms that have a partially full f shell in their ground-state configurations fit in at * (rare earths) and at † (heaviest elements). The first group has the $6s$ shell full and the second has the $7s$ shell full; the distribution of electrons in d and f shells for each group is shown below the main table.

A few of the periodicities are worth explicit mention. The first electron to go into each s shell beyond $1s$ gives an alkali, and the elements just before each of these (full $1s$ shell or a full p shell) are rare gases. The elements with the same number of electrons in a p shell have similar chemical properties; this is especially striking in the case of the halogens (one electron short of a full p shell). The elements with full $2s$ and $3s$ shells (Be and Mg) that are followed by p shells have somewhat different properties from the alkaline earths, which have full s shells followed by d or f shells. The filling of the $4s,3d$ shells gives elements somewhat similar to those arising from the filling of the $5s,4d$ shells. The elements that correspond to full bracketed shells (Zn, Cd, and Hg) are quite similar, as are the noble metals (Cu, Ag, and Au) in which an s electron is missing from the full bracketed shells.

THOMAS-FERMI STATISTICAL MODEL

We now turn to the first of the problems associated with the central-field approximation. Two methods have been used for the determination of the potential energy $V(r)$. The first of these, due to Thomas[1] and Fermi,[2] is discussed here, and the second, due to Hartree, is taken up later. The *Thomas-Fermi statistical model* assumes that $V(r)$ varies slowly enough in an electron wavelength so that many electrons can be localized within a volume over which the potential changes by a small fraction of itself. The electrons can then be treated by statistical mechanics and obey the

[1] L. H. Thomas, *Proc. Cambridge Phil. Soc.* **23**, 542 (1927).
[2] E. Fermi, *Z. Physik* **48**, 73 (1928).

Table 2 Ground-state electron configurations of the elements[1]

	s	s^2	p	p^2	p^3	p^4	p^5	p^6	d	d^2	d^3	d^4	d^5	d^6	d^7	d^8	d^9	d^{10}
$1s$	H 1	He 2																
$2s$	Li 3	Be 4																
$2p$			B 5	C 6	N 7	O 8	F 9	Ne 10										
$3s$	Na 11	Mg 12																
$3p$			Al 13	Si 14	P 15	S 16	Cl 17	A 18										
$4s,3d$ $4s^0$																		
$4s$	K 19												Cr 24					Cu 29
$4s^2$		Ca 20							Sc 21	Ti 22	V 23		Mn 25	Fe 26	Co 27	Ni 28		Zn 30
$4p$			Ga 31	Ge 32	As 33	Se 34	Br 35	Kr 36										
$5s,4d$ $5s^0$																		Pd 46
$5s$	Rb 37											Nb 41	Mo 42		Ru 44	Rh 45		Ag 47
$5s^2$		Sr 38							Y 39	Zr 40			Tc 43					Cd 48
$5p$			In 49	Sn 50	Sb 51	Te 52	I 53	Xe 54										
$6s,4f,5d$ $6s^0$																		
$6s$	Cs 55																Pt 78	Au 79
$6s^2$		Ba 56							La* 57	Hf 72	Ta 73	W 74	Re 75	Os 76	Ir 77			Hg 80
$6p$			Tl 81	Pb 82	Bi 83	Po 84	At 85	Rn 86										
$7s,5f,6d$ $7s^0$																		
$7s$	Fa 87																	
$7s^2$		Ra 88							Ac 89	Th† 90								

*$4f$:

		f	f^2	f^3	f^4	f^5	f^6	f^7	f^8	f^9	f^{10}	f^{11}	f^{12}	f^{13}	f^{14}
$5d^0$			Ce 58	Pr 59	Nd 60	Pm 61	Sm 62	Eu 63		Tb 65	Dy 66	Ho 67	Er 68	Tm 69	Yb 70
$5d$								Gd 64							Lu 71

† $5f$:

		f	f^2	f^3	f^4	f^5	f^6	f^7	f^8	f^9	f^{10}	f^{11}	f^{12}	f^{13}	f^{14}
$6d^0$															
$6d$			Pa 91	U 92	Np 93	Pu 94									

[1] This table is taken from Condon and Shortley, *op. cit.*, p. 333, with recent assignments from G. W. C. Kaye and T. H. Laby, "Tables of Physical and Chemical Constants," pp. 198–199 (Longmans, London, 1966). The heaviest elements, not included in the table, are americium (Am, 95), curium (Cm, 96), berkelium (Bk, 97), californium (Cf, 98), einsteinium (Es, 99), fermium (Fm, 100), mendelevium (Md, 101), nobelium (No, 102), and lawrencium (Lr, 103).

Fermi-Dirac statistics mentioned in Sec. 40. At normal temperatures, the thermal energy κT is very small in comparison with $V(r)$ everywhere except at the edge of the atom, where the chance of finding an electron is small. In this case, the Fermi-Dirac statistics requires that the electron states fill in order of increasing energy, as assumed above. The difference between the present treatment and the more general discussion given earlier in this section lies in the additional assumption that $V(r)$ is sensibly constant over a region in which many electrons can be localized.

The number of electron states in a cube of edge length L at the walls of which the wave functions obey periodic boundary conditions was computed in Sec. 11 to be $(L/2\pi)^3\, dk_x\, dk_y\, dk_z$. This must be multiplied by 2 to take account of the two possible spin states; then the number of states for which the magnitude of the momentum $\mathbf{p} = \hbar\mathbf{k}$ is less than or equal to p_0 is

$$2\left(\frac{L}{2\pi}\right)^3 \int_0^{p_0/\hbar} \int_0^{\pi} \int_0^{2\pi} k^2\, dk\, \sin\theta\, d\theta\, d\phi = \frac{p_0{}^3 L^3}{3\pi^2\hbar^3}$$

If all these states are occupied, the number of electrons per unit volume whose kinetic energy does not exceed $p_0{}^2/2m$ is $p_0{}^3/3\pi^2\hbar^3$. Now the maximum kinetic energy at any distance r from the nucleus is $-V(r)$, since otherwise electrons would escape from the atom. We thus obtain a relation between the volume density of electrons, $n(r)$, and the potential energy:

$$n(r) = \frac{[-2mV(r)]^{\frac{3}{2}}}{3\pi^2\hbar^3} \tag{47.1}$$

The electrostatic potential $-V(r)/e$ is also determined by Poisson's equation in terms of the charge density $-en(r)$:

$$-\frac{1}{e}\nabla^2 V = -\frac{1}{er^2}\frac{d}{dr}\left(r^2\frac{dV}{dr}\right) = 4\pi en(r) \tag{47.2}$$

Equations (47.1) and (47.2) are two simultaneous equations for n and V. The boundary conditions on the solutions can be expressed in terms of V alone for a neutral atom of atomic number Z. As $r \to 0$, the leading term in the potential energy must be due to the nucleus, so that $V(r) \to -Ze^2/r$. As $r \to \infty$, there must be no net charge inside the sphere of radius r, so that V falls off more rapidly than $1/r$, and $rV(r) \to 0$. The boundary condition at infinity is different from that assumed earlier in this section, where V was taken to have the asymptotic form $-e^2/r$. The V discussed earlier is the potential experienced by one of the atomic electrons, whereas the Thomas-Fermi potential is that experienced by an infinitesimal test charge. The difference between the two potentials emphasizes the statistical nature of the approximation made by Thomas and Fermi.

The solution for V is exact in the limit in which m becomes infinite and e becomes zero in such a way that m^3e^4 remains constant; then the electron wavelength becomes zero, and the density of particles becomes infinite. In this limit the potential is constant over many wavelengths, and enough particles are present so that statistical mechanics can be applied.

EVALUATION OF THE POTENTIAL

Elimination of $n(r)$ from Eqs. (47.1) and (47.2) leads to an equation for $-V(r)$

$$\frac{1}{r^2}\frac{d}{dr}\left[r^2\frac{d(-V)}{dr}\right] = \frac{4e^2[-2mV(r)]^{\frac{3}{2}}}{3\pi\hbar^3} \tag{47.3}$$

Equation (47.3) and the boundary conditions given above are conveniently expressed in a dimensionless form in which Z, E, m, and $\hbar$ appear only in scale factors. We put

$$V(r) = -\frac{Ze^2}{r}\chi \qquad r = bx$$

$$b = \frac{1}{2}\left(\frac{3\pi}{4}\right)^{\frac{2}{3}}\frac{\hbar^2}{me^2Z^{\frac{1}{3}}} = \frac{0.885a_0}{Z^{\frac{1}{3}}} \tag{47.4}$$

where $a_0 = \hbar^2/me^2$. With these substitutions, (47.3) becomes

$$x^{\frac{1}{2}}\frac{d^2\chi}{dx^2} = \chi^{\frac{3}{2}} \tag{47.5}$$

$$\chi = 1 \text{ at } x = 0 \qquad \chi = 0 \text{ at } x = \infty$$

The most accurate solution of Eq. (47.5) was computed by Bush and Caldwell[1] with the help of the original differential analyzer, and is expressed in the form of a numerical table.

Equations (47.4) show that the "radius" of an atom is inversely proportional to the cube root of the atomic number, if this radius is interpreted to be that of a sphere that encloses a fixed fraction of all the electrons (see Prob. 1). These equations can also be used to show that the Thomas-Fermi approximation improves with increasing Z. The potential at the atomic radius is proportional to $Z^{\frac{4}{3}}$, so that a typical electron wavelength is proportional to $Z^{-\frac{2}{3}}$. The distance over which the potential changes by a definite fraction of itself is proportional to the atomic radius, or $Z^{-\frac{1}{3}}$. Thus the fractional change of the potential in an electron wavelength is proportional to $Z^{-\frac{1}{3}}$ and decreases with increasing Z. Moreover, since the number of electrons is equal to Z, the use of the statistical method is better justified as Z increases.

[1] V. Bush and S. H. Caldwell, *Phys. Rev.* **38**, 1898 (1931).

HARTREE'S SELF-CONSISTENT FIELDS

The second method for obtaining a central field is due to Hartree.[1] This model assumes that each electron moves in a central field that can be calculated from the nuclear potential and the wave functions of all the other electrons, by assuming that the charge density associated with an electron is $-e$ times its position probability density. The Schrödinger equation is solved for each electron in its own central field, and the resulting wave functions made consistent with the fields from which they are calculated. Thus the kth electron is described by a normalized wave function $u_k(\mathbf{r}_k)$ that is a solution of the equation

$$\left[-\frac{\hbar^2}{2m}\nabla_k{}^2 - \frac{Ze^2}{r_k} + \sum_{j \neq k} \int |u_j(\mathbf{r}_j)|^2 \frac{e^2}{r_{jk}} d^3r_j \right] u_k(\mathbf{r}_k) \;=\; \epsilon_k u_k(\mathbf{r}_k) \quad (47.6)$$

where $r_{jk} = |\mathbf{r}_j - \mathbf{r}_k|$. If there are Z electrons in the atom, (47.6) constitutes a set of Z simultaneous nonlinear integrodifferential equations for the Z functions $u_k(\mathbf{r}_k)$. It is therefore not feasible to solve these equations directly, and Hartree used a method of successive approximations.

A potential energy that approximately represents the second and third terms in (47.6) is assumed, electron wave functions computed, and new potentials for each electron found from these wave functions. This process is continued until the potentials are self-consistent to a high order of accuracy. The principal approximation made is the averaging of the potential energy given as the third term in (47.6) over the angles of $\mathbf{r}_k$ to make it spherically symmetric. The solutions of (47.6) can then be expressed as products of radial functions and spherical harmonics. A further simplification is made so that the $2(2l + 1)$ or fewer electrons in a shell all move in the same potential and have the same radial wave function.

It is apparent that the Hartree approximation neglects correlations between the positions of the electrons, since the entire wave function for all the electrons is assumed to be a simple product of one-electron functions

$$\psi(\mathbf{r}_1,\mathbf{r}_2, \ldots ,\mathbf{r}_Z) = u_1(\mathbf{r}_1)u_2(\mathbf{r}_2) \cdots u_Z(\mathbf{r}_Z) \quad (47.7)$$

It is also clear from (47.7) that antisymmetrized wave functions are not employed. The antisymmetry is considered only insofar as the quantum numbers of the one-electron states u_k are chosen in agreement with the exclusion principle.[2]

---

[1] D. R. Hartree, *Proc. Cambridge Phil. Soc.* **24,** 111 (1928).

[2] Antisymmetrization is taken into account in the Hartree-Fock method; see, for example, Slater, *op. cit.*, chap. 17.

CONNECTION WITH THE VARIATION METHOD

We now show that the Hartree approximation results from an optimum variation calculation with the trial function (47.7).[1] The wave equation with inclusion of interelectronic interactions but neglect of spin-orbit terms (see below) is

$$H\psi = E\psi$$

$$H = \sum_k \left(-\frac{\hbar^2}{2m} \nabla^2{}_k - \frac{Ze^2}{r_k} \right) + \sum_{j>k}\sum \frac{e^2}{r_{jk}} \tag{47.8}$$

where $j > k$ implies a double summation over all different pairs of indices j and k. We wish to minimize the expectation value of H.

From (47.7) and (47.8) we obtain

$$\int \cdots \int \psi^* H\psi \, d^3r_1 \cdots d^3r_Z$$

$$= \sum_k \int u_k^*(\mathbf{r}_k) \left(-\frac{\hbar^2}{2m} \nabla_k{}^2 - \frac{Ze^2}{r_k} \right) u_k(\mathbf{r}_k) \, d^3r_k$$

$$+ \sum_{j>k}\sum \iint u_j^*(\mathbf{r}_j) u_k^*(\mathbf{r}_k) \frac{e^2}{r_{jk}} u_j(\mathbf{r}_j) u_k(\mathbf{r}_k) \, d^3r_j \, d^3r_k \quad (47.9)$$

since the u_k are normalized. The optimum ψ is obtained by varying each of the u_k separately to minimize (47.9). The only dependence of (47.9) on a particular one-electron function u_k is through the terms

$$\int u_k^*(\mathbf{r}_k) \left(-\frac{\hbar^2}{2m} \nabla_k{}^2 - \frac{Ze^2}{r_k} \right) u_k(\mathbf{r}_k) \, d^3r_k$$

$$+ \sum_{j \neq k} \iint u_j^*(\mathbf{r}_j) u_k^*(\mathbf{r}_k) \frac{e^2}{r_{jk}} u_j(\mathbf{r}_j) u_k(\mathbf{r}_k) \, d^3r_j \, d^3r_k$$

$$= \int u_k^*(\mathbf{r}_k) H_k u_k(\mathbf{r}_k) \, d^3r_k \quad (47.10)$$

$$H_k \equiv -\frac{\hbar^2}{2m} \nabla_k{}^2 - \frac{Ze^2}{r_k} + \sum_{j \neq k} \int |u_j(\mathbf{r}_j)|^2 \frac{e^2}{r_{jk}} \, d^3r_j$$

The integral in (47.10) is the expectation value of the operator H_k for the function u_k. From the discussion of Sec. 32, it follows that this is a minimum when u_k is an eigenfunction of H_k that corresponds to its lowest eigenvalue ϵ_k.

$$H_k u_k = \epsilon_k u_k \tag{47.11}$$

Since Eqs. (47.11) and (47.6) are identical, we see that the Hartree wave

[1] J. C. Slater, *Phys. Rev.* **35**, 210 (1930); V. Fock, *Z. Physik* **61**, 126 (1930).

functions are the best from the point of view of the variation method that can be written in the form (47.7).

The energy associated with this wave function is just the integral (47.9), which can be written with the help of (47.6)

$$\int \cdots \int \psi^* H \psi \, d^3 r_1 \cdots d^3 r_Z = \sum_k \epsilon_k$$

$$- \sum_{j>k} \sum \iint |u_j(\mathbf{r}_j)|^2 |u_k(\mathbf{r}_k)|^2 \frac{e^2}{r_{jk}} \, d^3 r_j \, d^3 r_k \quad (47.12)$$

The electrostatic interaction terms between electrons are counted twice in the summation over ϵ_k and so have to be subtracted out to give (47.12). Thus the energy of the atom is not just the sum of the ϵ_k, although each ϵ_k is roughly the energy of removal of the kth electron. This last is not strictly true, since the removal of an electron alters the self-consistent fields and hence the wave functions and ϵ's for the remaining electrons. However, ϵ_k is found to be an especially good approximation to the energy of removal in the case of an inner electron (x-ray level).

CORRECTIONS TO THE CENTRAL-FIELD APPROXIMATION

We now turn to the second problem mentioned at the beginning of this section, the correction of the approximate results obtained from the central field. Two terms are omitted in the central-field approximation: the difference between the actual electrostatic interaction between electrons and the average interaction that is included in the central field, and the spin-orbit energy. The latter is an interaction energy between the spin and the orbital motion of each electron and has the form

$$\sum_k \xi(r_k) \mathbf{L}_k \cdot \mathbf{S}_k \quad (47.13)$$

Here, $\mathbf{L}_k$ is the orbital angular momentum operator $\mathbf{r}_k \times \mathbf{p}_k$ of the kth electron and has the properties of the $\mathbf{J}$ operator introduced in Sec. 27; the eigenvalues of $\mathbf{L}_k^2$ and L_{kz} are given in terms of the quantum numbers l and m_l for the kth electron as $l(l + 1)\hbar^2$ and $m_l \hbar$, respectively. $\mathbf{S}_k$ is the spin angular momentum $\frac{1}{2}\hbar\mathbf{\sigma}_k$ of the kth electron that was introduced in Sec. 41. The function $\xi(r)$ is given by[1]

$$\xi(r) = \frac{1}{2m^2c^2} \frac{1}{r} \frac{dV}{dr} \quad (47.14)$$

in terms of the central-field potential energy $V(r)$.

[1] L. H. Thomas, *Nature* **117**, 514 (1926). This energy is a consequence of relativity and is derived as such in Chap. 13. It was first obtained from the precession of the spin axis of the electron, part of which is of electromagnetic origin (Larmor precession) and part of which comes from relativistic kinematics (Thomas precession).

In considering the effects of these terms, we shall assume that the perturbed eigenfunctions, which are linear combinations of various configuration wave functions, have only negligibly small amounts of all but one configuration mixed in them. From Eq. (31.10), it is apparent that this is the case if the interconfiguration matrix elements of the perturbation are small in comparison with the energy intervals between unperturbed configuration energies.

It can be shown that the part of the summation in (47.13) that includes electrons in full shells is zero, since the function ξ is the same for all electrons in a shell and the contributions from electrons with opposite m_l and m_s cancel. Thus the electrons in full shells can be ignored and the summation extended only over the remaining electrons. The case in which there is just one electron outside full shells is of interest in connection with the ground state and low excited states of the alkali atoms; it will be discussed in some detail in the next section. For the present, we consider very briefly the more general situation, always assuming that each atomic state is based on just one configuration of the electrons.

LS COUPLING SCHEME

There are, in general, a number of states that belong to the same configuration and that are degenerate in the central-field approximation. These states differ in the assignment of m_l and m_s quantum numbers to the individual electrons. The theory of complex spectra consists in determining the linear combinations of such suitably antisymmetrized wave functions that diagonalize the perturbation to first order (see Sec. 31), along with the corresponding perturbed energy levels.

The most usual situation is that in which the hitherto-neglected electrostatic terms are larger than the spin-orbit energy; this is called the *Russell-Saunders case*.[1] States of the same configuration can be classified as eigenfunctions of any dynamical variables that commute with the hamiltonian and hence are constants of the motion (see Sec. 24). When all perturbations are included, the only true constants of the motion are the total parity and the total angular momentum $\mathbf{J}$ of the electrons

$$\mathbf{J} = \mathbf{L} + \mathbf{S} = \sum_k (\mathbf{L}_k + \mathbf{S}_k) \tag{47.15}$$

$\mathbf{J}$ is a constant because the angles that specify the orientation of the atom as a whole, and that are the canonically conjugate variables to the components of $\mathbf{J}$, do not appear in the hamiltonian of an isolated atom. When the electrostatic perturbation is included but the spin-orbit energy neglected, the same argument can be applied to show that the total orbital

[1] H. N. Russell and F. A. Saunders, *Astrophys. J.* **61**, 38 (1925).

angular momentum **L** and the total spin angular momentum **S** are separately constants of the motion. The individual $\mathbf{S}_k$ need not be constants, even though no spin-dependent forces act in this approximation, since the use of antisymmetric wave functions couples the spins to the electrostatic energy (see the discussion of the excited states of helium in Sec. 41).

A state can be specified by the quantum numbers, J, L, S, M, M_L, and M_S, which are connected with eigenvalues of angular momentum operators through

$$\mathbf{J}^2 = J(J + 1)\hbar^2 \qquad J_z = M\hbar$$
$$\mathbf{L}^2 = L(L + 1)\hbar^2 \qquad L_z = M_L\hbar \qquad (47.16)$$
$$\mathbf{S}^2 = S(S + 1)\hbar^2 \qquad S_z = M_S\hbar$$

When the spin-orbit energy is neglected, the electrostatic energy separates states of different L; in some cases, only particular S values are permitted because of the exclusion principle. Only two of the other four quantum numbers are independent, and so we can use either LSM_LM_S or $LSJM$ to specify a state. Because of the spherical symmetry of the hamiltonian with respect to its space and spin parts separately, the energy is independent of the directional quantum numbers M_L and M_S, and there are $(2L + 1)(2S + 1)$ degenerate states. For given L and S, the states specified by J and M are linear combinations of those specified by M_L and M_S, so that the same amount of degeneracy appears in the $LSJM$ representation; these linear combinations can be expressed in terms of the Clebsch-Gordan coefficients discussed in Sec. 28. This is called the LS *coupling scheme*, since the individual L_k are coupled together to form the total L, and the individual S_k to form the total S.

If now the spin-orbit energy is included, L and S are no longer constants of the motion, although J and M still are. However, we assume that states of different L and S are sufficiently well separated by the electrostatic energy so that their mixing due to spin-orbit energy can be neglected. This is analogous to the earlier assumption that different configurations are sufficiently well separated by the central field so that their mixing due to the electrostatic energy can be neglected. States of different J in the $LSJM$ representation are now split apart by the spin-orbit energy; the energy is still independent of M, so that there are $2J + 1$ degenerate states. A Russell-Saunders state is usually written in the form $^4D_{\frac{1}{2}}$, where the superscript is the *multiplicity* $2S + 1$, the letter (now capitalized) is the L value according to the code given earlier in this section, and the subscript is the J value; in this case $S = \frac{3}{2}$, $L = 2$, and $J = \frac{1}{2}$. Since $\mathbf{J} = \mathbf{L} + \mathbf{S}$, the triangle rule discussed at the beginning of Sec. 28 shows that J can only be one of the numbers $L + S$, $L + S - 1$, . . . , $|L - S|$.

SELECTION RULES

The selection rules in the Russell-Saunders case can be obtained from the discussion of Sec. 46. Only one electron is involved in a transition, so that in an allowed transition the configuration changes through a change in one of the l's by one unit; this also changes the parity. Since the electric dipole moment does not involve the spins, and the spin functions for different S are orthogonal (see Prob. 4), S does not change in an allowed transition. The conservation of angular momentum between atom and radiation field further requires that J and L each change by 1 or 0. Transitions between states both of which have $J = 0$ are strictly forbidden.

Intersystem lines that join states of different multiplicity (change in S) sometimes occur and indicate a partial breakdown of LS coupling. The very intense mercury resonance line at 2537 Å is an intersystem line: $^3P_1 \rightarrow {}^1S_0$. This transition is allowed so far as the changes in J, L, configuration, and parity are concerned but not as regards the change in S. The $^3P_1$ state is partially mixed by the spin-orbit energy with a higher singlet ($S = 0$) state of the same J and parity, and this makes an electric dipole transition possible.

jj COUPLING SCHEME

The opposite approximation to that involved in LS coupling assumes that the spin-orbit energy is large in comparison with the electrostatic energy. If the latter is neglected, each electron can be characterized by the quantum numbers $nljm$ rather than nlm_lm_s, where $(\mathbf{L}_k + \mathbf{S}_k)^2 = j(j + 1)\hbar^2$ and $L_{kz} + S_{kz} = m\hbar$. The electrostatic energy then splits apart states of different J.

This is called the *jj coupling scheme*, since the orbital and spin angular momenta of the individual electrons are coupled together to form j's, from which the states are built up. It is mainly of interest in heavy atoms, where the large $V(r)$ makes the spin-orbit energy (47.13) the dominant perturbation.

48□THE ALKALI ATOMS

The ground-state configuration of an alkali atom consists of a series of full shells followed by a single s electron and so is $^2S_{\frac{1}{2}}$. The inner rare-gas configuration is so stable that all but quite high excited states of the atom involve only the valence electron. Thus the alkalis can be treated to quite good approximation in terms of a model in which a single electron moves in a spherically symmetric noncoulomb potential energy $V(r)$. In this section we calculate the energy levels and the intensities of allowed transitions in the absence and presence of an external magnetic field.

DOUBLET SEPARATION

The configuration of an alkali atom can be specified by a single pair of quantum numbers nl. Since there is only one electron, the perturbing electrostatic term mentioned in the preceding section does not appear. In the absence of external fields the hamiltonian, including the spin-orbit energy (47.13), is

$$H = -\frac{\hbar^2}{2m} \nabla^2 + V(r) + \xi(r)\mathbf{L} \cdot \mathbf{S} \qquad (48.1)$$

where $\xi(r)$ is given by (47.14). As in Sec. 47, we neglect the mixing of different configurations produced by the spin-orbit energy and regard this term as a perturbation that removes the $m_l m_s$ degeneracy within each configuration. The total angular momentum $\mathbf{J} = \mathbf{L} + \mathbf{S}$ of the valence electron is a constant of the motion (see Prob. 5), so that states can be designated by jm instead of $m_l m_s$, where $\mathbf{J}^2 = j(j + 1)\hbar^2$ and $J_z = m\hbar$. The states of different j have different energies, but there is still a $(2j + 1)$-fold degeneracy due to m. The removal of the m degeneracy by a magnetic field is discussed later in this section.

The difference in energy between states of different j is due to the $\mathbf{L} \cdot \mathbf{S}$ term in (48.1) and can be found from its expectation value or diagonal matrix element [see Eq. (31.8)]. We have the operator relation

$$\mathbf{J}^2 = (\mathbf{L} + \mathbf{S})^2 = \mathbf{L}^2 + \mathbf{S}^2 + 2\mathbf{L} \cdot \mathbf{S} \qquad (48.2)$$

Since l, j, and s are all good quantum numbers ($s = \frac{1}{2}$ for one electron), Eq. (48.2) can be solved for the diagonal matrix element of $\mathbf{L} \cdot \mathbf{S}$:

$$\langle lj|\mathbf{L} \cdot \mathbf{S}|lj \rangle = \tfrac{1}{2}[j(j + 1) - l(l + 1) - \tfrac{3}{4}]\hbar^2 \qquad (48.3)$$

Now if l is different from 0, j can be either $l + \frac{1}{2}$ or $l - \frac{1}{2}$. Thus the first-order perturbation arising from $\xi(r)\mathbf{L} \cdot \mathbf{S}$ is

$$\begin{array}{ll} \tfrac{1}{2}l\zeta_{nl} & \text{if } j = l + \tfrac{1}{2} \\ -\tfrac{1}{2}(l + 1)\zeta_{nl} & \text{if } j = l - \tfrac{1}{2} \\ \zeta_{nl} \equiv \hbar^2 \displaystyle\int_0^\infty |R_{nl}(r)|^2 \xi(r)\, r^2 dr & l > 0 \end{array} \qquad (48.4)$$

where $R_{nl}(r)$ is the normalized radial part of the unperturbed eigenfunction associated with the nl configuration. Since $V(r)$ represents an attractive potential energy, $\xi(r)$ given by (47.14) is positive and ζ_{nl} is positive. Thus (48.4) shows that the state with higher j has the higher energy. The pair of states is called a *doublet*; the doublet structure characterizes all the moderately excited levels of the alkali atoms except those for which $l = 0$, in which case j can only be $\frac{1}{2}$.

The doublet separations can be calculated from (48.4) if the radial function is known. We can get a rough estimate of their dependence on n by using the hydrogenic wave functions given in Eq. (16.24) and assuming that $V(r)$ has the coulomb form $-Ze^2/r$. Substitution into (47.14) and (48.4) gives, with the help of the generating function (16.21) for the associated Laguerre polynomials,

$$\zeta_{nl} = \frac{\hbar^2 Ze^2}{2m^2c^2} \int_0^\infty \frac{1}{r} R_{nl}^2(r)\, dr$$

$$= \frac{e^2\hbar^2 Z^4}{2m^2c^2 a_0{}^3 n^3 l(l+\frac{1}{2})(l+1)} \tag{48.5}$$

This is valid only for $l > 0$; the singularity in $\xi(r)$ at $r = 0$ makes the integral for ζ_{n0} diverge there, so that the perturbation approximation is not valid. It follows from (48.4) and (48.5) that the doublet separation is proportional to n^{-3}, and this is in fair agreement with observation. The absolute value of the doublet separation and its dependence on l are not given at all by this simple theory, since the effective Z is difficult to estimate and depends markedly on l because of penetration.[1]

DOUBLET INTENSITY

We now calculate the relative intensities of the two lines of the allowed doublet $^2P_{\frac{3}{2}} \to {}^2S_{\frac{1}{2}}$ and $^2P_{\frac{1}{2}} \to {}^2S_{\frac{1}{2}}$, under the assumption that the radial wave functions are the same for the two excited ^2P states. Transitions of this type give rise to the principal series in the alkali spectra. From Eq. (45.22), the spontaneous transition probabilities, and hence the observed intensities if the two P states are equally likely to be occupied, are proportional to the squares of the dipole matrix elements.[2]

The dependence of the two excited ^2P states and the ground ^2S state on the angular and spin coordinates of the electron is obtained by finding linear combinations of products of the four spherical harmonics $Y_{1,1}(\theta,\phi)$, $Y_{1,0}(\theta,\phi)$, $Y_{1,-1}(\theta,\phi)$, and $Y_{0,0}(\theta,\phi)$, and the two spin wave functions $(+)$ and $(-)$, that are eigenfunctions of $\mathbf{J}^2$ and J_z (see Secs. 14 and 41 for discussion of the angle and spin functions). These combinations can be obtained from the Clebsch-Gordan coefficients given in Eq. (28.13):

$$
\begin{aligned}
&{}^2P_{\frac{3}{2}}\begin{cases} m = & \frac{3}{2} & (+)Y_{1,1} \\ & \frac{1}{2} & 3^{-\frac{1}{2}}[2^{\frac{1}{2}}(+)Y_{1,0}+(-)Y_{1,1}] \\ & -\frac{1}{2} & 3^{-\frac{1}{2}}[2^{\frac{1}{2}}(-)Y_{1,0}+(+)Y_{1,-1}] \\ & -\frac{3}{2} & (-)Y_{1,-1} \end{cases} \\[4pt]
&{}^2P_{\frac{1}{2}}\begin{cases} m = & \frac{1}{2} & 3^{-\frac{1}{2}}[-(+)Y_{1,0}+2^{\frac{1}{2}}(-)Y_{1,1}] \\ & -\frac{1}{2} & 3^{-\frac{1}{2}}[(-)Y_{1,0}-2^{\frac{1}{2}}(+)Y_{1,-1}] \end{cases} \\[4pt]
&{}^2S_{\frac{1}{2}}\begin{cases} m = & \frac{1}{2} & (+)Y_{0,0} \\ & -\frac{1}{2} & (-)Y_{0,0} \end{cases}
\end{aligned}
\tag{48.6}
$$

[1] The effect of the spin-orbit interaction on the energy levels of hydrogen is found in the next chapter as part of an exact relativistic calculation.

[2] The energy difference between the two upper states is so small that the ω^3 factor in (45.22) does not affect the intensity ratio appreciably.

The wave functions (48.6) can be used to calculate the matrix elements of $x = r \sin \theta \cos \phi$, $y = r \sin \theta \sin \phi$, and $z = r \cos \theta$. We assume that the radial functions associated with (48.6) are all the same, so that the radial part of the matrix-element integral is a common factor throughout. The angle parts of the integrals are easily evaluated by making use of the explicit expressions for the Y's in terms of θ and ϕ given in (14.16).[1] The products of spin functions follow the simple rules $(+)^\dagger(+) = 1$, $(-)^\dagger(+) = 0$, etc. In this way we obtain the following values for the squares of the magnitudes of the indicated matrix elements, expressed in units of $\frac{1}{18}$ of the common radial factor:

$$
\begin{array}{llll}
^2P_{\frac{3}{2}} \rightarrow {}^2S_{\frac{1}{2}} \begin{cases}
m = \frac{3}{2} \text{ to } m = & \frac{1}{2} & |x|^2 = |y|^2 = 3 & |z|^2 = 0 \\
\frac{3}{2} \text{ to } & -\frac{1}{2} & |x|^2 = |y|^2 = |z|^2 = 0 & \\
\frac{1}{2} \text{ to } & \frac{1}{2} & |x|^2 = |y|^2 = 0 & |z|^2 = 4 \\
\frac{1}{2} \text{ to } & -\frac{1}{2} & |x|^2 = |y|^2 = 1 & |z|^2 = 0
\end{cases} \\[2em]
^2P_{\frac{1}{2}} \rightarrow {}^2S_{\frac{1}{2}} \begin{cases}
m = \frac{1}{2} \text{ to } m = & \frac{1}{2} & |x|^2 = |y|^2 = 0 & |z|^2 = 2 \\
\frac{1}{2} \text{ to } & -\frac{1}{2} & |x|^2 = |y|^2 = 2 & |z|^2 = 0
\end{cases}
\end{array}
$$

$$(48.7)$$

Similar results are obtained for the transitions that start from $m = -\frac{1}{2}$ and $-\frac{3}{2}$; altogether, they confirm the m selection rules of Sec. 46.

It follows from (48.7) that the sum of the intensities of all the lines that originate on each of the four $^2P_{\frac{3}{2}}$ states is equal to 6, in the above units. It is to be expected that these sums are equal since the four values of m differ only in the orientation of the angular momentum, and this should not affect the intensity. However, the total intensity from each of the two $^2P_{\frac{1}{2}}$ states is also equal to 6. The equality of total intensities from each state formed from a given L and S is a general property of LS coupling; this makes the observed intensity, which is that from all the states that are degenerate with respect to m, proportional to $2J + 1$.[2] In the example considered here, the two lines of the doublet have intensities in the ratio 2:1. This is observed for the lowest doublets of the alkalis, although for the higher doublets the intensity ratio exceeds 2. This is because the spin-orbit energy actually mixes different configurations (^2P states with the same j but different n); the amount of mixing is different for the two j values, so that the two radial functions are not the same. A small admixture of the low-intensity upper states in the high-intensity lowest ^2P states has little effect, whereas in the opposite case there is a large effect on the doublet intensity ratio.[3]

[1] In the general case in which Y_{lm}'s with $l > 1$ are involved, it is often easier to use a formula for the integral of the product of three spherical harmonics given by J. A. Gaunt; see Condon and Shortley, *op. cit.*, p. 176. Gaunt's formula can be derived by making use of the Clebsch-Gordan coefficients.

[2] Condon and Shortley, *op. cit.*, p. 238.

[3] E. Fermi, *Z. Physik* **59**, 680 (1929).

EFFECT OF A MAGNETIC FIELD[1]

We now consider the effect of a magnetic field on the energy levels and transition intensities of an alkali atom. As discussed in Sec. 31, a contant magnetic field can be represented by the vector potential

$$\mathbf{A} = \tfrac{1}{2}\mathbf{H} \times \mathbf{r} \tag{48.8}$$

and the extra energy associated with the orbital motion of an electron of charge $-e$ is

$$\frac{e}{2mc}\,\mathbf{H} \cdot \mathbf{L} + \frac{e^2}{8mc^2}\,\mathsf{H}^2 r^2 \sin^2 \theta \tag{48.9}$$

where $\mathbf{L} = \mathbf{r} \times \mathbf{p}$ and θ is the angle between $\mathbf{r}$ and $\mathbf{H}$.

The electron also has an intrinsic magnetic moment in the direction of its spin axis. The magnitude of this moment can be determined from comparison between experiment and the theory of the Zeeman effect presented below and is in agreement with the value deduced from Dirac's relativistic theory of the electron (see Chap. 13); it is $-e\hbar/2mc$, or $-e/mc$ times the spin angular momentum of the electron.[2] This is twice the ratio of magnetic moment to angular momentum of a classical charge distribution for which the ratio of charge to mass density is constant. The magnetic moment operator is $-(e/mc)\mathbf{S}$, and the extra energy in a magnetic field is

$$\frac{e}{mc}\,\mathbf{H} \cdot \mathbf{S} \tag{48.10}$$

The ratio of (48.9) to the kinetic energy is quite small for magnetic field strengths commonly attainable in the laboratory (see Prob. 6). It is therefore permissible to use perturbation theory to find the effect of the H terms on the wave functions and energy levels. In most cases, only the linear terms need be considered. However, for very strong fields and large orbits, the quadratic terms can become of interest (see the discussion of the quadratic Zeeman effect below). Also, the diamagnetic susceptibility can be obtained from the terms in the energy that are proportional to H^2.

WEAK-FIELD CASE

For the present, we consider only the first-order effects of H. The hamiltonian (48.1) then becomes, with (48.9) and (48.10),

$$H = -\frac{\hbar^2}{2m}\,\nabla^2 + V(r) + \xi(r)\mathbf{L} \cdot \mathbf{S} + \epsilon(L_z + 2S_z),\ \epsilon \equiv \frac{e\mathsf{H}}{2mc} \tag{48.11}$$

---

[1] W. Heisenberg and P. Jordan, *Z. Physik* **37**, 263 (1926).

[2] The quantity $e\hbar/2mc$ is called the *Bohr magneton*, and is equal to 0.927×10^{-20} erg/oersted.

where the field is along the z axis. The magnetic field can now be classified as weak or strong according as the last term in (48.11) is small or large in comparison with the spin-orbit energy. The *Zeeman effect* usually refers to the weak-field case, and the *Paschen-Back effect* to the strong-field case, although the term Zeeman effect is sometimes used to include all magnetic effects.

In the weak-field case, we can make use of the wave functions (48.6), which are eigenfunctions of $\mathbf{J}^2$ and J_z. It is easily verified that the magnetic energy $\epsilon(L_z + 2S_z) = \epsilon(J_z + S_z)$ has matrix elements between states of different j but not between states of the same j and different m. We neglect the former, because of the relatively large energy separation between states of different j. Thus the magnetic energy is diagonal with respect to m for each j and shifts the energy of each of the states (48.6) by its expectation value for that state. In each case, J_z is diagonal, and so its expectation value is $m\hbar$. The expectation value of S_z for the $^2P_{\frac{3}{2}}$ state with $m = \frac{1}{2}$, for example, is

$$\iint 3^{-\frac{1}{2}}[2^{\frac{1}{2}}(+)^\dagger Y_{1,0}^* + (-)^\dagger Y_{1,1}^*]\tfrac{1}{2}\hbar\sigma_z 3^{-\frac{1}{2}}[2^{\frac{1}{2}}(+)Y_{1,0}$$
$$+ (-)Y_{1,1}] \sin\theta \, d\theta \, d\phi$$
$$= \frac{\hbar}{6} \iint [2^{\frac{1}{2}}(+)^\dagger Y_{1,0}^* + (-)^\dagger Y_{1,1}^*][2^{\frac{1}{2}}(+)Y_{1,0}$$
$$- (-)Y_{1,1}] \sin\theta \, d\theta \, d\phi$$
$$= \frac{\hbar}{6}(2 - 1) = \frac{\hbar}{6}$$

with the help of (41.5) and the orthonormality of the spin functions and the Y's. Thus the magnetic energy of this state is $\epsilon\hbar(\frac{1}{2} + \frac{1}{6}) = \frac{2}{3}\epsilon\hbar$. This and the similar results for the other states (48.6) can be expressed in terms of the *Landé g factor*; the magnetic energy is

$$\epsilon m\hbar g$$

$$g = \tfrac{4}{3} \text{ for } {}^2P_{\frac{3}{2}} \qquad g = \tfrac{2}{3} \text{ for } {}^2P_{\frac{1}{2}} \qquad g = 2 \text{ for } {}^2S_{\frac{1}{2}} \qquad (48.12)$$

The weak-field transition intensities are given directly by (48.7). According to the discussion of Sec. 46, the radiation from the transitions in which m changes by unity is circularly polarized when viewed along the field and linearly polarized perpendicular to the field when viewed in the xy plane; these are called the σ components (from the German *senkrecht*). When m does not change in a transition, the radiation does not appear along the field and is polarized parallel to the field (π components) when viewed in the xy plane. For observation in the xy plane, the π intensity is proportional to $|z|^2$ in (48.7) and the σ intensity is proportional to either $|x|^2$ or $|y|^2$ (but not to their sum).

STRONG-FIELD CASE

If the magnetic energy is large in comparison with the spin-orbit energy in (48.11), the field is said to be strong. In this case the states within a given nl configuration are better specified by m_l and m_s than by j and m as in (48.6). The magnetic energy is then diagonal and has the value

$$\epsilon\hbar(m_l + 2m_s) \tag{48.13}$$

If the spin-orbit energy is neglected for the moment, the eight wave functions that correspond to (48.6), and their energy shifts (48.13), are

$$
\begin{array}{lll}
{}^2P \left\{ \begin{array}{ll}
(+)Y_{1,1} & 2\epsilon\hbar \\
(+)Y_{1,0} & \epsilon\hbar \\
(+)Y_{1,-1} & 0 \\
(-)Y_{1,1} & 0 \\
(-)Y_{1,0} & -\epsilon\hbar \\
(-)Y_{1,-1} & -2\epsilon\hbar
\end{array} \right. \\[2em]
{}^2S \left\{ \begin{array}{ll}
(+)Y_{0,0} & \epsilon\hbar \\
(-)Y_{0,0} & -\epsilon\hbar
\end{array} \right.
\end{array}
\tag{48.14}
$$

In the event that the magnetic field is very strong, the spin-orbit energy is most simply treated as a perturbation on the wave functions (48.14). We consider instead the general case, which includes all relative magnitudes of the magnetic and spin-orbit energies. This is done by working with the matrix of the last two terms in (48.11) in either of the representations (48.6) or (48.14). The eigenvalues of the matrix are the energy levels, and the transformation that diagonalizes the matrix gives the wave functions in accordance with the discussion of Sec. 31. We start from (48.14), and notice at once that the two ^2S wave functions are the same as the $^2S_{\frac{1}{2}}$ functions of (48.6). We ignore the effect of the spin-orbit energy on these two states, since it does not shift them with respect to each other; the energy shifts due to the magnetic field are $\pm\epsilon\hbar$. Similarly, the first and last of the six ^2P wave functions are the same as the $^2P_{\frac{3}{2}}$ functions of (48.6) with $m = \pm\frac{3}{2}$; their energies are $\frac{1}{2}\zeta \pm 2\epsilon\hbar$, where ζ is given by (48.4).

The four remaining ^2P wave functions combine in pairs, according to whether $m = m_l + m_s$ is equal to $\frac{1}{2}$ or $-\frac{1}{2}$. It is enough to consider just one of these pairs, say that for which $m = \frac{1}{2}$: $(+)Y_{1,0}$ and $(-)Y_{1,1}$. The matrix of the magnetic and spin-orbit energies in the representation specified by these two states can be found with the help of the angular momentum matrices (27.26):

$$
\begin{bmatrix}
\epsilon\hbar & 2^{-\frac{1}{2}}\zeta \\
2^{-\frac{1}{2}}\zeta & -\frac{1}{2}\zeta
\end{bmatrix}
\tag{48.15}
$$

In accordance with the discussion of Eq. (22.21), the eigenvalues of the matrix (48.15) are found by solving the secular equation

$$\begin{vmatrix} \epsilon\hbar - \lambda & 2^{-\frac{1}{2}}\zeta \\ 2^{-\frac{1}{2}}\zeta & -\frac{1}{2}\zeta - \lambda \end{vmatrix} = \lambda^2 + (\tfrac{1}{2}\zeta - \epsilon\hbar)\lambda - \tfrac{1}{2}\zeta(\epsilon\hbar + \zeta) = 0$$

In this way we obtain for the energy shifts of these two states

$$\lambda_\pm = \tfrac{1}{2}[\epsilon\hbar - \tfrac{1}{2}\zeta \pm (\epsilon^2\hbar^2 + \epsilon\hbar\zeta + \tfrac{9}{4}\zeta^2)^{\frac{1}{2}}] \tag{48.16}$$

In the weak- and strong-field limits, the upper and lower signs in (48.16) lead to

$$\lambda_+ \to \tfrac{1}{2}\zeta + \tfrac{2}{3}\epsilon\hbar \qquad \text{and} \qquad \lambda_- \to -\zeta + \tfrac{1}{3}\epsilon\hbar \qquad \text{for } \frac{\epsilon\hbar}{\zeta} \to 0$$

$$\lambda_+ \to \epsilon\hbar \qquad \text{and} \qquad \lambda_- \to -\tfrac{1}{2}\zeta \qquad \text{for } \frac{\zeta}{\epsilon\hbar} \to 0 \tag{48.17}$$

Equations (48.17) show that the state that corresponds to the upper sign in (48.16) is the weak-field state $j = \tfrac{3}{2}$, $m = \tfrac{1}{2}$ and the strong-field state $m_l = 0$, $m_s = \tfrac{1}{2}$. Similarly, the lower sign in (48.16) corresponds to the weak-field state $j = \tfrac{1}{2}$, $m = \tfrac{1}{2}$ and to the strong field state $m_l = 1$, $m_s = -\tfrac{1}{2}$.

The transition intensities can be found in the general case by calculating the matrix elements of x, y, and z with the help of the eigenfunctions of $\xi(r)\mathbf{L} \cdot \mathbf{S} + \epsilon(L_z + 2S_z)$. These eigenfunctions are the first, sixth, seventh, and eighth of (48.14) and linear combinations of the other four functions that are obtained from the matrix that diagonalizes (48.15).

QUADRATIC ZEEMAN EFFECT

For very strong magnetic fields and large orbits or n values, effects of second order in H become appreciable. From (48.5), it is apparent that the effect of the spin-orbit energy becomes very small for large n, and a useful approximation is obtained by neglecting this part of the energy entirely. In this case the electron spin commutes with the hamiltonian, so that m_s is a constant of the motion, and the spin can be ignored. The hamiltonian (48.11) is then replaced by

$$H = -\frac{\hbar^2}{2m} \nabla^2 + V(r) + \epsilon L_z + \tfrac{1}{2}m\epsilon^2 r^2 \sin^2\theta \tag{48.18}$$

Since $L_z = -i\hbar\partial/\partial\phi$ commutes with (48.18), m_l is a good quantum number, and the only effect of the term ϵL_z is to displace each energy level by the amount $\epsilon\hbar m_l$. Thus for large n we need be concerned only with the effect of the last term $H' \equiv \tfrac{1}{2}m\epsilon^2 r^2 \sin^2\theta$ in (48.18), for particular values of m_l and m_s.[1]

[1] L. I. Schiff and H. Snyder, *Phys. Rev.* **55**, 59 (1939).

It follows from the work of Sec. 16 that the effective radius of a hydrogen atom is roughly proportional to n^2. For alkali-atom states of large n, $V(r)$ has practically the coulomb form, and the wave functions are very nearly hydrogenic functions. Thus H' increases about as n^4. This means that n is no longer a good quantum number for sufficiently large n. For smaller n, l may not be a good quantum number since H' has off-diagonal matrix elements between states of different l, and the unperturbed energies of these states lie close together (they fail to be degenerate only because the wave functions for the smallest values of l penetrate the inner full shells). In this region, the perturbed energy levels can be found by diagonalizing the matrix of H' for given values of n, m_l, and m_s, when the $n - |m_l|$ rows and columns are labeled by l. The structure of the H' matrix can be inferred from Gaunt's formula (footnote 1, page 439); since $\sin^2 \theta$ can be expressed in terms of spherical harmonics of order 0 and 2, the only nonvanishing matrix elements $\langle l|H'|l'\rangle = H'_{ll'}$ are for $l - l' = 0$, ± 2. Thus the H' matrix has the form (if, for example, $m_l = 0$)

$$\begin{bmatrix} H'_{00} & 0 & H'_{02} & 0 & 0 & \cdots \\ 0 & H'_{11} & 0 & H'_{13} & 0 & \cdots \\ H'_{20} & 0 & H'_{22} & 0 & H'_{24} & \cdots \\ 0 & H'_{31} & 0 & H'_{33} & 0 & \cdots \\ 0 & 0 & H'_{42} & 0 & H'_{44} & \cdots \\ \cdots & \cdots & \cdots & \cdots & \cdots & \cdots \end{bmatrix} \tag{48.19}$$

The matrix (48.19) is equivalent to two independent matrices, one for even and the other for odd l, each with about $\frac{1}{2}n$ rows and columns. Direct diagonalization of these would be quite arduous for large n. However, the resulting energy levels are so close together that they cannot be resolved spectroscopically, so that there is little reason to determine the individual levels. What can be observed is the aggregate of transitions between the ^2S ground state ($l = 0$) and the group of states that are obtained by diagonalization of (48.19); these appear to be a single broadened "line". Allowed transitions occur only by virtue of the state with $l = 1$ that is mixed into each of the eigenfunctions of (48.19), so that m_l can be only 0 or ± 1. This makes it possible to find the center of gravity of this line and its mean-square breadth without diagonalizing H', as we now show.

The unperturbed wave functions can be chosen so that H' is a real matrix. Then the unitary matrix S that diagonalizes H' can be real, so that Eq. (22.23) or Eq. (23.12) can be written

$$SH'S^\dagger = E \tag{48.20}$$

where $S^\dagger$ is now the transpose of S and E is diagonal. In terms of matrix elements, this equation is

$$\sum_{k,l} S_{ik} H'_{kl} S_{jl} = E_i \delta_{ij}$$

The new eigenfunctions u_i that correspond to the energy eigenvalues E_i are given in terms of the unperturbed wave functions v_l by (23.6):

$$u_i = \sum_l S_{il} v_l$$

If now we neglect the dependence of the radiative transition probability on energy over the small range of energies involved in this group of states, the transition probability is proportional to the square of the amount of v_1 in each u_i, or to S_{i1}^2. Thus the energy levels E_i should be weighted in proportion to S_{i1}^2. The center of gravity of the group of perturbed energy levels is given by

$$E_{av} = \sum_i E_i S_{i1}^2 = H'_{11}$$

since (48.20) can be inverted to give $H' = S^\dagger E S$. In similar fashion, the the mean-square breadth of the line is

$$\sum_i (E_i - E_{av})^2 S_{i1}^2 = \sum E_i^2 S_{i1}^2 - E_{av}^2$$

$$= \sum_l H'^2_{1l} - E_{av}^2 = H'^2_{13}$$

Thus only two of the matrix elements of H' need be calculated. It is apparent that both the displacement (apart from the factor $e\hbar m_l$) and the breadth of the line are proportional to H^2.

49□MOLECULES

Molecules are considerably more complex in structure than atoms, and correspondingly less has been accomplished in the quantitative application of quantum mechanics to molecular problems. In this section, a general account of the nature of molecular energy levels is followed by a simple explicit calculation for the hydrogen molecule and a somewhat more general treatment of diatomic molecules.[1]

[1] For more detailed discussions, see G. Herzberg, "Molecular Spectra and Molecular Structure," 2d ed. (Van Nostrand, Princeton, N.J., 1950); L. Pauling and E. B. Wilson, Jr., "Introduction to Quantum Mechanics," chaps. X, XII, and XIII (McGraw-Hill, New York, 1935); J. C. Slater, "Quantum Theory of Molecules and Solids," vol. 1 (McGraw-Hill, New York, 1963).

CLASSIFICATION OF ENERGY LEVELS

The simplifying feature that is the basis of all molecular approximations is the large ratio of nuclear mass to electron mass. As we shall see shortly, this implies that the energy associated with the motion of the nuclei is much smaller than that associated with the motion of the electrons about the nuclei. Since the period of a motion is of the order of $\hbar$ divided by its energy, the nuclear periods are correspondingly longer than the electronic periods. It is then a good approximation to regard the nuclei as fixed in calculating the electronic motion. Moreover, the nuclear motion can be calculated under the assumption that the electrons have their steady motion for each instantaneous arrangement of the nuclei (adiabatic approximation).

The nuclei are expected to have a stable equilibrium arrangement somewhere between a completely collapsed structure (which is unstable, since the nuclei are positively charged and repel each other at short distances) and a completely dispersed structure (which is not the most stable structure if a molecule exists). The nuclear motions can then be classified into translations and rotations of the quasi-rigid equilibrium arrangement and internal vibrations of the nuclei about equilibrium. As with atoms, the translational motion is the same as that of a free particle [see the discussion of Eqs. (16.5)] and gives rise to no nonclassical features.

We thus arrive at a classification of molecular energy levels into *electronic*, *vibrational*, and *rotational* types and proceed to estimate their relative orders of magnitude. Suppose that the molecule has linear dimensions of order a. Then the energy E_e associated with the motion of a valence electron (one that occupies roughly the whole of the molecular volume, rather than one that is bound in an inner shell close to a nucleus) is of order $\hbar^2/ma^2$, where m is the electronic mass. This can be inferred by an argument like that given near the beginning of Sec. 9, by noting that the momentum uncertainty of the electron is at least of order $\hbar/a$, so that its minimum kinetic energy is $\hbar^2/ma^2$. We thus obtain

$$E_e \sim \frac{\hbar^2}{ma^2} \tag{49.1}$$

For values of a of the order of a few angstrom units, this corresponds to transition frequencies in the visible and ultraviolet regions of the spectrum.

To estimate the vibrational energy, we regard each of the normal modes as a harmonic oscillator with which is associated a mass M and a stiffness constant K_0. M will be of the order of a typical nuclear mass. K_0 can be estimated by noting that a displacement along a normal mode by the order of the molecular size a must produce an energy change of the order of the electronic energy E_e, since such a large displacement would produce a substantial distortion of the electronic wave function; we thus put $K_0 \sim E_e/a^2$. Then the energy E_v associated with a fairly low mode of vibration is, from (13.8),

$$E_v \sim \hbar \left(\frac{K_0}{M}\right)^{\frac{1}{2}} \sim \frac{\hbar^2}{(mM)^{\frac{1}{2}}a^2} \sim \left(\frac{m}{M}\right)^{\frac{1}{2}} E_e \tag{49.2}$$

where use has been made of (49.1). E_v is roughly a hundred times smaller than E_e and corresponds to transitions in the near infrared.

The rotational energy E_r can be estimated from the moment of inertia of the molecule, which is of order Ma^2. As would be expected, the angular momentum of a fairly low mode of rotation turns out to be of order $\hbar$, so that

$$E_r \sim \frac{\hbar^2}{Ma^2} \sim \frac{m}{M} E_e \tag{49.3}$$

This is about a hundred times smaller than E_v and corresponds to transitions in the far infrared.

It might be expected from Eqs. (49.2) and (49.3) that the electronic, vibrational, and rotational energy levels can be obtained as successively higher orders in an approximation that is based in some way on the small ratio m/M (which is usually in the range 10^{-3} to 10^{-4}). This was shown to be the case by Born and Oppenheimer.[1] They used as expansion parameter the ratio of a typical nuclear vibrational displacement to the internuclear distance (which is of order a). An oscillator of energy E_v and stiffness constant K_0 has a displacement of order

$$\left(\frac{E_v}{K_0}\right)^{\frac{1}{2}} \sim a \left(\frac{E_v}{E_e}\right)^{\frac{1}{2}}$$

so that the expansion parameter is

$$\left(\frac{E_v}{E_e}\right)^{\frac{1}{2}} \sim \left(\frac{m}{M}\right)^{\frac{1}{4}} \tag{49.4}$$

In terms of this, the electronic energy is of zero order, the vibrational energy of second order, and the rotational energy of fourth order; the first- and third-order energies vanish.

WAVE EQUATION

The time-independent Schrödinger equation for a molecule is readily written down:

$$\left(-\frac{\hbar^2}{2m} \sum_{i=1}^{n} \nabla_i^2 - \sum_{j=1}^{N} \frac{\hbar^2}{2M_j} \nabla_j^2 + V\right)\psi = E\psi \tag{49.5}$$

[1] M. Born and J. R. Oppenheimer, *Ann. Physik* **84,** 457 (1927).

There are n electrons and N nuclei, and V is the sum of the electrostatic interactions between all pairs of them. It is apparent that the nuclear kinetic-energy terms are of fourth order in the expansion parameter (49.4). If they are neglected, the wave function ψ involves the nuclear coordinates $\mathbf{R}_j$ only parametrically, and (49.5) is a wave equation in the $\mathbf{r}_i$ for the motion of the electrons with respect to nuclei that are fixed in space. In this case, ψ is approximately $u_{\mathbf{R}_j}(\mathbf{r}_i)$ and corresponds to the energy eigenvalue $U(\mathbf{R}_j)$. The nuclear motion can then be found by regarding $U(\mathbf{R}_j)$ as a potential function and using it to obtain a nuclear wave function $w(\mathbf{R}_j)$.

We therefore write ψ in the form

$$\psi(\mathbf{r}_i,\mathbf{R}_j) = u_{\mathbf{R}_j}(\mathbf{r}_i)w(\mathbf{R}_j) \tag{49.6}$$

where u satisfies the equation

$$\left(-\frac{\hbar^2}{2m}\sum_{i=1}^{n}\nabla_i^2 + V\right)u_{\mathbf{R}_j}(\mathbf{r}_i) = U(\mathbf{R}_j)u_{\mathbf{R}_j}(\mathbf{r}_i) \tag{49.7}$$

For each arrangement of the nuclei, $U(\mathbf{R}_j)$ is obtained as an eigenvalue of Eq. (49.7). There will, in general, be several solutions that correspond to different electronic states of the molecule; care must be taken to ensure that u and U change continuously with $\mathbf{R}_j$, especially if the system is degenerate. Substitution of (49.6) into (49.5) gives, with the help of (49.7),

$$\left[-\sum_{j=1}^{N}\frac{\hbar^2}{2M_j}\nabla_j^2 + U(\mathbf{R}_j)\right]\psi = E\psi$$

which can be rewritten

$$u_{\mathbf{R}_j}(\mathbf{r}_i)\left[-\sum_{j=1}^{N}\frac{\hbar^2}{2M_j}\nabla_j^2 + U(\mathbf{R}_j) - E\right]w(\mathbf{R}_j)$$

$$= \sum_{j=1}^{N}\frac{\hbar^2}{2M_j}[w(\mathbf{R}_j)\nabla_j^2 u_{\mathbf{R}_j}(\mathbf{r}_i) + 2\nabla_j w(\mathbf{R}_j)\cdot\nabla_j u_{\mathbf{R}_j}(\mathbf{r}_i)] \tag{49.8}$$

If now the dependence of u on $\mathbf{R}_j$ is neglected, the right side of (49.8) drops out, and an approximate wave equation for the nuclear motion is obtained:

$$\left[-\sum_{j=1}^{N}\frac{\hbar^2}{2M_j}\nabla_j^2 + U(\mathbf{R}_j)\right]w(\mathbf{R}_j) = Ew(\mathbf{R}_j) \tag{49.9}$$

The neglect of the $\nabla_j u$ terms derives physically from the smallness of the amplitudes of the nuclear motion in comparison with the equilibrium internuclear distances [smallness of the expansion parameter (49.4)]; this implies that the electronic part u of the wave function does not change much as the nuclei move. Born and Oppenheimer showed formally that this approximation is justified so long as not too high vibrational and rotational modes are excited.

THE HYDROGEN MOLECULE

It is clear from the foregoing discussion that two distinct problems arise in connection with molecular structure. The first is the solution of Eq. (49.7) to obtain electronic wave functions and a potential energy function $U(\mathbf{R}_j)$ of the nuclear coordinates. The second is the solution of (49.9) for the nuclear motion. The first problem can be solved only in the simplest cases. As an example, we now consider in outline an approximate solution for the hydrogen molecule due to Heitler and London.[1] Following this, we discuss the solution of Eq. (49.9) for a general diatomic molecule, making simple assumptions concerning the potential energy U.

The only nuclear coordinate $\mathbf{R}_j$ that appears in (49.7) in the case of the hydrogen molecule is the magnitude R of the distance between the two hydrogen nuclei. The hamiltonian is that given in Eq. (32.11) (see Fig. 27); however, R is no longer large in comparison with $a_0 = \hbar^2/me^2$ so that the approximations implied in (32.11) and (32.12) are no longer useful. Nevertheless, an approximate wave function based on a simple product of two ground-state hydrogen-atom functions gives remarkably good results. The reason for this is that exchange degeneracy (see Sec. 40) is taken into account; the degenerate wave functions for which electron 1 is on nucleus A and electron 2 on nucleus B, and for which electron 1 is on nucleus B and electron 2 on nucleus A, are both used at once. The new feature of the work of Heitler and London was the recognition that an appropriate linear combination of unperturbed degenerate wave functions gives a significantly lower energy than the separate wave functions; it is the basis of the present-day theory of *homopolar binding* in molecules. This property of degeneracy is sometimes referred to as *resonance*. An analogous situation is that in which an interaction between two classical oscillators that are in resonance (same unperturbed frequency) gives rise to a normal mode that has a lower frequency (and also one that has a higher frequency). In a similar way, an interaction between two resonant (degenerate) states in quantum mechanics gives rise to a lower energy eigenvalue (as well as to a higher one).[2] There may of course be more than two degenerate unperturbed states, and the degeneracy need not be of the exchange type.

[1] W. Heitler and F. London, Z. *Physik* **44,** 455 (1927).

[2] This use of the word "resonance" is only remotely related to that which appeared in Sec. 19 in connection with scattering.

POTENTIAL-ENERGY FUNCTION

Equation (49.7) for the hydrogen molecule is

$$[H - U(R)]u_R(\mathbf{r}_1,\mathbf{r}_2) = 0$$

$$H = -\frac{\hbar^2}{2m}(\nabla_1^2 + \nabla_2^2)$$

$$+ e^2\left(\frac{1}{R} + \frac{1}{r_{12}} - \frac{1}{r_{1A}} - \frac{1}{r_{2B}} - \frac{1}{r_{1B}} - \frac{1}{r_{2A}}\right) \quad (49.10)$$

We wish to base our approximate calculation of $U(R)$ on the approximate wave functions

$$u_1(\mathbf{r}_1,\mathbf{r}_2) = u_A(\mathbf{r}_1)u_B(\mathbf{r}_2)$$
$$u_2(\mathbf{r}_1,\mathbf{r}_2) = u_A(\mathbf{r}_2)u_B(\mathbf{r}_1)$$

$$(49.11)$$

where u_A and u_B are ground-state hydrogen wave functions [u_{100} in the notation of (16.24)] based on nuclei A and B, respectively. It must first be noticed that the u_1 and u_2 of (49.11) are eigenfunctions of different unperturbed hamiltonians, so that the degenerate perturbation theory of Sec. 31 is not applicable. This is unlike the situation with the helium atom [see the discussion of (41.7)], where the two exchange-degenerate wave functions are solutions of the same unperturbed hamiltonian.

We can, however, use the variation method of Sec. 32, in which case it is natural to adopt as the trial function an arbitrary linear combination of u_1 and u_2

$$\psi(\mathbf{r}_1,\mathbf{r}_2) = u_1(\mathbf{r}_1,\mathbf{r}_2) + Au_2(\mathbf{r}_1,\mathbf{r}_2) \quad (49.12)$$

where A is the variation parameter. Substitution of (49.12) into (32.5) gives

$$U(R) \leq \frac{(1 + A^2)H_{11} + 2AH_{12}}{1 + A^2 + 2A\gamma} \qquad \gamma \equiv \iint u_1 u_2 \, d^3r_1 \, d^3r_2$$

$$H_{11} = H_{22} \equiv \iint u_1 H u_1 \, d^3r_1 \, d^3r_2 \qquad H_{12} = H_{21}$$
$$\equiv \iint u_1 H u_2 \, d^3r_1 \, d^3r_2 \quad (49.13)$$

These equalities between matrix elements are easily established with the help of Eq. (23.21) when it is remembered that the u's are real and that H is hermitian and symmetrical in the two electrons.

The matrix elements and γ depend on R. For any particular value of R, the derivative of the right side of (49.13) with respect to A is

$$\frac{2(1 - A^2)(H_{12} - \gamma H_{11})}{(1 + A^2 + 2A\gamma)^2}$$

which is zero for $A = \pm 1$. Since the right side of (49.13) is equal to H_{11} when A is $-\infty$, 0, and $+\infty$, one of the points $A = \pm 1$ must be a minimum and the other a maximum. The integrals in (49.13) can be expressed in terms of tabulated functions, and the minimum expectation value of H is obtained with $A = +1$:

$$\psi = u_1 + u_2$$

$$U(R) \leq \frac{H_{11} + H_{12}}{1 + \gamma} \qquad (49.14)$$

The upper limit on $U(R)$ given in (49.14) has the general appearance that is characteristic of the internuclear potential energy of a diatomic molecule (see Fig. 39) and is in good agreement with experiment.[1] Since ψ in (49.14) is symmetric in an interchange of the space coordinates of the two electrons, it must be multiplied by the antisymmetric singlet spin function given as the last of Eqs. (41.6).

It is interesting to compare the symmetry characters of the ground state of the hydrogen molecule and the excited states of the helium atom considered in Sec. 41, from a physical point of view. Because of the exclusion principle, electrons must be in different space states if they have parallel spins and hence tend to keep away from each other. In the excited $1s2s$ state of helium, for example, this reduces the electrostatic repulsion of the electrons and lowers the energy. Thus the triplet states of helium tend to lie lower than the singlet state of the same configuration. (The situation is different for the ground state, since only the singlet state can exist for the $1s^2$ configuration.) In the ground state of the hydrogen molecule, on the other hand, the lowest energy (strongest binding) is obtained when the electrons tend to concentrate between the two nuclei, since then the repulsion between the electrons is more than compensated by the attraction of both nuclei for each electron. This occurs when the electrons can occupy the same space state and hence when they have antiparallel spins. Thus it is the singlet state that leads to a stable molecule.

THE MORSE POTENTIAL

We now turn to diatomic molecules in general and consider the nature of the solutions of Eq. (49.9) for the nuclear motion. If the nuclei have masses M_1 and M_2 and their relative position vector R has polar coordinates R, θ, ϕ, the equation for the relative motion becomes [see Eqs. (16.5)]

$$\left[-\frac{\hbar^2}{2M} \nabla^2 + U(R) \right] w(R,\theta,\phi) = Ew(R,\theta,\phi) \qquad (49.15)$$

where $M = M_1M_2/(M_1 + M_2)$ is the reduced mass.

[1] Pauling and Wilson, *op. cit.*, sec. 43a.

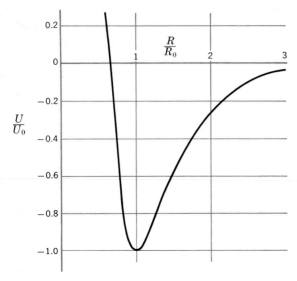

Fig. 39 The Morse potential (49.16), with $a = \tfrac{1}{2}R_0$.

It has been found by experience that the potential-energy function for the lowest electronic states of actual diatomic molecules can be represented quite accurately by a simple analytic function that contains three adjustable parameters

$$U(R) = U_0(e^{-2(R-R_0)/a} - 2e^{-(R-R_0)/a}) \tag{49.16}$$

Equation (49.16) represents the *Morse potential*[1] and is drawn in Fig. 39. U approaches zero exponentially for large R, has the minimum value $-U_0$ at $R = R_0$, and becomes large and positive as R approaches zero if the "breadth" a of the attractive region is somewhat smaller than the equilibrium distance R_0.

Figure 39 has the general appearance that would be expected for a diatomic molecule. The zero of energy is arbitrarily chosen to occur when the neutral atoms are far apart; then U becomes negative at first as R decreases, because of the van der Waals attraction.[2] For smaller R this is replaced by the much stronger Heitler-London resonance attraction. As R continues to decrease, the close approach of the nuclei (or ionic cores) gives rise to a repulsion that causes U to increase and eventually become large and positive.[3]

[1] P. M. Morse, *Phys. Rev.* **34**, 57 (1929).

[2] One of the inaccuracies of the Morse potential is its replacement of the $1/R^6$ van der Waals term (see the end of Sec. 32) by an exponential; however, the behavior of U at such large R has little influence on molecular energy levels.

[3] Unlike the true interaction, the Morse potential is finite at $R = 0$.

ROTATION AND VIBRATION OF DIATOMIC MOLECULES

Equation (49.15) can be separated in spherical coordinates, as was Eq. (14.1), to give

$$w(R,\theta,\phi) = \frac{\chi(R)}{R} Y_{KM_K}(\theta,\phi)$$

K and M_K are the angular momentum quantum numbers that are analogous to l and m, respectively, for a single particle in a central field. The radial equation is

$$-\frac{\hbar^2}{2M}\frac{d^2\chi}{dR^2} + W(R)\chi = E\chi$$

$$W(R) = U(R) + \frac{\hbar^2 K(K+1)}{2MR^2} \qquad K = 0, 1, 2, \ldots$$

(49.17)

Equation (49.17) is the wave equation for the one-dimensional motion of a particle of mass M in a potential $W(R)$, with the boundary condition that χ vanish at $R = 0$. If K is not too large, the general shape of W resembles that of U shown in Fig. 39. In this case, we are primarily interested in vibrations of small amplitude about the minimum. We can then expand W about its minimum at R_1, which is only the same as R_0 if $K = 0$, to give

$$W(R) = W_0 + \tfrac{1}{2}K_0(R - R_1)^2 + b(R - R_1)^3 + c(R - R_1)^4 \quad (49.18)$$

where higher-order terms are neglected. If the b and c terms are also neglected and the domain of R is extended to $-\infty$, the eigenvalues of (49.17) are those of a linear harmonic oscillator with an additive term W_0. This is a good approximation for moderate values of the *rotational quantum number* K and the *vibrational quantum number* v. A somewhat better approximation can be obtained by regarding the b and c terms in (49.18) as perturbations on the oscillator. Since the b term produces only a second-order effect (see Prob. 2, Chap. 8), whereas the c term appears in first order (its expectation value can be computed by matrix methods), both make contributions to E that have the same order of magnitude.

ENERGY LEVELS

The eigenvalues of (49.17) to lowest order in b and c are then

$$E = W_0 + \hbar\left(\frac{K_0}{M}\right)^{\frac{1}{2}}\left(v + \frac{1}{2}\right) - \frac{\hbar^2 b^2}{MK_0^2}\left[\frac{15}{4}\left(v + \frac{1}{2}\right)^2 + \frac{7}{16}\right]$$

$$+ \frac{3\hbar^2 c}{2MK_0}\left[\left(v + \frac{1}{2}\right)^2 + \frac{1}{4}\right] \qquad v = 0, 1, 2, \ldots \qquad (49.19)$$

W_0, K_0, b, and c can all be expanded in powers of $K(K + 1)$, where the coefficients depend on the parameters of the function $U(R)$. If U has the form (49.16), the following expressions can be obtained:

$$R_1 = R_0 + \frac{\hbar^2 K(K + 1)a^2}{2MR_0^3 U_0}$$

$$W_0 = -U_0 + \frac{\hbar^2 K(K + 1)}{2MR_0^2} - \frac{\hbar^4 K^2(K + 1)^2 a^2}{4M^2 R_0^6 U_0}$$

$$K_0 = \frac{2U_0}{a^2} - \frac{3\hbar^2 K(K + 1)}{MR_0^2 a^2} \frac{a}{R_0}\left(1 - \frac{a}{R_0}\right)$$

$$b = -\frac{U_0}{a^3} \qquad c = \frac{7U_0}{12a^4}$$

(49.20)

Only enough terms have been retained to give E correctly to second order in $v + \frac{1}{2}$ and $K(K + 1)$.

The first of Eqs. (49.20) shows that the molecule stretches owing to rotation. The second equation is the equilibrium energy $-U_0$, plus the rotational energy to second order. The first-order rotational energy is $\hbar^2 K(K + 1)/2I_0$, where $I_0 = MR_0^2$ is the moment of inertia of the molecule about an axis perpendicular to the line joining the nuclei; this energy is the same as for a rigid rotator (see Prob. 12). The third equation includes the change in the stiffness due to stretching. The corrections for stretching in the anharmonic terms b and c can be neglected to this order. The second term on the right side of (49.19) can be expanded with the help of the expression for K_0 to give

$$\hbar\left(\frac{2U_0}{Ma^2}\right)^{\frac{1}{2}}\left(v + \frac{1}{2}\right)\left[1 - \frac{3\hbar^2 K(K + 1)}{4MR_0^2 U_0} \frac{a}{R_0}\left(1 - \frac{a}{R_0}\right)\right]$$

The last two terms in (49.19) give the second-order vibrational energy

$$\left(-\frac{15}{16} + \frac{7}{16}\right)\frac{\hbar^2}{Ma^2}\left(v + \frac{1}{2}\right)^2 = -\frac{\hbar^2}{2Ma^2}\left(v + \frac{1}{2}\right)^2$$

(49.21)

since the constant factors cancel.

It is apparent that the rotational and vibrational energy levels agree in order of magnitude with the estimates made at the beginning of this section. As either v or K increases, the spacing between levels becomes smaller than that predicted from the simple rigid rotator and harmonic oscillator.

EFFECT OF NUCLEAR IDENTITY

In the event that the two nuclei of a diatomic molecule are identical, the wave function must be symmetric with respect to an interchange of their space and spin coordinates if the nuclei have zero or integer spin, or antisymmetric if they have half-odd-integer spin (see Sec. 41). The discussion of Sec. 14 shows that the parity of the nuclear wave function is determined by the angular function $Y_{KM_K}(\theta,\phi)$ and is even or odd according as K is even or odd. An interchange of the space coordinates of the two nuclei is equivalent to a change in sign of their relative position vector **R**, so that the parity determines the space symmetry of the wave function. We thus see that for nuclei of zero or integer spin, the spin function must be symmetric for even K and antisymmetric for odd K; for nuclei of half-odd-integer spin, the spin function must be antisymmetric for even K and symmetric for odd K.

The discussion of Sec. 41 shows that for two nuclei of spin $I\hbar$ each, the total of $(2I + 1)^2$ spin states can be divided into $(I + 1)(2I + 1)$ symmetric states and $I(2I + 1)$ antisymmetric states. Thus, in a gas that is in statistical equilibrium, the ratio of the number of molecules with even K to the number with odd K will be $(I + 1)/I$ if I is zero or an integer, and $I/(I + 1)$ if I is half an odd integer.[1] This effect gives rise to alternating intensities in the band (rotational) spectrum of homonuclear diatomic molecules. Both the spin and the statistics of appropriate nuclei can be determined in this way, and the results are in agreement with the general statement in Sec. 41.

50☐ATOMIC NUCLEI

The application of quantum mechanics to the investigation of the structure of atomic nuclei entails great mathematical complexities in all but the simplest cases. In this section we mention very briefly some general properties of nuclei and then consider the nuclear two-body problem.[2]

GENERAL PROPERTIES OF NUCLEI

Atomic nuclei consist of protons and neutrons, both of which are called *nucleons*. Other particles such as mesons, which have a transient existence within nuclei, are usually ignored in structure theories. Protons

---

[1] This ratio is, of course, modified by the Boltzmann factor if the spacing between rotational levels is not small in comparison with the thermal energy κT.

[2] For more detailed discussions at various levels, see W. E. Meyerhof, "Elements of Nuclear Physics" (McGraw-Hill, New York, 1967); M. A. Preston, "Physics of the Nucleus" (Addison-Wesley, Reading, Mass., 1962); R. D. Evans, "The Atomic Nucleus" (McGraw-Hill, New York, 1955); A. E. S. Green, "Nuclear Physics" (McGraw-Hill, New York, 1955); R. G. Sachs, "Nuclear Theory" (Addison-Wesley, Reading, Mass., 1953); G. Gamow and C. L. Critchfield, "Theory of Atomic Nucleus and Nuclear Energy Sources" (Oxford, New York, 1949); J. M. Blatt and V. F. Weisskopf, "Theoretical Nuclear Physics" (Wiley, New York, 1952); M. G. Mayer and J. H. D. Jensen, "Elementary Theory of Nuclear Shell Structure" (Wiley, New York, 1955); A. de-Shalit and I. Talmi, "Nuclear Shell Theory" (Academic, New York, 1963); E. J. Konopinski, "The Theory of Beta Radioactivity" (Oxford, London, 1966).

are nuclei of hydrogen atoms, and neutrons are particles that have about the same mass, no electric charge, and the same spin and statistics as protons (spin $\frac{1}{2}\hbar$, Fermi-Dirac statistics). A nucleus can be characterized by its charge Ze, where Z is an integer and e is the positive proton charge, and its mass M, which is measured in units of $\frac{1}{16}$ of the mass of O^{16} (oxygen isotope of mass number 16). M is always found to be close to an integer A, called the *mass number*. The number of neutrons in a nucleus is equal to $A - Z$; thus the deuteron (heavy-hydrogen nucleus) H^2 consists of one proton and one neutron, the alpha particle (helium nucleus) He^4 of two protons and two neutrons, and the gold nucleus Au^{197} of 79 protons and 118 neutrons.

According to the theory of relativity, the difference between the sum of the masses of the Z protons and $A - Z$ neutrons in a nucleus and the mass M of that nucleus, multiplied by the square of the speed of light, is the energy evolved when the separate nucleons are brought together to form the nucleus. This energy is called the *binding energy* of the nucleus and is conveniently measured in units of a million electron volts (Mev). The *nuclear radius* R is a reasonably well-defined quantity. It can be measured in several ways, for example, from the scattering of high-energy neutrons, protons, and electrons. It is found experimentally that both the binding energy per nucleon and the volume per nucleon are roughly constant over most of the periodic system. The former is about 8 Mev, and the latter is usually expressed in the form $R = r_0 A^{\frac{1}{3}}$, where $r_0 \approx 1.2$ to 1.4×10^{-13} cm. The approximate constancy of the binding energy and volume per nucleon is a consequence of the *saturation* property of nuclear forces.

TWO-NUCLEON INTERACTION

The most fundamental problem to be solved in connection with nuclei is the determination of the parameters of the interaction energy between pairs of nucleons. It is possible that once these are known the problem of the structure of nuclei heavier than the deuteron would become merely an exceedingly complicated exercise in the application of quantum mechanics. This situation would be analogous to that which obtains in atomic and molecular structure, where the main interaction is known to be given by Coulomb's law. On the other hand, it is possible that knowledge of the two-body interactions is not enough to determine the structure of heavier nuclei, even in principle. This would be the case if there were additional interactions which occur only when three, four, or more nucleons are close together, so that their existence and character could not be inferred from a study of the two-nucleon system. The question of whether or not appreciable many-body interactions exist has not yet been settled, and we shall not discuss it further here.

We devote the remainder of this chapter to the two-nucleon system and assume that the main interaction is of short range. It is reasonable to expect this range to be substantially less than the radii of heavy nuclei, and calculations of the type described below show that it is of the order of 2×10^{-13} cm. We put aside for the present any possible dependence of the interaction potential energy $V(r)$ on quantities other than the magnitude of the separation distance r between the two nucleons. Our first problem then is to solve the Schrödinger equation for the relative motion of two particles of reduced mass μ in the potential $V(r)$. Since neutrons and protons have about the same mass, μ is very nearly equal to half the mass of either of them.

NEUTRON-PROTON SYSTEM

A simple assumption for the shape of $V(r)$ is the square well form (see Fig. 13, page 83): $V(r) = -V_0$ for $r < a$, $V(r) = 0$ for $r > a$. It was shown in Sec. 15 that there is no bound state of a particle of mass μ in this potential unless $V_0 a^2 > \pi^2 \hbar^2 / 8\mu$, which is equal to 1.0×10^{-24} Mev-cm² for the neutron-proton system. If we assume that $a \approx 2 \times 10^{-13}$ cm, V_0 must exceed 25 Mev in order for the deuteron to exist. Since the deuteron has only one bound state, it is reasonable to suppose that it corresponds to $l = 0$. Then the solution of Prob. 7, Chap. 4, shows that the measured binding energy of approximately 2.23 Mev is obtained with $V_0 \approx 36$ Mev.

The scattering cross section for neutrons of very low energy on protons can then be obtained from Eq. (19.28). If we neglect E in comparison with V_0, we find that $\sigma \approx 3.6 \times 10^{-24}$ cm². The measured cross section for neutrons of a few electron volts energy in hydrogen is about 20.4×10^{-24} cm²; this energy is small enough so that it can be neglected in comparison with V_0 and large enough so that the binding of the proton in the hydrogen molecule does not affect the result. An explanation of this discrepancy in terms of the dependence of the neutron-proton interaction on the spin state was suggested in 1935 by E. Wigner (unpublished). The deuteron is known to have spin $\hbar$ and so is in a triplet spin state. However, as discussed in Sec. 43 in connection with exchange collisions of electrons with hydrogen atoms, the colliding neutron and proton will be in a triplet state in three-fourths of the collisions and in a singlet spin state in one-fourth of the collisions. Thus the discrepancy is removed if the singlet cross section is taken to be about 70×10^{-24} cm².

If we assume that a is also equal to 2×10^{-13} cm for the singlet interaction, Eq. (19.28) shows that this cross section is obtained for a potential depth of either 24 or 27 Mev. It is apparent that this is the resonance scattering case discussed in Sec. 19 and that these two potentials correspond to virtual and bound singlet states, respectively. The decision as to which is correct cannot be made on the basis of the dependence of the scattering cross section on incident neutron energy; it is shown in Sec. 19 that, with $l = 0$, σ is a monotonic decreasing function of E in both cases, and there is not enough difference in the behavior of the two functions. It is found from other considerations[1] that the singlet state is virtual, so that the depth corresponding to this range is about 24 Mev.

ARBITRARY SHAPE OF POTENTIAL

The interaction potential energy between a pair of nucleons is characterized by a short range a and a large magnitude V_0. Here, a and V_0 do not apply only to the square well shape but rather refer to the distance within which $V(r)$ is appreciably different from zero and to the approximate magnitude of $V(r)$ in this region, respectively. For collisions of moderate energy, up to a few Mev, ka is fairly small compared with unity, where $k = (2\mu E)^{\frac{1}{2}}/\hbar$ and E is the kinetic energy in the center-of-mass coordinate system. For example, with $a = 2 \times 10^{-13}$ cm, ka is equal to unity when the energy of the incident nucleon in the laboratory system is about 20 Mev. Thus for moderate energies, only the $l = 0$ partial wave need be considered. Also, both E and ϵ, the binding energy of the deuteron, are fairly small in comparison with V_0. It follows that the form of the $l = 0$ radial wave function depends only slightly on the energy within the potential range and has its simple asymptotic form outside this range. This suggests that the binding and the low-energy scattering produced by such a potential should depend primarily on the "strength" of the potential, measured roughly by $V_0 a^2$, and on the distance at which the wave function attains its asymptotic form, measured roughly by a.

It turns out that any strong, short-range, predominantly attractive potential can actually be represented by two parameters, which may be chosen to be a strength and a range, and which between them specify the bound-state energy $-\epsilon$ and the dependence of the scattering phase shift on energy for moderate values of E.[2] Thus low-energy experiments can be expected to determine only these two parameters and not the shape of the potential $V(r)$; this expectation is confirmed by the experimental results.

[1] Most reliably from the scattering of very slow neutrons in ortho- and parahydrogen; the possibility of such a determination was first pointed out by J. Schwinger and E. Teller, *Phys. Rev.* **52**, 286 (1937).

[2] Although suspected earlier, this result was first established by J. Schwinger in unpublished lectures (1947), using a variational method; the present treatment follows that of H. A. Bethe, *Phys. Rev.* **76**, 38 (1949).

RELATIONS FOR THE PHASE SHIFT

We work entirely with the $l = 0$ partial wave, and let $u(r)$ be the product of r and the radial wave function. The normalization of u is so chosen that its asymptotic form is

$$u(r) \rightarrow \psi(r) \tag{50.1}$$

outside the range of the potential, where

$$\psi(r) \equiv \frac{\sin{(kr + \delta)}}{\sin{\delta}} \tag{50.2}$$

for all r. The phase shift δ agrees with definition given in Eq. (19.8), and the total cross section is

$$\sigma = \frac{4\pi}{k^2} \sin^2{\delta} \tag{50.3}$$

as in Eq. (19.13).

The wave equations for particular energies E_1 and E_2 are

$$\frac{d^2u_1}{dr^2} + k_1{}^2u_1 - Uu_1 = 0$$
$$\frac{d^2u_2}{dr^2} + k_2{}^2u_2 - Uu_2 = 0 \tag{50.4}$$

where $U(r) = 2\mu V(r)/\hbar^2$. We multiply the first of Eqs. (50.4) by u_2, the second by u_1, and integrate the difference between them over r from $r = 0$ to a distance R that is somewhat larger than the range of the potential:

$$\left(u_2 \frac{du_1}{dr} - u_1 \frac{du_2}{dr}\right)\bigg|_0^R = (k_2{}^2 - k_1{}^2) \int_0^R u_1u_2 \, dr \tag{50.5}$$

The ψ's satisfy the same Eqs. (50.4) as the u's, except that the U terms are absent. Therefore Eq. (50.5) holds for the ψ's as well:

$$\left(\psi_2 \frac{d\psi_1}{dr} - \psi_1 \frac{d\psi_2}{dr}\right)\bigg|_0^R = (k_2{}^2 - k_1{}^2) \int_0^R \psi_1\psi_2 \, dr \tag{50.6}$$

If now Eq. (50.5) is subtracted from Eq. (50.6), the contributions to the left side from the upper limit R cancel, since $u(R) = \psi(R)$. Then the limit $R \rightarrow \infty$ can be taken, to yield

$$\left(\psi_1 \frac{d\psi_2}{dr} - \psi_2 \frac{d\psi_1}{dr}\right)_{r=0} - \left(u_1 \frac{du_2}{dr} - u_2 \frac{du_1}{dr}\right)_{r=0}$$
$$= (k_2{}^2 - k_1{}^2) \int_0^\infty (\psi_1\psi_2 - u_1u_2) \, dr \tag{50.7}$$

From Eq. (50.2), the first parenthesis on the left side is equal to $k_2 \cot \delta_2 - k_1 \cot \delta_1$. Also, since $u(0) = 0$, the second parenthesis on the left side is zero. Thus Eq. (50.7) can be written

$$k_2 \cot \delta_2 - k_1 \cot \delta_1 = \tfrac{1}{2}(k_2{}^2 - k_1{}^2)\rho(E_1,E_2)$$

$$\rho(E_1,E_2) \equiv 2 \int_0^\infty (\psi_1\psi_2 - u_1u_2)\, dr \tag{50.8}$$

A modification of Eqs. (50.8) that is of interest is obtained by replacing E_1 by $-\epsilon$, $\psi_1(r)$ by $\psi_g(r) \equiv e^{-\beta r}$, where $\beta^2 = 2\mu\epsilon/\hbar^2$, and $u_1(r)$ by the ground-state wave function $u_g(r)$ normalized in analogy with (50.1). The result is

$$k_2 \cot \delta_2 + \beta = \tfrac{1}{2}(k_2{}^2 + \beta^2)\rho(-\epsilon,E_2)$$

$$\rho(-\epsilon,E_2) \equiv 2 \int_0^\infty (\psi_g\psi_2 - u_gu_2)\, dr \tag{50.9}$$

Another modification consists in allowing E_1 to become zero:

$$k_2 \cot \delta_2 + \frac{1}{a_t} = \frac{1}{2} k_2{}^2 \rho(0,E_2)$$

$$\rho(0,E_2) \equiv 2 \int_0^\infty (\psi_0\psi_2 - u_0u_2)\, dr \tag{50.10}$$

$$\psi_0 \equiv 1 - \frac{r}{a_t} \qquad \frac{1}{a_t} = - \lim_{E \to 0} (k \cot \delta)$$

where the subscripts on u_0 and ψ_0 denote zero energy. The quantity a_t is the scattering length defined below Eq. (39.39); from Eq. (50.3) the scattering cross section at zero energy is equal to $4\pi a_t{}^2$. The subscript on a_t implies that it refers to the triplet, not the singlet, interaction.

EFFECTIVE RANGE

Equations (50.8) to (50.10) are exact. We now make an approximation with regard to ρ that is suggested by the general form of the potential. It is apparent that Eq. (50.1) makes the integrand of ρ vanish outside the potential. Inside the potential, all the ψ's are very nearly equal to unity since kr and βr are small in comparison with unity; also, the u's are very nearly equal to each other since U is much larger than k^2 or β^2. Thus ρ depends only slightly on its arguments and can be calculated for any convenient energies. Our approximation, then, is to replace ρ in the above equations by

$$r_t \equiv \rho(0,0) = 2 \int_0^\infty (\psi_0{}^2 - u_0{}^2)\, dr \tag{50.11}$$

which is the effective range introduced in Sec. 39; again, the subscript on r_t implies that it refers to the triplet interaction. Alternatively, the effective range could be defined, for example, as

$$\rho(-\epsilon, -\epsilon) = 2 \int_0^\infty (\psi_g{}^2 - u_g{}^2) \, dr \tag{50.12}$$

It is shown in Prob. 17 that the effective ranges computed from Eqs. (50.11) and (50.12) in a typical case agree with each other within a few percent.

With this approximation, the scattering phase shift is given by Eq. (50.9) as (dropping the subscript 2)

$$k \cot \delta + \beta \approx \tfrac{1}{2} r_t (k^2 + \beta^2) \tag{50.13}$$

and by Eq. (50.10) as

$$k \cot \delta + \frac{1}{a_t} \approx \tfrac{1}{2} r_t k^2 \tag{50.14}$$

Equations (50.13) and (50.14) are the same as Eqs. (39.40) and (39.39), respectively, when β is identified with κ and use is made of (39.41). Comparison of (50.13) and (50.14) gives the following relation between a_t, β, and r_t:

$$\frac{1}{a_t} \approx \beta - \tfrac{1}{2} r_t \beta^2 \tag{50.15}$$

which is the same as (39.42).

Either of the quantities β or a_t may be thought of as a strength parameter for the potential and r_t as a range parameter; however, $1/\beta$ and a_t differ enough so that specification of any two of the three fixes the third. Thus, according to this shape-independent effective-range theory, all the binding and low-energy scattering properties of the potential are determined by just two parameters for each spin state. The experimental results show that this is actually the case and so confirm the assumption of a strong, short-range interaction on which the theory is based.

Experimental values are $1/\beta = 4.32 \times 10^{-13}$ cm for the triplet spin state ($\epsilon = 2.225$ Mev), $a_t = 5.40 \times 10^{-13}$ cm, and $r_t = 1.72 \times 10^{-13}$ cm; these are consistent with Eq. (50.15). The corresponding square well interaction has a depth of 35.5 Mev and a radius of 2.03×10^{-13} cm. For the singlet spin state, $a_s = -23.7 \times 10^{-13}$ cm, where the negative sign means that there is no bound state; the effective range is not very well determined experimentally but probably lies between 2.5 and 2.7×10^{-13} cm.[1] A square well of depth 16.8 Mev and radius 2.37×10^{-13} cm corresponds to the above a_s and $r_s = 2.47 \times 10^{-13}$ cm; the depth 14.2 Mev and radius 2.57×10^{-13} cm corresponds to $r_s = 2.68 \times 10^{-13}$ cm.[2]

[1] H. P. Noyes, *Nucl. Phys.* **74**, 508 (1965).

[2] The square-well parameters were kindly supplied by B. F. Gibson and A. Goldberg.

EXCHANGE OPERATORS

The spin dependence of the neutron-proton interaction noted above can be expressed in terms of the *spin-exchange operator* $\frac{1}{2}(1 + \mathbf{\sigma}_N \cdot \mathbf{\sigma}_P)$, where $\mathbf{\sigma}_N$ and $\mathbf{\sigma}_P$ are the Pauli spin matrices for the neutron and proton, respectively, defined as in Eqs. (27.30) or (41.3). As shown in Prob. 18, a triplet spin function is an eigenfunction of this operator with eigenvalue $+1$; similarly, a singlet spin function is an eigenfunction with eigenvalue -1. Equations (41.6) show that a triplet function of two spin $\frac{1}{2}$ particles is symmetric in an interchange of the spins and hence has eigenvalue $+1$ for an exchange operator; similarly, a singlet function is antisymmetric and hence has eigenvalue -1 for an exchange operator. Thus the above operator actually does have the effect of interchanging neutron and proton spins.

A *space-exchange operator*[1] multiplies wave functions of even l by $+1$ and wave functions of odd l by -1; it has no effect on the results obtained thus far, which are all for $l = 0$. For higher energy scattering, the discussion of Sec. 19 shows that the partial wave with $l = 1$ can be significant. If the phase shift δ_1 for $l = 1$ is small in magnitude and the higher phase shifts can be neglected, Eq. (19.32) can be approximated as

$$\sigma(\theta) \approx \frac{1}{k^2} \left(\sin^2 \delta_0 + 3\delta_1 \sin 2\delta_0 \cos \theta \right)$$

For energies high enough so that δ_1 is appreciable, the $l = 0$ phase shift δ_0 is likely to be between 0 and 90°, so that the sign of the angular asymmetry is determined by the sign of δ_1.

If the interaction were predominantly of the non-space-exchange type, the potential would be negative (attractive) for $l = 1$, and δ_1 would be positive. Then neutrons incident on protons would be preferentially scattered forward in both the center-of-mass and laboratory coordinate systems. If, on the other hand, the space-exchange operator were to dominate the interaction, the potential energy would be repulsive for $l = 1$, and δ_1 would be negative. Then the neutrons would be preferentially scattered backward in the center-of-mass system or at right angles in the laboratory system, and the protons would tend to recoil in the forward direction in both systems. This effect can be regarded physically as a non-space-exchange type scattering accompanied by an exchange of identity between the neutron and the proton.

Moderate-energy scattering experiments show that the differential cross section is nearly symmetric about 90° in the center-of-mass system. If it were exactly symmetric, the simplest and most likely situation

---

[1] This was introduced by E. Majorana, *Z. Physik* **82**, 137 (1933), as a modification of the original suggestion of W. Heisenberg, *Z. Physik* **77**, 1 (1932).

would be either that all the even l phase shifts are zero or that all the odd l phase shifts are zero. The first case is impossible, since it is known that $\delta_0 \neq 0$. We are thus led to the *Serber interaction* as a rough approximation to the space-exchange character of the neutron-proton potential at moderate energies: The coefficients of the space-exchange and non-space-exchange parts of the neutron-proton potential are equal and of the same sign, so that there is no interaction in odd l states.

PROTON-PROTON SCATTERING

The scattering of fast protons in hydrogen can be treated by the methods outlined in Sec. 21, with suitable allowance for the identity and spin of the two colliding protons (see Sec. 41). When the interaction is a pure coulomb field, combination of Eqs. (21.10) and (41.2) yields the *Mott scattering formula*[1]

$$\sigma(\theta) = \left(\frac{e^2}{2\mu v^2}\right)^2 \left\{ \operatorname{cosec}^4 \tfrac{1}{2}\theta + \sec^4 \tfrac{1}{2}\theta \right.$$

$$\left. - \operatorname{cosec}^2 \tfrac{1}{2}\theta \sec^2 \tfrac{1}{2}\theta \cos \left[\frac{e^2}{\hbar v} \ln \left(\tan^2 \tfrac{1}{2}\theta\right) \right] \right\} \quad (50.16)$$

which is expressed in the center-of-mass coordinate system. This formula represents only the experiments for protons of less than about 0.2 Mev bombarding energy, since for higher energies the protons approach closely enough so that the specifically nuclear interaction becomes appreciable. Up to several Mev energy, only the δ_0 term in (21.27) need be included. It must be remembered that, because of the exclusion principle, the partial wave with $l = 0$ is associated with a singlet spin state. Thus experiments with fast protons are required if information concerning the triplet proton-proton interaction is to be obtained. An effective-range theory can be made for the singlet proton-proton interaction and leads to roughly the same parameters as for the singlet neutron-proton interaction.[2]

PROBLEMS

1. Find an expression for the electron density $n(r)$ in the Thomas-Fermi model in terms of the dimensionless function χ, and show that the radius of a sphere that encloses a fixed fraction of all the electrons is proportional to $Z^{-\frac{1}{3}}$.

[1] N. F. Mott, *Proc. Roy. Soc. (London)* **A126,** 259 (1930). μ is half the proton mass, and v is the relative speed.

[2] The nucleon-nucleon interactions for a wide range of energy are reviewed by A. E. S. Green, M. H. MacGregor, and R. Wilson, *Rev. Mod. Phys.* **39,** 498 (1967), and other articles in the same issue of that journal.

2. Use Lagrange's method of undetermined multipliers to show that the condition that the integral in (47.9) is stationary, when the u's are varied but kept normalized, is given by (47.11).

3. Two p electrons ($l = 1$) can have $L = 0$, 1, or 2 and $S = 0$ or 1 in the Russell-Saunders case. Are all combinations of L and S permitted if the n values of the two electrons are different? Are they all permitted if the n values are the same?

4. Show that spin wave functions in the Russell-Saunders case that are eigenfunctions of S^2 with different values of the total-spin quantum number S are orthogonal. Use a method like that employed in Sec. 10 to show that energy eigenfunctions corresponding to different eigenvalues are orthogonal.

5. Show by direct computation that $\mathbf{J} = \mathbf{L} + \mathbf{S}$ commutes with $\mathbf{L} \cdot \mathbf{S}$ and hence with the hamiltonian (48.1).

6. Estimate the ratio of the term in (48.9) that is linear in H to the kinetic-energy term for a hydrogen atom in a magnetic field of 10^5 gauss.

7. Show that the Landé g factor for a one-electron state, analogous to (48.12) but applicable for $j = l \pm \frac{1}{2}$, is

$$g = \frac{2l + 1 \pm 1}{2l + 1}$$

Make use of the extension of the Clebsch-Gordan coefficients (28.13) to the case $j_1 = l$, $j_2 = \frac{1}{2}$.

8. Estimate the magnitude of the magnetic field strength for which the two perturbation terms in (48.11) are equal for an alkali atom.

9. Construct a diagram that shows the relative displacements and intensities of the π and σ Zeeman components of the $^2P \rightarrow {}^2S$ transitions in an alkali atom when the magnetic field is weak. Construct a similar diagram when the field is strong.

10. Show that the ratio of the distance traveled by the nuclei of a molecule during a period of the electronic motion to the dimensions of the molecule is of order $(m/M)^{\frac{3}{4}}$ in the case of vibrational motion, and (m/M) in the case of rotational motion. Do these results justify an adiabatic type of approximation?

11. Does the internuclear potential (49.14) obtained for the hydrogen molecule approach the $-1/R^6$ form obtained in Sec. 32 for large R? If not, why not?

12. Set up and solve the wave equation for a rigid rotator that has no kinetic energy of rotation about a particular axis and has equal moments of inertia about the two perpendicular axes.

13. Derive the selection rules for transitions between rotational levels of a diatomic molecule.

14. Discuss the selection rules for vibrational transitions when the two nuclei of a diatomic molecule are the same and when they are different.

15. Calculate the contributions to the vibrational energy of a diatomic molecule of the neglected fifth- and sixth-power terms in the expansion (49.18), and show that their neglect is justified in arriving at the $(v + \frac{1}{2})^2$ energy given in (49.21). Use matrix methods to get the needed matrix elements of x^5 and x^6 for a harmonic oscillator.

16. Suppose that the interaction between a neutron and a proton is the same in the singlet as in the triplet state and is represented by a square well. Is there any value of a that will fit both the deuteron binding energy ($l = 0$) and the slow-neutron scattering cross section? If so, what is it?

17. Use the value of the binding energy of the deuteron to calculate the triplet effective range of a square well potential from Eq. (50.11) and from Eq. (50.12), and compare them with each other. Assume that $a = 2 \times 10^{-13}$ cm.

18. Show that the spin-exchange operator $\frac{1}{2}(1 + \mathbf{d}_N \cdot \mathbf{d}_P)$ has the properties ascribed to it in the text. Then make use of Eqs. (23.38) to construct triplet and singlet projection operators. Finally, if the triplet potential energy is $V_t(r)$ and the singlet is $V_s(r)$, construct a single spin-dependent potential energy that describes the neutron-proton interaction.

19. Make use of the work of Sec. 21 to obtain an expression for the ratio of the proton-proton scattering with a phase shift δ_0 (and no others) to the Mott scattering given by Eq. (50.16).

13
Relativistic Wave Equations

In this chapter we extend the nonrelativistic Schrödinger wave equation to the description of the motion of a particle that has a speed approaching that of light. This extension can be made in many ways, each of which is consistent with the Lorentz transformation equations of the special theory of relativity.[1] A characteristic feature of relativistic wave equations is that the spin of the particle is built into the theory from the beginning and cannot be added afterward, as Pauli added the electron spin to Schrödinger's nonrelativistic equation. This feature provides a useful gauge of the applicability of a particular equation to the description of a particular kind of particle. Two relativistic equations are considered here: the spin 0 equation due to Schrödinger that has since been found to describe a π meson, and the spin $\frac{1}{2}$ equation due to Dirac that

---

[1] For a review of special relativity, see, for example, H. M. Schwartz, "Introduction to Special Relativity," chaps. 3, 4, 8 (McGraw-Hill, New York, 1968); P. G. Bergmann, "Introduction to the Theory of Relativity," pt. I (Prentice-Hall, Englewood Cliffs, N.J., 1946); C. Møller, "The Theory of Relativity," chaps. I–III (Oxford, London, 1952).

describes an electron. In discussing these equations, we devote our attention mainly to the deductions that can be made from them and do not attempt to establish their Lorentz invariance. We shall, therefore, continue to use three-dimensional vector notation rather than the more elegant four-dimensional notation of special relativity theory. The invariance of an equation can usually be inferred quite convincingly from its symmetry between the space coordinates and the time.

51□SCHRÖDINGER'S RELATIVISTIC EQUATION

At the time when Schrödinger developed his nonrelativistic wave equation, he also proposed an extension of it that meets the requirements of special relativity.[1]   This equation follows quite naturally from the transition in classical dynamics from the nonrelativistic relation

$$E = \frac{\mathbf{p}^2}{2m} \tag{51.1}$$

between the energy and momentum of a free particle to the corresponding relativistic relation

$$E^2 = c^2\mathbf{p}^2 + m^2c^4 \tag{51.2}$$

where now E includes the rest-mass energy mc^2.   We proceed by adopting the substitutions (6.13) for E and $\mathbf{p}$

$$E \rightarrow i\hbar \frac{\partial}{\partial t} \qquad \mathbf{p} \rightarrow -i\hbar\nabla \tag{51.3}$$

FREE PARTICLE

A relativistic wave equation for a free particle can be obtained by substituting (51.3) into (51.2) and operating on a wave function $\psi(\mathbf{r},t)$, just as the substitution of (51.3) into (51.1) yields Eq. (6.11).   The result is

$$-\hbar^2 \frac{\partial^2\psi}{\partial t^2} = -\hbar^2c^2\nabla^2\psi + m^2c^4\psi \tag{51.4}$$

Equation (51.4) has plane wave solutions of the form

$$\exp i(\mathbf{k}\cdot\mathbf{r} - \omega t) \tag{51.5}$$

which are eigenfunctions of the operators E and $\mathbf{p}$ in (51.3) with eigenvalues $\hbar\omega$ and $\hbar\mathbf{k}$, respectively.   It is apparent that (51.5) satisfies Eq. (51.4) if

$$\hbar\omega = \pm(\hbar^2c^2\mathbf{k}^2 + m^2c^4)^{\frac{1}{2}} \tag{51.6}$$

[1] E. Schrödinger, *Ann. Physik* **81,** 109 (1926), Sec. 6.

The positive and negative square roots in (51.6) correspond to an ambiguity in the sign of the energy that also results from the classical expression (51.2). We take only the positive square root for the present and return to the negative-energy solutions at the end of Sec. 53.

Expressions for the charge and current densities can be found in analogy with those obtained in Sec. 7. The conservation equation

$$\frac{\partial}{\partial t} P(\mathbf{r},t) + \mathbf{\nabla} \cdot \mathbf{S}(\mathbf{r},t) = 0 \tag{51.7}$$

turns out to be invariant with respect to Lorentz transformations. We multiply (51.4) on the left by ψ^*, the complex conjugate equation on the left by ψ, and subtract one from the other. Then (51.7) results, if we define real quantities

$$P(\mathbf{r},t) = \frac{i\hbar}{2mc^2}\left(\psi^*\frac{\partial\psi}{\partial t} - \psi\frac{\partial\psi^*}{\partial t}\right)$$

$$\mathbf{S}(\mathbf{r},t) = \frac{\hbar}{2im}(\psi^*\mathbf{\nabla}\psi - \psi\mathbf{\nabla}\psi^*) \tag{51.8}$$

This expression for $\mathbf{S}$ is identical with the nonrelativistic form (7.3), and the expression for P can be shown to reduce to (7.1) in the non-relativistic limit (see Prob. 1). It should be noted that P given by (51.8) is not necessarily positive and hence cannot be interpreted as a position probability density. It can, however, be multiplied by e and interpreted as an electric charge density, since charge density can have either sign so long as it is real.

ELECTROMAGNETIC POTENTIALS

We can include the electromagnetic potentials $\mathbf{A}(\mathbf{r},t)$, $\phi(\mathbf{r},t)$ in the wave equation by making use of the fact that ϕ and $(1/c)\mathbf{A}$ have the same Lorentz-transformation properties as E and $\mathbf{p}$. In analogy with the nonrelativistic expression (24.29), we replace (51.2) by

$$(E - e\phi)^2 = (c\mathbf{p} - e\mathbf{A})^2 + m^2c^4 \tag{51.9}$$

for a particle of charge e. The substitutions (51.3) then give

$$\left(-\hbar^2\frac{\partial^2}{\partial t^2} - 2ie\hbar\phi\frac{\partial}{\partial t} - ie\hbar\frac{\partial\phi}{\partial t} + e^2\phi^2\right)\psi$$
$$= [-\hbar^2c^2\nabla^2 + 2ie\hbar c\mathbf{A}\cdot\mathbf{\nabla} + ie\hbar c(\mathbf{\nabla}\cdot\mathbf{A}) + e^2\mathbf{A}^2 + m^2c^4]\psi \tag{51.10}$$

We can now find the connection between Eq. (51.10) and the similar Eq. (24.39) in the nonrelativistic limit. We make the substitution

$$\psi(\mathbf{r},t) = \psi'(\mathbf{r},t)e^{-imc^2t/\hbar} \tag{51.11}$$

in (51.10) and assume that operation with $i\hbar(\partial/\partial t)$ on ψ' gives a result that is of the same order as $e\phi\psi'$ and small in comparison with $mc^2\psi'$. This is equivalent to subtracting out the rest energy and assuming that the remaining energies are small in comparison with it. Differentiation of (51.11) gives

$$\frac{\partial\psi}{\partial t} = \left(\frac{\partial\psi'}{\partial t} - \frac{imc^2}{\hbar}\psi'\right)e^{-imc^2t/\hbar}$$

$$\frac{\partial^2\psi}{\partial t^2} = \left(\frac{\partial^2\psi'}{\partial t^2} - \frac{2imc^2}{\hbar}\frac{\partial\psi'}{\partial t} - \frac{m^2c^4}{\hbar^2}\psi'\right)e^{-imc^2t/\hbar}$$

The first term in each of these derivatives can be neglected, as can the last two terms on the left side of (51.10), which then becomes

$$\left(2i\hbar mc^2\frac{\partial\psi'}{\partial t} + m^2c^4\psi' - 2emc^2\phi\psi'\right)e^{-imc^2t/\hbar}$$

With these approximations, Eq. (51.10) becomes the same as (24.39) if ψ' is replaced by ψ.

There is no way in which the Pauli spin matrices (41.3) can be included in Eq. (51.10) without destroying the invariance of the theory. This is not surprising, since the spin matrices transform like the components of a three-dimensional, rather than a four-dimensional, vector and since ψ has one component rather than two components like the spin functions (33.4). Thus the Schrödinger relativistic equation represents a particle that has no spin.

The structure of Eq. (51.9) shows that a "potential-energy" term cannot be added arbitrarily to (51.10), as the term $V\psi$ was added to (24.39) to give Eq. (44.1). The Lorentz transformation properties of any such term must be investigated first. If it transforms like part of a four-dimensional vector, the rest of this vector must be included in some such manner as ϕ and $(1/c)\mathbf{A}$ were included in (51.9). If it is an invariant with respect to Lorentz transformations, it can be included as part of the rest energy mc^2.

SEPARATION OF THE EQUATION

The wave equation (51.10) can be separated with respect to $\mathbf{r}$ and t if the potentials $\mathbf{A}$, ϕ are independent of the time. We then put

$$\psi(\mathbf{r},t) = u(\mathbf{r})e^{-iEt/\hbar}$$

and substitute into (51.10) to obtain

$$(E - e\phi)^2 u = [-\hbar^2c^2\nabla^2 + 2ie\hbar c\mathbf{A}\cdot\nabla$$
$$+ ie\hbar c(\nabla\cdot\mathbf{A}) + e^2\mathbf{A}^2 + m^2c^4]u \quad (51.12)$$

We now specialize to the case in which $\mathbf{A} = 0$ and $\phi(\mathbf{r})$ is spherically symmetric. Equation (51:12) then becomes

$$(-\hbar^2 c^2 \nabla^2 + m^2 c^4) u(\mathbf{r}) = [E - e\phi(r)]^2 u(\mathbf{r}) \tag{51.13}$$

which can be separated in spherical coordinates (see Sec. 14) to give

$$u(r,\theta,\phi) = R(r) Y_{lm}(\theta,\phi)$$

$$\left[-\frac{1}{r^2} \frac{d}{dr}\left(r^2 \frac{d}{dr}\right) + \frac{l(l+1)}{r^2} \right] R = \frac{(E - e\phi)^2 - m^2 c^4}{\hbar^2 c^2} R$$

$$l = 0, 1, 2, \ldots \tag{51.14}$$

This reduces to the nonrelativistic radial equation if we put $E = mc^2 + E'$ and assume that E' and $e\phi$ can be neglected in comparison with mc^2. Then the fraction on the right side of (51.14) becomes $(2m/\hbar^2)(E' - e\phi)$, as it should.

ENERGY LEVELS IN A COULOMB FIELD

An exact solution of (51.14) can easily be obtained if we put $e\phi = -Ze^2/r$, by making use of the results of Sec. 16. This situation would represent a hydrogen atom were it not for the fact that the particle described by (51.10) has no spin and so cannot be an electron.

If we put $\rho = \alpha r$, Eq. (51.14) can be written as

$$\frac{1}{\rho^2} \frac{d}{d\rho}\left(\rho^2 \frac{dR}{d\rho}\right) + \left[\frac{\lambda}{\rho} - \frac{1}{4} - \frac{l(l+1) - \gamma^2}{\rho^2} \right] R = 0$$

$$\gamma \equiv \frac{Ze^2}{\hbar c} \qquad \alpha^2 \equiv \frac{4(m^2 c^4 - E^2)}{\hbar^2 c^2} \qquad \lambda \equiv \frac{2E\gamma}{\hbar c \alpha} \tag{51.15}$$

This has precisely the form of Eq. (16.7) except that $l(l+1)$ has been replaced by $l(l+1) - \gamma^2$. The parameter λ is determined by the boundary condition on R when $\rho = \infty$, and E is expressed in terms of λ by eliminating α from the last two of Eqs. (51.15):

$$E = mc^2 \left(1 + \frac{\gamma^2}{\lambda^2}\right)^{-\frac{1}{2}} \tag{51.16}$$

A study of the way in which Eq. (16.7) was solved shows that solutions of (51.15) that are finite at $\rho = 0$ and ∞ exist only if

$$\lambda = n' + s + 1 \tag{51.17}$$

where n' is zero or a positive integer and s is the nonnegative solution of the equation

$$s(s + 1) = l(l + 1) - \gamma^2 \tag{51.18}$$

Equation (51.18) has the two solutions

$$s = -\tfrac{1}{2} \pm \tfrac{1}{2}[(2l + 1)^2 - 4\gamma^2]^{\frac{1}{2}} \tag{51.19}$$

of which one is positive and the other negative for $l > 0$.

For $l = 0$, both the s values given by (51.19) are negative, so that $R(r)$, which behaves like r^s near $r = 0$, is singular at the origin. However, γ is quite small (very nearly equal to $Z/137$ if e is the electronic charge), so that use of the upper sign in (51.19) gives a value of s that is close to zero for physically interesting values of Z, whereas the lower sign makes s close to -1. The choice between these two values of s can be made in the following way. In a physically realizable case, the source of the coulomb field has some small but finite size a that corresponds, say, to the nuclear radius, so that $\phi(r)$ is finite everywhere. Then the solution $R(r)$ that is finite at $r = 0$ can be shown to approach the point coulomb solution that corresponds to the upper sign in (51.19) when $a \to 0$ (see Prob. 3). We then use the upper sign in (51.19) for all l and obtain from (51.17)

$$\lambda = n' + \tfrac{1}{2} + [(l + \tfrac{1}{2})^2 - \gamma^2]^{\frac{1}{2}} \tag{51.20}$$

Equations (51.16) and (51.20) give a fine structure to the non-relativistic energy levels (16.15). This can be seen by expanding the expression for the energy levels in powers of γ^2. The result to terms of order γ^4 is

$$E = mc^2 \left[1 - \frac{\gamma^2}{2n^2} - \frac{\gamma^4}{2n^4} \left(\frac{n}{l + \frac{1}{2}} - \frac{3}{4} \right) \right] \tag{51.21}$$

where $n = n' + l + 1$ is the total quantum number of Eq. (16.14) and can take on positive integer values. The first term on the right side of (51.21) is the rest energy. The second term is

$$-\frac{mc^2\gamma^2}{2n^2} = -\frac{mZ^2e^4}{2\hbar^2n^2}$$

and agrees with (16.15). The third term is the fine-structure energy, which removes the degeneracy between states of the same n and different l. The total spread of the fine-structure levels for a given n is easily seen from (51.21) to be

$$\frac{mc^2\gamma^4}{n^3} \frac{n - 1}{n - \frac{1}{2}} \tag{51.22}$$

This is much larger than is observed experimentally in the spectrum of hydrogen.

52□DIRAC'S RELATIVISTIC EQUATION

Dirac[1] approached the problem of finding a relativistic wave equation by starting from the hamiltonian form (24.1)

$$i\hbar \frac{\partial}{\partial t} \psi(\mathbf{r},t) = H\psi(\mathbf{r},t) \tag{52.1}$$

The classical relativistic hamiltonian for a free particle is the positive square root of the right side of Eq. (51.2). However, if this is substituted into (52.1) and $\mathbf{p}$ is replaced by $-i\hbar\nabla$, the resulting wave equation is unsymmetrical with respect to space and time derivatives and hence not relativistic. Dirac therefore modified the hamiltonian in such a way as to make it linear in the space derivatives.

FREE-PARTICLE EQUATION

The simplest hamiltonian that is linear in the momentum and mass term is

$$H = c\boldsymbol{\alpha} \cdot \mathbf{p} + \beta mc^2 \tag{52.2}$$

Substitution into (52.1) leads to the wave equation

$$(E - c\boldsymbol{\alpha} \cdot \mathbf{p} - \beta mc^2)\psi = 0$$

or   (52.3)

$$\left(i\hbar \frac{\partial}{\partial t} + i\hbar c\, \boldsymbol{\alpha} \cdot \nabla - \beta mc^2\right) \psi = 0$$

We now consider the four quantities α_x, α_y, α_z, and β. If (52.3) is to describe a free particle, there can be no terms in the hamiltonian that depend on the space coordinates or the time, since such terms would have the properties of space-time-dependent energies and give rise to forces. Also, the space and time derivatives are to appear only in $\mathbf{p}$ and E, and not in $\boldsymbol{\alpha}$ and β, since (52.3) is to be linear in all these derivatives. We thus conclude that $\boldsymbol{\alpha}$ and β are independent of $\mathbf{r}$, t, $\mathbf{p}$, and E and hence commute with all of them. This does not necessarily mean that $\boldsymbol{\alpha}$ and β are numbers, since they need not commute with each other.

We can learn more about $\boldsymbol{\alpha}$ and β by requiring that any solution ψ of (52.3) also be a solution of Schrödinger's relativistic equation (51.4) (the converse need not be true). This is a reasonable requirement since, in the absence of external fields, the wave-packet solutions of (52.3) whose

[1] P. A. M. Dirac, *Proc. Roy. Soc. (London)* **A117,** 610 (1928); "The Principles of Quantum Mechanics," 4th ed., chap. XI (Oxford, New York, 1958). See also J. D. Bjorken and S. D. Drell, "Relativistic Quantum Mechanics" (McGraw-Hill, New York, 1964); H. A. Bethe and E. E. Salpeter, "Quantum Mechanics of One- and Two-electron Atoms," chap. I(b) (Springer, Berlin, 1957).

motions resemble those of classical particles must have the classical relation (51.2) between energy, momentum, and mass. We therefore multiply the first of Eqs. (52.3) on the left by $(E + c\boldsymbol{\alpha} \cdot \mathbf{p} + \beta mc^2)$ to obtain

$$\{E^2 - c^2[\alpha_x{}^2 p_x{}^2 + \alpha_y{}^2 p_y{}^2 + \alpha_z{}^2 p_z{}^2 + (\alpha_x\alpha_y + \alpha_y\alpha_x)p_xp_y$$
$$+ (\alpha_y\alpha_z + \alpha_z\alpha_y)p_yp_z + (\alpha_z\alpha_x + \alpha_x\alpha_z)p_zp_x] - m^2c^4\beta^2$$
$$- mc^3[(\alpha_x\beta + \beta\alpha_x)p_x + (\alpha_y\beta + \beta\alpha_y)p_y + (\alpha_z\beta + \beta\alpha_z)p_z]\}\psi = 0$$

$$(52.4)$$

where the substitutions (51.3) for E and $\mathbf{p}$ in terms of differential operators are implied. Equation (52.4) agrees with (51.4) if $\boldsymbol{\alpha}$, β satisfy the relations

$$\alpha_x{}^2 = \alpha_y{}^2 = \alpha_z{}^2 = \beta^2 = 1$$
$$\alpha_x\alpha_y + \alpha_y\alpha_x = \alpha_y\alpha_z + \alpha_z\alpha_y = \alpha_z\alpha_x + \alpha_x\alpha_z = 0 \qquad (52.5)$$
$$\alpha_x\beta + \beta\alpha_x = \alpha_y\beta + \beta\alpha_y = \alpha_z\beta + \beta\alpha_z = 0$$

The four quantities are said to *anticommute* in pairs, and their squares are unity.

Since $\boldsymbol{\alpha}$, β anticommute rather than commute with each other, they cannot be numbers. We have seen in Chap. 6 that quantities of this type can be expressed in terms of matrices, and it is convenient for calculation to have a matrix representation of them. We note first that, since the H given by (52.2) is hermitian, each of the four matrices $\boldsymbol{\alpha}$, β must be hermitian and hence square. Our problem is to find an explicit representation in which, say, one of these matrices is diagonal (then the others cannot be diagonal since they do not commute with this one). In the interests of simplicity, we shall require the representation to have as low a rank as possible.

MATRICES FOR α AND β

The squares of all four matrices are unity, so that their eigenvalues are $+1$ and -1. We arbitrarily choose β as the matrix that is to be diagonal, and we rearrange its rows and columns so that all the $+1$ eigenvalues are grouped together in a matrix of rank n, and all the -1 eigenvalues are grouped in a matrix of rank m. Since β anticommutes with $\boldsymbol{\alpha}$, it cannot be a constant matrix, and so both n and m must be greater than zero. The β matrix can be represented schematically as

$$\beta = \begin{bmatrix} 1 & 0 \\ 0 & -1 \end{bmatrix} \qquad (52.6)$$

which is an abbreviation for

$$\begin{bmatrix} 1 & 0 & . & . & 0 & 0 & . & . \\ 0 & 1 & . & . & 0 & 0 & . & . \\ . & . & . & . & . & . & . & . \\ . & . & . & . & . & . & . & . \\ 0 & 0 & . & . & -1 & 0 & . & . \\ 0 & 0 & . & . & 0 & -1 & . & . \\ . & . & . & . & . & . & . & . \\ . & . & . & . & . & . & . & . \end{bmatrix} \tag{52.7}$$

The dashed lines in (52.7) separate the submatrices 1, 0, 0, and -1 that appear in (52.6).[1] We now consider the matrix equation $\alpha_x\beta + \beta\alpha_x = 0$, the jl element of which is

$$(\alpha_x)_{jl}(\beta_j + \beta_l) = 0$$

Here β_j and β_l are two of the eigenvalues of β, which are arranged in accordance with (52.6) or (52.7). If $\beta_j = \beta_l$, then $(\alpha_x)_{jl} = 0$, whereas if β_j and β_l have opposite signs, $(\alpha_x)_{jl}$ need not be zero. Thus the matrix for α_x can be written in the form

$$\alpha_x = \begin{bmatrix} 0 & \alpha_{x1} \\ \alpha_{x2} & 0 \end{bmatrix} \tag{52.8}$$

where α_{x1} has n rows and m columns, and α_{x2} has m rows and n columns. Since the square of (52.8) is a unit matrix, we see also that

$$\alpha_{x1}\alpha_{x2} = 1 \qquad \alpha_{x2}\alpha_{x1} = 1 \tag{52.9}$$

The unit matrix that appears on the right side of the first of Eqs. (52.9) has n rows and columns, and the unit matrix in the second equation has m rows and columns. It is not difficult to show that no matrices can be found that satisfy (52.9) if n, m equal 1, 2 or 2, 1. We therefore consider the two possibilities $n = m = 1$ and $n = m = 2$ as giving matrices of minimum rank.[2] It is apparent that α_y and α_z can be written in forms similar to (52.8).

We have already obtained three anticommuting matrices of the form (52.6) or (52.8) with $n = m = 1$. These are the Pauli spin matrices (41.3)

$$\sigma_x = \begin{bmatrix} 0 & 1 \\ 1 & 0 \end{bmatrix} \qquad \sigma_y = \begin{bmatrix} 0 & -i \\ i & 0 \end{bmatrix} \qquad \sigma_z = \begin{bmatrix} 1 & 0 \\ 0 & -1 \end{bmatrix} \tag{52.10}$$

[1] The matrices 1, 0 are the same as the unit and null matrices **1**, $\bigcirc$ defined in Sec. 22.
[2] Higher-rank matrices correspond to particles with spin greater than $\frac{1}{2}$.

which satisfy the equations

$$\sigma_x\sigma_y = -\sigma_y\sigma_x = i\sigma_z \tag{52.11}$$

together with the two similar relations obtained by permuting x, y, z. Any matrix with two rows and columns has four elements and so can be expressed as a linear combination of the four linearly independent matrices σ_x, σ_y, σ_z, and 1. Then it is not difficult to show that a fourth matrix that anticommutes with all three of those in (52.10) cannot be found.

We therefore try $n = m = 2$ and for simplicity take $\alpha_{x1} = \alpha_{x2}$, etc. Then Eqs. (52.9) become $\alpha_{x1}{}^2 = 1$, and the equation $\alpha_x\alpha_y + \alpha_y\alpha_x = 0$ becomes $\alpha_{x1}\alpha_{y1} + \alpha_{y1}\alpha_{x1} = 0$. From these and the similar relations obtained by permuting x, y, z, we see at once that we can identify α_{x1} with σ_x, etc. We thus arrive at an explicit matrix representation for β, $\boldsymbol{\alpha}$:

$$\beta = \begin{bmatrix} 1 & 0 & 0 & 0 \\ 0 & 1 & 0 & 0 \\ 0 & 0 & -1 & 0 \\ 0 & 0 & 0 & -1 \end{bmatrix} \qquad \alpha_x = \begin{bmatrix} 0 & 0 & 0 & 1 \\ 0 & 0 & 1 & 0 \\ 0 & 1 & 0 & 0 \\ 1 & 0 & 0 & 0 \end{bmatrix}$$

$$\alpha_y = \begin{bmatrix} 0 & 0 & 0 & -i \\ 0 & 0 & i & 0 \\ 0 & -i & 0 & 0 \\ i & 0 & 0 & 0 \end{bmatrix} \qquad \alpha_z = \begin{bmatrix} 0 & 0 & 1 & 0 \\ 0 & 0 & 0 & -1 \\ 1 & 0 & 0 & 0 \\ 0 & -1 & 0 & 0 \end{bmatrix} \tag{52.12}$$

These matrices are evidently hermitian; we abbreviate them as

$$\beta = \begin{bmatrix} 1 & 0 \\ 0 & -1 \end{bmatrix} \qquad \boldsymbol{\alpha} = \begin{bmatrix} 0 & \boldsymbol{\sigma} \\ \boldsymbol{\sigma} & 0 \end{bmatrix} \tag{52.13}$$

where each "element" is a matrix with two rows and columns.[1]

FREE–PARTICLE SOLUTIONS

Now that $\boldsymbol{\alpha}$ and β are represented by matrices, Eq. (52.3) has no meaning unless the wave function ψ is itself a matrix with four rows and one column:

$$\psi(\mathbf{r},t) = \begin{bmatrix} \psi_1(\mathbf{r},t) \\ \psi_2(\mathbf{r},t) \\ \psi_3(\mathbf{r},t) \\ \psi_4(\mathbf{r},t) \end{bmatrix} \tag{52.14}$$

[1] The relativistic character of the Dirac equation can be made more apparent if (52.3) is multiplied through on the left by β; this enhances the symmetry between space and time derivatives, since the four matrices β, $\beta\boldsymbol{\alpha}$ have properties similar to the four matrices β, $\boldsymbol{\alpha}$.

Then (52.3) is equivalent to four simultaneous first-order partial differential equations that are linear and homogeneous in the four ψ's.

Plane wave solutions of the form

$$\psi_j(\mathbf{r},t) = u_j \exp i(\mathbf{k} \cdot \mathbf{r} - \omega t) \qquad j = 1, 2, 3, 4 \tag{52.15}$$

can now be found, where the u_j are numbers. These are eigenfunctions of the energy and momentum operators (51.3) with eigenvalues $\hbar\omega$ and $\hbar\mathbf{k}$, respectively. Substitution of (52.15) and (52.12) into (52.13) gives a set of algebraic equations for the u_j, where $E = \hbar\omega$ and $\mathbf{p} = \hbar\mathbf{k}$ are now numbers:

$$
\begin{aligned}
(E - mc^2)u_1 - cp_z u_3 - c(p_x - ip_y)u_4 &= 0 \\
(E - mc^2)u_2 - c(p_x + ip_y)u_3 + cp_z u_4 &= 0 \\
(E + mc^2)u_3 - cp_z u_1 - c(p_x - ip_y)u_2 &= 0 \\
(E + mc^2)u_4 - c(p_x + ip_y)u_1 + cp_z u_2 &= 0
\end{aligned}
\tag{52.16}
$$

These equations are homogeneous in the u_j and hence have solutions only if the determinant of the coefficients is zero. This determinant is $(E^2 - m^2c^4 - c^2\mathbf{p}^2)^2$, so that the relation between E and $\mathbf{p}$ is in agreement with (51.2).

Explicit solutions can be obtained for any momentum $\mathbf{p}$ by choosing a sign for the energy, say $E_+ = +(c^2\mathbf{p}^2 + m^2c^4)^{\frac{1}{2}}$. Then there are two linearly independent solutions, which are conveniently written as

$$
u_1 = 1 \qquad u_2 = 0 \qquad u_3 = \frac{cp_z}{E_+ + mc^2}
$$
$$
u_4 = \frac{c(p_x + ip_y)}{E_+ + mc^2}
$$
$$
u_1 = 0 \qquad u_2 = 1 \qquad u_3 = \frac{c(p_x - ip_y)}{E_+ + mc^2}
$$
$$
u_4 = -\frac{cp_z}{E_+ + mc^2}
\tag{52.17}
$$

Similarly, if we choose the negative square root $E_- = -(c^2\mathbf{p}^2 + m^2c^4)^{\frac{1}{2}}$, we obtain two new solutions, which are conveniently written as

$$
u_1 = \frac{cp_z}{E_- - mc^2} \qquad u_2 = \frac{c(p_x + ip_y)}{E_- - mc^2}
$$
$$
u_3 = 1 \qquad u_4 = 0
$$
$$
u_1 = \frac{c(p_x - ip_y)}{E_- - mc^2} \qquad u_2 = -\frac{cp_z}{E_- - mc^2}
$$
$$
u_3 = 0 \qquad u_4 = 1
\tag{52.18}
$$

Each of these four solutions can be normalized, in the sense that $\psi^\dagger\psi = 1$, by multiplying it by the factor $\{1 + [c^2\mathbf{p}^2/(E_+ + mc^2)^2]\}^{-\frac{1}{2}}$; $\psi^\dagger$ is the hermitian adjoint of ψ and is a matrix with one row and four columns.

It is apparent that the solutions (52.17) correspond to positive energy and the solutions (52.18) to negative energy. In the nonrelativistic limit, in which $E_+ = -E_-$ is close to mc^2 and large in comparison with $c|\mathbf{p}|$, u_3 and u_4 are of the order of v/c times u_1 or u_2 for the positive-energy solutions (v is the speed of the particle); the opposite is true for the negative-energy solutions. The physical distinction between the two solutions for each sign of the energy can be seen by defining three new spin matrices σ'_x, σ'_y, σ'_z that have four rows and columns:

$$\boldsymbol{\sigma}' = \begin{bmatrix} \boldsymbol{\sigma} & 0 \\ 0 & \boldsymbol{\sigma} \end{bmatrix} \tag{52.19}$$

We shall see at the beginning of Sec. 53 that $\frac{1}{2}\hbar\boldsymbol{\sigma}'$ can be interpreted as the operator that represents spin angular momentum. When the small components of the wave function can be neglected, it is easy to see that ψ is an eigenfunction of σ'_z with eigenvalue $+1$ for the first of each pair of solutions (52.17) and (52.18), and eigenvalue -1 for the second solution of each pair.

CHARGE AND CURRENT DENSITIES

We can obtain a conservation equation by multiplying the second of Eqs. (52.3) on the left by $\psi^\dagger$, the hermitian adjoint equation

$$-i\hbar \frac{\partial \psi^\dagger}{\partial t} - i\hbar c(\nabla\psi^\dagger) \cdot \boldsymbol{\alpha} - \psi^\dagger \beta mc^2 = 0$$

on the right by ψ, and taking the difference of the two results. We then get Eq. (51.7) if we define the real quantities

$$P(\mathbf{r},t) = \psi^\dagger \psi \qquad \mathbf{S}(\mathbf{r},t) = c\psi^\dagger \boldsymbol{\alpha} \psi \tag{52.20}$$

The expression for P has the nonrelativistic form (7.1); since it is never negative, it can be interpreted as a position probability density. It can be shown that the expression (52.20) for $\mathbf{S}$ reduces to (7.3) in the non-relativistic limit except for a term that involves $\boldsymbol{\sigma}'$ (see Prob. 6).

The second of Eqs. (52.20) suggests that the operator $c\boldsymbol{\alpha}$ can be interpreted as a particle velocity. This can be verified by calculating the time derivative of the position vector $\mathbf{r}$ from Eq. (24.10) in the Heisenberg picture. With the hamiltonian (52.2) and the commutation relations (24.31), we obtain

$$\frac{dx}{dt} = \frac{1}{i\hbar}(xH - Hx) = c\alpha_x \tag{52.21}$$

ELECTROMAGNETIC POTENTIALS

Terms that involve the electromagnetic potentials can be added to Eq. (52.3) in a relativistic way by making the usual replacements $c\mathbf{p} \to c\mathbf{p} - e\mathbf{A}$ and $E \to E - e\phi$, where the particle described by the equation has electric charge e. We thus obtain

$$[E - e\phi - \boldsymbol{\alpha} \cdot (c\mathbf{p} - e\mathbf{A}) - \beta mc^2]\psi = 0 \qquad (52.22)$$

Here E and $\mathbf{p}$ stand for the operators (51.3). This equation can be reduced to a form that is similar to (51.10) by multiplying it on the left with $[E - e\phi + \boldsymbol{\alpha} \cdot (c\mathbf{p} - e\mathbf{A}) + \beta mc^2]$. The result is

$$\{(E - e\phi)^2 - [\boldsymbol{\alpha} \cdot (c\mathbf{p} - e\mathbf{A})]^2 - m^2c^4$$
$$- (E - e\phi)\boldsymbol{\alpha} \cdot (c\mathbf{p} - e\mathbf{A}) + \boldsymbol{\alpha} \cdot (c\mathbf{p} - e\mathbf{A})(E - e\phi)\}\psi = 0$$
$$(52.23)$$

The second operator in (52.23) can be reduced by making use of the following relation:

$$(\boldsymbol{\alpha} \cdot \mathbf{B})(\boldsymbol{\alpha} \cdot \mathbf{C}) = \mathbf{B} \cdot \mathbf{C} + i\boldsymbol{\sigma}' \cdot (\mathbf{B} \times \mathbf{C}) \qquad (52.24)$$

where $\mathbf{B}$ and $\mathbf{C}$ commute with $\boldsymbol{\alpha}$ but not necessarily with each other (see Prob. 7). We identify both $\mathbf{B}$ and $\mathbf{C}$ with $c\mathbf{p} - e\mathbf{A}$; we also require the relation

$$(c\mathbf{p} - e\mathbf{A}) \times (c\mathbf{p} - e\mathbf{A}) = -ce(\mathbf{A} \times \mathbf{p} + \mathbf{p} \times \mathbf{A}) = ie\hbar c\boldsymbol{\nabla} \times \mathbf{A} = ie\hbar c\mathbf{H}$$

where use has been made of (24.30). With this substitution, Eq. (52.24) becomes

$$[\boldsymbol{\alpha} \cdot (c\mathbf{p} - e\mathbf{A})]^2 = (c\mathbf{p} - e\mathbf{A})^2 - e\hbar c\boldsymbol{\sigma}' \cdot \mathbf{H}$$

The last two operators in (52.23) can be written as

$$e\boldsymbol{\alpha} \cdot (E\mathbf{A} - \mathbf{A}E) + ce\boldsymbol{\alpha} \cdot (\phi\mathbf{p} - \mathbf{p}\phi)$$
$$= ie\hbar\boldsymbol{\alpha} \cdot \frac{\partial A}{\partial t} + ie\hbar c\boldsymbol{\alpha} \cdot \boldsymbol{\nabla}\phi = -ie\hbar c\boldsymbol{\alpha} \cdot \mathbf{E}$$

where use has again been made of (24.30). Equation (52.23) then becomes

$$[(E - e\phi)^2 - (c\mathbf{p} - e\mathbf{A})^2 - m^2c^4 + e\hbar c\boldsymbol{\sigma}' \cdot \mathbf{H} - ie\hbar c\boldsymbol{\alpha} \cdot \mathbf{E}]\psi = 0 \qquad (52.25)$$

The first three terms are precisely the same as (51.10). The physical significance of the last two terms will now be shown from consideration of the nonrelativistic limit of the entire equation.

We could proceed just as we did in obtaining the nonrelativistic limit of Eq. (51.10).   A slightly different approach consists in putting

$$E = E' + mc^2 \tag{52.26}$$

and assuming that E' and $e\phi$ are small in comparison with mc^2; this is equivalent to the substitution (51.11) and the subsequent approximations.   We can then make the replacement

$$(E - e\phi)^2 - m^2c^4 \approx 2mc^2(E' - e\phi)$$

in (52.25) to obtain

$$E'\psi = \left[\frac{1}{2m} \left(\mathbf{p} - \frac{e}{c}\mathbf{A} \right)^2 + e\phi - \frac{e\hbar}{2mc}\, \boldsymbol{\sigma}' \cdot \mathbf{H} + \frac{ie\hbar}{2mc}\, \boldsymbol{\alpha} \cdot \mathbf{E} \right] \psi \tag{52.27}$$

Now E' is equivalent to the time derivative operator $i\hbar(\partial/\partial t)$ if a factor $e^{-imc^2t/\hbar}$ is taken out of ψ.   Thus (52.27) is the nonrelativistic Schrödinger equation (24.39), with two additional terms that involve $\mathbf{H}$ and $\mathbf{E}$ directly.

The $\mathbf{H}$ term has the form associated with the energy of a magnetic dipole of moment $(e\hbar/2mc)\boldsymbol{\sigma}'$.   It was shown in (52.18), for a free particle, that the first and second components of the wave function are large in comparison with the third and fourth components for the positive-energy solutions in the nonrelativistic limit.   This can also be shown without difficulty, when the particle is not free, from the structure of the general equation (52.22).   Equation (52.19) shows that $\boldsymbol{\sigma}'$ operating on the four-component wave function is the same as $\boldsymbol{\sigma}$ operating on the large components alone.   Thus the two large components of (52.27) with the $\mathbf{H}$ term give just the nonrelativistic equation with the Pauli spin matrices and the correct coefficient for the magnetic moment of an electron [see Eq. (48.10), in which the electron charge is $-e$].

We now show that in practical cases the $\mathbf{E}$ term in (52.27) is of order $(v/c)^2$ times the $e\phi$ term and so is to be neglected in the nonrelativistic limit.[1]   We note first that the expectation value of $\boldsymbol{\alpha}$ is of order $(v/c)\int\psi^\dagger\psi\, d^3r$, since (52.13) shows that $\boldsymbol{\alpha}$ mixes the large and small components (we also saw earlier that $c\boldsymbol{\alpha}$ is the velocity operator).   For an electron that is part of a system of linear dimensions a, $e\phi$ is of order eEa, and $\hbar/a \sim p \sim mv$.   Thus the ratio of the $\mathbf{E}$ to the $e\phi$ terms in (52.27) is of order

$$\frac{e\hbar v E}{mc^2} \frac{1}{eEa} \sim \frac{v^2}{c^2}$$

In contrast with this, we have already seen in Eqs. (48.9) and (48.10) that the $\mathbf{H}$ term in (52.27) is of the same order as the other magnetic terms that are linear in $\mathbf{A}$.   Although the $\mathbf{E}$ term must be omitted from (52.27)

---

[1] For a spherically symmetric electrostatic potential it leads to the spin-orbit energy, which is actually of order $(v/c)^2 e\phi$; see Eq. (53.8).

for a consistent nonrelativistic approximation, it cannot be dropped from the relativistic equation (52.25), where it is required to preserve Lorentz invariance.

53☐DIRAC'S EQUATION FOR A CENTRAL FIELD

In the preceding section, the existence of the magnetic moment of an electron was demonstrated explicitly by showing that the expected extra magnetic energy appears in the nonrelativistic approximation. The electron spin carries no energy in itself and so can be observed only through its coupling with the orbital motion of the electron. In the first part of this section, we make this coupling apparent in two ways: through conservation of total angular momentum and through the spin-orbit energy that was introduced in Sec. 47. In both cases we work with such potentials $\mathbf{A}$, ϕ that there is no transfer of angular momentum to the electron; this implies that we have a central field ($\mathbf{A} = 0$ and ϕ spherically symmetric). In the latter part of this section, we separate the Dirac equation for a general central field and find the energy levels of the hydrogen atom.

SPIN ANGULAR MOMENTUM

With $\mathbf{A}(\mathbf{r},t) = 0$ and $\phi(\mathbf{r},t) = \phi(r)$, Eq. (52.22) can be written as

$$i\hbar \frac{\partial \psi}{\partial t} = H\psi$$

$$H = c\boldsymbol{\alpha} \cdot \mathbf{p} + \beta mc^2 + V \tag{53.1}$$

where $V = e\phi$. We might expect that the orbital angular momentum $\mathbf{L} = \mathbf{r} \times \mathbf{p}$ is a constant of the motion in such a central field. In order to investigate this point, we calculate the time rate of change of $\mathbf{L}$ in the Heisenberg picture with the help of Eqs. (24.10) and (24.31):

$$i\hbar \frac{dL_x}{dt} = L_x H - H L_x$$

$$= c\boldsymbol{\alpha} \cdot [(yp_z - zp_y)\mathbf{p} - \mathbf{p}(yp_z - zp_y)]$$

$$= -i\hbar c(\alpha_z p_y - \alpha_y p_z) \tag{53.2}$$

since $\mathbf{L}$ commutes with any spherically symmetric function such as $V(r)$. It is apparent that $\mathbf{L}$ does not commute with H and hence is not a constant of the motion. However, we expect on physical grounds that it is possible to define a total angular momentum that is constant in a central field of force. This means that we must find another operator such that the commutator of its x component with H is the negative of the right side of (53.2); the sum of this operator and $\mathbf{L}$ is then a constant of the motion and can be interpreted as the total angular momentum.

It is not difficult to see that the desired operator is a multiple of the σ' defined in (52.19). From (52.11) and (52.13), we find that σ'_x commutes with α_x and β, although not with the other components of $\boldsymbol{\alpha}$:

$$\sigma'_x \alpha_y - \alpha_y \sigma'_x = \begin{bmatrix} \sigma_x & 0 \\ 0 & \sigma_x \end{bmatrix} \begin{bmatrix} 0 & \sigma_y \\ \sigma_y & 0 \end{bmatrix} - \begin{bmatrix} 0 & \sigma_y \\ \sigma_y & 0 \end{bmatrix} \begin{bmatrix} \sigma_x & 0 \\ 0 & \sigma_x \end{bmatrix}$$

$$= \begin{bmatrix} 0 & i\sigma_z \\ i\sigma_z & 0 \end{bmatrix} - \begin{bmatrix} 0 & -i\sigma_z \\ -i\sigma_z & 0 \end{bmatrix} = 2i\alpha_z$$

The time rate of change of $\boldsymbol{\sigma}'$ can now be obtained:

$$i\hbar \frac{d\sigma'_x}{dt} = \sigma'_x H - H \sigma'_x = 2ic(\alpha_z p_y - \alpha_y p_z) \tag{53.3}$$

It is apparent from (53.2) and (53.3) that the quantity $\mathbf{L} + \frac{1}{2}\hbar\boldsymbol{\sigma}'$ commutes with H and can therefore be taken to be the total angular momentum. We refer to the operator

$$\mathbf{S} = \tfrac{1}{2}\hbar\boldsymbol{\sigma}' \tag{53.4}$$

as the spin angular momentum of the electron.

APPROXIMATE REDUCTION; SPIN–ORBIT ENERGY

We now wish to show that the spin-orbit energy (47.13) is a consequence of the Dirac equation. This term can be shown to be of order $(v/c)^2$ times the potential energy:

$$\frac{1}{V} \frac{1}{2m^2c^2} \frac{1}{r} \frac{dV}{dr} (\mathbf{L} \cdot \mathbf{S}) \sim \frac{1}{V} \frac{1}{m^2c^2} \frac{V}{a^2} pa\hbar \sim \frac{v^2}{c^2}$$

where a represents the linear dimensions of the system, and

$$\frac{\hbar}{a} \sim p \sim mv$$

Thus the approximations that led to (52.27) are not adequate for the present purpose.

In order to obtain a consistent approximation that is expressed in terms of the more familiar two-component wave functions, we replace ψ in (53.1) by ψ_1 and ψ_2, which now represent the first two and the last two components of ψ, respectively. We assume that ψ_1, ψ_2 together constitute a nonrelativistic energy eigenfunction, which means that

$$E = E' + mc^2$$

is regarded as a number rather than an operator; E' and V are assumed to be small in comparison with mc^2. The wave equation then becomes

$$(E' - V)\psi_1 - c\boldsymbol{\sigma} \cdot \mathbf{p}\psi_2 = 0 \tag{53.5}$$

$$(E' + 2mc^2 - V)\psi_2 - c\boldsymbol{\sigma} \cdot \mathbf{p}\psi_1 = 0$$

where $\mathbf{p}$ is still an operator. It is apparent from the second of these equations that ψ_2 is of the order of v/c times ψ_1, and so we eliminate it to obtain an equation in terms of ψ_1 alone. The substitution

$$\psi_2 = (E' + 2mc^2 - V)^{-1}c\mathbf{\sigma} \cdot \mathbf{p}\psi_1$$

in the first of Eqs. (53.5) gives

$$E'\psi_1 = \frac{1}{2m} (\mathbf{\sigma} \cdot \mathbf{p}) \left(1 + \frac{E' - V}{2mc^2}\right)^{-1} (\mathbf{\sigma} \cdot \mathbf{p})\psi_1 + V\psi_1 \qquad (53.6)$$

Thus far, no approximations have been made.

The desired approximation is obtained by keeping the lowest terms in an expansion in powers of $(E' - V)/2mc^2$. The following relations are easily established:

$$\left(1 + \frac{E' - V}{2mc^2}\right)^{-1} \approx 1 - \frac{E' - V}{2mc^2}$$

$$\mathbf{p}V = V\mathbf{p} - i\hbar\nabla V$$

$$(\mathbf{\sigma} \cdot \nabla V)(\mathbf{\sigma} \cdot \mathbf{p}) = (\nabla V) \cdot \mathbf{p} + i\mathbf{\sigma} \cdot [(\nabla V) \times \mathbf{p}]$$

With the help of these, (53.6) becomes

$$E'\psi_1 = \left[\left(1 - \frac{E' - V}{2mc^2}\right) \frac{\mathbf{p}^2}{2m} + V\right]\psi_1$$
$$- \frac{\hbar^2}{4m^2c^2} (\nabla V) \cdot (\nabla\psi_1) + \frac{\hbar^2}{4m^2c^2} \mathbf{\sigma} \cdot [(\nabla V) \times \mathbf{p}\psi_1] \quad (53.7)$$

Further simplications can be made if V is spherically symmetric. We use the relations

$$(\nabla V) \cdot \nabla = \frac{dV}{dr} \frac{\partial}{\partial r}$$

$$\nabla V = \frac{1}{r} \frac{dV}{dr} \mathbf{r}$$

and note that $E' - V$ is approximately equal to $\mathbf{p}^2/2m$, the accuracy being sufficient to replace the second-order term $(E' - V)\mathbf{p}^2$ in (53.7) by $\mathbf{p}^4/2m$. We can then rewrite (53.7) as

$$E'\psi_1 = \left(\frac{\mathbf{p}^2}{2m} - \frac{\mathbf{p}^4}{8m^3c^2} + V - \frac{\hbar^2}{4m^2c^2} \frac{dV}{dr} \frac{\partial}{\partial r} + \frac{1}{2m^2c^2} \frac{1}{r} \frac{dV}{dr} \mathbf{S} \cdot \mathbf{L}\right)\psi_1$$
$$(53.8)$$

where now $\mathbf{S} = \frac{1}{2}\hbar\mathbf{\sigma}$ and $\mathbf{L} = \mathbf{r} \times \mathbf{p}$.

The first and third terms on the right side of (53.8) give the non-relativistic Schrödinger equation. The second term has the form of the classical relativistic mass correction, which can be obtained by expanding the square root of (51.2):

$$E' = E - mc^2 = (c^2\mathbf{p}^2 + m^2c^4)^{\frac{1}{2}} - mc^2 \approx \frac{\mathbf{p}^2}{2m} - \frac{\mathbf{p}^4}{8m^3c^2}$$

The last term is the spin-orbit energy (47.14), which is now seen to appear as an automatic consequence of the Dirac equation. The fourth term is a similar relativistic correction to the potential energy, which does not have a classical analog. Since it does not involve the angular momenta, it is much more difficult to demonstrate experimentally than the spin-orbit energy.[1]

SEPARATION OF THE EQUATION

The Dirac equation for a central field can be separated without approximation in spherical coordinates. The procedure is more complicated than for either of the Schrödinger equations because of the interdependence of orbital and spin angular momenta. We start by defining radial momentum and velocity operators

$$p_r = r^{-1}(\mathbf{r} \cdot \mathbf{p} - i\hbar) \qquad \alpha_r = r^{-1}(\boldsymbol{\alpha} \cdot \mathbf{r}) \qquad (53.9)$$

both of which can be shown to be hermitian. We also define an operator k that will shortly be seen to be related to the total angular momentum:

$$\hbar k = \beta(\boldsymbol{\sigma}' \cdot \mathbf{L} + \hbar) \qquad (53.10)$$

where $\mathbf{L} = \mathbf{r} \times \mathbf{p}$. It can be shown by direct substitution, with the help of (52.24), that

$$\alpha_r p_r + i\hbar r^{-1}\alpha_r\beta k = \boldsymbol{\alpha} \cdot \mathbf{p}$$

The hamiltonian (53.1) then becomes

$$H = c\alpha_r p_r + \frac{i\hbar c}{r}\alpha_r\beta k + \beta mc^2 + V \qquad (53.11)$$

The following relations can be established with the help of the definitions (53.9) and (53.10) and the relations of Sec. 52:

$$\alpha_r k - k\alpha_r = 0 \qquad \beta k - k\beta = 0 \qquad p_r k - kp_r = 0$$

$$\alpha_r p_r - p_r\alpha_r = 0$$

These show that k commutes with the hamiltonian (53.11) and so is a constant of the motion. The eigenvalues of k can be inferred by squaring (53.10):

$$\hbar^2 k^2 = (\boldsymbol{\sigma}' \cdot \mathbf{L})^2 + 2\hbar(\boldsymbol{\sigma}' \cdot \mathbf{L}) + \hbar^2 = (\mathbf{L} + \tfrac{1}{2}\hbar\boldsymbol{\sigma}')^2 + \tfrac{1}{4}\hbar^2 \qquad (53.12)$$

The quantity $(\mathbf{L} + \tfrac{1}{2}\hbar\boldsymbol{\sigma}')^2$ is the square of the total angular momentum

[1] For further discussion of this term, see E. U. Condon and G. H. Shortley, "The Theory of Atomic Spectra," p. 130 (Cambridge, London, 1935).

and has eigenvalues $j(j + 1)\hbar^2$, where j is half a positive odd integer. Thus k^2 has eigenvalues $(j + \frac{1}{2})^2$, so that k can be ± 1, ± 2, ...

We now choose a representation in which H and k are diagonal and represented by the numbers E and k, respectively. α_r and β can then be represented by any hermitian matrices that satisfy the relations

$$\alpha_r{}^2 = \beta^2 = 1 \qquad \alpha_r\beta + \beta\alpha_r = 0$$

which are not difficult to verify. Such matrices can have two rows and columns; for example, we can put

$$\beta = \begin{bmatrix} 1 & 0 \\ 0 & -1 \end{bmatrix} \qquad \alpha_r = \begin{bmatrix} 0 & -i \\ i & 0 \end{bmatrix} \tag{53.13}$$

Now the angular and spin parts of the wave function are fixed by the requirement that ψ be an eigenfunction of the k operator (53.10). For such purposes as the computation of energy levels, we need be concerned only with the radial part; because of the structure of (53.13), this has two components, which we write

$$\begin{bmatrix} r^{-1}F(r) \\ r^{-1}G(r) \end{bmatrix} \tag{53.14}$$

Substitution of (53.13) and (53.14) into the wave equation with the hamiltonian (53.11) gives us the radial equations for an electron moving in a central field. We make use of the relation

$$p_r = -i\hbar\left(\frac{\partial}{\partial r} + \frac{1}{r}\right)$$

to obtain

$$(E - mc^2 - V)F + \hbar c\frac{dG}{dr} + \frac{\hbar ck}{r}G = 0$$

$$(E + mc^2 - V)G - \hbar c\frac{dF}{dr} + \frac{\hbar ck}{r}F = 0 \tag{53.15}$$

It is convenient to make the numerical substitutions

$$\alpha_1 = \frac{mc^2 + E}{\hbar c} \qquad \alpha_2 = \frac{mc^2 - E}{\hbar c} \qquad \rho = \alpha r$$

$$\alpha = +(\alpha_1\alpha_2)^{\frac{1}{2}} = \frac{(m^2c^4 - E^2)^{\frac{1}{2}}}{\hbar c} \tag{53.16}$$

in terms of which Eqs. (53.15) become

$$\left(\frac{d}{d\rho} + \frac{k}{\rho}\right)G - \left(\frac{\alpha_2}{\alpha} + \frac{V}{\hbar c\alpha}\right)F = 0$$

$$\left(\frac{d}{d\rho} - \frac{k}{\rho}\right)F - \left(\frac{\alpha_1}{\alpha} - \frac{V}{\hbar c\alpha}\right)G = 0 \tag{53.17}$$

THE HYDROGEN ATOM

We now find the energy eigenvalues of (53.17) when $V(r) = -Ze^2/r$; with $\gamma \equiv Ze^2/\hbar c$, the quantity $V/\hbar c\alpha$ becomes $-\gamma/\rho$. We follow a procedure that is analogous to that of Sec. 16 and put

$$F(\rho) = f(\rho)e^{-\rho} \qquad G(\rho) = g(\rho)e^{-\rho} \tag{53.18}$$

The equations for f and g are

$$g' - g + \frac{kg}{\rho} - \left(\frac{\alpha_2}{\alpha} - \frac{\gamma}{\rho}\right)f = 0$$

$$f' - f - \frac{kf}{\rho} - \left(\frac{\alpha_1}{\alpha} + \frac{\gamma}{\rho}\right)g = 0 \tag{53.19}$$

We look for solutions of (53.19) in the form of power series:

$$f = \rho^s(a_0 + a_1\rho + \cdots) \qquad a_0 \neq 0$$

$$g = \rho^s(b_0 + b_1\rho + \cdots) \qquad b_0 \neq 0 \tag{53.20}$$

Since (53.14) is supposed to be finite at $r = 0$, we expect that s is greater than or equal to 1. However, in analogy with the solution of the Schrödinger relativistic equation (51.15) for the coulomb field, we shall admit a value of s slightly less than 1.

We substitute (53.20) into (53.19) and equate the coefficients of $\rho^{s+\nu-1}$ to zero:

$$(s + \nu + k)b_\nu - b_{\nu-1} + \gamma a_\nu - \frac{\alpha_2}{\alpha}a_{\nu-1} = 0$$

$$(s + \nu - k)a_\nu - a_{\nu-1} - \gamma b_\nu - \frac{\alpha_1}{\alpha}b_{\nu-1} = 0 \tag{53.21}$$

for $\nu > 0$. When $\nu = 0$, the equations analogous to (53.21) are

$$(s + k)b_0 + \gamma a_0 = 0$$

$$(s - k)a_0 - \gamma b_0 = 0 \tag{53.22}$$

Equations (53.22) have the required nonvanishing solution for a_0 and b_0 only if the determinant of their coefficients vanishes; this gives

$$s = \pm(k^2 - \gamma^2)^{\frac{1}{2}} \tag{53.23}$$

Because of the boundary condition at the origin, we take the upper sign for s in (53.23).

A relation between a_ν and b_ν can be obtained by multiplying the first of Eqs. (53.21) by α, the second by α_2, and subtracting:

$$b_\nu[\alpha(s + \nu + k) + \alpha_2\gamma] = a_\nu[\alpha_2(s + \nu - k) - \alpha\gamma] \tag{53.24}$$

where use has been made of (53.16). We can now examine the behavior of the solution at large r. Unless both the series (53.20) terminate, this behavior is determined by their high terms, and so we can neglect constant factors in comparison with ν. We then obtain from (53.21) and (53.24)

$$a_\nu \approx \frac{2}{\nu} a_{\nu-1} \qquad b_\nu \approx \frac{2}{\nu} b_{\nu-1}$$

This means that both series have the asymptotic form $e^{2\rho}$, and regular solutions are obtained only if they terminate. Suppose that this occurs at $\nu = n'$, so that $a_{n'+1} = b_{n'+1} = 0$. Then both Eqs. (53.21) give the relation

$$\alpha_2 a_{n'} = -\alpha b_{n'} \qquad n' = 0, 1, 2, \ldots \qquad (53.25)$$

We obtain energy levels by setting $\nu = n'$ in (53.24) and making use of (53.25). With the help of (53.16), we find that

$$2\alpha(s + n') = \gamma(\alpha_1 - \alpha_2) = \frac{2E\gamma}{\hbar c}$$

which incidentally shows that $E > 0$. The square of this is

$$(m^2 c^4 - E^2)(s + n')^2 = E^2 \gamma^2$$

which is easily solved to give

$$E = mc^2 \left[1 + \frac{\gamma^2}{(s + n')^2} \right]^{-\frac{1}{2}} \qquad (53.26)$$

Equations (53.23) and (53.26) are equivalent to the formula first derived by Sommerfeld[1] on the basis of the old quantum theory. This formula accounts quite well for the spectrum of hydrogen.[2] The fine structure is made evident by expanding (53.26) in powers of γ^2. The result to terms of order γ^4 resembles (51.21) but is not quite the same:

$$E = mc^2 \left[1 - \frac{\gamma^2}{2n^2} - \frac{\gamma^4}{2n^4} \left(\frac{n}{|k|} - \frac{3}{4} \right) \right] \qquad (53.27)$$

where $n = n' + |k|$ is the total quantum number of Eq. (16.14), and $|k|$ can take on positive integer values. The total spread in energy of the fine-structure levels for a given n is easily seen from (53.27) to be

$$\frac{mc^2 \gamma^4}{n^3} \frac{n-1}{2n}$$

This is substantially less than the value (51.22) obtained from the Schrödinger relativistic equation and is in agreement with experiment.

[1] A. Sommerfeld, *Ann. Physik.* **51**, 1 (1916).

[2] There are, however, small but important deviations from this formula; see W. E. Lamb, *Rept. on Progr. Phys.* **14**, 19 (1951).

CLASSIFICATION OF ENERGY LEVELS

For $n' > 0$, all positive and negative integer values of k are permissible [we saw from (53.12) that k cannot be zero]. For $n' = 0$, however, a contradiction can arise between (53.22) and (53.25); these give

$$\frac{b_0}{a_0} = -\frac{\gamma}{s+k} \quad \text{and} \quad \frac{b_0}{a_0} = -\frac{\alpha_2}{\alpha} \quad (53.28)$$

respectively. Since $s < |k|$, the first of these expressions is positive or negative according as k is negative or positive, whereas the second is always negative. Thus, for $n' = 0$, k can assume only positive integer values.

Thus far we have shown only that the j value of a level is equal to $|k| - \frac{1}{2}$. In order to connect l with the level, we must make the non-relativistic approximation that the orbital angular momentum is well defined. Since in this case F in (53.14) is much larger than G, we can replace β by -1 and $\boldsymbol{\sigma}'$ by $\boldsymbol{\sigma}$ in (53.10). In this approximation, $(\mathbf{L} + \frac{1}{2}\hbar\boldsymbol{\sigma})^2 = [l(l+1) + \frac{3}{4}]\hbar^2 + \hbar\boldsymbol{\sigma} \cdot \mathbf{L}$ and is also equal to $j(j+1)\hbar^2$. We obtain in this way

$$k = j(j+1) - l(l+1) + \frac{1}{4} = \begin{cases} l+1 & j = l + \frac{1}{2} \\ -l & j = l - \frac{1}{2} \end{cases}$$

As an example of the energy levels in hydrogen, we consider the case $n = 3$. The radial quantum number n' can be 0, 1, or 2, and k can be $\pm(3 - n')$ except that k can be only $+3$ when $n' = 0$. The levels with their nonrelativistic classifications are

n'	k	l	j	
0	3	2	$\frac{5}{2}$	$^2D_{\frac{5}{2}}$
1	-2	2	$\frac{3}{2}$	$^2D_{\frac{3}{2}}$
1	2	1	$\frac{3}{2}$	$^2P_{\frac{3}{2}}$
2	-1	1	$\frac{1}{2}$	$^2P_{\frac{1}{2}}$
2	1	0	$\frac{1}{2}$	$^2S_{\frac{1}{2}}$

According to (53.23) and (53.26), states with the same $|k|$ or j have the same energy; Eq. (53.27) shows that the energy increases with increasing $|k|$.

NEGATIVE ENERGY STATES

We have seen that both the Schrödinger and Dirac relativistic equations admit of solutions for which a particle has negative kinetic energy and negative rest mass. These solutions correspond to the negative square root of the classical energy equation (51.2).   The negative-energy solutions cannot be ignored in the quantum theory, as they are in the classical theory, since there is nothing to prevent a charged particle from making a radiative transition from a state of positive energy to a state of negative energy.

Dirac proposed that we regard the negative energy states of Eq. (52.22) as being full, in which case the exclusion principle prevents transitions into such occupied states.   The normal state of the vacuum then consists of an infinite density of negative-energy electrons.   It is assumed that there are no electromagnetic or gravitational effects of these electrons but that deviations from the norm produced by emptying one or more of the negative energy states can be observed.   The absence of a negatively charged electron that has negative mass and kinetic energy would then be expected to manifest itself as a positively charged particle that has an equal positive mass and kinetic energy.   In this way, a "hole" theory of *positrons* can be formulated.

With so many electrons present, however, the theory is no longer the one-particle theory contemplated when the wave equation was set up.   A many-particle theory can be based on the Dirac equation in accordance with the formalism of quantized fields discussed in the next chapter, and a theory of positrons can be developed without recourse to holes.

It might at first be thought that a similar technique cannot be applied to the Schrödinger relativistic equation, since it describes a particle of zero spin, which we expect to obey Einstein-Bose statistics rather than the exclusion principle.   However, Pauli and Weisskopf[1] showed that the quantized field energy is always positive in this case, even though the parameter E in the wave equation can be either positive or negative.   Moreover, the charge in the quantized field can have either sign, corresponding to the ambiguity of the sign of P noted after Eq. (51.8).   Thus both the theories discussed in this chapter predict the existence of particles that have positive energies and both signs of electric charge.   The appearance of spin angular momentum as a consequence of the Dirac equation shows that this is the theory that describes electrons.

PROBLEMS

1.   Use the nonrelativistic approximation implied in (51.11) and in the immediately following discussion to show that the expression (51.8) for P reduces to (7.1) in the proper limit.

2.   Solve the Schrödinger relativistic equation for an attractive square well potential of depth V_0 and radius a, after determining the continuity conditions at $r = a$.

[1] W. Pauli and V. Weisskopf, *Helv. Phys. Acta* **7**, 709 (1934).

Obtain an explicit expression for the minimum V_0 with given a that just binds a particle of mass m.

3. Find the solution of the Schrödinger relativistic equation that is finite at $r = 0$ and corresponds to the potential energy $e\phi = -Ze^2/a$ for $r < a$ and $e\phi = -Ze^2/r$ for $r > a$, when a is very small. Note that only the first two terms of each power series in r need be retained. Show that the solution for $r > a$ approaches that which corresponds to the upper sign in (51.19) when $a \to 0$.

4. Show that any matrix with two rows and columns can be expressed as a linear combination of σ_x, σ_y, σ_z, and 1. Use this result to show that there is no matrix that anticommutes with each of the first three of these.

5. Show explicitly that the wave functions (52.17) and (52.18) are not eigenfunctions of any component of the spin angular momentum $\frac{1}{2}\hbar\sigma'$.

6. Obtain an expression for the current density given by (52.20) for a free-particle wave function in the nonrelativistic limit.

7. Make use of Eqs. (52.11), (52.13), and (52.19) to verify Eq. (52.24).

8. Prove that the operators α_r and k defined by Eqs. (53.9) and (53.10) commute with each other and that $\hbar^2 k^2$ is given by the right side of (53.12).

9. Discuss the connection between the $\boldsymbol{\alpha} \cdot \mathbf{E}$ term in Eq. (52.27) and the spin-orbit energy.

10. Show that the negative square roots that could appear in arriving at Eqs. (51.16) and (53.26) actually do not correspond to bound states.

11. Use the selection rules $\Delta l = \pm 1$, $\Delta j = 0$, ± 1 to list the frequencies of the allowed transitions between the states with $n = 2$ and $n = 3$ for the coulomb field, in both the Schrödinger and Dirac relativistic theories. In particular, show that the latter theory gives seven lines, of which five are distinct, whereas the former gives three lines that are much more spread apart.

12. Solve the Dirac equation for an attractive square well potential of depth V_0 and radius a, after determining the continuity conditions at $r = a$. Obtain an explicit expression for the minimum V_0 with given a that just binds a particle of mass m, and compare with the answer to Prob. 2.

14

The Quantization of Wave Fields

The theory of quantum mechanics presented thus far in this book has dealt with systems that, in the classical limit, consist of material particles. We wish now to extend the theory so that it can be applied to the electromagnetic field and thus provide a consistent basis for the quantum theory of radiation. The quantization of a wave field imparts to it some particle properties; in the case of the electromagnetic field, a theory of light quanta (photons) results. The field quantization technique can also be applied to a ψ field, such as that described by the nonrelativistic Schrödinger equation (6.16) or by one of the relativistic equations (51.4) or (52.3). As we shall see in the nonrelativistic case (Sec. 55), it then converts a one-particle theory into a many-particle theory, in a manner equivalent to the transition from Eq. (6.16) to (16.1) or (40.7). Because of this equivalence, it might seem that the quantization of ψ fields merely provides another formal approach to the many-particle problem. However, the new formalism can deal as well with processes that involve the creation or destruction of material particles (radioactive beta decay, meson-nucleon interaction).

This chapter is intended to serve as an introduction to quantum field theory.[1] We start in Sec. 54 with a discussion of the classical and quantum equations of motion for a wave field, without specifying the detailed nature of the field. The application to Eq. (6.16) is used as a first example in Sec. 55. Several other particle wave equations (including the relativistic Schrödinger and Dirac equations) have also been quantized but are not discussed here. The electromagnetic field is considered in the last two sections.

54☐CLASSICAL AND QUANTUM FIELD EQUATIONS

A general procedure for the quantization of the equations of motion of a classical system was obtained in Sec. 24. We start with the lagrangian function for the system and verify that it gives the correct classical equations. The momenta canonically conjugate to the coordinates of the system are found from the lagrangian, and a hamiltonian function is set up. The classical hamiltonian equations of motion are then converted into quantum equations by the substitution of commutator brackets for Poisson brackets; this gives the change of the dynamical variables with time in the Heisenberg picture. We now show how this procedure can be applied in its entirety to a wave field $\psi(\mathbf{r},t)$, which we assume for the present to be real.[2]

COORDINATES OF THE FIELD

A wave field is specified by its amplitudes at all points of space and the dependence of these amplitudes on the time, in much the same way as a system of particles is specified by the positional coordinates q_i and their dependence on the time. The field evidently has an infinite number of degrees of freedom and is analogous to a system that consists of an infinite number of particles. It is natural, then, to use the amplitudes $\psi(\mathbf{r},t)$ at all points $\mathbf{r}$ as coordinates, in analogy with the particle coordinates $q_i(t)$ of Sec. 24.

It is not necessary, however, to proceed in this way. As an alternative, we can expand ψ in some complete orthonormal set of functions

---

[1] For further discussion, see P. A. M. Dirac, "The Principles of Quantum Mechanics," 4th ed., chaps. X, XII (Oxford, New York, 1958); H. Goldstein, "Classical Mechanics," chap. 11 (Addison-Wesley, Reading, Mass., 1950); J. D. Bjorken and S. D. Drell, "Relativistic Quantum Fields" (McGraw-Hill, New York, 1965); E. Henley and W. Thirring, "Elementary Quantum Field Theory" (McGraw-Hill, New York, 1962); S. S. Schweber, "An Introduction to Relativistic Quantum Field Theory" (Harper & Row, New York, 1961); J. J. Sakurai, "Advanced Quantum Mechanics" (Addison-Wesley, Reading, Mass., 1967).

[2] W. Heisenberg and W. Pauli, Z. *Physik* **56**, 1 (1929); **59**, 168 (1930).

u_k:

$$\psi(\mathbf{r},t) = S_k a_k(t) u_k(\mathbf{r}) \tag{54.1}$$

The expansion coefficients a_k in (54.1) can be regarded as the field coordinates, and the field equations can be expressed in terms of either ψ or the a_k. We shall use the wave amplitudes at all points as the field coordinates in this section. It will be convenient for some of the later work to make use of the coefficients a_k.

TIME DERIVATIVES

It is important to have clearly in mind the meaning of time derivatives in classical and quantum field theories. In classical particle theory, both total and partial time derivatives were defined in connection with a function $F(q_i,p_i,t)$ of the coordinates, momenta, and time; these derivatives are related through Eq. (24.22). Similarly, both derivatives were defined for a Heisenberg-picture operator and related to each other as in Eq. (24.10). In classical field theory, $\psi(\mathbf{r})$ is the analog of q_i, and the only time derivative that can be defined is $\partial\psi/\partial t$; we refer to it as $\dot\psi$ in analogy with $\dot q_i$ in the particle case. Thus, in the classical hamiltonian equations of motion of the field [(54.19) below], we interpret $\dot\psi$, and also $\dot\pi$, as partial time derivatives. However a functional $F(\psi,\pi,t)$ can depend explicitly on the time as well as on the field, so that it is important to distinguish between dF/dt and $\partial F/\partial t$ in Eq. (54.20).

The same situation appears in quantum field theory. No distinction can be made between $d\psi/dt$ and $\partial\psi/\partial t$, and both are referred to as $\dot\psi$. On the other hand, a Heisenberg-picture operator can depend explicitly on the time, and the distinction between the two time derivatives must be made in Eq. (54.23).

CLASSICAL LAGRANGIAN EQUATION

The lagrangian $L(q_i,\dot q_i,t)$ used in Sec. 24 is a function of the time and a functional of the possible paths $q_i(t)$ of the system. The actual paths are derived from the variational principle (24.17):

$$\delta \int_{t_1}^{t_2} L\, dt = 0 \qquad \delta q_i(t_1) = \delta q_i(t_2) = 0$$

By analogy, we expect the field lagrangian to be a functional of the field amplitude $\psi(\mathbf{r},t)$. It can usually be expressed as the integral over all space of a *lagrangian density* L:

$$L = \int L(\psi,\nabla\psi,\dot\psi,t)\, d^3r \tag{54.2}$$

where, as remarked above, $\dot\psi$ is $\partial\psi/\partial t$ or $d\psi/dt$. The appearance of $\nabla\psi$ as an argument of L is a consequence of the continuous dependence of ψ

on $\mathbf{r}$ (continuously infinite number of degrees of freedom); higher derivatives of ψ could also be present but do not seem to arise in problems of physical interest. The variational principle that corresponds to (24.17) is

$$\delta \int_{t_1}^{t_2} L \, dt = \delta \int_{t_1}^{t_2} \int L \, dt \, d^3r = \int_{t_1}^{t_2} \int (\delta L) \, dt \, d^3r = 0 \qquad (54.3)$$

where the infinitesimal variation $\delta\psi$ of ψ is subject to the restrictions

$$\delta\psi(\mathbf{r},t_1) = \delta\psi(\mathbf{r},t_2) = 0 \qquad (54.4)$$

If L has the form indicated in (54.2), its variation can be written

$$\delta L = \frac{\partial L}{\partial \psi} \delta\psi + \sum_{xyz} \frac{\partial L}{\partial(\partial\psi/\partial x)} \delta\left(\frac{\partial\psi}{\partial x}\right) + \frac{\partial L}{\partial \dot\psi} \delta\dot\psi \qquad (54.5)$$

where the summation over x, y, z implies the sum of three terms with y and z substituted for x. Now $\delta\dot\psi$ is the difference between the original and varied $\dot\psi$ and hence is the time derivative of the variation of ψ. This and the similar expression for $\delta(\partial\psi/\partial x)$ can be written

$$\delta\dot\psi = \frac{\partial}{\partial t}(\delta\psi) \qquad \delta\left(\frac{\partial\psi}{\partial x}\right) = \frac{\partial}{\partial x}(\delta\psi)$$

Equation (54.3) then becomes

$$\int_{t_1}^{t_2} \int \left[\frac{\partial L}{\partial \psi} \delta\psi + \sum_{xyz} \frac{\partial L}{\partial(\partial\psi/\partial x)} \frac{\partial}{\partial x}(\delta\psi) + \frac{\partial L}{\partial \dot\psi} \frac{\partial}{\partial t}(\delta\psi) \right] dt \, d^3r = 0 \quad (54.6)$$

The summation terms in (54.6) can be integrated by parts with respect to the space coordinates; the surface terms vanish, either because ψ falls off rapidly enough at infinite distance, or because ψ obeys periodic boundary conditions at the walls of a large but finite box. The last term of (54.6) can be integrated by parts with respect to the time, and the boundary terms vanish because of (54.4). Equation (54.6) can therefore be written

$$\int_{t_1}^{t_2} \int \left\{ \frac{\partial L}{\partial \psi} - \sum_{xyz} \frac{\partial}{\partial x}\left[\frac{\partial L}{\partial(\partial\psi/\partial x)} \right] - \frac{\partial}{\partial t}\left(\frac{\partial L}{\partial \dot\psi}\right) \right\} \delta\psi \, dt \, d^3r = 0 \qquad (54.7)$$

Since (54.3) is valid for an arbitrary variation $\delta\psi$ at each point in space, Eq. (54.7) is equivalent to the differential equation

$$\frac{\partial L}{\partial \psi} - \sum_{xyz} \frac{\partial}{\partial x}\left[\frac{\partial L}{\partial(\partial\psi/\partial x)} \right] - \frac{\partial}{\partial t}\left(\frac{\partial L}{\partial \dot\psi}\right) = 0 \qquad (54.8)$$

Equation (54.8) is the classical field equation derived from the lagrangian density $L(\psi,\nabla\psi,\dot\psi,t)$.

FUNCTIONAL DERIVATIVE

In order to pursue further the analogy with particle mechanics, it is desirable to rewrite Eq. (54.8) in terms of L rather than $\mathbf{L}$. Since the aggregate of values of ψ and $\dot\psi$ at all points is analogous to the q_i and $\dot q_i$ of particle theory, we require derivatives of L with respect to ψ and $\dot\psi$ at particular points. These are called *functional derivatives* and are denoted by $\partial L/\partial\psi$ and $\partial L/\partial\dot\psi$. Expressions for them can be obtained by dividing up all space into small cells and replacing volume integrals by summations over these cells. The average values of quantities such as ψ, $\nabla\psi$, and $\dot\psi$ in the ith cell are denoted by subscripts i, and the volume of that cell by $\delta\tau_i$. Then

$$\sum_i L[\psi_i, (\nabla\psi)_i, \dot\psi_i, t]\, \delta\tau_i$$

approaches L in the limit in which all the $\delta\tau_i$ approach zero.

In similar fashion, the t integrand in Eq. (54.6) or (54.7) can be replaced by

$$\sum_i \left\{ \frac{\partial L}{\partial\psi} - \sum_{xyz} \frac{\partial}{\partial x}\left[\frac{\partial L}{\partial(\partial\psi/\partial x)} \right] \right\}_i \delta\psi_i\, \delta\tau_i + \sum_i \left(\frac{\partial L}{\partial\dot\psi} \right)_i \delta\dot\psi_i\, \delta\tau_i$$

where the variation in L is now produced by independent variations in the ψ_i and the $\dot\psi_i$. Suppose now that all the $\delta\psi_i$ and $\delta\dot\psi_i$ are zero except for a particular $\delta\psi_j$. It is natural to relate the functional derivative of L with respect to ψ for a point in the jth cell to the ratio of δL to $\delta\psi_j$; we therefore define

$$\frac{\partial L}{\partial\psi} = \lim_{\delta\tau_j\to 0} \frac{\delta L}{\delta\psi_j\, \delta\tau_j} = \frac{\partial L}{\partial\psi} - \sum_{xyz} \frac{\partial}{\partial x}\left[\frac{\partial L}{\partial(\partial\psi/\partial x)} \right] \tag{54.9}$$

Similarly, the functional derivative of L with respect to $\dot\psi$ is defined by setting all the $\delta\psi_i$ and $\delta\dot\psi_i$ equal to zero except for a particular $\delta\dot\psi_j$:

$$\frac{\partial L}{\partial\dot\psi} = \lim_{\delta\tau_j\to 0} \frac{\delta L}{\delta\dot\psi_j\, \delta\tau_j} = \frac{\partial L}{\partial\dot\psi} \tag{54.10}$$

Here again the point $\mathbf{r}$ at which the functional derivative is evaluated is in the jth cell. Substitution of (54.9) and (54.10) into (54.8) gives

$$\frac{\partial}{\partial t}\frac{\partial L}{\partial\dot\psi} - \frac{\partial L}{\partial\psi} = 0 \tag{54.11}$$

which closely resembles the lagrangian equations (24.18) for a system of particles.

CLASSICAL HAMILTONIAN EQUATIONS

The momentum canonically conjugate to ψ_j can be defined as in particle mechanics to be the ratio of δL to the infinitesimal change $\delta\dot\psi_j$ when all the other $\delta\dot\psi_i$ and all the $\delta\psi_i$ are zero. We thus obtain

$$P_j = \frac{\delta L}{\delta\dot\psi_j} = \delta\tau_j\left(\frac{\partial L}{\partial\dot\psi}\right)_j \tag{54.12}$$

It follows from (54.11) and (54.12) that

$$\dot P_j = \delta\tau_j\left(\frac{\partial L}{\partial\psi}\right)_j \tag{54.13}$$

The analogy with Eq. (24.19) then gives for the hamiltonian

$$H = \sum_i P_i\dot\psi_i - L = \sum_i\left(\frac{\partial L}{\partial\dot\psi}\right)_i\dot\psi_i\,\delta\tau_i - L \tag{54.14}$$

We write H as the volume integral of a *hamiltonian density* $\boldsymbol{H}$ and assume that the cells are small enough so that the difference between a volume integral and the corresponding cell summation can be ignored; we then have

$$H = \int \boldsymbol{H}\,d^3r \qquad \boldsymbol{H} = \pi\dot\psi - \boldsymbol{L} \qquad \pi \equiv \frac{\partial\boldsymbol{L}}{\partial\dot\psi} = \frac{\partial L}{\partial\dot\psi} \tag{54.15}$$

The approximate hamiltonian (54.14), with the relations (54.12) and (54.13), can be manipulated in precisely the same way as the hamiltonian for a system of particles. Instead of showing this explicitly, we now work with the true field hamiltonian H given in (54.15), which is a functional of ψ and π from which $\dot\psi$ has been eliminated. The classical hamiltonian equations of motion will be derived without further recourse to the cell approximation. The variation of L produced by variations of ψ and $\dot\psi$ can be written, with the help of (54.11) and (54.15),

$$\delta L = \int\left(\frac{\partial L}{\partial\psi}\,\delta\psi + \frac{\partial L}{\partial\dot\psi}\,\delta\dot\psi\right)d^3r = \int(\dot\pi\,\delta\psi + \pi\,\delta\dot\psi)\,d^3r$$

$$= \int[\delta(\pi\dot\psi) + \dot\pi\,\delta\psi - \dot\psi\,\delta\pi]\,d^3r$$

$$= \delta H + \delta L + \int(\dot\pi\,\delta\psi - \dot\psi\,\delta\pi)\,d^3r \tag{54.16}$$

The variation of H produced by the corresponding variations of ψ and π can be written

$$\delta H = \int\left(\frac{\partial H}{\partial\psi}\,\delta\psi + \frac{\partial H}{\partial\pi}\,\delta\pi\right)d^3r \tag{54.17}$$

It follows from the earlier discussion of functional derivatives that

$$\frac{\partial H}{\partial \psi} = \frac{\partial H}{\partial \psi} - \sum_{xyz} \frac{\partial}{\partial x} \frac{\partial H}{\partial(\partial\psi/\partial x)}$$

$$\frac{\partial H}{\partial \pi} = \frac{\partial H}{\partial \pi} - \sum_{xyz} \frac{\partial}{\partial x} \frac{\partial(\partial\pi/\partial x)}{\partial H}$$

(54.18)

Comparison of Eqs. (54.16) and (54.17) for arbitrary variations $\delta\psi$ and $\delta\pi$ then gives the classical field equations in hamiltonian form:

$$\dot{\psi} = \frac{\partial H}{\partial \pi} \qquad \dot{\pi} = -\frac{\partial H}{\partial \psi}$$

(54.19)

The hamiltonian equation for the time rate of change of a functional F of ψ and π can now be found. We express F as the volume integral of the corresponding functional density $F(\psi,\pi,t)$, which for simplicity is assumed not to depend explicitly on the time or on the gradients of ψ or π. The foregoing analysis can be used to show that

$$\frac{dF}{dt} = \frac{\partial F}{\partial t} + \int \left(\frac{\partial F}{\partial \psi} \dot{\psi} + \frac{\partial F}{\partial \pi} \dot{\pi} \right) d^3r$$

$$= \frac{\partial F}{\partial t} + \int \left(\frac{\partial F}{\partial \psi} \frac{\partial H}{\partial \pi} - \frac{\partial F}{\partial \pi} \frac{\partial H}{\partial \psi} \right) d^3r$$

$$= \frac{\partial F}{\partial t} + \{F,H\}$$

(54.20)

This equation also serves to define the Poisson bracket expression for two functionals of the field variables. The right side of Eq. (54.20) is not changed if F also depends on $\nabla\psi$ or $\nabla\pi$ (see Prob. 2). It is apparent from (54.20) that H is a constant of the motion if it does not depend explicitly on the time; in this case, H is the total energy of the field.

QUANTUM EQUATIONS FOR THE FIELD

The analogy between particle coordinates and momenta q_i, p_i and the cell averages ψ_i, P_i suggests that we choose as quantum conditions for the field

$$[\psi_i,\psi_j] = [P_i,P_j] = 0 \qquad [\psi_i,P_j] = i\hbar\delta_{ij}$$

(54.21)

This means that we have converted the wave field from a real numerical function to a hermitian operator in the Heisenberg picture.

We now assume that the cell volumes are very small. Then Eqs. (54.21) can be rewritten with the help of (54.12) and (54.15) in terms of

ψ and π:

$$[\psi(\mathbf{r},t),\psi(\mathbf{r}',t)] = [\pi(\mathbf{r},t),\pi(\mathbf{r}',t)] = 0$$
$$[\psi(\mathbf{r},t),\pi(\mathbf{r}',t)] = i\hbar\delta(\mathbf{r},\mathbf{r}')$$

where $\delta(\mathbf{r},\mathbf{r}') = 1/\delta\tau_i$ if $\mathbf{r}$ and $\mathbf{r}'$ are in the same cell and zero otherwise. The function $\delta(\mathbf{r},\mathbf{r}')$ has the property that $\int f(\mathbf{r})\delta(\mathbf{r},\mathbf{r}')\,d^3r$ is equal to the average value of f for the cell in which $\mathbf{r}'$ is situated. Thus, in the limit in which the cell volumes approach zero, $\delta(\mathbf{r},\mathbf{r}')$ can be replaced by the three-dimensional Dirac δ function $\delta^3(\mathbf{r} - \mathbf{r}')$. The quantum conditions for the canonical field variables then become

$$[\psi(\mathbf{r},t),\psi(\mathbf{r}',t)] = [\pi(\mathbf{r},t),\pi(\mathbf{r}',t)] = 0$$
$$[\psi(\mathbf{r},t),\pi(\mathbf{r}',t)] = i\hbar\delta^3(\mathbf{r} - \mathbf{r}')$$

$$(54.22)$$

The equation of motion for any quantum dynamical variable F is obtained from Eq. (24.10) or by replacing the Poisson bracket in Eq. (54.20) by the commutator bracket divided by $i\hbar$.

$$\frac{dF}{dt} = \frac{\partial F}{\partial t} + \frac{1}{i\hbar}[F,H] \qquad (54.23)$$

The commutator bracket can be evaluated with the help of (54.22) when explicit expressions for F and H in terms of ψ and π are given. Thus Eqs. (54.22) and (54.23) completely describe the behavior of the quantized field that is specified by the hamiltonian H.

FIELDS WITH MORE THAN ONE COMPONENT

Thus far in this section we have dealt with fields that can be described by a single real amplitude. If the field has more than one component $\psi_1, \psi_2, \ldots$, the lagrangian density has the form $L(\psi_1, \Delta\psi_1, \dot{\psi}_1, \psi_2, \Delta\psi_2, \dot{\psi}_2, \ldots, t)$. Then if each of the field components is varied independently, the variational equation (54.3) leads to an equation of the form (54.8) or (54.11) for each of $\psi_1, \psi_2, \ldots$. A momentum canonically conjugate to each ψ_s can be defined as in Eq. (54.15) to be $\pi_s = \partial L/\partial\dot{\psi}_s$. The hamiltonian density has the form

$$H = \sum_s \pi_s\dot{\psi}_s - L \qquad (54.24)$$

and the hamiltonian equations consist of a pair like (54.19) for each s. Equation (54.23) is unchanged, and the commutation relations (54.22) are replaced by

$$[\psi_s(\mathbf{r},t),\psi_{s'}(\mathbf{r}',t)] = [\pi_s(\mathbf{r},t),\pi_{s'}(\mathbf{r}',t)] = 0$$
$$[\psi_s(\mathbf{r},t),\pi_{s'}(\mathbf{r}',t)] = i\hbar\delta_{ss'}\delta^3(\mathbf{r} - \mathbf{r}')$$

$$(54.25)$$

COMPLEX FIELD

Thus far we have dealt with fields that are real numerical functions in the classical case and hermitian operators in the Heisenberg picture in the quantum case. A different situation that is of immediate interest for the nonrelativistic Schrödinger equation is a single ψ field that is complex or nonhermitian.

In the classical case we can express ψ in terms of real fields ψ_1 and ψ_2 as

$$\psi = 2^{-\frac{1}{2}}(\psi_1 + i\psi_2) \qquad \psi^* = 2^{-\frac{1}{2}}(\psi_1 - i\psi_2) \qquad (54.26)$$

We show first that the lagrangian equations of the form (54.8) obtained by independent variation of ψ and ψ^* are equivalent to those obtained by variation of ψ_1 and ψ_2. It follows from (54.26) that

$$\frac{\partial}{\partial\psi} = 2^{-\frac{1}{2}}\left(\frac{\partial}{\partial\psi_1} - i\frac{\partial}{\partial\psi_2}\right) \qquad \frac{\partial}{\partial\psi^*} = 2^{-\frac{1}{2}}\left(\frac{\partial}{\partial\psi_1} + i\frac{\partial}{\partial\psi_2}\right)$$

Thus the ψ, ψ^* equations are obtained by adding and subtracting the ψ_1, ψ_2 equations.

In similar fashion, the classical momenta canonically conjugate to ψ and ψ^* are seen to be

$$\pi = 2^{-\frac{1}{2}}(\pi_1 - i\pi_2) \qquad \tilde{\pi} = 2^{-\frac{1}{2}}(\pi_1 + i\pi_2) \qquad (54.27)$$

The second momentum is written as $\tilde{\pi}$ rather than π^* in order to emphasize the fact that it is defined as being canonically conjugate to ψ^* and is not necessarily the complex conjugate of π. Indeed, as we shall see in the next section, $\tilde{\pi}$ is identically zero for the nonrelativistic Schrödinger equation. However, whenever the lagrangian is real, π_1 and π_2 are independent of each other and $\tilde{\pi} = \pi^*$. In this case $\pi_1\dot{\psi}_1 + \pi_2\dot{\psi}_2 = \pi\dot{\psi} + \pi^*\dot{\psi}^*$, and the hamiltonian is unchanged.

The corresponding quantum case is obtained from the commutation relations (54.25) with $s = 1, 2$. If π_1 and π_2 are independent, then all pairs of variables except the following commute:

$$[\psi(\mathbf{r},t),\pi(\mathbf{r}',t)] = [\psi^\dagger(\mathbf{r},t),\pi^\dagger(\mathbf{r}',t)] = i\hbar\delta^3(\mathbf{r} - \mathbf{r}') \qquad (54.28)$$

55☐QUANTIZATION OF THE NONRELATIVISTIC SCHRÖDINGER EQUATION

As a first example of the application of the field-quantization technique developed in the preceding section, we consider here the quantization of the nonrelativistic Schrödinger equation (6.16). The application implies that we are treating Eq. (6.16) as though it were a classical equation that describes the motion of some kind of material fluid. As we shall see, the resulting quantized field theory is equivalent to a many-particle Schrö-dinger equation, like (16.1) or (40.7). For this reason, field quantization is often called *second quantization;* this term implies that the transition from classical particle mechanics to Eq. (6.16) constitutes the first quantization.

CLASSICAL LAGRANGIAN AND HAMILTONIAN EQUATIONS

The lagrangian density may be taken to be

$$L = i\hbar\psi^*\dot{\psi} - \frac{\hbar^2}{2m}\nabla\psi^* \cdot \nabla\psi - V(\mathbf{r},t)\psi^*\psi \tag{55.1}$$

As shown at the end of the preceding section, ψ and ψ^* can be varied separately to obtain the lagrangian equations of motion. The equation of the form (54.8) that results from variation of ψ is

$$-i\hbar\dot{\psi}^* = -\frac{\hbar^2}{2m}\nabla^2\psi^* + V(\mathbf{r},t)\psi^*$$

which is the complex conjugate of Eq. (6.16). Variation of ψ^* gives Eq. (6.16):

$$i\hbar\dot{\psi} = -\frac{\hbar^2}{2m}\nabla^2\psi + V(\mathbf{r},t)\psi \tag{55.2}$$

The momentum canonically conjugate to ψ is

$$\pi = \frac{\partial L}{\partial\dot{\psi}} = i\hbar\psi^* \tag{55.3}$$

However $\dot{\psi}^*$ does not appear in the lagrangian density, so that $\tilde{\pi}$ is identically zero. It is therefore impossible to satisfy the second of the commutation relations (54.28) (or the corresponding classical Poisson-bracket relation), so that ψ^*, $\tilde{\pi}$ cannot be regarded as a pair of canonically conjugate variables. They can easily be eliminated from the hamiltonian since π^* never appears and Eq. (55.3) gives ψ^* in terms of π.[1]

The hamiltonian density is

$$H = \pi\dot{\psi} - L = -\frac{i\hbar}{2m}\nabla\pi \cdot \nabla\psi - \frac{i}{\hbar}V\pi\psi \tag{55.4}$$

---

[1] The conclusion that π can be identified with ψ^* is related to the appearance of only the first-order time derivative in the wave equation (55.2), since in this case $\dot{\psi}$ can be expressed in terms of ψ and its space derivatives through the wave equation. If the wave equation is of second order in the time derivative, ψ and $\dot{\psi}$ are independent; then π is related to $\dot{\psi}^*$ rather than to ψ^*, and both ψ, π and ψ^*, $\tilde{\pi}$ are pairs of canonical variables. The nonrelativistic Schrödinger equation and the Dirac equation are of the former type, whereas the relativistic Schrödinger equation is of the latter type.

The hamiltonian equations of motion obtained from (54.19), with the help of (54.18), are

$$\dot{\psi} = -\frac{i}{\hbar} V\psi + \frac{i\hbar}{2m} \nabla^2\psi$$

$$\dot{\pi} = \frac{i}{\hbar} V\pi - \frac{i\hbar}{2m} \nabla^2\pi$$

The first of these equations is the same as (55.2), and the second equation, together with (55.3), is the complex conjugate of (55.2). We have thus shown, from the point of view of classical field theory, that the lagrangian density (55.1) and the canonical variables and hamiltonian derived from it are in agreement with the wave equation (6.16) or (55.2).

QUANTUM EQUATIONS

The quantum equations are obtained by adopting the volume integral of (55.4) as the hamiltonian, (54.23) as the equation of motion, and the first of Eqs. (54.28) as the quantum condition on the wave field. Since ψ is now a Heisenberg-picture operator rather than a numerical function, ψ^* is replaced by $\psi^\dagger$, which is the hermitian adjoint of ψ rather than its complex conjugate. Further, as remarked above, the Heisenberg-picture operators ψ, $\psi^\dagger$ have no explicit dependence on the time, so that their equations of motion are given by (54.23) or (24.10), with the first term on the right side omitted and $d\psi/dt$ on the left side identified with $\dot{\psi}$. The hamiltonian is conveniently written with replacement of π by $i\hbar\psi^\dagger$ and becomes

$$H = \int \left(\frac{\hbar^2}{2m} \nabla\psi^\dagger \cdot \nabla\psi + V\psi^\dagger\psi \right) d^3r \qquad (55.5)$$

Application of Eqs. (22.15) and (22.16) then shows that H is hermitian. The quantized hamiltonian given in (55.5) is the operator that represents the total energy of the field; it is not to be confused with the operator (23.2), which is the energy operator for a single particle that is described by the wave equation (6.16). We have as yet given no explicit representation for the new operators ψ and H and therefore cannot say on what they might operate. The choice of a particular representation is not necessary so far as the Heisenberg equations of motion are concerned but is desirable for the physical interpretation of the formalism that we give later in this section.

The commutation relations are

$$[\psi(\mathbf{r}),\psi(\mathbf{r}')] = [\psi^\dagger(\mathbf{r}),\psi^\dagger(\mathbf{r}')] = 0$$

$$[\psi(\mathbf{r}),\psi^\dagger(\mathbf{r}')] = \delta^3(\mathbf{r} - \mathbf{r}') \qquad (55.6)$$

The omission of t from the argument of the field variables implies that both fields in a commutator bracket refer to the same time. In accordance with the earlier discussion, the equation of motion for ψ is

$$i\hbar\dot{\psi} = [\psi, H]$$

$$= \left[\psi, \int \frac{\hbar^2}{2m} \nabla'\psi^{\dagger\prime} \cdot \nabla'\psi' \, d^3r'\right] + \left[\psi, \int V'\psi^{\dagger\prime}\psi' \, d^3r'\right] \quad (55.7)$$

where primes indicate that an integration variable $\mathbf{r}'$ has been substituted for $\mathbf{r}$. The second term on the right side is easily evaluated with the help of (55.6) to give

$$\int V'(\psi\psi^{\dagger\prime}\psi' - \psi^{\dagger\prime}\psi'\psi) \, d^3r' = \int V'(\psi\psi^{\dagger\prime} - \psi^{\dagger\prime}\psi)\psi' \, d^3r'$$

$$= \int V'\psi' \, \delta^3(\mathbf{r} - \mathbf{r}') \, d^3r' = V\psi \quad (55.8)$$

ψ commutes with V, which is a numerical function. Evaluation of the first term on the right side of (55.7) is simplified by performing a partial integration on $\int \nabla\psi^{\dagger\prime} \cdot \nabla\psi' \, d^3r'$ to obtain $-\int \psi^{\dagger\prime}\nabla'^2\psi' \, d^3r'$; the surface terms vanish because ψ either vanishes at infinity or obeys periodic boundary conditions. We thus obtain

$$[\psi, \int \nabla'\psi^{\dagger\prime} \cdot \nabla'\psi' \, d^3r'] = -[\psi, \int \psi^{\dagger\prime}\nabla'^2\psi' \, d^3r']$$

$$= -\int [\psi, \psi^{\dagger\prime}]\nabla'^2\psi' \, d^3r' = -\int (\nabla'^2\psi') \, \delta^3(\mathbf{r} - \mathbf{r}') \, d^3r' = -\nabla^2\psi \quad (55.9)$$

Substitution of (55.8) and (55.9) into (55.7) yields Eq. (55.2), so that the equations obtained from classical and quantum field theories agree. A similar calculation shows that the equation $i\hbar\dot{\psi}^{\dagger} = [\psi^{\dagger}, H]$ yields the hermitian adjoint of Eq. (55.2); it can also be seen directly that this equation is the hermitian adjoint of the equation $i\hbar\dot{\psi} = [\psi, H]$ so long as H is hermitian.

If V is independent of t, H has no explicit dependence on the time, and Eq. (54.23) shows that H is a constant of the motion. Thus the energy in the field is constant. Another interesting operator is

$$N = \int \psi^{\dagger}\psi \, d^3r$$

which we assume represents the number of particles in the field. We note first that N is hermitian. Its time derivative is given by

$$i\hbar\dot{N} = [N, H]$$

$$= \left[\int \psi^{\dagger}\psi \, d^3r, \int \left(\frac{\hbar^2}{2m} \nabla'\psi^{\dagger\prime} \cdot \nabla'\psi' + V'\psi^{\dagger\prime}\psi'\right) d^3r'\right] \quad (55.10)$$

The commutator of N with the V part of H can be written as

$$\int\int V'(\psi^{\dagger}\psi\psi^{\dagger\prime}\psi' - \psi^{\dagger\prime}\psi'\psi^{\dagger}\psi) \, d^3r \, d^3r'$$

With the help of (55.6) the parenthesis in the integrand is

$$\psi^\dagger\psi\psi^{\dagger\prime}\psi' - \psi^{\dagger\prime}\psi'\psi^\dagger\psi = \psi^\dagger[\psi^{\dagger\prime}\psi + \delta^3(\mathbf{r} - \mathbf{r}')]\psi' - \psi^{\dagger\prime}\psi'\psi^\dagger\psi$$

$$= \psi^{\dagger\prime}\psi^\dagger\psi\psi' + \psi^\dagger\psi'\delta^3(\mathbf{r} - \mathbf{r}') - \psi^{\dagger\prime}\psi'\psi^\dagger\psi$$

$$= \psi^{\dagger\prime}[\psi'\psi^\dagger - \delta^3(\mathbf{r} - \mathbf{r}')]\psi + \psi^\dagger\psi'\delta^3(\mathbf{r} - \mathbf{r}')$$
$$- \psi^{\dagger\prime}\psi'\psi^\dagger\psi$$

$$= 0$$

since the δ function vanishes unless $\mathbf{r} = \mathbf{r}'$. A similar but slightly more complicated calculation shows that

$$[\psi^\dagger\psi, \, \boldsymbol{\nabla}'\psi^{\dagger\prime} \cdot \boldsymbol{\nabla}'\psi'] = [\psi^\dagger\boldsymbol{\nabla}'\psi' - (\boldsymbol{\nabla}'\psi^{\dagger\prime})\psi] \cdot \boldsymbol{\nabla}'\delta^3(\mathbf{r} - \mathbf{r}')$$

The double integral of this over $\mathbf{r}$ and $\mathbf{r}'$ is zero. Thus Eq. (55.10) shows that N is a constant of the motion.

It can also be shown that the commutator brackets in (55.6) are constants of the motion, so that these equations are always valid if they are at a particular time.

THE N REPRESENTATION

We now specialize to a representation in which the operator N is diagonal. Since N is hermitian, its eigenvalues are real. A convenient and general way of specifying this representation is by means of an expansion like (54.1) in terms of some complete orthonormal set of functions $u_k(\mathbf{r})$, which we assume for definiteness to be discrete. We put

$$\psi(\mathbf{r},t) = \sum_k a_k(t)u_k(\mathbf{r}) \qquad \psi^\dagger(\mathbf{r},t) = \sum_k a_k^\dagger(t)u_k^*(\mathbf{r}) \qquad (55.11)$$

where the u_k are numerical functions of the space coordinates and the a_k are Heisenberg-picture operators that depend on the time. Equations (55.11) can be solved for the a_k:

$$a_k(t) = \int u_k^*(\mathbf{r})\psi(\mathbf{r},t)\, d^3r \qquad a_k^\dagger(t) = \int u_k(\mathbf{r})\psi^\dagger(\mathbf{r},t)\, d^3r$$

Thus, if we multiply the last of the commutation relations (55.6) by $u_k^*(\mathbf{r})u_l(\mathbf{r}')$ on both sides and integrate over $\mathbf{r}$ and $\mathbf{r}'$, we obtain

$$[a_k(t),a_l^\dagger(t)] = \int\int u_k^*(\mathbf{r})u_l(\mathbf{r}')\, \delta^3(\mathbf{r} - \mathbf{r}')\, d^3r\, d^3r' = \delta_{kl} \qquad (55.12)$$

because of the orthonormality of the u_k. In similar fashion, it is apparent that a_k and a_l commute and that $a_k^\dagger$ and $a_l^\dagger$ commute, for all k and l. Substitution of (55.11) into the expression for N shows that

$$N = \sum_k N_k \qquad \text{where} \qquad N_k = a_k^\dagger a_k \qquad (55.13)$$

It is easily seen that each N_k commutes with all the others, so that they can be diagonalized simultaneously.

CREATION, DESTRUCTION, AND NUMBER OPERATORS

The commutation relations (55.12) for the operators a_k and $a_k^\dagger$ were solved in Sec. 25 in connection with the harmonic oscillator. There it was found that the solution of Eq. (25.10), in the representation in which $a^\dagger a$ is diagonal, consists of the matrices (25.12). It follows that the states of the quantized field, in the representation in which each N_k is diagonal, are the kets

$$|n_1, n_2, \ldots n_k, \ldots \rangle \tag{55.14}$$

where each n_k is an eigenvalue of N_k and must be a positive integer or zero. We also have the relations

$$a_k|n_1, \ldots n_k, \ldots \rangle = n_k^{\frac{1}{2}}|n_1, \ldots n_k - 1, \ldots \rangle$$
$$a_k^\dagger|n_1, \ldots n_k, \ldots \rangle = (n_k + 1)^{\frac{1}{2}}|n_1, \ldots n_k + 1, \ldots \rangle \tag{55.15}$$

Thus $a_k^\dagger$ and a_k are called *creation* and *destruction operators* for the state k of the field.

The *number operator* N_k need not be a constant of the motion, although we have seen from Eq. (55.10) that $N = \Sigma N_k$ is a constant. The rate of change of N_k is given by

$$i\hbar \dot{N}_k = [a_k^\dagger a_k, H]$$

where H is obtained from (55.5) and (55.11):

$$H = \sum_{jl} a_j^\dagger a_l \int \left(\frac{\hbar^2}{2m} \nabla u_j^* \cdot \nabla u_l + V u_j^* u_l \right) d^3r$$
$$= \sum_{jl} a_j^\dagger a_l \int u_j^* \left(-\frac{\hbar^2}{2m} \nabla^2 + V \right) u_l \, d^3r \tag{55.16}$$

It is not difficult to show from (55.12) that a particular N_k is constant if and only if all the volume integrals in (55.16) are zero for which either j or l is equal to k. These integrals are just the matrix elements of the one-particle hamiltonian (23.2), so that the necessary and sufficient condition that N_k be a constant of the motion is that all such off-diagonal elements that involve the state u_k be zero.[1]

The case in which the u_k are eigenfunctions of (23.2) with eigenvalues E_k is of particular interest. The integrals in (55.16) are then $E_l \delta_{jl}$, and the field hamiltonian becomes

$$H = \sum_k a_k^\dagger a_k E_k = \sum_k N_k E_k \tag{55.17}$$

This particular N representation is the one in which H is also diagonal;

---

[1] This result for the quantized field is closely related to the corresponding result, contained in Eq. (35.5), for the one-particle probability amplitude.

the ket $|n_1, \ldots n_k, \ldots \rangle$ has the eigenvalue $\Sigma n_k E_k$ for the total energy operator H. It is apparent that all the N_k are constant in this case.

CONNECTION WITH THE MANY-PARTICLE SCHRÖDINGER EQUATION

The quantized field theory is closely related to the many-particle Schrödinger equation discussed in Sec. 40. If the u_k are eigenfunctions of the one-particle hamiltonian (23.2), the field theory shows that stationary solutions exist for which the number of particles n_k in the kth state is a constant positive integer or zero, and the energy is $\Sigma n_k E_k$. Each solution can be described by a ket $|n_1, \ldots n_k, \ldots \rangle$; these kets form a complete orthonormal set, and there is just one solution for each set of numbers $n_1, \ldots$. On the other hand, a stationary many-particle wave function like the ψ in Eq. (40.1) can be written as a product of one-particle wave functions $u_k(\mathbf{r})e^{-iE_k t/\hbar}$ if there is no interaction between the particles. The linear combination of such products that is symmetric with respect to interchange of any pair of particle coordinates can be specified uniquely by stating the number of particles in each state. Again, the number of particles in each state is a positive integer or zero, and the energy is the sum of all the particle energies.

We see then that the quantized field theory developed thus far in this section is equivalent to the Schrödinger equation for several non-interacting particles, provided that only the symmetric solutions are retained in the latter case. We are thus led to a theory of particles that obey Einstein-Bose statistics. It can be shown that the two theories are completely equivalent even if interactions between particles are taken into account.[1]

It is natural to see if there is some way in which the quantized-field formalism can be modified to yield a theory of particles that obey Fermi-Dirac statistics. As discussed in Sec. 40, a system of such particles can be described by a many-particle wave function that is antisymmetric with respect to interchange of any pair of particle coordinates. The required linear combination of products of one-particle wave functions can be specified uniquely by stating the number of particles in each state, provided that each of these numbers is either 0 or 1. The desired modification of the theory must, therefore, limit the eigenvalues of each operator N_k to 0 and 1.

ANTICOMMUTATION RELATIONS

A review of the foregoing theory shows that the conclusion that the eigenvalues of each N_k are the positive integers and zero stems from the commutation relations (55.12) for the a_k and $a_k^\dagger$. Equations (55.12) in turn

[1] See W. Heisenberg, "The Physical Principles of the Quantum Theory," App., sec. 11 (University of Chicago Press, Chicago, 1930).

arise from the commutation relations (55.6) for ψ and $\psi^\dagger$. Thus we must modify Eqs. (55.6) if we are to obtain a theory of particles that obey the exclusion principle. It is reasonable to require that this modification be made in such a way that the quantum equation of motion for ψ is the wave equation (55.2) when the hamiltonian has the form (55.5).

It was found by Jordan and Wigner[1] that the desired modification consists in the replacement of the commutator brackets

$$[A,B] \equiv AB - BA$$

in Eqs. (54.22) and (55.6) by anticommutator brackets

$$[A,B]_+ \equiv AB + BA$$

This means that Eqs. (55.6) are replaced by

$$[\psi(\mathbf{r}),\psi(\mathbf{r}')]_+ = \psi(\mathbf{r})\psi(\mathbf{r}') + \psi(\mathbf{r}')\psi(\mathbf{r}) = 0$$
$$[\psi^\dagger(\mathbf{r}),\psi^\dagger(\mathbf{r}')]_+ = \psi^\dagger(\mathbf{r})\psi^\dagger(\mathbf{r}') + \psi^\dagger(\mathbf{r}')\psi^\dagger(\mathbf{r}) = 0 \qquad (55.18)$$
$$[\psi(\mathbf{r}),\psi^\dagger(\mathbf{r}')]_+ = \psi(\mathbf{r})\psi^\dagger(\mathbf{r}') + \psi^\dagger(\mathbf{r}')\psi(\mathbf{r}) = \delta^3(\mathbf{r} - \mathbf{r}')$$

It then follows directly from Eqs. (55.11) and (55.18) that

$$[a_k,a_l]_+ = a_k a_l + a_l a_k = 0$$
$$[a_k{}^\dagger,a_l{}^\dagger]_+ = a_k{}^\dagger a_l{}^\dagger + a_l{}^\dagger a_k{}^\dagger = 0 \qquad (55.19)$$
$$[a_k,a_l{}^\dagger]_+ = a_k a_l{}^\dagger + a_l{}^\dagger a_k = \delta_{kl}$$

We define $N_k = a_k{}^\dagger a_k$ as before and notice first that each N_k commutes with all the others, so that they can be diagonalized simultaneously. The eigenvalues of N_k can be obtained from the matrix equation

$$N_k{}^2 = a_k{}^\dagger a_k a_k{}^\dagger a_k = a_k{}^\dagger(1 - a_k{}^\dagger a_k)a_k = a_k{}^\dagger a_k = N_k \qquad (55.20)$$

where use has been made of Eqs. (55.19). If N_k is in diagonal form and has the eigenvalues n_k', n_k'', . . . , it is apparent that $N_k{}^2$ is also in diagonal form and has the eigenvalues $n_k'^2$, $n_k''^2$, ... Thus the matrix equation (55.20) is equivalent to the algebraic equations

$$n_k'^2 = n_k' \qquad n_k''^2 = n_k'' \qquad \cdot\ \cdot\ \cdot$$

for the eigenvalues. These are quadratic equations that have two roots: 0 and 1. Thus the eigenvalues of each N_k are 0 and 1, and the particles obey the exclusion principle. The eigenvalues of $N = \Sigma N_k$ are the positive integers and zero, as before. The earlier expressions (55.16) and (55.17) for the hamiltonian are unchanged, and the energy eigenvalues are $\Sigma n_k E_k$.

[1] P. Jordan and E. Wigner, Z. *Physik* **47,** 631 (1928).

EQUATION OF MOTION

In order to find the quantum equation of motion for ψ when the hamiltonian is given by (55.5), we must decide whether or not the general equation of motion (54.23) is to be retained. The latter equation was obtained by replacing the Poisson bracket by the commutator bracket in the classical equation (54.20). This replacement was justified by analogy with the particle theory of Sec. 24, by the identical algebraic properties of the two kinds of bracket expressions given in (24.27), and by the correspondence-theory argument of Prob. 9, Chap. 6. Thus abandonment of Eq. (54.23) means that the classical equation (54.20) is likewise abandoned. Since many of the quantities with which we are concerned (number of particles, energy, etc.) have well-defined classical analogs, we wish to retain (54.23) as the general quantum equation of motion.

The equation for ψ is then given by (55.7), where now the anti-commutation relations (55.18) are to be used in evaluating the right side. This causes (55.8) to be replaced by

$$\int V'(\psi\psi^{\dagger\prime}\psi' - \psi^{\dagger\prime}\psi'\psi)\, d^3r' = \int V'(\psi\psi^{\dagger\prime} + \psi^{\dagger\prime}\psi)\psi'\, d^3r'$$
$$= \int V'\psi'\delta^3(\mathbf{r} - \mathbf{r}')\, d^3r' = V\psi$$

Similar treatment of the first term on the right side of (55.7) causes no change in the right side of (55.9). Thus the wave equation (55.2) is unaffected by the substitution of anticommutation for commutation relations between the wave amplitudes. It can also be shown without difficulty that N and the anticommutator brackets in (55.18) are constants of the motion.

PHYSICAL IMPLICATIONS OF ANTICOMMUTATION

Since anticommutator brackets do not possess the algebraic properties of Poisson brackets, we can conclude that there is no classical analog for the quantities ψ and a_k that satisfy the relations (55.18) and (55.19). This does not mean, however, that N and H do not possess classical limits, for they are constructed of bilinear combinations of ψ or a_k and commute with each other.

These conclusions can be confirmed on the basis of physical considerations. In order that a field amplitude be strong enough to be classically measurable, it must be possible to have a very large number of particles in the same state so that their fields can be coherent. This implies that such particles obey Einstein-Bose statistics. We can, for example, conclude that light quanta or photons obey Einstein-Bose statistics, since it is known that strong electromagnetic fields can be produced and are classically measurable. In the case of metallic electrons, which obey Fermi-Dirac statistics, quantities like energy, and charge and current density, are classically measurable since they can be expressed as bilinear combinations of the field amplitude, whereas the electron field amplitude itself is not.[1]

REPRESENTATION OF THE ANTICOMMUTING a_k OPERATORS

An explicit representation for the operators that appear in (55.19) is easily obtained in the hypothetical but instructive case in which the system has only one state. The matrix equations to be solved are

$$a^2 = a^{\dagger 2} = 0 \qquad aa^\dagger + a^\dagger a = 1 \qquad N = a^\dagger a \qquad (55.21)$$

Equations (55.21) are just those solved in Prob. 4, Chap. 6. We have already seen in (55.20) that $N^2 = N$, so that N has the eigenvalues 0 and 1. If there is no degeneracy, N can be represented by the diagonal matrix

$$N = \begin{bmatrix} 0 & 0 \\ 0 & 1 \end{bmatrix} \qquad (55.22)$$

It is interesting to note that a cannot be diagonalized since N has a non-vanishing eigenvalue. If it could be, the first of Eqs. (55.21) would show that the square of each of its eigenvalues is zero; this would mean that a and hence $a^\dagger$ and N are identically zero, so that N could not have the form (55.22) in any representation.

Explicit matrices for a and $a^\dagger$ that agree with (55.21) and (55.22) are

$$a = \begin{bmatrix} 0 & 1 \\ 0 & 0 \end{bmatrix} \qquad a^\dagger = \begin{bmatrix} 0 & 0 \\ 1 & 0 \end{bmatrix} \qquad (55.23)$$

The two kets that represent the two possible states of this system can be expressed as

$$|0\rangle = \begin{bmatrix} 1 \\ 0 \end{bmatrix} \qquad |1\rangle = \begin{bmatrix} 0 \\ 1 \end{bmatrix} \qquad (55.24)$$

It is easily seen that the first ket in (55.24) has the eigenvalue 0 for the operator N given in (55.22), and the second has the eigenvalue 1. The following relations are easily obtained from (55.23) and (55.24):

$$a|n\rangle = n|1 - n\rangle \qquad a^\dagger|n\rangle = (1 - n)|1 - n\rangle \qquad (55.25)$$

Thus a and $a^\dagger$ again play the roles of destruction and creation operators, respectively.

In the actual problem, the number of states of the system is infinite, and it is not convenient to write explicit matrices like those in (55.23).

---

[1] The classical measurability of the field amplitude for any charged particle (Einstein-Bose or Fermi-Dirac statistics) implies that ψ appears linearly in H, since the energy must then depend on ψ itself as well as on bilinear combinations of ψ. This in turn implies that terms linear in a_k or $a_k{}^\dagger$ appear in the hamiltonian, so that single charged particles can be destroyed or created. Thus ψ cannot be measured classically if the theory is such that electric charge is conserved.

We can, however, find the effects of operating with a_k and $a_k{}^\dagger$ on a ket $|n_1, \ldots, n_k, \ldots\rangle$ that has the eigenvalue n_k ($= 0$ or 1) for the operator N_k. The desired relations would have the form (55.25) were it not that a series of such equations (with subscripts added) would not agree with the first two of Eqs. (55.19).

We therefore proceed in the following way. We order the states k of the system in an arbitrary but definite way: $1, 2, \ldots, k, \ldots$ Then operation with each a_k or $a_k{}^\dagger$ has the form (55.25), except that a multiplying plus or minus sign is introduced, according as the kth state is preceded in the assumed order by an even or an odd number of occupied states. We thus replace the Einstein-Bose equations (55.15) by the exclusion-principle equations

$$a_k|n_1, \ldots n_k, \ldots\rangle = \theta_k n_k|n_1, \ldots, 1 - n_k, \ldots\rangle$$

$$a_k{}^\dagger|n_1, \ldots n_k, \ldots\rangle = \theta_k(1 - n_k)|n_1, \ldots, 1 - n_k, \ldots\rangle \quad (55.26)$$

$$\theta_k = (-1)^{\nu_k} \qquad \nu_k = \sum_{j=1}^{k-1} n_j$$

As an example, we calculate the effect of operating with $a_k a_l$ and with $a_l a_k$ on some ket, where we assume for definiteness that the order is such that $l > k$. If each operation is not to give a zero result, both n_k and n_l in the original ket must equal unity. Operation with $a_k a_l$ empties first the lth and then the kth state and introduces a factor $\theta_l \theta_k$. Operation with $a_l a_k$ empties the kth state first, so that θ_k is unchanged. But when the lth state is emptied in this case, there is one less particle in the states below the lth than there was in the previous case, since the kth state is now empty, whereas it was occupied before. Thus the sign of θ_l is changed. We find in this way that

$$a_k a_l|\ldots n_k \ldots n_l \ldots\rangle = -a_l a_k|\ldots n_k \ldots n_l \ldots\rangle$$

in agreement with the first of Eqs. (55.19). In similar fashion, it can be shown that Eqs. (55.26) agree with the result of operating with the other two of Eqs. (55.19) on any ket. Since the aggregate of kets represents all possible states of the many-particle system, they constitute a complete set, and Eqs. (55.19) follow as operator equations from Eqs. (55.26).

56□ELECTROMAGNETIC FIELD IN VACUUM[1]

We now apply the methods developed in Sec. 54 to the quantization of the electromagnetic field in vacuum. Since we are not concerned with

[1] For further discussion of the material in this section and the next, see the references cited in footnote 1, page 491, and also E. Fermi, *Rev. Mod. Phys.* **4**, 87 (1932); L. Rosenfeld, *Ann. Inst. Henri Poincaré* **1**, 25 (1931); W. Heitler, "The Quantum Theory of Radiation," 3d ed. (Oxford, New York, 1954).

establishing the Lorentz invariance of the theory, we use three-dimensional rather than four-dimensional notation throughout. We start by finding a lagrangian whose variation yields Maxwell's equations. From this, canonical momenta can be defined, and a hamiltonian can be set up. Quantization is effected by replacing the classical Poisson brackets by commutator brackets. We shall not consider the possible existence of anticommutation relations between the field variables, since experiment shows that strong electromagnetic fields are classically measurable and that photons obey Einstein-Bose statistics.

LAGRANGIAN EQUATIONS

Maxwell's equations in empty space are obtained by setting ρ and $\mathbf{J}$ equal to zero in Eqs. (44.2):

$$\boldsymbol{\nabla} \times \mathbf{E} + \frac{1}{c} \frac{\partial \mathbf{H}}{\partial t} = 0 \qquad \boldsymbol{\nabla} \times \mathbf{H} - \frac{1}{c} \frac{\partial \mathbf{E}}{\partial t} = 0$$

$$\boldsymbol{\nabla} \cdot \mathbf{E} = 0 \qquad \boldsymbol{\nabla} \cdot \mathbf{H} = 0 \tag{56.1}$$

The lagrangian is most conveniently expressed in terms of the potentials $\mathbf{A}, \phi$ that are partially defined by

$$\mathbf{E} = -\frac{1}{c} \frac{\partial \mathbf{A}}{\partial t} - \boldsymbol{\nabla}\phi \qquad \mathbf{H} = \boldsymbol{\nabla} \times \mathbf{A} \tag{56.2}$$

As discussed in Sec. 44, this does not specify the potentials completely, since gauge transformations of the potentials can still be made without altering the electric and magnetic field strengths computed from (56.2).

The lagrangian density can be taken to be

$$L = \frac{1}{8\pi} \left(\frac{1}{c} \frac{\partial \mathbf{A}}{\partial t} + \boldsymbol{\nabla}\phi \right)^2 - \frac{1}{8\pi} (\boldsymbol{\nabla} \times \mathbf{A})^2 \tag{56.3}$$

The lagrangian equations are obtained from (54.8) if we regard A_x, A_y, A_z, and ϕ as the field variables. Variation of the components of $\mathbf{A}$ gives three equations that can be written together as

$$-\frac{1}{4\pi} \boldsymbol{\nabla} \times \boldsymbol{\nabla} \times \mathbf{A} - \frac{1}{4\pi c} \frac{\partial}{\partial t} \left(\frac{1}{c} \frac{\partial \mathbf{A}}{\partial t} + \boldsymbol{\nabla}\phi \right) = 0$$

This is the same as the second of Eqs. (56.1). Variation of ϕ gives

$$-\frac{1}{4\pi} \boldsymbol{\nabla} \cdot \left(\frac{1}{c} \frac{\partial \mathbf{A}}{\partial t} + \boldsymbol{\nabla}\phi \right) = 0$$

which is the same as the third of Eqs. (56.1). The definitions (56.2) for the potentials automatically satisfy the other two of Maxwell's equations.

HAMILTONIAN EQUATIONS

The momentum canonically conjugate to A_x is found from (54.15) and (56.3) to be

$$P_x = \frac{1}{4\pi c} \left(\frac{1}{c} \frac{\partial A_x}{\partial t} + \frac{\partial \phi}{\partial x} \right) \tag{56.4}$$

with similar expressions for the other two momenta. The momentum canonically conjugate to ϕ vanishes identically, since $\dot{\phi}$ does not appear in the lagrangian density. A similar situation was encountered with ψ^* in the nonrelativistic Schrödinger equation (Sec. 55); as before, it means that ϕ cannot be treated as a field variable and must be eliminated from the hamiltonian.

The hamiltonian density is obtained from (54.24):

$$H = \mathbf{P} \cdot \frac{\partial \mathbf{A}}{\partial t} - L = 2\pi c^2 \mathbf{P}^2 + \frac{1}{8\pi} (\nabla \times \mathbf{A})^2 - c\mathbf{P} \cdot \nabla\phi \tag{56.5}$$

where use has been made of (56.4) to replace $\partial \mathbf{A}/\partial t$ by terms involving $\mathbf{P}$. The hamiltonian equations of motion (54.19) are

$$\frac{\partial \mathbf{A}}{\partial t} = 4\pi c^2 \mathbf{P} - c\nabla\phi \qquad \frac{\partial \mathbf{P}}{\partial t} = -\frac{1}{4\pi} \nabla \times \nabla \times \mathbf{A} \tag{56.6}$$

The first of these equations is the same as (56.4); it is necessary that (56.4) be obtained over again in this way, since the hamiltonian formalism consists only of (56.5) and the canonical variables $\mathbf{A}$ and $\mathbf{P}$. We can now make use of this equation to define a quantity $\mathbf{E}$ that is equal to $-4\pi c\mathbf{P}$. Then the second of Eqs. (56.6) agrees with the second of Maxwell's equations (56.1), if we also define a quantity $\mathbf{H}$ to be equal to $\nabla \times \mathbf{A}$. The first and fourth of Eqs. (56.1) are satisfied because of the way in which $\mathbf{E}$ and $\mathbf{H}$ are defined.

The third of Maxwell's equations cannot be obtained as a hamiltonian equation based on (56.5). We can, however, say that we shall be concerned only with those solutions of the hamiltonian equations for which $\nabla \cdot \mathbf{E} = 0$, or $\nabla \cdot \mathbf{P} = 0$, at some definite time. If then we can show that this restriction is maintained at all times, the solutions so chosen form a consistent and satisfactory set. The time derivative of $\nabla \cdot \mathbf{P}$ is found from the second of Eqs. (56.6) to be

$$\frac{\partial}{\partial t} \nabla \cdot \mathbf{P} = -\frac{1}{4\pi} \nabla \cdot \nabla \times \nabla \times \mathbf{A} = 0$$

Since the field equations are of first order in the time derivatives, we have shown that the restriction that $\nabla \cdot \mathbf{E} = 0$ at one instant of time is equivalent to the validity of the third of Eqs. (56.1) at all times.

We now see that the last term in the hamiltonian density (56.5) contributes nothing to the field hamiltonian. Its volume integral can be transformed by means of a partial integration into $c \int \phi \nabla \cdot \mathbf{P} \, d^3r$, which is equal to zero; the surface term vanishes because $\mathbf{P}$ either vanishes sufficiently rapidly at infinity or obeys periodic boundary conditions at the walls of a large box. The hamiltonian is then

$$H = \int \left[2\pi c^2 \mathbf{P}^2 + \frac{1}{8\pi} (\nabla \times \mathbf{A})^2 \right] d^3r \tag{56.7}$$

and ϕ has disappeared. This is in agreement with the usual expression $(1/8\pi) \int (\mathbf{E}^2 + \mathbf{H}^2) \, d^3r$ for the total energy in the electromagnetic field.

QUANTUM EQUATIONS

The classical electromagnetic field is converted into a quantum field in the following way. We start with the hamiltonian (56.7) and the canonical field variables $\mathbf{A}$, $\mathbf{P}$. Since ϕ no longer appears, it is convenient to choose the gauge so that $\phi = 0$. The general equation of motion is (54.23), and the commutation relations (54.25) between the field variables become

$$[A_s(\mathbf{r},t),A_{s'}(\mathbf{r}',t)] = [P_s(\mathbf{r},t),P_{s'}(\mathbf{r}',t)] = 0$$
$$[A_s(\mathbf{r},t),P_{s'}(\mathbf{r}',t)] = i\hbar \delta_{ss'} \delta^3(\mathbf{r} - \mathbf{r}') \tag{56.8}$$

Each of the indices s, s' can be x, y, or z.

The equation of motion for a typical component of $\mathbf{A}$ is

$$i\hbar \dot{A}_x(\mathbf{r},t) = [A_x(\mathbf{r},t),H]$$

A_x commutes with the $(\nabla \times \mathbf{A})^2$ term in H and also with that part of the $\mathbf{P}^2$ term that involves $P_y^2 + P_z^2$; thus we need calculate only the commutator of A_x and the P_x^2 term in H. This is $2\pi c^2$ times the integral over $\mathbf{r}'$ of $[A_x, P_x'^2]$, where the prime indicates that the argument is $\mathbf{r}'$ rather than $\mathbf{r}$.

$$\begin{aligned} [A_x(\mathbf{r},t),P_x^2(\mathbf{r}',t)] &= A_x P_x'^2 - P_x'^2 A_x \\ &= [P_x' A_x + i\hbar \delta^3(\mathbf{r} - \mathbf{r}')]P_x' - P_x'^2 A_x \\ &= P_x'[P_x' A_x + i\hbar \delta^3(\mathbf{r} - \mathbf{r}')] + i\hbar \delta^3(\mathbf{r} - \mathbf{r}')P_x' - P_x'^2 A_x \\ &= 2i\hbar \delta^3(\mathbf{r} - \mathbf{r}')P_x(\mathbf{r}',t) \end{aligned}$$

Integration over $\mathbf{r}'$ gives the relation

$$\begin{aligned} i\hbar \dot{A}_x(\mathbf{r},t) &= 2\pi c^2 \int 2i\hbar \delta^3(\mathbf{r} - \mathbf{r}')P_x(\mathbf{r}',t) \, d^3r' \\ &= 4\pi c^2 i\hbar P_x(\mathbf{r},t) \end{aligned} \tag{56.9}$$

This is the same as the corresponding classical equation, which is the first of Eqs. (56.6), when $\phi = 0$.

The equation of motion for a typical component of **P** is

$$i\hbar \dot{P}_x(\mathbf{r},t) = [P_x(\mathbf{r},t),H]$$

P_x commutes with all the integrand of H except for that part which contains the sum of the squares of the y and z components of $\boldsymbol{\nabla} \times \mathbf{A}$. The calculation of this commutator bracket is straightforward but tedious (see Prob. 10) and yields an expression for $\dot{\mathbf{P}}$ that is in agreement with the second of Eqs. (56.6). Thus if we define $\mathbf{E} = -4\pi c\mathbf{P}$ and $\mathbf{H} = \boldsymbol{\nabla} \times \mathbf{A}$, the quantum equations of motion for **A** and **P** agree with the first, second, and fourth of Maxwell's equations (56.1).

The third of Maxwell's equations must be imposed as a *supplementary condition*, as in the classical case. If we set $\boldsymbol{\nabla} \cdot \mathbf{P}$ equal to zero at a particular time, it is always zero since its time derivative is zero. Equation (56.9) then shows that the time derivative of $\boldsymbol{\nabla} \cdot \mathbf{A}$ is always zero, or that $\boldsymbol{\nabla} \cdot \mathbf{A}$ is a constant in time. It is convenient to restrict the choice of gauge further so that $\boldsymbol{\nabla} \cdot \mathbf{A}$ is zero everywhere at a particular time, in which case we see that it is zero at all space-time points. It is apparent, however, that the introduction of the supplementary condition is inconsistent with the commutation relations (56.8). For example, the commutator bracket of A_x and $\boldsymbol{\nabla} \cdot \mathbf{P}$ should be zero, since $\boldsymbol{\nabla} \cdot \mathbf{P}$ is zero, but is computed from (56.8) to be

$$[A_x(\mathbf{r},t), \boldsymbol{\nabla}' \cdot \mathbf{P}(\mathbf{r}',t)] = i\hbar \frac{\partial}{\partial x'} \delta^3(\mathbf{r} - \mathbf{r}')$$

It is not surprising that this inconsistency should arise, since Eqs. (56.8) imply that there are three independent pairs of canonical variables, whereas the restrictions $\boldsymbol{\nabla} \cdot \mathbf{P} = 0$ and $\boldsymbol{\nabla} \cdot \mathbf{A} = 0$ cause only two of these pairs to be linearly independent. We should therefore modify the commutation relations so that they are consistent with the supplementary condition.

The nature of this modification is established in Prob. 11. It turns out that the commutator brackets of $\mathbf{A}(\mathbf{r},t)$ and $\mathbf{P}(\mathbf{r}',t)$ do not vanish when $\mathbf{r} - \mathbf{r}'$ is finite. This would appear at first to contradict the physical principle that there can be no interference between electromagnetic field measurements performed at different places and the same time since this field has a finite speed of propagation. However, the vector potential **A** is not in itself a physical quantity; only the electric and magnetic fields are directly measurable. We shall now show with the help of (56.8) that the commutation relations of **E** and **H** have the required infinitesimal character and are, moreover, consistent with the supplementary condition $\boldsymbol{\nabla} \cdot \mathbf{E} = 0$. It can also be shown (see Prob. 12) that the same results are obtained by starting with the modified canonical commutation relations of Prob. 11.

COMMUTATION RELATIONS FOR É AND H

The electric and magnetic fields are defined by the equations

$$\mathbf{E} = -4\pi c \mathbf{P} \qquad \mathbf{H} = \nabla \times \mathbf{A} \tag{56.10}$$

where the commutation relations for $\mathbf{A}$ and $\mathbf{P}$ are assumed to have the form (56.8). We see at once that

$$[\mathsf{E}_s(\mathbf{r},t), \mathsf{E}_{s'}(\mathbf{r}',t)] = [\mathsf{H}_s(\mathbf{r},t), \mathsf{H}_{s'}(\mathbf{r}',t)] = 0 \tag{56.11}$$

where each of the indices s, s' can be x, y, or z. The commutator bracket for typical parallel components of $\mathbf{E}$ and $\mathbf{H}$ is

$$[\mathsf{E}_x(\mathbf{r},t), \mathsf{H}_x(\mathbf{r}',t)] = -4\pi c \left[P_x, \left(\frac{\partial A'_z}{\partial y'} - \frac{\partial A'_y}{\partial z'} \right) \right] = 0 \tag{56.12}$$

For typical perpendicular components of $\mathbf{E}$ and $\mathbf{H}$, we obtain

$$\begin{aligned}
[\mathsf{E}_x(\mathbf{r},t), \mathsf{H}_y(\mathbf{r}',t)] &= -4\pi c \left[P_x, \left(\frac{\partial A'_x}{\partial z'} - \frac{\partial A'_z}{\partial x'} \right) \right] \\
&= -4\pi c \frac{\partial}{\partial z'} [P_x, A'_x] \\
&= 4\pi c i\hbar \frac{\partial}{\partial z'} \delta^3(\mathbf{r} - \mathbf{r}')
\end{aligned} \tag{56.13}$$

Other relations similar to (56.13) are obtained by cyclic permutation of x, y, z.

It follows at once from (56.11) that $\nabla \cdot \mathbf{E}$ commutes with all components of $\mathbf{E}$. The commutator bracket of $\nabla \cdot \mathbf{E}$ and a typical component of $\mathbf{H}$ is, with the help of (56.13),

$$\begin{aligned}
[\nabla \cdot \mathbf{E}, \mathsf{H}'_x] &= \left[\frac{\partial \mathsf{E}_y}{\partial y}, \mathsf{H}'_x \right] + \left[\frac{\partial \mathsf{E}_z}{\partial z}, \mathsf{H}'_x \right] \\
&= 4\pi c i\hbar \left[-\frac{\partial}{\partial y} \frac{\partial}{\partial z'} \delta^3(\mathbf{r}' - \mathbf{r}) + \frac{\partial}{\partial z} \frac{\partial}{\partial y'} \delta^3(\mathbf{r}' - \mathbf{r}) \right]
\end{aligned} \tag{56.14}$$

Since $(\partial/\partial y')\delta^3(\mathbf{r}' - \mathbf{r}) = -(\partial/\partial y)\delta^3(\mathbf{r}' - \mathbf{r})$, we see that the right side of (56.14) is zero. Thus $\nabla \cdot \mathbf{E}$ commutes with $\mathbf{E}$ and $\mathbf{H}$ and hence also with the hamiltonian, which from (56.7) can be written as

$$H = \frac{1}{8\pi} \int (\mathbf{E}^2 + \mathbf{H}^2)\, d^3r \tag{56.15}$$

This means that $\nabla \cdot \mathbf{E}$ is a constant of the motion and so is zero at all space-time points if it is made to vanish everywhere at a particular time.

As would be expected, the field commutation relations (56.11) to (56.13), together with the hamiltonian (56.15), can be used in place of the canonical formalism originally developed in terms of $\mathbf{A}$ and $\mathbf{P}$. We have already seen that $\nabla \cdot \mathbf{E}$ is a constant of the motion; a similar calculation shows that $\nabla \cdot \mathbf{H}$ is constant, so that it can also be made to vanish at all space-time points. The first two of Maxwell's equations (56.1) then follow as special cases of the general equation of motion (54.23) (see Prob. 14):

$$
\begin{aligned}
i\hbar\dot{E}_x &= [E_x, H] = \frac{1}{8\pi} \int [E_x, (H_y'^2 + H_z'^2)] \, d^3r' \\
&= i\hbar c(\nabla \times \mathbf{H})_x \\
i\hbar\dot{H}_x &= [H_x, H] = \frac{1}{8\pi} \int [H_x, (E_y'^2 + E_z'^2)] \, d^3r' \\
&= -i\hbar c(\nabla \times \mathbf{E})_x
\end{aligned}
\tag{56.16}
$$

PLANE WAVE REPRESENTATION

For many applications, a representation of the potentials and fields in a complete orthonormal set of plane waves is useful. These plane waves are taken to be vector functions of $\mathbf{r}$ that are polarized perpendicular to the propagation vector so that the conditions $\nabla \cdot \mathbf{A} = \nabla \cdot \mathbf{P} = 0$ are satisfied.

$$
\mathbf{u}_{k\lambda}(\mathbf{r}) = L^{-\frac{3}{2}}\varepsilon_{k\lambda} \exp{(i\mathbf{k} \cdot \mathbf{r})} \qquad \lambda = 1, 2
$$

The vectors $\mathbf{k}$ are chosen as in (11.3), so that the $\mathbf{u}_{k\lambda}$ satisfy periodic boundary conditions at the walls of a large cubical box of volume L^3. The $\varepsilon_{k\lambda}$ are unit vectors, and ε_{k1}, ε_{k2}, and $\mathbf{k}$ form a right-handed set, so that $\mathbf{k} \cdot \varepsilon_{k\lambda} = 0$ and $\nabla \cdot \mathbf{u}_{k\lambda} = 0$. It is easily verified that the orthonormality property assumes the form

$$
\int \mathbf{u}_{k\lambda}^* \cdot \mathbf{u}_{k'\lambda'} \, d^3r = \delta_{kk'}\delta_{\lambda\lambda'}
$$

We expand $\mathbf{A}$ and $\mathbf{P}$ in terms of the $\mathbf{u}_{k\lambda}$:

$$
\begin{aligned}
\mathbf{A}(\mathbf{r},t) &= {\sum_{k\lambda}}' [q_{k\lambda}(t)\mathbf{u}_{k\lambda}(\mathbf{r}) + q_{k\lambda}^\dagger(t)\mathbf{u}_{k\lambda}^*(\mathbf{r})] \\
\mathbf{P}(\mathbf{r},t) &= {\sum_{k\lambda}}' [p_{k\lambda}(t)\mathbf{u}_{k\lambda}(\mathbf{r}) + p_{k\lambda}^\dagger(t)\mathbf{u}_{k\lambda}^*(\mathbf{r})]
\end{aligned}
\tag{56.17}
$$

The operators $q_{k\lambda}^\dagger$ and $p_{k\lambda}^\dagger$ are the hermitian adjoints of $q_{k\lambda}$ and $p_{k\lambda}$, respectively; thus $\mathbf{A}$ and $\mathbf{P}$ are hermitian. The primes indicate that the summations extend over half the $\mathbf{k}$ space, so that the plane waves $\mathbf{u}_{k\lambda}^*$ do not duplicate $\mathbf{u}_{-k\lambda}$.

We take for the commutation relations between the q's and p's

$$
[q_{k\lambda}(t), p_{k'\lambda'}^\dagger(t)] = [q_{k\lambda}^\dagger(t), p_{k'\lambda'}(t)] = i\hbar\delta_{kk'}\delta_{\lambda'\lambda}
\tag{56.18}
$$

with all other pairs commuting, and verify that they give the correct commutation relations between $\mathbf{A}$ and $\mathbf{P}$. It is apparent that

$$[A_s(\mathbf{r},t), A_{s'}(\mathbf{r}',t)] = [P_s(\mathbf{r},t), P_{s'}(\mathbf{r}',t)] = 0$$

We also obtain from (56.17) and (56.18)

$$\begin{aligned}[A_s(\mathbf{r},t), P_{s'}(\mathbf{r}',t)] &= \sum_{\mathbf{k}\lambda}{}' \sum_{\mathbf{k}'\lambda'}{}' \{[q_{\mathbf{k}\lambda}(t), p_{\mathbf{k}'\lambda'}{}^\dagger(t)]u_{\mathbf{k}\lambda,s}(\mathbf{r})u^*_{\mathbf{k}'\lambda',s'}(\mathbf{r}') \\ &\qquad + [q_{\mathbf{k}\lambda}{}^\dagger(t), p_{\mathbf{k}'\lambda'}(t)]u^*_{\mathbf{k}\lambda,s}(\mathbf{r})u_{\mathbf{k}'\lambda',s'}(\mathbf{r}')\} \\ &= i\hbar L^{-3} \sum_{\mathbf{k}\lambda} \epsilon_{\mathbf{k}\lambda,s}\epsilon_{\mathbf{k}\lambda,s'} \exp\left[i\mathbf{k}\cdot(\mathbf{r}-\mathbf{r}')\right] \qquad (56.19)\end{aligned}$$

The subscripts s, s' denote cartesian components of the vectors on which they appear; the prime has been removed from the last summation in (56.19) since the primed summation over terms with both $\mathbf{k}$ and $-\mathbf{k}$ is equivalent to a summation of $\mathbf{k}$ terms over the entire $\mathbf{k}$ space.

If there were three mutually perpendicular unit vectors $\boldsymbol{\epsilon}_{\mathbf{k}\lambda}$, then the three numbers $\epsilon_{\mathbf{k}\lambda,s}$ would be the direction cosines of the cartesian direction s, and we would have that $\sum_\lambda \epsilon_{\mathbf{k}\lambda,s}\epsilon_{\mathbf{k}\lambda,s'} = \delta_{ss'}$. Since there are just two unit vectors $\boldsymbol{\epsilon}_{\mathbf{k}\lambda}$ that are perpendicular to each other and to $\mathbf{k}$, we can write

$$\sum_\lambda \epsilon_{\mathbf{k}\lambda,s}\epsilon_{\mathbf{k}\lambda,s'} = \delta_{ss'} - \frac{k_s k_{s'}}{k^2}$$

We also have that

$$k_s k_{s'} \exp\left[i\mathbf{k}\cdot(\mathbf{r}-\mathbf{r}')\right] = \frac{\partial}{\partial r_s}\frac{\partial}{\partial r'_{s'}} \exp\left[i\mathbf{k}\cdot(\mathbf{r}-\mathbf{r}')\right]$$

With these substitutions and with the replacement of $L^{-3}\sum_\mathbf{k}$ by $(2\pi)^{-3}\int d^3k$ when L is large, we can rewrite (56.19) as

$$\begin{aligned}[A_s(\mathbf{r},t), P_{s'}(\mathbf{r}',t)] &= i\hbar\delta_{ss'}\{(2\pi)^{-3}\int \exp\left[i\mathbf{k}\cdot(\mathbf{r}-\mathbf{r}')\right] d^3k\} \\ &\quad - i\hbar\frac{\partial}{\partial r_s}\frac{\partial}{\partial r'_{s'}}\left\{(2\pi)^{-3}\int \frac{1}{k^2}\exp\left[i\mathbf{k}\cdot(\mathbf{r}-\mathbf{r}')\right] d^3k\right\} \qquad (56.20)\end{aligned}$$

The first brace expression in (56.20) is equal to $\delta^3(\mathbf{r}-\mathbf{r}')$. The second brace can be calculated as a special case of Eq. (37.18) and is equal to $(4\pi|\mathbf{r}-\mathbf{r}'|)^{-1}$. The commutator bracket (56.20) then becomes

$$[A_s(\mathbf{r},t), P_{s'}(\mathbf{r}',t)] = i\hbar\delta_{ss'}\delta^3(\mathbf{r}-\mathbf{r}') - \frac{i\hbar}{4\pi}\frac{\partial}{\partial r_s}\frac{\partial}{\partial r'_{s'}}\left(\frac{1}{|\mathbf{r}-\mathbf{r}'|}\right) \qquad (56.21)$$

which is that assumed in Prob. 11; the other commutator brackets vanish. This confirms the choice of the commutation relations (56.18).

QUANTIZED FIELD ENERGY

Substitution of (56.17) into the field hamiltonian (56.7) gives

$$H = \sum_{\mathbf{k}\lambda}{}' \left(4\pi c^2 p_{\mathbf{k}\lambda} p_{\mathbf{k}\lambda}{}^\dagger + \frac{k^2}{4\pi} q_{\mathbf{k}\lambda} q_{\mathbf{k}\lambda}{}^\dagger \right) \tag{56.22}$$

since $q_{\mathbf{k}\lambda}$ and $q_{\mathbf{k}\lambda}{}^\dagger$, and $p_{\mathbf{k}\lambda}$ and $p_{\mathbf{k}\lambda}{}^\dagger$ commute; here use has been made of the restriction on the summation to half the $\mathbf{k}$ space, which makes all integrals of the form $\int \mathbf{u}_{\mathbf{k}\lambda} \cdot \mathbf{u}_{\mathbf{k}'\lambda'}\, d^3r$ vanish.

We wish now to find the eigenvalues of H when the commutation relations are as given in (56.18). This can be done by choosing linear combinations of the plane wave amplitudes that make H formally equivalent to the sum of the energies of a number of harmonic oscillators (see Sec. 55). Now each index pair $\mathbf{k}$, λ corresponds to two linearly polarized plane waves that travel in opposite senses along the $\mathbf{k}$ direction. Thus we want our new linear combinations of $q_{\mathbf{k}\lambda}\mathbf{u}_{\mathbf{k}\lambda}$ and $p_{\mathbf{k}\lambda}\mathbf{u}_{\mathbf{k}\lambda}$ to have the general forms

$$a_{\mathbf{k}\lambda} \exp i(\mathbf{k}\cdot\mathbf{r} - kct) \qquad a_{\mathbf{k}\lambda}'{}^\dagger \exp i(\mathbf{k}\cdot\mathbf{r} + kct) \tag{56.23}$$

where $a_{\mathbf{k}\lambda}$ and $a_{\mathbf{k}\lambda}'$ are operators that are independent of $\mathbf{r}$ and t. The first of these is a plane wave that travels in the positive $\mathbf{k}$ direction and has the positive angular frequency kc, and the second is the hermitian adjoint of a plane wave that travels in the negative $\mathbf{k}$ direction and has the same frequency.

With the remarks of the preceding paragraph as a guide, we proceed to find the time dependence of $q_{\mathbf{k}\lambda}$ and $p_{\mathbf{k}\lambda}$. Their equations of motion are given by (54.23):

$$\begin{aligned}
i\hbar \dot{q}_{\mathbf{k}\lambda} &= [q_{\mathbf{k}\lambda}, H] = 4\pi i\hbar c^2 p_{\mathbf{k}\lambda} \\
i\hbar \dot{p}_{\mathbf{k}\lambda} &= [p_{\mathbf{k}\lambda}, H] = -\frac{i\hbar k^2}{4\pi} q_{\mathbf{k}\lambda}
\end{aligned} \tag{56.24}$$

Elimination of $p_{\mathbf{k}\lambda}$ gives a second-order equation for $q_{\mathbf{k}\lambda}$:

$$\ddot{q}_{\mathbf{k}\lambda} = 4\pi c^2 \dot{p}_{\mathbf{k}\lambda} = -k^2 c^2 q_{\mathbf{k}\lambda}$$

This is easily integrated to give

$$q_{\mathbf{k}\lambda}(t) = a_{\mathbf{k}\lambda} e^{-ikct} + a_{\mathbf{k}\lambda}'{}^\dagger e^{ikct} \tag{56.25}$$

where we have followed the pattern indicated by (56.23). We then obtain from the first of Eqs. (56.24)

$$p_{\mathbf{k}\lambda}(t) = -\frac{ik}{4\pi c} a_{\mathbf{k}\lambda} e^{-ikct} + \frac{ik}{4\pi c} a_{\mathbf{k}\lambda}'{}^\dagger e^{ikct} \tag{56.26}$$

Equations (56.25) and (56.26) can be solved for the a's.

$$a_{k\lambda} = \tfrac{1}{2}\left(q_{k\lambda} + \frac{4\pi ic}{k}\, p_{k\lambda}\right) e^{ikct}$$
$$a_{k\lambda}'^{\dagger} = \tfrac{1}{2}\left(q_{k\lambda} - \frac{4\pi ic}{k}\, p_{k\lambda}\right) e^{-ikct} \tag{56.27}$$

Similar relations hold for their hermitian adjoints. The commutation relations for the a's can be obtained from (56.27) and (56.18):

$$[a_{k\lambda}, a_{k'\lambda'}^{\dagger}] = [a_{k\lambda}', a_{k'\lambda'}'^{\dagger}] = \frac{2\pi\hbar c}{k}\, \delta_{kk'}\delta_{\lambda\lambda'} \tag{56.28}$$

with all other pairs commuting; these are independent of the time, as they should be.

Substitution of (56.25) and (56.26) into the hamiltonian (56.22) gives

$$H = {\sum_{k\lambda}}' \frac{k^2}{2\pi}\,(a_{k\lambda}a_{k\lambda}^{\dagger} + a_{k\lambda}'^{\dagger}a_{k\lambda}') \tag{56.29}$$

If we adopt the definitions

$$N_{k\lambda} = \frac{k}{2\pi\hbar c}\, a_{k\lambda}^{\dagger}a_{k\lambda} \qquad N_{k\lambda}' = \frac{k}{2\pi\hbar c}\, a_{k\lambda}'^{\dagger}a_{k\lambda}' \tag{56.30}$$

we see from the work of Sec. 55 that $N_{k\lambda}$ and $N_{k\lambda}'$ each have the eigenvalues $0, 1, 2, \ldots$. In terms of the N's, the hamiltonian (56.29) becomes

$$H = {\sum_{k\lambda}}' \hbar ck(N_{k\lambda} + N_{k\lambda}' + 1) \tag{56.31}$$

Because of the structure of (56.23) and (56.25), we can identify $a_{k\lambda}'$ with $a_{-k\lambda}$, and $N_{k\lambda}'$ with $N_{-k\lambda}$. Then the restriction on the summation of (56.31) to half the k space can be removed to give

$$H = \sum_{k\lambda} \hbar ck(N_{k\lambda} + \tfrac{1}{2}) \tag{56.32}$$

Equation (56.32) is equivalent to Planck's quantum hypothesis: The energy associated with each plane electromagnetic wave is an integer multiple of the fundamental quantum $h\nu = \hbar kc$. In addition to the Planck energy, however, there is the harmonic-oscillator zero-point energy of one-half quantum per state of the field, which is infinite since there are an infinite number of states. This infinite energy is not objectionable since it does not interact with charged matter.[1]

[1] See also the discussion at the end of Sec. 57.

QUANTIZED FIELD MOMENTUM

The momentum density of an electromagnetic field is the Poynting vector $(c/4\pi)\mathbf{E}(\mathbf{r},t) \times \mathbf{H}(\mathbf{r},t)$ divided by c^2. The total momentum in the field can then be written in terms of the canonical variables, with the help of (56.10),

$$\mathbf{G} = \frac{1}{4\pi c} \int \mathbf{E} \times \mathbf{H} \, d^3r = - \int \mathbf{P} \times (\nabla \times \mathbf{A}) \, d^3r$$

Substitution from (56.17), (56.25), (56.26), and (56.30) gives

$$\mathbf{G} = i \sideset{}{'}\sum_{\mathbf{k}\lambda} \mathbf{k}(p_{\mathbf{k}\lambda}q_{\mathbf{k}\lambda}{}^\dagger - p_{\mathbf{k}\lambda}{}^\dagger q_{\mathbf{k}\lambda})$$

$$= \frac{1}{4\pi c} \sideset{}{'}\sum_{\mathbf{k}\lambda} \mathbf{k}k[(a_{\mathbf{k}\lambda}a_{\mathbf{k}\lambda}{}^\dagger + a_{\mathbf{k}\lambda}{}^\dagger a_{\mathbf{k}\lambda}) - (a'_{\mathbf{k}\lambda}a'_{\mathbf{k}\lambda}{}^\dagger + a'_{\mathbf{k}\lambda}{}^\dagger a'_{\mathbf{k}\lambda})]$$

$$= \sideset{}{'}\sum_{\mathbf{k}\lambda} \hbar\mathbf{k}[(N_{\mathbf{k}\lambda} + \tfrac{1}{2}) - (N'_{\mathbf{k}\lambda} + \tfrac{1}{2})] = \sum_{\mathbf{k}\lambda} \hbar\mathbf{k}N_{\mathbf{k}\lambda} \qquad (56.33)$$

where the restriction on the summation is removed as in the transition from (56.31) to (56.32). In this case, the zero-point terms cancel for plane waves that travel in opposite directions.

Equations (56.32) and (56.33) show that the energy and momentum of each plane wave are quantized in units of $\hbar k c$ for the energy and $\hbar \mathbf{k}$ for the momentum. It will also be shown explicitly at the end of this section that the quantized electromagnetic field propagates with the classical speed of light.

A(r,t) IN THE PLANE WAVE REPRESENTATION

The vector potential appears in the interaction between charged particles and the electromagnetic field that is discussed in the next section. We shall therefore require an expression for $\mathbf{A}(\mathbf{r},t)$ in the plane wave representation that is specified by the eigenvalues $n_{\mathbf{k}\lambda}$ of the operators $N_{\mathbf{k}\lambda}$. A typical ket for this representation can be written $| \cdots n_{\mathbf{k}\lambda} \cdots \rangle$, which describes a state of the electromagnetic field in which there are $n_{\mathbf{k}\lambda}$ light quanta with momentum $\hbar\mathbf{k}$ and polarization $\boldsymbol{\varepsilon}_{\mathbf{k}\lambda}$. We then see from Eq. (56.28) and the work of Sec. 55 that the operators $a_{\mathbf{k}\lambda}$ and $a_{\mathbf{k}\lambda}{}^\dagger$ have the properties

$$a_{\mathbf{k}\lambda} \Big| \cdots n_{\mathbf{k}\lambda} \cdots \rangle = \left(\frac{2\pi\hbar c n_{\mathbf{k}\lambda}}{k}\right)^{\frac{1}{2}} \Big| \cdots n_{\mathbf{k}\lambda} - 1 \cdots \rangle$$

$$a_{\mathbf{k}\lambda}{}^\dagger \Big| \cdots n_{\mathbf{k}\lambda} \cdots \rangle = \left[\frac{2\pi\hbar c(n_{\mathbf{k}\lambda} + 1)}{k}\right]^{\frac{1}{2}} \Big| \cdots n_{\mathbf{k}\lambda} + 1 \cdots \rangle$$

$$\qquad\qquad\qquad\qquad\qquad\qquad\qquad (56.34)$$

We obtain from (56.17) and (56.25)

$$\mathbf{A}(\mathbf{r},t) = L^{-\frac{3}{2}} \sum_{\mathbf{k}\lambda}{}' \boldsymbol{\varepsilon}_{\mathbf{k}\lambda}[(a_{\mathbf{k}\lambda}e^{-ikct} + a'_{\mathbf{k}\lambda}{}^\dagger e^{ikct}) \exp (i\mathbf{k} \cdot \mathbf{r})$$
$$+ (a_{\mathbf{k}\lambda}{}^\dagger e^{ikct} + a'_{\mathbf{k}\lambda}e^{-ikct}) \exp (-i\mathbf{k} \cdot \mathbf{r})]$$
$$= L^{-\frac{3}{2}} \sum_{\mathbf{k}\lambda} \boldsymbol{\varepsilon}_{\mathbf{k}\lambda}\{a_{\mathbf{k}\lambda} \exp [i(\mathbf{k} \cdot \mathbf{r} - kct)]$$
$$+ a_{\mathbf{k}\lambda}{}^\dagger \exp [-i(\mathbf{k} \cdot \mathbf{r} - kct)]\} \quad (56.35)$$

Here again the restriction has been removed from the summation by identifying $a'_{\mathbf{k}\lambda}$ with $a_{-\mathbf{k}\lambda}$. This expression for the vector potential is easily seen to be hermitian, as it must be. It follows from the structure of (56.34) that $a_{\mathbf{k}\lambda}$ and $a_{\mathbf{k}\lambda}{}^\dagger$ are destruction and creation operators, respectively, for a light quantum in the state $\mathbf{k}$, λ. Thus a term in the hamiltonian linear in $\mathbf{A}$ would give rise to the absorption and emission of light quanta.

COMMUTATION RELATIONS AT DIFFERENT TIMES

It is interesting to generalize the commutation relations (56.11) to (56.13) for the components of $\mathbf{E}$ and $\mathbf{H}$ to the case in which the times are different.[1] The results show under what circumstances measurements of the electromagnetic fields at different space-time points affect each other.

Expansions for $\mathbf{E}$ and $\mathbf{H}$, in terms of the $a_{\mathbf{k}\lambda}$ that are analogous to (56.35), can be found without difficulty:

$$\mathbf{E}(\mathbf{r},t) = L^{-\frac{3}{2}} \sum_{\mathbf{k}\lambda} ik\boldsymbol{\varepsilon}_{\mathbf{k}\lambda}\{a_{\mathbf{k}\lambda} \exp [i(\mathbf{k} \cdot \mathbf{r} - kct)]$$
$$- a_{\mathbf{k}\lambda}{}^\dagger \exp [-i(\mathbf{k} \cdot \mathbf{r} - kct)]\} \quad (56.36)$$
$$\mathbf{H}(\mathbf{r},t) = L^{-\frac{3}{2}} \sum_{\mathbf{k}\lambda} i(\mathbf{k} \times \boldsymbol{\varepsilon}_{\mathbf{k}\lambda})\{a_{\mathbf{k}\lambda} \exp [i(\mathbf{k} \cdot \mathbf{r} - kct)]$$
$$- a_{\mathbf{k}\lambda}{}^\dagger \exp [-i(\mathbf{k} \cdot \mathbf{r} - kct)]\}$$

The commutator bracket for two cartesian components of the electric field strength is

$$[E_s(\mathbf{r},t), E_{s'}(\mathbf{r}',t')] = L^{-3} \sum_{\mathbf{k}\lambda} 4\pi i\hbar ck\epsilon_{\mathbf{k}\lambda,s}\epsilon_{\mathbf{k}\lambda,s'} \sin (\mathbf{k} \cdot \boldsymbol{\varrho} - kc\tau) \quad (56.37)$$

$$\boldsymbol{\varrho} = \mathbf{r} - \mathbf{r}' \qquad \tau = t - t'$$

where use has been made of (56.28). The summation over the polarization index λ can be evaluated by the technique used on the similar summa-

[1] These commutation relations are due to P. Jordan and W. Pauli, *Z. Physik* **47**, 151 (1928).

tion in (56.19):

$$\sum_\lambda \epsilon_{k\lambda,s}\epsilon_{k\lambda,s'} \sin(\mathbf{k}\cdot\boldsymbol{\varrho} - kc\tau) = \frac{1}{k^2}(k^2\delta_{ss'} - k_s k_{s'}) \sin(\mathbf{k}\cdot\boldsymbol{\varrho} - kc\tau)$$

$$= \frac{1}{k^2}\left(\frac{\delta_{ss'}}{c^2}\frac{\partial}{\partial t}\frac{\partial}{\partial t'} - \frac{\partial}{\partial r_s}\frac{\partial}{\partial r'_{s'}}\right) \sin(\mathbf{k}\cdot\boldsymbol{\varrho} - kc\tau) \qquad (56.38)$$

The summation over $\mathbf{k}$ can be evaluated by replacing it with an integral for large L:

$$L^{-3}\sum_\mathbf{k} k^{-1}\sin(\mathbf{k}\cdot\boldsymbol{\varrho} - kc\tau) \xrightarrow[L\to\infty]{} (2\pi)^{-3}\int k^{-1}\sin(\mathbf{k}\cdot\boldsymbol{\varrho} - kc\tau)\,d^3k$$

$$= -(4\pi^2\rho)^{-1}\int_0^\infty [\cos(k\rho - kc\tau) - \cos(k\rho + kc\tau)]\,dk$$

after performing the integration over the angle between $\mathbf{k}$ and $\boldsymbol{\varrho}$; we call this expression $D(\boldsymbol{\varrho},\tau)$. Equation (11.10) can then be used to express D in terms of δ functions:

$$D(\boldsymbol{\varrho},\tau) = (4\pi\rho)^{-1}[\delta(\rho + c\tau) - \delta(\rho - c\tau)] \qquad (56.39)$$

It then follows from (56.37) and (56.38) that

$$[E_s(\mathbf{r},t), E_{s'}(\mathbf{r}',t')]$$
$$= 4\pi i\hbar c\left(\frac{\delta_{ss'}}{c^2}\frac{\partial}{\partial t}\frac{\partial}{\partial t'} - \frac{\partial}{\partial r_s}\frac{\partial}{\partial r'_{s'}}\right) D(\mathbf{r} - \mathbf{r}', t - t') \quad (56.40)$$

The commutator bracket for two cartesian components of the magnetic field strength can be found in the same way and is

$$[H_s(\mathbf{r},t), H_{s'}(\mathbf{r}',t')] = [E_s(\mathbf{r},t), E_{s'}(\mathbf{r}',t')] \qquad (56.41)$$

An expression for the commutation relation between components of $\mathbf{E}$ and $\mathbf{H}$ can also be obtained from (56.36).

$$[E_s(\mathbf{r},t), H_{s'}(\mathbf{r}',t')]$$
$$= L^{-3}\sum_\mathbf{k} 4\pi i\hbar ck(\epsilon_{k1,s}\epsilon_{k2,s'} - \epsilon_{k2,s}\epsilon_{k1,s'}) \sin(\mathbf{k}\cdot\boldsymbol{\varrho} - kc\tau) \quad (56.42)$$

It is apparent that (56.42) vanishes if $s = s'$, so that parallel components of the electric and magnetic field strengths commute at all space-time points. If $s \neq s'$, we can put $s = x$, $s' = y$, where x, y, z form a right-handed set of axes, in which case we see that

$$\epsilon_{k1,x}\epsilon_{k2,y} - \epsilon_{k2,x}\epsilon_{k1,y} = (\boldsymbol{\varepsilon}_{k1} \times \boldsymbol{\varepsilon}_{k2})_z = \frac{k_z}{k}$$

An analysis similar to that which led from (56.37) to (56.40) then shows that

$$[E_x(\mathbf{r},t), H_y(\mathbf{r}',t')] = -4\pi i\hbar \frac{\partial}{\partial z}\frac{\partial}{\partial t'} D(\mathbf{r} - \mathbf{r}', t - t') \qquad (56.43)$$

The subscripts x, y, z can be permuted cyclically in (56.43).

Since all these commutation relations involve the D function (56.39), we see that all components of the field strengths commute except in the infinitesimal neighborhood of the hypersurfaces $c(t - t') = \pm |\mathbf{r} - \mathbf{r}'|$ in four-dimensional space-time. These hypersurfaces constitute the *light cone*, which is the locus of all light pulses that pass through the space point $\mathbf{r} = \mathbf{r}'$ at the time $t = t'$. Thus the field strengths at space-time points so situated that a light signal cannot pass from either one to the other commute with each other, and both can be measured precisely. This shows that the quantized electromagnetic field is propagated with the classical speed of light, c. A discussion of the connection between these commutation relations and the uncertainty principle has been given by Bohr and Rosenfeld.[1]

57☐INTERACTION BETWEEN CHARGED PARTICLES AND THE ELECTROMAGNETIC FIELD

We now wish to combine the quantization of the nonrelativistic Schrödinger equation (Sec. 55) with that of Maxwell's equations (Sec. 56), to obtain a quantum theory of the interaction of charged particles with the electromagnetic field. As before, we start with a classical lagrangian, use it to obtain the canonical variables and the hamiltonian, and then carry through the quantization. We shall apply the resulting formalism to the calculation of the coulomb interaction between charged particles and also the emission and absorption of radiation. The latter will enable us to place the theory of Chap. 11 on a sounder basis.

LAGRANGIAN AND HAMILTONIAN EQUATIONS

Our lagrangian must yield the nonrelativistic Schrödinger equation (44.1) and its complex conjugate through variation of ψ^* and ψ, respectively, and also the inhomogeneous Maxwell equations (44.2) through variation of $\mathbf{A}$ and ϕ. The sum of the lagrangian densities (55.1) and (56.3) has these properties, provided that we make the substitutions

$$i\hbar \frac{\partial \psi}{\partial t} \rightarrow i\hbar \frac{\partial \psi}{\partial t} - e\phi\psi \qquad -i\hbar\nabla\psi \rightarrow -i\hbar\nabla\psi - \frac{e}{c}\mathbf{A}\psi \qquad (57.1)$$

in the former, where e is the charge of the particle. This means that the electric charge and current densities that appear in (44.2) are those obtained by multiplying Eqs. (7.1) and (7.3) by e and making the substitutions (57.1):

$$\rho = e\psi^*\psi \qquad \mathbf{J} = \frac{e\hbar}{2im}[\psi^*\nabla\psi - (\nabla\psi^*)\psi] - \frac{e^2}{mc}\mathbf{A}\psi^*\psi \qquad (57.2)$$

[1] N. Bohr and L. Rosenfeld, *Kgl. Danske Videnskab. Selskab, Mat.-Fys. Medd.* **12,** 8 (1933).

It was shown in Prob. 2, Chap. 11, that this ρ and $\mathbf{J}$ satisfy the equation of continuity when ψ is a solution of (44.1). We thus arrive at the lagrangian density

$$L = \psi^* \left(i\hbar \frac{\partial \psi}{\partial t} - e\phi\psi \right) - \frac{1}{2m} \left[\left(i\hbar\nabla - \frac{e}{c}\mathbf{A} \right) \psi^* \right] \cdot \left[\left(-i\hbar\nabla - \frac{e}{c}\mathbf{A} \right) \psi \right]$$
$$- V\psi^*\psi + \frac{1}{8\pi} \left(\frac{1}{c} \frac{\partial \mathbf{A}}{\partial t} + \nabla\phi \right)^2 - \frac{1}{8\pi} (\nabla \times \mathbf{A})^2 \quad (57.3)$$

It is shown in Prob. 17 that Eqs. (44.1) and (44.2) do indeed follow from Eqs. (57.3) and (54.8).

Equation (57.3) suffers from the defects noted earlier in connection with (55.1) and (56.3). Since the time derivatives of ψ^* and ϕ do not appear, their canonical momenta cannot be defined, and they must be eliminated as coordinate variables from the hamiltonian theory. As before, the momentum canonically conjugate to ψ is $i\hbar\psi^*$, and the momenta canonically conjugate to the components of $\mathbf{A}$ are the components of $\mathbf{P} = (4\pi c)^{-1}[(1/c)(\partial \mathbf{A}/\partial t) + \nabla\phi]$. The hamiltonian then becomes

$$H = \int \left(i\hbar\psi^* \frac{\partial \psi}{\partial t} + \mathbf{P} \cdot \frac{\partial \mathbf{A}}{\partial t} \right) d^3r - L$$
$$= \int \left\{ \frac{1}{2m} \left[\left(i\hbar\nabla - \frac{e}{c}\mathbf{A} \right) \psi^* \right] \cdot \left[\left(-i\hbar\nabla - \frac{e}{c}\mathbf{A} \right) \psi \right] + e\phi\psi^*\psi \right.$$
$$\left. + V\psi^*\psi + 2\pi c^2 \mathbf{P}^2 + \frac{1}{8\pi} (\nabla \times \mathbf{A})^2 - c\mathbf{P} \cdot \nabla\phi \right\} d^3r \quad (57.4)$$

and ψ^* appears as a canonical momentum variable. It is not difficult to show that the hamiltonian equations of motion for ψ and its canonical momentum $i\hbar\psi^*$ are (44.1) and its complex conjugate, respectively. The hamiltonian equations for $\mathbf{A}$ and $\mathbf{P}$ are

$$\frac{\partial \mathbf{A}}{\partial t} = 4\pi c^2 \mathbf{P} - c\nabla\phi$$
$$\frac{\partial \mathbf{P}}{\partial t} = -\frac{1}{4\pi} \nabla \times \nabla \times \mathbf{A} + \frac{1}{c} \mathbf{J} \quad (57.5)$$

where $\mathbf{J}$ is given in (57.2). Thus if we define $\mathbf{E} = -4\pi c\mathbf{P}$ and $\mathbf{H} = \nabla \times \mathbf{A}$, as in Sec. 56, we obtain the first, second, and fourth of Maxwell's equations (44.2).

ELIMINATION OF ϕ

The third of Maxwell's equations (44.2) must be obtained as a supplementary condition, as was the corresponding equation in Sec. 56. We shall therefore be concerned only with those solutions of the hamiltonian equations for which $\nabla \cdot \mathbf{E} - 4\pi e \psi^* \psi = 0$ at some definite time. If then the time derivative of this quantity is zero, the restriction is maintained at all times, and the solutions so chosen form a consistent and satisfactory set. With the help of the first of Eqs. (57.2), the second of Eqs. (57.5), and the definition of $\mathbf{E}$, we see that

$$\frac{\partial}{\partial t} (\nabla \cdot \mathbf{E} - 4\pi e \psi^* \psi) = -4\pi \nabla \cdot \mathbf{J} - 4\pi \frac{\partial \rho}{\partial t}$$

This is zero because of the equation of continuity for the electric charge and current densities.

We can now see that the two terms on the right side of (57.4) that involve ϕ cancel each other. The second ϕ term can be integrated by parts to give

$$-c \int \mathbf{P} \cdot \nabla \phi \, d^3 r = c \int \phi \nabla \cdot \mathbf{P} \, d^3 r = -\int \phi \rho \, d^3 r$$

which is equal to and opposite in sign from the first ϕ term $e \int \phi \psi^* \psi \, d^3 r$. Thus ϕ has disappeared from the hamiltonian and may be chosen in any convenient way. The choice is made so that, when $\mathbf{P}$ (or $\mathbf{E}$) is divided into *solenoidal* and *irrotational* parts, the latter part is expressed entirely in terms of ϕ. We put

$$\mathbf{P} = \mathbf{P}_1 + \mathbf{P}_2$$

$$\nabla \cdot \mathbf{P}_1 = 0 \qquad \mathbf{P}_1 \text{ is solenoidal} \tag{57.6}$$

$$\nabla \times \mathbf{P}_2 = 0 \qquad \mathbf{P}_2 \text{ is irrotational}$$

If now we put $\mathbf{P}_2 = (4\pi c)^{-1} \nabla \phi$, we see that the third of Eqs. (57.6) is satisfied and that the first of Eqs. (57.5) becomes

$$\frac{\partial \mathbf{A}}{\partial t} = 4\pi c^2 \mathbf{P}_1 \tag{57.7}$$

It is now possible to have $\nabla \cdot \mathbf{A} = 0$ at all times if it is true at any one time, since (57.7) and the second of Eqs. (57.6) show that $(\partial/\partial t)\nabla \cdot \mathbf{A} = 0$; we therefore choose the gauge so that $\nabla \cdot \mathbf{A} = 0$. This choice is usually referred to as the *radiation gauge* or the *coulomb gauge*, since there is a clear separation between the radiation field, described by $\mathbf{P}_1$ or $\mathbf{A}$, and the coulomb interaction, which we shall see below is described by $\mathbf{P}_2$ or ϕ.

The ϕ potential reappears in the hamiltonian (57.4) through the $\mathbf{P}^2$ term. The volume integral of $\mathbf{P}^2$ can be written, with the help of the expression for $\mathbf{P}_2$ and a partial integration,

$$\int \mathbf{P}^2 \, d^3r = \int \mathbf{P}_1{}^2 \, d^3r + \int (2\mathbf{P}_1 + \mathbf{P}_2) \cdot \mathbf{P}_2 \, d^3r$$

$$= \int \mathbf{P}_1{}^2 \, d^3r + \frac{1}{4\pi c} \int (2\mathbf{P}_1 + \mathbf{P}_2) \cdot \boldsymbol{\nabla}\phi \, d^3r$$

$$= \int \mathbf{P}_1{}^2 \, d^3r - \frac{1}{4\pi c} \int \phi \boldsymbol{\nabla} \cdot (2\mathbf{P}_1 + \mathbf{P}_2) \, d^3r$$

Now $\boldsymbol{\nabla} \cdot \mathbf{P}_1 = 0$, and the supplementary condition is that $\boldsymbol{\nabla} \cdot \mathbf{P}_2 = -\rho/c$; thus the $\mathbf{P}^2$ term in H becomes

$$2\pi c^2 \!\int\! \mathbf{P}^2 \, d^3r = 2\pi c^2 \!\int\! \mathbf{P}_1{}^2 \, d^3r + \tfrac{1}{2}\!\int\! \phi\rho \, d^3r \tag{57.8}$$

The choice of ϕ tells us that

$$\nabla^2\phi = 4\pi c \boldsymbol{\nabla} \cdot \mathbf{P}_2 = -4\pi\rho$$

This equation can be integrated by making use of the free-particle Green's function (37.19) with $k = 0$; the result is

$$\phi(\mathbf{r},t) = \int \frac{\rho(\mathbf{r}',t)}{|\mathbf{r} - \mathbf{r}'|} \, d^3r' \tag{57.9}$$

The hamiltonian (57.4) can now be rewritten, with the help of (57.8) and (57.9),

$$H = \int \left\{ \frac{1}{2m} \left[\left(i\hbar\boldsymbol{\nabla} - \frac{e}{c}\mathbf{A} \right) \psi^* \right] \cdot \left[\left(-i\hbar\boldsymbol{\nabla} - \frac{e}{c}\mathbf{A} \right) \psi \right] + V\psi^*\psi \right\} d^3r$$

$$+ \int \left[2\pi c^2 \mathbf{P}_1{}^2 + \frac{1}{8\pi} (\boldsymbol{\nabla} \times \mathbf{A})^2 \right] d^3r$$

$$+ \tfrac{1}{2} \iint \frac{\rho(\mathbf{r},t)\rho(\mathbf{r}',t)}{|\mathbf{r} - \mathbf{r}'|} \, d^3r \, d^3r' \tag{57.10}$$

Here, $\boldsymbol{\nabla} \cdot \mathbf{P}_1 = \boldsymbol{\nabla} \cdot \mathbf{A} = 0$, and $\rho(\mathbf{r},t) = e\psi^*(\mathbf{r},t)\psi(\mathbf{r},t)$. The last term in (57.10) is the internal coulomb energy of the electric charge distribution $\rho(\mathbf{r},t)$; it results from the elimination of ϕ and the irrotational part of $\mathbf{P}$ and does not have to be inserted into the theory as a separate assumption.

The solenoidal field vectors ($\mathbf{P}_1$ and $\mathbf{A}$) are usually referred to as the *transverse* part of the electromagnetic field, since the electric and magnetic field strengths in the corresponding plane-wave solutions are transverse to the direction of propagation, as in Sec. 56. The irrotational coulomb field vector ($\mathbf{P}_2$) is called the *longitudinal* part of the field, since Eq. (57.9) shows that the contribution to $\mathbf{P}_2$ at one point from an infinitesimal element of charge at another point is along the line joining the two points.

QUANTIZATION OF THE FIELDS

We can now obtain a quantum theory of the interacting particle and electromagnetic fields by adopting the equation of motion (54.23), the particle field commutation or anticommutation relations (55.6) or (55.18), and the electromagnetic field commutation relations (56.21) with $\mathbf{P}_1$ substituted for $\mathbf{P}$. It will also be assumed that all components of ψ and $\psi^\dagger$ commute with all components of $\mathbf{A}$ and $\mathbf{P}_1$.

The order of factors like ψ^* and ψ that are multiplied together in the hamiltonian (57.10) is immaterial in the unquantized case. In the quantum theory, however, $\psi^\dagger$ and ψ do not commute with each other, and the result of a particular calculation will depend on the order in which they appear in the hamiltonian. We shall see later on in this section that a suitable hamiltonian is obtained if all terms are left as they are, except for a change in the integrand of the coulomb term. This integrand in (57.10) contains the term

$$\rho(\mathbf{r},t)\rho(\mathbf{r}',t) = e^2\psi^\dagger(\mathbf{r},t)\psi(\mathbf{r},t)\psi^\dagger(\mathbf{r}',t)\psi(\mathbf{r}',t) \tag{57.11}$$

which we replace by[1]

$$e^2\psi^\dagger(\mathbf{r},t)\psi^\dagger(\mathbf{r}',t)\psi(\mathbf{r}',t)\psi(\mathbf{r},t) \tag{57.12}$$

It can be shown with the help of (55.6) and (55.18) that (57.11) is equal to (57.12) plus

$$e^2\psi^\dagger(\mathbf{r},t)\psi(\mathbf{r}',t)\delta^3(\mathbf{r} - \mathbf{r}')$$

regardless of whether commutation or anticommutation relations are used. Thus the change from (57.11) to (57.12) is equivalent to the subtraction from the hamiltonian (57.10) of the quantity

$$\frac{e^2}{2} \iint \frac{\psi^\dagger(\mathbf{r},t)\psi(\mathbf{r}',t)\delta^3(\mathbf{r} - \mathbf{r}')}{|\mathbf{r} - \mathbf{r}'|} \, d^3r \, d^3r' \tag{57.13}$$

This is evidently infinite unless $\psi^\dagger(\mathbf{r},t)\psi(\mathbf{r},t)$ is zero; it will be shown below that this can happen only if there are no particles present in the field.

The quantum equations of motion are obtained from (54.23) when the hamiltonian (57.10) is modified by substitution of (57.12) for (57.11). The electromagnetic field equations agree with those obtained in Sec. 56, except that $\mathbf{P}_1$ replaces $\mathbf{P}$ and the electric current term appears as in the second of Eqs. (57.5). The particle field equation is the same as (44.1) except that ϕ is replaced by

$$e \iint \frac{\psi^\dagger(\mathbf{r}',t)\psi(\mathbf{r}',t)}{|\mathbf{r} - \mathbf{r}'|} \, d^3r'$$

It can then be shown that the time derivatives of the bracket expressions

[1] Note that both (57.11) and (57.12) give hermitian contributions to H.

in (55.6) or (55.18) and (56.21) are zero, so that these equations hold for all time if they are valid initially, as was assumed (see Prob. 19).

INCLUSION OF STATIC FIELDS

Thus far we have assumed that the electric charge and current densities arise entirely from charged particles that are described by the ψ field. The effect of a static charge distribution can easily be included by the addition of a term $4\pi\rho_s$ to the right side of the third of Eqs. (44.2), and a term $e\phi_s\psi$ to the right side of (44.1), where $\nabla^2\phi_s = -4\pi\rho_s$. It is not difficult to see that the only effect on the hamiltonian (57.10) is to add a term $\int e\phi_s\psi^*\psi \, d^3r$.

The situation of greatest practical interest is that for which $e\phi_s = -Ze^2/r$. This corresponds to an electron in the vicinity of a fixed (infinitely massive) point nucleus of atomic number Z, placed at the origin. With this addition and the modification (57.12), the quantized version of the hamiltonian (57.10) becomes

$$H = \int \left\{ \frac{1}{2m} \left[\left(i\hbar\nabla - \frac{e}{c}\mathbf{A} \right) \psi^\dagger \right] \cdot \left[\left(-i\hbar\nabla - \frac{e}{c}\mathbf{A} \right) \psi \right] \right.$$
$$\left. + V\psi^\dagger\psi - \frac{Ze^2}{r}\psi^\dagger\psi \right\} d^3r + \int \left[2\pi c^2 \mathbf{P}_1^2 + \frac{1}{8\pi}(\nabla \times \mathbf{A})^2 \right] d^3r$$
$$+ \frac{e^2}{2} \iint \frac{\psi^\dagger\psi^{\dagger\prime}\psi^\prime\psi}{|\mathbf{r} - \mathbf{r}'|} d^3r \, d^3r' \quad (57.14)$$

where the primes in the last term indicate that the arguments are $\mathbf{r}'$ rather than $\mathbf{r}$. Thus the nuclear coulomb interaction enters in the same way as a special choice of V, as would be expected.

PERTURBATION THEORY OF THE INTERPARTICLE INTERACTION

In the remainder of this section we shall consider two perturbation calculations based on the hamiltonian (57.14). First, we shall ignore the transverse part of the electromagnetic field ($\mathbf{P}_1$ and $\mathbf{A}$) and regard the coulomb interaction between particles [last term of (57.14)] as a perturbation. It is not necessary to retain both the V and Z terms, and we drop the latter in order to conform to the notation used in Secs. 23 and 55. This example is of interest since it shows how the replacement of (57.11) by (57.12) eliminates the infinite electrostatic self-energy of each charged particle, which is a carry-over from classical theory. It also shows how the exchange interaction between charged particles, including its dependence on particle statistics, emerges from the quantized field theory. Second, we shall consider the interaction of a single charged particle with the transverse electromagnetic field; in this case the last term of (57.14) does not contribute since only one particle is present.

The unperturbed hamiltonian ($e = 0$ and neglect of the transverse field) is just (55.5), so that the unperturbed states can be described by the kets $|n_1, n_2, \ldots n_k, \ldots \rangle$ in the N representation. This means that ψ is expanded in accordance with (55.11). We choose the u_k to be eigenfunctions of (23.2) with eigenvalues E_k, so that our kets are eigenstates of (55.5) with energy eigenvalues $\Sigma n_k E_k$. Our object is to find the first-order perturbed energy that arises from the last term in (57.14). In accordance with the general theory of Sec. 31, this is the expectation value of

$$\frac{e^2}{2} \iint \frac{\psi^\dagger \psi^{\dagger\prime} \psi^\prime \psi}{|\mathbf{r} - \mathbf{r}^\prime|} d^3r \, d^3r^\prime$$

$$= \frac{e^2}{2} \sum_{jklm} a_j^\dagger a_k^\dagger a_l a_m \iint |\mathbf{r} - \mathbf{r}^\prime|^{-1} u_j^*(\mathbf{r}) u_k^*(\mathbf{r}^\prime) u_l(\mathbf{r}^\prime) u_m(\mathbf{r}) \, d^3r \, d^3r^\prime$$

$$(57.15)$$

for an unperturbed ket. It is apparent from the first of Eqs. (55.15) in the Einstein-Bose case, or from the first of Eqs. (55.26) in the Fermi-Dirac case, that $a_l a_m |n_1, \ldots \rangle = 0$ unless there are at least two particles present. With symmetric statistics, we require $n_l \geq 1$ and $n_m \geq 1$ if $l \neq m$, or $n_l \geq 2$ if $l = m$, in order to get a nonvanishing result. With the exclusion principle, only the first case is possible.

In similar fashion, it is apparent that the subtracted quantity (57.13) is equal to

$$\frac{e^2}{2} \sum_{kl} a_k^\dagger a_l \iint |\mathbf{r} - \mathbf{r}^\prime|^{-1} u_k^*(\mathbf{r}) u_l(\mathbf{r}^\prime) \, \delta^3(\mathbf{r} - \mathbf{r}^\prime) \, d^3r \, d^3r^\prime$$

The integral associated with any term in this summation for which $k = l$ is evidently infinite. Thus (57.13) gives an infinite contribution to the energy of the system unless $a_k |n_1, \ldots \rangle = 0$ for all k, that is, unless $n_k = 0$ for all k so that there are no particles present. This infinite contribution is the electrostatic self-energy of a classical point charge; it is eliminated from the quantum theory by subtraction of (57.13) from the field hamiltonian.

EINSTEIN–BOSE CASE

The expectation value or diagonal matrix element of (57.15) for a ket that corresponds to two or more Einstein-Bose particles is a sum of terms, each of which involves one or two occupied states. The term that refers to a single occupied state k, for example, contains the matrix element of $a_k^\dagger a_k^\dagger a_k a_k = a_k^\dagger(a_k a_k^\dagger - 1)a_k = N_k^2 - N_k$. Thus the expectation value of this part of (57.15) is

$$\frac{e^2}{2} n_k(n_k - 1) \iint |\mathbf{r} - \mathbf{r}'|^{-1} |u_k(\mathbf{r})|^2 |u_k(\mathbf{r}')|^2 \, d^3r \, d^3r' \qquad (57.16)$$

This is equal to zero if $n_k = 1$, and to e^2 times the volume integral if $n_k = 2$, as expected (see also Prob. 20).

The term that refers to different occupied states k and l contains the matrix elements of $a_k{}^\dagger a_l{}^\dagger a_k a_l$, $a_l{}^\dagger a_k{}^\dagger a_k a_l$, $a_k{}^\dagger a_l{}^\dagger a_l a_k$, and $a_l{}^\dagger a_k{}^\dagger a_l a_k$, each of which is equal to $N_k N_l$. Thus the expectation value of this part of (57.15) is

$$e^2 n_k n_l [\iint |\mathbf{r} - \mathbf{r}'|^{-1} |u_k(\mathbf{r})|^2 |u_l(\mathbf{r}')|^2 \, d^3r \, d^3r'$$
$$+ \iint |\mathbf{r} - \mathbf{r}'|^{-1} u_k^*(\mathbf{r}) u_l^*(\mathbf{r}') u_k(\mathbf{r}') u_l(\mathbf{r}) \, d^3r \, d^3r'] \quad (57.17)$$

In the case $n_k = n_l = 1$, this is just what would be expected from a symmetric two-particle wave function of the form (40.6). As with Eq. (41.8), the first term in (57.17) is called the direct or coulomb energy, and the second term the exchange energy.

FERMI–DIRAC CASE

The expectation value of (57.15) for a ket that corresponds to two or more Fermi-Dirac particles is again a sum of terms, each of which now involves two different occupied states k and l. Equations (55.19) show that

$$a_k{}^\dagger a_l{}^\dagger a_k a_l = -a_l{}^\dagger a_k{}^\dagger a_k a_l = -a_k{}^\dagger a_l{}^\dagger a_l a_k = a_l{}^\dagger a_k{}^\dagger a_l a_k = -N_k N_l$$

Since $n_k = n_l = 1$, the expectation value of this part of (57.15) is

$$e^2 [\iint |\mathbf{r} - \mathbf{r}'|^{-1} |u_k(\mathbf{r})|^2 |u_l(\mathbf{r}')|^2 \, d^3r \, d^3r'$$
$$- \iint |\mathbf{r} - \mathbf{r}'|^{-1} u_k^*(\mathbf{r}) u_l^*(\mathbf{r}') u_k(\mathbf{r}') u_l(\mathbf{r}) \, d^3r \, d^3r'] \quad (57.18)$$

As would be expected from an antisymmetric two-particle wave function of the form (40.6), the direct and exchange energies have opposite signs in (57.18).

RADIATION THEORY

As our final example, we now show how the absorption and emission of electromagnetic radiation by a charged particle can be obtained from quantum field theory. The calculation reproduces the principal results obtained from the semiclassical theory of Secs. 44 and 45 but places them on a sounder basis. As in Eqs. (44.13), we break up the hamiltonian into an unperturbed part H_0 and a perturbation H'. H_0 is now the sum of the particle hamiltonian (55.5) and the transverse part of the electromagnetic hamiltonian (56.7), and can also be written in the N

representation:

$$H_0 = \int \left[\frac{\hbar^2}{2m} \nabla\psi^\dagger \cdot \nabla\psi + V\psi^\dagger\psi + 2\pi c^2 \mathbf{P}_1{}^2 + \frac{1}{8\pi} (\nabla \times \mathbf{A})^2 \right] d^3r$$

$$= \sum_l N_l E_l + \sum_{\mathbf{k}\lambda} \hbar ck(N_{\mathbf{k}\lambda} + \tfrac{1}{2}) \qquad (57.19)$$

H' is the remainder of the total hamiltonian (57.14). Certain parts of it can, however, be ignored. As before, we drop the Z term since we are keeping the V term. We also drop the last term since we are no longer concerned with the coulomb interaction between particles. Further, we note from the discussion of Eq. (56.35) that a term in the hamiltonian linear in $\mathbf{A}$ is linear in the light quantum destruction and creation operators $a_{\mathbf{k}\lambda}$ and $a_{\mathbf{k}\lambda}{}^\dagger$, which respectively cause the absorption and emission of single photons. In similar fashion the $\mathbf{A}^2$ term in (57.14) gives rise to the absorption and emission of pairs of photons and to the simultaneous absorption of one photon and emission of another. We therefore keep only the part of H' that is linear in $\mathbf{A}$. With the help of a partial integration, and making use of the fact that $\nabla \cdot \mathbf{A} = 0$, we obtain

$$H' = \frac{ie\hbar}{mc} \int \psi^\dagger \mathbf{A} \cdot \nabla\psi \, d^3r \qquad (57.20)$$

We now change from the Heisenberg picture, in which the ψ's and $\mathbf{A}$ depend on the time but the kets do not, to the interaction picture. To zero order in H', the ψ's and $\mathbf{A}$, and hence also H' itself, are the same in the interaction as in the Heisenberg picture. The kets are no longer strictly constant in time but show a secular change that is proportional to the zero-frequency part of H' (compare with Secs. 35 and 37). We therefore write H' in a form that shows its explicit dependence on the time. It follows from Eq. (55.11) and the solution to Prob. 5 that $\psi = \Sigma a_l e^{-iE_l t/\hbar} u_l(\mathbf{r})$, where the argument $t = 0$ has been dropped from a_l. Then on substituting this and the expansion (56.35) into (57.20), we obtain

$$H' = \frac{ie\hbar}{mcL^{\frac{3}{2}}} \sum_{jl} \sum_{\mathbf{k}\lambda} a_j{}^\dagger a_l \mathbf{\varepsilon}_{\mathbf{k}\lambda} \cdot \left[a_{\mathbf{k}\lambda} e^{i(E_j - E_l - \hbar ck)t/\hbar} \int \exp{(i\mathbf{k} \cdot \mathbf{r})} \, u_j^* \nabla u_l \, d^3r \right.$$

$$\left. + a_{\mathbf{k}\lambda}{}^\dagger \, e^{i(E_j, -E_l + \hbar ck)t/\hbar} \int \exp{(-i\mathbf{k} \cdot \mathbf{r})} \, u_j^* \nabla u_l \, d^3r \right] \quad (57.21)$$

A typical $a_{\mathbf{k}\lambda}$ term in (57.21) corresponds to the destruction of a photon of energy $\hbar ck = \hbar\omega$ and a particle of energy E_l and the creation of a particle of energy E_j; in other words, a photon is absorbed and the particle makes a transition from state l to state j. Since, as remarked above, the kets are essentially time-independent, this process occurs only if the frequency of the corresponding part of H' is practically zero, that is, if $E_j \approx E_l + \hbar\omega$. Similarly, a typical $a_{k\lambda}{}^\dagger$ term corresponds to the emission of a photon, and this process occurs only if $E_j \approx E_l - \hbar\omega$. Thus energy conservation appears automatically as a result of the calculation.[1]

TRANSITION PROBABILITY FOR ABSORPTION

We consider first a transition from a ket $|\alpha\rangle$, in which there is a particle in the state l and a number of photons with a range of energies, to a ket $|\beta\rangle$ in which there is a particle in the state j $(E_j > E_l)$ and one less photon of approximate energy $E_j - E_l$. The matrix element of H' for this transition is seen from (55.15) and (56.34) to be

$$\langle\beta|H'(t)|\alpha\rangle = \langle\beta|T_B|\alpha\rangle e^{i\omega_{\beta\alpha}t} \qquad \omega_{\beta\alpha} \equiv \frac{E_j - E_l - \hbar\omega}{\hbar} \qquad (57.22)$$

where we have separated out the time dependence by defining the first-order or Born approximation T matrix element

$$\langle\beta|T_B|\alpha\rangle \equiv \frac{ie\hbar}{mcL^{\frac{3}{2}}}\left(\frac{2\pi\hbar cn_{k\lambda}}{k}\right)^{\frac{1}{2}} \int u_j^* \exp(i\mathbf{k}\cdot\mathbf{r})\, \boldsymbol{\varepsilon}_{k\lambda}\cdot\boldsymbol{\nabla}u_l\, d^3r \qquad (57.23)$$

Here $n_{k\lambda}$ is the number of photons of the type absorbed that are present in the initial ket $|\alpha\rangle$. The transition probability per unit time can then be calculated as in Secs. 35 and 37:

$$\begin{aligned}
w &= \frac{1}{t}\sum_{k\lambda}\hbar^{-2}\left|\int_0^t \langle\beta|H'(t')|\alpha\rangle\, dt'\right|^2 \\
&= \sum_{k\lambda}\hbar^{-2}|\langle\beta|T_B|\alpha\rangle|^2\frac{1}{t}\left|\int_0^t e^{i\omega_{\beta\alpha}t'}\, dt'\right|^2 \\
&= \sum_{k\lambda}\hbar^{-2}|\langle\beta|T_B|\alpha\rangle|^2\frac{4\sin^2\frac{1}{2}\omega_{\beta\alpha}t}{\omega_{\beta\alpha}{}^2 t} \qquad (57.24)
\end{aligned}$$

We now suppose, as in Sec. 44, that the particle states j and l are discrete and that the incident radiation can be described by an intensity $I(\omega)\, d\omega$ for the infinitesimal frequency range $d\omega$. Then the summation over states $\mathbf{k}$ of the radiation field can be replaced by an integration over k or $\omega_{\beta\alpha}$. Each photon contributes an amount $\hbar\omega/L^3$ to the energy density or an amount $\hbar c\omega/L^3$ to the intensity. We can therefore replace

$$\sum_{k\lambda}\{\quad\}n_{k\lambda} \qquad \text{by} \qquad \sum_\lambda\int\{\quad\}\frac{L^3 I(\omega)\, d\omega}{\hbar c\omega} \qquad (57.25)$$

---

[1] Although we have assumed in this discussion that the particles are bosons, it is apparent that the same results are obtained if they are fermions. Particle statistics cannot be significant as long as only one particle is present.

Combination of (57.23) to (57.25), together with the substitution of $d\omega_{\beta\alpha}$ for $d\omega$, gives for a particular polarization λ

$$w = \frac{8\pi e^2}{m^2 c} \left| \int u_j^* \exp (i\mathbf{k} \cdot \mathbf{r}) \, \boldsymbol{\epsilon}_{\mathbf{k}\lambda} \cdot \boldsymbol{\nabla} u_l \, d^3r \right|^2 \int \frac{I(\omega) \sin^2 \frac{1}{2}\omega_{\beta\alpha}t}{\omega^2 \omega_{\beta\alpha}^2 t} \, d\omega_{\beta\alpha}$$

The $\omega_{\beta\alpha}$ integrand is sharply peaked at $\omega_{\beta\alpha} = 0$, and so we proceed as in Sec. 35 to extend the limits to $\pm \infty$ and make use of the result $\int_{-\infty}^{\infty} x^{-2} \sin^2 x \, dx = \pi$:

$$w = \frac{4\pi^2 e^2 I(\omega)}{m^2 c \omega^2} \left| \int u_j^* \exp (i\mathbf{k} \cdot \mathbf{r}) \, \boldsymbol{\epsilon}_{\mathbf{k}\lambda} \cdot \boldsymbol{\nabla} u_l \, d^3r \right|^2 \qquad \omega = \frac{E_j - E_l}{\hbar}$$

$$(57.26)$$

This is in agreement with Eq. (44.17).

TRANSITION PROBABILITY FOR EMISSION

We now use the $a_{\mathbf{k}\lambda}^\dagger$ part of (57.21) to calculate the transition probability for emission of a photon. In order to make the result comparable with that obtained in the preceding subsection, we suppose that the particle destroyed is in the state j and that created is in the state l, where again $E_j > E_l$. The T matrix element (57.23) is then replaced by

$$\frac{ie\hbar}{mcL^{\frac{3}{2}}} \left[\frac{2\pi\hbar c(n_{\mathbf{k}\lambda} + 1)}{k} \right]^{\frac{1}{2}} \int u_l^* \exp (-i\mathbf{k} \cdot \mathbf{r}) \, \boldsymbol{\epsilon}_{\mathbf{k}\lambda} \cdot \boldsymbol{\nabla} u_j \, d^3r \qquad (57.27)$$

Use has been made of the second of Eqs. (56.34), and it is important to remember that $n_{\mathbf{k}\lambda}$ is the number of photons of the type emitted that are present *initially*. A calculation similar to that which led from (57.23) to (57.26) gives for the emission probability per unit time

$$\frac{4\pi^2 e^2 I(\omega)}{m^2 c \omega^2} \left| \int u_l^* \exp (-i\mathbf{k} \cdot \mathbf{r}) \, \boldsymbol{\epsilon}_{\mathbf{k}\lambda} \cdot \boldsymbol{\nabla} u_j \, d^3r \right|^2$$
$$+ \sum_{\mathbf{k}\lambda} \frac{8\pi e^2 \hbar}{m^2 \omega L^3} \left| \int u_l^* \exp (-i\mathbf{k} \cdot \mathbf{r}) \, \boldsymbol{\epsilon}_{\mathbf{k}\lambda} \cdot \boldsymbol{\nabla} u_j \, d^3r \right|^2 \frac{\sin^2 \frac{1}{2}\omega_{\beta\alpha}t}{\omega_{\beta\alpha}^2 t} \quad (57.28)$$

where $\omega_{\beta\alpha}$ is still given by (57.22).

The two terms of (57.28) evidently arise from $n_{\mathbf{k}\lambda}$ and 1, respectively, in the factor $(n_{\mathbf{k}\lambda} + 1)^{\frac{1}{2}}$ of (57.27). The first term is proportional to the intensity of the incident radiation and agrees with the expression (44.19) for the induced emission probability. The second term is independent of the intensity of the radiation present initially; we now show that it agrees with the spontaneous emission probability obtained in Sec. 45.

We can simplify the second term in (57.28) by replacing the summation over $\mathbf{k}$ with an integral over ω or $\omega_{\beta\alpha}$. In order to do this, we require an expression for the number of states of the electromagnetic field that lie in the angular frequency range ω to $\omega + d\omega$. It follows from the discussion of periodic boundary conditions in Sec. 11 that there are $(L/2\pi)^3 \, dk_x \, dk_y \, dk_z$ plane waves with propagation vectors in the range $dk_x \, dk_y \, dk_z$. Thus if we specify the direction of the propagation vector $\mathbf{k}$ by the polar angles θ, ϕ with respect to some fixed set of axes, the number of plane waves with angular frequency in the range $d\omega$ that have directions of propagation in the angular range $d\theta \, d\phi$ is

$$(L^3\omega^2/8\pi^3c^3) \sin\theta \, d\theta \, d\phi \, d\omega$$

The integration over ω in the second term of (57.28) can be carried out as before; the result is

$$\int_0^\pi \int_0^{2\pi} \sum_\lambda \frac{e^2\hbar\omega}{2\pi m^2 c^3} \left| \int u_l^* \exp\left(-i\mathbf{k}\cdot\mathbf{r}\right) \boldsymbol{\varepsilon}_{\mathbf{k}\lambda} \cdot \boldsymbol{\nabla} u_j \, d^3r \right|^2 \sin\theta \, d\theta \, d\phi$$

$$(57.29)$$

The expression to the right of the summation in (57.29) is the probability per unit time for spontaneous emission of a light quantum with propagation vector $\mathbf{k}$ in the angular range $d\theta \, d\phi$ and with polarization λ. Thus (57.29) is the total spontaneous emission probability associated with the transition $j \to l$. In order to compare it with the corresponding expression in Sec. 45, we specialize to the dipole case by replacing $\exp\left(-i\mathbf{k}\cdot\mathbf{r}\right)$ by unity and $\boldsymbol{\nabla}$ by $-(m\omega/\hbar)\mathbf{r}$ in the integrand of the matrix element [see Eq. (44.20)]:

$$\int_0^\pi \int_0^{2\pi} \sum_\lambda \frac{e^2\omega^3}{2\pi\hbar c^3} \left| \boldsymbol{\varepsilon}_{\mathbf{k}\lambda} \cdot \int u_l^*\mathbf{r}u_j \, d^3r \right|^2 \sin\theta \, d\theta \, d\phi \qquad (57.30)$$

The two directions of polarization for each propagation vector can be chosen in any way so long as they are perpendicular to each other and to $\mathbf{k}$. If we choose one in the plane of $\mathbf{k}$ and the matrix element $\langle l|\mathbf{r}|j\rangle$, and the other perpendicular to this plane, only the former is emitted; then a factor $\sin^2\theta$ appears in the integrand, where θ is the angle between $\mathbf{k}$ and $\langle l|\mathbf{r}|j\rangle$. Thus the polarization and angular distribution of the emitted radiation are in agreement with those found in Sec. 45. The total spontaneous dipole emission probability obtained from (57.30) is

$$\int_0^\pi \int_0^{2\pi} \frac{e^2\omega^3}{2\pi\hbar c^3} \sin^2\theta \left(\int u_l^*\mathbf{r}u_j \, d^3r \right)^* \cdot \left(\int u_l^*\mathbf{r}u_j \, d^3r \right) \sin\theta \, d\theta \, d\phi$$

$$= \frac{4e^2\omega^3}{3\hbar c^3} |\langle l|\mathbf{r}|j\rangle|^2 \quad (57.31)$$

which agrees with (45.22).

Both the spontaneous and induced emission probabilities appear as the result of a single calculation in quantum field theory, whereas these two effects were calculated in quite different ways in Chap. 11. As was pointed out above, the spontaneous emission arises from the 1 in the factor $(n_{k\lambda} + 1)^{\frac{1}{2}}$ that appears in the second of Eqs. (56.34). This in turn comes from the commutation relations (56.28) and hence is a purely quantum-mechanical effect. From a formal point of view, we can say that the spontaneous emission probability is equal to the probability of emission that would be induced by the presence of one quantum in each state of the electromagnetic field (see also Prob. 6, Chap. 11). Now we have already seen in Eq. (56.32) that the smallest possible energy of the field corresponds to the presence of one-half quantum per state. This suggests that we regard the spontaneous emission as being induced by the zero-point oscillations of the electromagnetic field; note, however, that these oscillations are twice as effective in producing emissive transitions as are real photons and are of course incapable of producing absorptive transitions.

PROBLEMS

1. Make use of Eqs. (54.12) to (54.14) to show that the classical hamiltonian equations of motion for a field agree with the lagrangian equations in the cell approximation.

2. Show that Eq. (54.20) is valid even if the functional density F depends on $\nabla\psi$ and $\nabla\pi$ as well as on ψ and π.

3. The wave amplitude $\psi(\mathbf{r}_0,t)$ can be regarded as a functional to which corresponds the functional density $\psi(\mathbf{r},t)\delta^3(\mathbf{r} - \mathbf{r}_0)$, and similarly for π. Show that Eq. (54.20) gives the correct equations of motion for ψ and π when use is made of these functional densities.

4. Extend (55.11) and the following equations to the situation in which the u_k constitute a continuous set of functions. Then make use of Prob. 2, Chap. 3, to show that the measured number of particles in the infinitesimal neighborhood of any point is a positive integer or zero.

5. Find the equation of motion of the Heisenberg-picture operator $a_k(t)$ defined by Eq. (55.11) when H has the form (55.17). Integrate this equation to find $a_k(t)$ in terms of $a_k(0)$.

6. Show that the anticommutator bracket has different algebraic properties from the commutator bracket and the Poisson bracket.

7. Show that N is a constant of the motion for nonrelativistic Fermi-Dirac particles.

8. Consider a system of Fermi-Dirac particles for which there are two states. Obtain explicitly the matrices and kets that are analogous to (55.23) and (55.24).

9. Show that $[\rho(\mathbf{r},t),\rho(\mathbf{r}',t)] = 0$ for both quantizations of the nonrelativistic Schrödinger equation, where $\rho(\mathbf{r},t) \equiv e\psi^\dagger(\mathbf{r},t)\psi(\mathbf{r},t)$.

10. Calculate the commutator bracket of $[\nabla \times \mathbf{A}(\mathbf{r},t)]^2$ and $P_x(\mathbf{r}',t)$. Use the result to show that the equation of motion for the quantity $\mathbf{P}$ in a vacuum electromagnetic field is given by the second of Eqs. (56.6).

11. Show that if the commutator bracket of two cartesian components of $\mathbf{A}$ and $\mathbf{P}$ is given by

$$[A_s(\mathbf{r},t),P_{s'}(\mathbf{r}',t)] = i\hbar\delta_{ss'}\delta^3(\mathbf{r}-\mathbf{r}) - \frac{i\hbar}{4\pi}\frac{\partial}{\partial r_s}\frac{\partial}{\partial r'_{s'}}\left(\frac{1}{|\mathbf{r}-\mathbf{r}'|}\right)$$

then $\mathbf{A}$ and $\nabla\cdot\mathbf{P}$ at different space points commute with each other.

12. Show that the replacement of the last of the commutation relations (56.8) by that of Prob. 11 does not affect those commutator brackets that involve the field strengths.

13. Show that $\nabla\cdot\mathbf{H}$ commutes with the electromagnetic-field hamiltonian (56.15) and hence is a constant of the motion.

14. Carry through the calculations implied in Eqs. (56.16), and show that the first two of Maxwell's equations are obtained.

15. Calculate the commutator bracket of each of the bracket expressions in (56.18) with the hamiltonian (56.22), and show that the bracket expressions are constant in time. This means that these commutation laws are consistent with the equations of motion.

16. Derive the expression (56.43) for the commutator bracket of $E_z(\mathbf{r},t)$ and $H_y(\mathbf{r}',t')$.

17. Obtain the lagrangian equations of motion for ψ, ψ^*, $\mathbf{A}$, and ϕ from Eq. (57.3).

18. Find the quantum equation of motion for ψ when the hamiltonian is given by (57.10) with the substitution of (57.12) for (57.11). Show that it agrees with (44.1) if ϕ is replaced by $e\int|\mathbf{r}-\mathbf{r}'|^{-1}\psi^\dagger(\mathbf{r}',t)\psi(\mathbf{r}',t)\,d^3r'$. What result is obtained if the above substitution is not made?

19. Show that the bracket expressions in (55.6) or (55.18) and (56.21) are constant in time for the hamiltonian of Prob. 18.

20. Show that the expression (57.16) is obtained from the theory of Sec. 40 if there are n_k Einstein-Bose particles in the same state k, for any value of n_k.

Index

MacDonald, J. K. L., 256
MacGregor, M. H., 463
Majorana, E., 462
Massey, H. S. W., 139, 325, 327
Matrix, 149
  element, 164, 167, 223
    second-order, 250, 337
  function of, 153
  hermitian, 151
  of infinite rank, 153
  of one column, 161
  on one row, 162
  representation of group, 192, 366
  singular and nonsingular, 151
  trace or spur of, 151
  unitary, 152
Maxwell's equations, 398, 509
Mayer, M. G., 455
Messiah, A., 56, 191, 365, 366
Metropolis, N., 215
Meyerhof, W. E., 455
Miller, S. C., Jr., 269
Molecule, 445
  classification of levels, 446
  effect of nuclear identity, 454
Molière, G., 339
Møller, C., 308, 310, 466
Momentum, eigenfunction, 53
  of field, 518
  operator, 23
  probability function, 59
Momentum determination experiment,
    11
Morse, P. M., 15, 85, 256, 452
Morse potential, 452
Mott, N. F., 139, 327, 463
Mott scattering formula, 463
Multiplication, group, 192
  matrix, 149
Multiplicity, 435
Multipole moments, permitted cases of,
    224, 243, 254, 383

N representation, 502
Ne'eman, Y., 210
Negative energy states, 488
Neumann, J. von, 149, 154
Newton, R. G., 299, 344, 345, 352, 355
Nieto, M. M., 8

Nishijima, K., 205, 226
Nondegenerate perturbation theory, 245
Norm, 162
Normalization, 25
  box, 47, 54
  δ function, 56
  of scattering wave function, 102, 116
Noyes, H. P., 461
Nucleon, 455
  interaction of, 457
Nucleus, 455
  radius of, 456
Number operator, 183, 503

$O(3)$ group, 195
$O(4)$ group, 237
Old quantum theory, 4, 212, 277, 375,
    486
Operator, 148
  antilinear, 228
  antiunitary, 229
  Casimir, 209, 210, 238, 241
  creation and destruction, 183, 503,
    507
  irreducible tensor, 219
  linear, 46
  number, 183
  projection, 166, 378
  raising and lowering, 182, 200, 241
  representation of, 159
  rotation, 200
  scalar, 219
  space displacement, 189
  space inversion, 225
  tensor, 219
  time displacement, 193
  time reversal, 229
  unitary, 164
  vector, 219
Oppenheimer, J. R., 265, 370, 390, 447
Optical model potential, 130
Optical theorem, 137, 342, 360
  generalized, 136, 360
Orthogonal group, 195, 237
Orthogonality, 48, 163
Orthonormality, 156
  and closure, 51
  of energy eigenfunctions, 49
  of momentum eigenfunctions, 55
  of spherical harmonics, 80